INTERSCIENCE MONOGRAPHS AND TEXTS IN PHYSICS AND ASTRONOMY

Edited by R. E. MARSHAK

Volume I: E. R. Cohen, K. M. Crowe, and J. W. M. DuMond
THE FUNDAMENTAL CONSTANTS OF PHYSICS

Volume II: G. J. Dienes and G. H. Vineyard
RADIATION EFFECTS IN SOLIDS

Volume III: M. N. Bogoliubov and D. V. Shirkov
INTRODUCTION TO THE THEORY OF QUANTIZED FIELDS

Volume IV: J. B. Marion and J. L. Fowler, *Editors*
FAST NEUTRON PHYSICS *In two parts*
Part I: Techniques
Part II: Experiments and Theory

Volume V: D. M. Ritson, *Editor*
TECHNIQUES OF HIGH ENERGY PHYSICS

Volume VI: R. N. Thomas and R. G. Athay
PHYSICS OF THE SOLAR CHROMOSPHERE

Volume VII: Lawrence H. Aller
THE ABUNDANCE OF THE ELEMENTS

Volume VIII: E. N. Parker
INTERPLANETARY DYNAMICAL PROCESSES

Volume IX: Conrad L. Longmire
ELEMENTARY PLASMA PHYSICS

Volume X: R. Brout and P. Carruthers
LECTURES ON THE MANY-ELECTRON PROBLEM

Volume XI: A. I. Akhiezer and V. B. Berestetskii
QUANTUM ELECTRODYNAMICS

Volume XII: John L. Lumley and Hans A. Panofsky
THE STRUCTURE OF ATMOSPHERIC TURBULENCE

Volume XIII: Robert D. Heidenreich
FUNDAMENTALS OF TRANSMISSION ELECTRON MICROSCOPY

Volume XIV: G. Rickayzen
THEORY OF SUPERCONDUCTIVITY

Volume XV: Raymond J. Seeger and G. Temple, *Editors*
RESEARCH FRONTIERS IN FLUID DYNAMICS

Volume XVI: C. S. Wu and S. A. Moszkowski
BETA DECAY

Volume XVII: Klaus G. Steffen
HIGH ENERGY BEAM OPTICS

INTERSCIENCE MONOGRAPHS AND TEXTS IN PHYSICS AND ASTRONOMY

Edited by R. E. MARSHAK
University of Rochester, Rochester, New York

VOLUME XVI

Editorial Advisory Board

A. ABRAGAM, *Collège de France, Paris, France*
H. ALFVÉN, *Royal Institute of Technology, Stockholm, Sweden*
V. A. AMBARTSUMIAN, *Astronomical Institute, Academy of Sciences, Erevan, Armenia, U.S.S.R.*
L. V. BERKNER, *Graduate Research Center of the Southwest, Dallas, Texas*
H. J. BHABHA, *Tata Institute for Fundamental Research, Bombay, India*
L. BIERMANN, *Max-Planck Institut für Physik und Astrophysik, Munich, Germany*
C. BLOCH, *Centre d'Etudes Nucléaires, Saclay, France*
N. N. BOGOLUBOV, *J.I.N.R., Dubna, U.S.S.R.*
A. BOHR, *Universitets Institut for Teoretisk Fysik, Copenhagen, Denmark*
J. G. BOLTON, *C.S.I.R.O. Radiophysics Laboratory, Sydney, Australia*
S. CHANDRASEKHAR, *Enrico Fermi Institute for Nuclear Studies, Chicago, Illinois*
J. W. DuMOND, *California Institute of Technology, Pasadena, California*
J. FRIEDEL, *University of Paris, Orsay, France*
L. GOLDBERG, *Harvard College Observatory, Cambridge, Massachusetts*
M GOLDHABER, *Brookhaven National Laboratory, Upton, New York*
H. E. GOVE, *University of Rochester, Rochester, New York*
S. HAYAKAWA, *University of Nagoya, Nagoya, Japan*
C. HERRING, *Bell Telephone Laboratories, Murray Hill, New Jersey*
J. KAPLAN, *University of California, Los Angeles, California*
B. LAX, *Massachusetts Institute of Technology, Cambridge, Massachusetts*
C. MØLLER, *Universitets Institut for Teoretisk Fysik, Copenhagen, Denmark*
W. K. H. PANOFSKY, *Stanford University, Stanford, California*
R. E. PEIERLS, *University of Oxford, Oxford, England*
F. PRESS, *Massachusetts Institute of Technology, Cambridge, Massachusetts*
B. ROSSI, *Massachusetts Institute of Technology, Cambridge, Massachusetts*
A. SALAM, *International Theoretical Physics Centre, Trieste, Italy*
M. P. SAVEDOFF, *University of Rochester, Rochester, New York*
E. SCHATZMAN, *University of Paris, Paris, France*
A. L. SCHAWLOW, *Stanford University, Stanford, California*
D. A. SHIRKOV, *Institute for Mathematics, Academy of Sciences, Novosibirsk, U.S.S.R.*
R. A. SMITH, *Massachusetts Institute of Technology, Cambridge, Massachusetts*
L. SPITZER, Jr., *Princeton University Observatory, Princeton, New Jersey*
B. STRÖMGREN, *Institute for Advanced Study, Princeton, New Jersey*
W. B. THOMPSON, *University of Oxford, Oxford, England*
G. TORALDO di FRANCIA, *Università di Firenze, Florence, Italy*
G. E. UHLENBECK, *Rockefeller Institute, New York, New York*
L. VAN HOVE, *C.E.R.N., Geneva, Switzerland*
V. F. WEISSKOPF, *C.E.R.N., Geneva, Switzerland*
H. YUKAWA, *University of Kyoto, Kyoto, Japan*

BETA DECAY

C. S. WU
Columbia University

S. A. MOSZKOWSKI
University of California,
Los Angeles

INTERSCIENCE PUBLISHERS
a division of John Wiley & Sons New York · London · Sydney

 Library of Congress Catalog Card Number: 65-21452. Printed in the United States of America

Preface

The realization that parity is not conserved in beta decay has greatly stimulated interest in the whole field of elementary-particle physics. The recently reported discovery of two kinds of neutrinos and the successful venturing into the high-energy neutrino field will undoubtedly greatly accelerate our inquiries into the intrinsic nature of weak interactions. We now have strong evidence that beta decay is only one of the many branches of the universal Fermi interaction, but it is the one that has been most closely studied and is best understood.

The amazing progress in this area has been due both to evidence provided by experimental observations and to theoretical attempts to interpret the observations. We shall try to understand the phenomena of beta decay in both its experimental and theoretical aspects. This book covers the main features of beta decay and, for completeness, includes the essential feature of other weak interactions with leptonic decays.

This book is not meant to be complete and encyclopedic in scope, however, or to take the place of the many fine reference books and compilations of data which are available in the literature. On the other hand, it has seemed to us that something has been lacking in the presentation of the subject. In some reference books theoretical results are simply stated, and the reader is referred to the literature where rigorous derivations are indeed given. Such material is, of course, essential for specialists in the field, but for others the treatments are often somewhat abstract. It seemed to us, therefore, that a book giving a complete, self-contained, but not too specialized treatment of the most important topics of beta decay would be useful. We hope that the present book will fulfill this need.

We have attempted to derive most of the results, but we have grouped them in the appendices so that the reader's attention would not be diverted from the main topics. Nonrelativistic quantum mechanics is presupposed but not the relativistic version. In particular, the problems of inversions and of transformations, both nonrelativistic and relativistic, are considered in some detail in Appendix I and III; this information is essential to an understanding of the invariance relations involved in beta decay. The formulation and the interpretation of the Dirac equations for a free particle are also given in Appendix II.

In Chapter 1 we present a historical introduction which outlines the development and progress of the field of beta decay. This chapter gives the reader a descriptive account of the many interesting highlights of this fascinating subject.

In Chapter 2 a simple theory of beta decay is introduced. We attempt to give a clear picture of the basic Fermi formulation of beta decay by using the analogy with electromagnetic radiation theory. The basic terms are introduced and explained and the familiar formulas are derived using the simplest version of the theory.

In Chapter 3 we generalize the treatment to take into account the spins of the elementary particles involved and the invariance requirements. We then discuss the classification of beta transitions, and to illustrate the pertinent points many decay schemes are introduced as examples. The use of the analysis of beta decay as a tool in the study of nuclear structure is treated in these sections, and the determination of the beta interaction by classical beta decay (before the overthrow of parity in weak interactions) is also treated at some length. The investigation of the β-γ (polarized or unpolarized) angular correlation, spectrum shape determination, and ft values constitute a powerful new tool, based on the $V - A$ theory, to determine the various nuclear matrix elements in first forbidden beta transitions.

The discovery of the nonconservation of parity and charge conjugation, the implications for the theory of the two-component neutrino and lepton conservation, and many of the possibilities opened up for further exploration as a result of these discoveries are discussed in Chapter 4. In Chapter 5 we discuss electron capture and other pertinent processes which are intrinsically related to nuclear beta decay.

Since 1957, investigation has revealed many similarities between nuclear beta decay and other leptonic-decay weak interactions, for example, the violation of space and charge conjugation invariance, the two-component neutrino, $V - A$ interactions, etc. In Chapter 6 we have tried to present the essential points of some of the weak interactions to show the significant connections between them and nuclear beta decay and finally to comprehend the meaning of the universal Fermi interaction. Formulas for these processes were derived by using the two-component neutrino theory and can be found in the appendices.

The last chapter of this book was written with great emotion and enthusiasm. The extensive study of nuclear beta decay has been fruitful, and a new era of high-energy weak interaction has been opened up to us. In the days ahead, we may expect exciting, and sometimes puzzling, results from the continuing work on weak interactions. We believe, however, that the formulation and interpretation of beta decay will, in general, remain substantially unaltered, and that the main topics of this book will continue to serve as a useful introduction to this field for some time to come.

We wish to thank Professor R. Marshak for his constant interest and for the encouragement that he gave us in the preparation of this book. We are also indebted to Dr. M. Morita for his contribution to the preparation of Section 3-5. To many of our former and present colleagues and associates, particularly Dr. N. Benczer Koller, Dr. R. J. Finkelstein, Dr. C. Ryan, Dr. E. C. G. Sudershan, Dr. J. Sunier, and Dr. R. van Lieshout, we express our deep appreciation for the care with which they have read our manuscript and for the criticism which they have given us.

C. S. Wu
S. A. Moszkowski

New York and Los Angeles
November 1965

Contents

BETA DECAY

CHAPTER 1

Historical Introduction*

No one who has followed the development of the theory of β decay could fail to be impressed with the way that, from its first, very confused appearance, it gradually developed into a consistent picture and finally assumed a role of great importance in particle interactions. As is well known, β decay is full of surprises and subtleties. Its apparent perversities have threatened us not once but twice with the abandonment of some of our cherished conservation laws. However, now it seems quite clear that the first riddle—the continuous β spectra—was merely a coded clue which nature had chosen as a means of revealing the existence of an elusive, undetectable particle (neutrino). Otherwise, how would this elusive, undetectable particle ever be discovered directly? In the second crisis, when the laws of parity and charge conjugation were both found to be violated in β decay, the world of physics was shocked and puzzled. Then it again turned out that by removing these restrictions, gates were opened wide for a much better understanding of β decay. A great advance in the theory of the neutrino (two components) immediately followed, and the possibility of a broader and deeper symmetry connecting space and charge (*CP* combined inversion) thus emerged. We were all pleasantly surprised.

As one reminisces about the history of the theory of β decay, the fascinating story unfolds in several outstanding periods.

1-1 THE FIRST PERIOD

The first period, which lasted from the discovery of radioactivity to approximately 1930, was the longest and most perplexing one. Unlike

* This chapter is mainly based on "History of Beta Decay" by C. S. Wu, which appeared in *Beiträge zur Physik und Chemie des 20. Jahrhunderts*, O. R. Frisch et al., eds., Friedr. Vieweg und Sohn, Braunschweig, 1959.

an α spectrum, which consists of one or several monoenergetic α lines of nuclear origin, β spectra showed up with quite complicated compositions. There were many sharp lines superimposed on a continuous distribution of electrons. Which of these groups was the real disintegration electron? And where did those not of nuclear origin come from?

The homogeneous groups of electrons in the β spectra were soon identified as of secondary origin and ceased to be considered as the disintegration electrons from the nucleus. In spite of the prominent appearance of the sharp electron lines on a photographic plate, these electrons contribute only a small fraction of the total emission. It was shown by Chadwick (Ch-14) that the continuous distribution of electrons forms the main portion of the β spectrum, and they can be identified as the disintegration electrons.

By that time, the quantum theory—in particular, the idea of discrete energy states—was already well accepted. Thus, in 1922 Meitner (Me-22) raised the important point that a nucleus, presumably quantized, ought not to emit electrons of varying energy. What, then, caused the inhomogeneity of electrons as represented by the continuous distribution? Could it be introduced after the actual expulsion from the nucleus? If the inhomogeneity were actually introduced after the expulsion from the nucleus, it would imply that the electrons all had the same disintegration energy, equal to the upper limit of the spectrum. If, on the contrary, the disintegration electron were actually ejected from the nucleus with various energies, then the average energy of disintegration should correspond to the mean energy of the continuous spectrum. A final decision between these two views would thus be reached by measuring the average energy of disintegration of a β emitter whose spectrum was well known. The average energy of disintegration can be measured by finding the heat produced when a known number of atoms disintegrates inside a calorimeter, the wall of which is so thick that all β rays are stopped in it. RaE was perfectly suited for this purpose. The results of Ellis and Wooster (El-27) gave (350 ± 40) kev, in striking agreement with the mean energy of the emitted β particles as shown by the continuous spectrum (390 ± 60) kev, and entirely incompatible with the value of 1050 kev predicted by the assumption that all electrons have the same disintegration energy to start with. These results were strongly confirmed by an independent measurement with several improvements by Meitner and Orthmann (Me-30).

Thus, by the end of this first period the various components of the β spectra had been correctly identified and the theoretical difficulty implied by the continuous distribution of the disintegration electrons, namely the apparent breakdown of energy conservation in β decay, was fully comprehended.

1-2 THE SECOND PERIOD

As soon as the experimental evidence proved beyond a doubt that continuous distribution is the intrinsic characteristic of disintegration electrons, physicists knew that they were confronted with something very puzzling. In particular, W. Pauli, who had closely followed these experimental polemics with great interest, was convinced that the results from the calorimetric measurements were very conclusive and extremely significant.

At about the same time, wave mechanics had been taking hold in physics. Our understanding of the spins and statistics of nuclei gradually became clear. However, the fundamental constituents of nuclei were still supposed to be protons and electrons. Therefore the N^{14} nucleus was supposed to obey Fermi-Dirac statistics. The argument for this supposition is as follows: N^{14} should consist of 21 particles, 14 protons and 7 electrons. All 21 particles obey Fermi-Dirac statistics. According to the Ehrenfest and Oppenheimer theorem (Eh-31) the N^{14} nucleus should also obey Fermi-Dirac statistics. To everyone's dismay, however, the analysis of the band spectrum of N^{14} (He-29; Ra-30) revealed Bose-Einstein statistics contrary to expectation and, therefore, provided a strong argument against the proton-electron hypothesis. The determinations of nuclear spins led to the same conclusion. So electrons would have to be excluded in the nucleus. But no better ideas about the possible constituents of the nuclei were advanced at that time to replace the old proton-electron hypothesis.

Based purely on the spin and statistics considerations, Pauli pointed out in a letter (Pa-30) to Geiger and Meitner in December of 1930 that in β decay not only was the energy apparently not conserved; neither were the spin and the statistics. Consider the well-known case of the β decay of RaE:

$$_{83}\mathrm{RaE}^{210} \rightarrow {}_{84}\mathrm{RaF}^{210} + \beta^-$$

The nuclear angular momentum of RaE (mass number is 210) and RaF (mass number is also 210) are integral multiples of $\hbar$, namely $\hbar$ and 0, respectively. Thus the possible change of the nuclear angular momentum $I\hbar$ during the transition must be an integral amount (in this case it is $\Delta I = \hbar$). On the other hand, the intrinsic angular momentum of the electron is $\frac{1}{2}\hbar$. The orbital angular momentum is always an integral of $\hbar$. So the angular momentum is clearly not conserved in the β^- decay if the β^- particle is the only particle emitted. Pauli went on to propose the outlandish idea of introducing into β decay a very penetrating new neutral particle of vanishingly small mass—the "neutrino"—in order to save the situation. He made public his proposal of this strange new particle at the American Physical Society meeting in Pasadena in June, 1931. Considering that the proton, electron, and photon were the only known elementary particles at the time, it is not surprising that Pauli's hypothesis of a new undetectable particle met with considerable skepticism.

Then came the big breakthrough with the discovery of neutrons by Chadwick (Ch-32). The proton-neutron hypothesis (He-32) of nuclear constitution immediately resolved the puzzle concerning nuclear spins and statistics. In fact, modern nuclear physics dates from this time.

At the Solvay Congress in Brussels in 1933, Pauli (Pa-33b) was greatly encouraged by this favorable development and put aside whatever reservations he might have had previously about his neutrino hypothesis. The neutrino was already well qualified to be a full-fledged member of the family of elementary particles.

In fact, in recent years the neutrino has been identified in both the low- and high-energy inverse β processes and is destined to play an increasingly important role in weak interactions. Commenting on this exciting episode concerning the continuous β spectrum, Bohr is known to have remarked at the time: "One should be prepared for further surprises with β decay." Later this prophecy came true, but in a much more dramatic way than had been anticipated.

Fermi was also present at the Solvay Congress, and this meeting precipitated the famous Fermi theory of β decay (Fe-34) soon after its close. It should be mentioned that independently of Fermi, F. Perrin, who attended the Solvay Congress too, discussed qualitatively the form of the β spectrum, including the correct phase-space factors. In Fermi's theory of β decay, the β^- particle is created at the moment of emission in the same way as a photon is formed at the moment of its emission from an atom. The neutrino is also created at the moment of emission. We may express the β^- decay of a neutron as follows:

$$n \rightarrow p + \beta^- + \nu \tag{1-1}$$

For a more complex nucleus, the decay is of the form

$$Z^A \rightarrow (Z + 1)^A + \beta^- + \nu \tag{1-2}$$

The β particle and neutrino carry off practically all the energy released in the decay (except for a small recoil caused by the nucleus). The energy release is given by

$$E_0 = ({}_ZM^A - {}_{Z+1}M^A)c^2 \tag{1-3}$$

where M refers to the atomic mass of the nuclide indicated. Positron decay may be expressed as

$$Z^A \rightarrow (Z - 1)^A + \beta^+ + \nu \tag{1-4}$$

Here the energy release is

$$E_0 = ({}_ZM^A - {}_{Z-1}M^A - 2m_e)c^2 \tag{1-5}$$

where m_e is the electron rest mass.

Whenever positron emission is possible, it is also possible to make the transition by orbital electron capture,

$$Z^A + e^- \rightarrow (Z - 1)^A + \nu \tag{1-6}$$

where e^- is a bound electron, most often a K electron. If the binding energy of the captured electron is ϵ_e, the energy release is

$$({}_ZM^A - {}_{Z-1}M^A)c^2 - \epsilon_e \tag{1-7}$$

The existence of this process was first suggested by Yukawa and Sakata (Yu-35) in 1935 and found by Alvarez (Al-38) in 1938 for the nucleus Ga^{67}.

In the Fermi theory of β decay, a new kind of interaction between the four Fermi particles had to be introduced. Fermi was guided in this totally new field by the analogy with electromagnetic theory. With his characteristic simplicity and directness, he assumed that the probability of decay from an n state to a $p + \beta^- + \nu$ state is simply proportional to the squares of all the probability amplitudes ψ_n, ψ_p, ψ_{β^-} and ψ_ν. However, the field amplitudes ψ are spinors with four components. There are various ways of multiplying them together. It was later shown that all relativistically invariant combinations of the four wave functions could be included. These are known as scalar, vector, tensor, axial-vector, and pseudoscalar coupling. Fermi used only the vector interaction as an illustration in his original paper (Fe-34), and even after evidence against a pure vector interaction was developed, he is reputed to have said, "I still believe it is the vector interaction." Fermi never liked the idea that the interaction was an arbitrary combination of the five linear invariants. Subsequent developments have largely vindicated his position. The currently accepted universal Fermi interaction can, in fact, be obtained by a slight modification of the vector interaction.

The Fermi theory of β decay is *now* known to predict with remarkable accuracy both the relation between the rate of β decay and the energy of disintegration, and also the shape of β spectra. However, the Fermi theory unfortunately met an unfair test at the very beginning. Until the time when artificial radioactive nuclei could be copiously produced, RaE was the only candidate that beautifully fulfilled many experimental requirements as a β source for the investigation of its spectrum shape. How could we have known then that the β spectrum of RaE would turn out to be only a very special case, one whose spectrum has, in fact, been understood only very recently. Its peculiar energy dependence defied what was expected of the simple Fermi theory of β decay and greatly slackened the pace of the theory's initial progress.

Only a year after Fermi's original paper, many believed that it was necessary to use the more complicated form of interaction proposed by Konopinski and Uhlenbeck (Ko-35), which contained derivatives of the neutrino wave function. Later, however, more accurate measurements of β spectra (La-40; Wu-50) proved that it is unnecessary to introduce the Konopinski-Uhlenbeck modification.

1-3 THE THIRD PERIOD

Interrupted by World War II, the study of β decay was inevitably slowed down. However, during the war years nuclear reactors and the isotope separators were fully developed. As a result, the β radioactive sources of high specific activities, which are so essential for β investigation, were made available. In the meantime, many new designs of magnetic spectrometers emphasizing iron-free, moderate resolution and large transmission were proposed and built. Moreover, the surprising success of the nuclear shell model in interpreting results of β spectroscopy added further incentive to rapid progress in this field. So, in the third period (Wu-50, 55; Ri-56; All-57) we enjoyed great prosperity in β-ray spectroscopy. Not only were many laboratories engaged in active research in this field; many interesting and significant findings were actually made.

In the forties, although the major portion of an allowed β spectrum followed the Fermi distribution closely, there were always some deviations present in the very low-energy region—below 200 kev. Had these discrepancies in the very low-energy region remained real, it would have been necessary to revise Fermi's theory of β decay. To clarify this situation, many laboratories concentrated their efforts on the low-energy region of the spectrum.

The investigation of very low-energy electrons involves many difficulties. The most serious of these is the absorption and scattering effect in the finite and nonuniform source thickness and its backing material. The absorption effect of the counter window at the very low-energy region is also quite troublesome.

Wu and Albert (Wu-49) investigated the positron and electron spectra from Cu^{64} in their solenoid magnetic spectrometer. The superior transmission of this type of spectrometer permitted them to use a source strength of a few microcuries. Nevertheless, they still exercised great caution in the uniformity as well as the thinness of the source preparation. The β decay of Cu^{64} is an ideal test of the theory of β decay from the point of view that both positrons and negatrons from Cu^{64} are of nearly equal energy and comparable intensity. Therefore, the ratio of positrons to electrons should be affected less by elastic scattering. Their experimental results were indeed in excellent accord with the theoretical value predicted by the Fermi theory of β decay. They concluded that the Fermi theory predicts the true distribution for electrons and positrons at very low energies.

Eliminating the excess low-energy electrons of the allowed β spectrum also removed the obvious discrepancies standing in the way of acceptance of the Fermi theory of β decay. However, it could hardly be considered a crucial test of the theory, because the allowed spectrum is given by a statistical factor $pE(E_0 - E)^2$ (Eq. 2-21), which is the calculated phase volume corresponding to the sharing of the disintegration energy between the electron and the neutrino. Nothing about this shape is very sophisticated.

On the other hand, there also must be some "forbidden" spectra radically different from the allowed shape. Such spectra were indeed being uncovered in rapid succession in various laboratories (La-49b; Wu-50, 55) starting in 1949, and they looked altogether different from the familiar allowed shapes. Some of these spectra were known as *the unique first forbidden spectra* of transitions involving a change of spin angular momentum of two units ($\Delta I = 2$) and a change of parity (yes). A unique energy dependence is predicted for those differing from the allowed shape by the factor (see p. 96)

$$p^2 + q^2 \sim (E^2 - 1) + (E_0 - E)^2 \tag{1-8}$$

Here E is the electron energy and E_0 is the total energy release, both in units of the electron rest energy $m_e c^2$. The factor emphasizes the relative number of high-energy particles and may also emphasize low-energy particles if $E_0 > 2$. Therefore, the uncorrected Kurie plot (Sec. 2-4, p. 35)—essentially a plot of the energy spectrum divided by the statistical factor—tends to bulge upward at high energy and may also curve upward at low energy, thereby producing an inversion point at $E = \frac{1}{2}E_0$.

It was good to see a real forbidden spectrum after seeing so many allowed ones! And the maxim "It never rains but it pours" seemed to apply in this case. Not only were abundant examples of unique first forbidden spectra observed, but even the rare types of unique second and third forbidden spectra were soon identified. The experimental observation of the three unique first, second, and third forbidden spectra of Y^{91} (La-49b; Wu-50), Be^{10} (Fe-49a, Fel-50; Be-49, 50a; Fu-49; Al-50a), and K^{40} (Fe-49b, 52; Be-50b; Al-50b), as theoretically predicted, is a triumphant proof for the theory of β decay.

One of the goals in the study of β decay is to determine its interaction form. Altogether, there are five possible basic interaction forms, known as scalar, vector, tensor, axial vector, and pseudoscalar. There are certain special bilinear combination of the Dirac components (and their complex conjugates) of the particles involved, which behave like a scalar, a vector, etc., under relativistic transformations. These five forms can be classified into two types according to their selection rules. In an allowed β transition, if the two leptons (electron and neutrino) are emitted with spins in parallel so that together they carry away one unit of angular momentum (in an allowed transition the orbital angular momentum is zero), the interaction is called the *Gamow-Teller type*. Tensor and axial-vector forms belong to this type. If the two leptons are emitted with opposite spin directions so that no angular momentum is carried away by them, the interaction is the *Fermi type*. Scalar and vector forms belong to this type.

The necessity for the presence of the Gamow-Teller interaction (Ga-36) was known for some time, as concluded from the He^6 β decay. This decay, involving the spin sequence $0 \rightarrow 1$ and no parity change, must be governed by the Gamow-Teller selection rule only. The presence of the Fermi interaction was made certain through the later discoveries of the class of β decay of $0^+ \rightarrow 0^+$ transitions in O^{14}, C^{10}, etc. (Sh-53; Ar-53). Only Fermi selection rules would allow $0^+ \rightarrow 0^+$ transitions to occur. However, nature seems to be impartial to these two selection rules. They are found to be nearly equally present. We even learned through the good behavior of the allowed spectra that no evidence of an energy dependence of $1/E$ was ever observed. This observation implied that both S and V in Fermi type and both A and T in Gamow-Teller type cannot be present with comparable strength. If one of them is dominant, the other is very weak. This $1/E$ energy-dependence term is known as the *Fierz interference term* (Fi-37).

Much other evidence derived from the shapes of spectra indicated that only two combinations, ST and VA, were permissible. ST had been the favorite choice based solely on the results (Rus-53) of the β-ν angular correlation of He^6, a pure Gamow-Teller-type β emitter. The long-awaited results of the β-ν angular correlation in A^{35}, a pure Fermi-type β emitter, never arrived on the scene to challenge or confirm this (ST) deduction prior to the parity period.

This period also saw the beginning of the concept of "*the universal Fermi interaction*." Already during the 1940's other processes such as π-μ and μ-e decay and muon capture were observed. Their comparatively long lifetime identified them with the same family as β decay and suggested that there is a distinct group of weak interactions.

How weak this β interaction is may be seen by comparing it with the electromagnetic and nuclear interaction. The magnitude of the electromagnetic interaction may be characterized by means of the well-known fine-structure constant $G_e^2 = e^2/\hbar c$ which is about $\frac{1}{137}$. The dimensionless coupling constant in the nuclear (strong) case say for a pion) is represented by $G_N^2 = f^2/4\pi$ and is about 15. The corresponding dimensionless coupling constant in β decay is

$$G_\beta{}^2 = (g^2/m_e{}^2c^4)(m_ec/\hbar)^6 \sim 10^{-23}.*$$

(For a definition of g see p. 23.)

The lifetime of nuclei with respect to β decay is in the range of normal human experience, that is, seconds to years; but this span is very *long* on a nuclear time scale. In the latter, the unit is about 10^{-21} sec which is very roughly the time required for a nuclear particle, say with $v \sim 0.1c$, to traverse a nucleus, say of diameter $\sim 10^{-12}$ cm. This happens to be of the same order as the time $\hbar/m_ec^2$, required for a relativistic electron to travel a distance of a Compton wavelength.

On the other hand, weak as the β-decay interaction is, its strength is still much greater than that of the gravitational interaction which is characterized by Newton's constant $G_G{}^2 = \gamma m_p{}^2/\hbar c \sim 10^{-38}$ where m_p is the proton mass. Thus gravitational effects are only observable when large masses are involved.

1-4 THE FOURTH PERIOD

The Neutrino

The elusive neutrino appears to most physicists not only to be real but also to have a distinctive personality. Its presence has been detected in the cloud-chamber picture of the recoil nucleus and the emitted β^- particle from a β^- decay (Cr-38). These two tracks are not emitted in directions opposite to each other. We could also measure the discrete recoil energy of the nucleus in an electron-capture process. This recoil must be due to the emission of the neutrino. In recent years the gigantic and intricate experimentation of Reines and Cowan (Re-56) could actually show us the disintegrations caused by the reverse reaction in which an antineutrino and a proton are transformed into a neutron and positron. Now, the success of the two-component theory of the neutrino indicates that the neutrino is provided with handedness, and these intrinsic helicities have been much used lately for prying into nature's

---

* Some authors, for instance Marshak and Sudarshan (Mar-61), use m_π instead of m_e in their definition of $G_\beta{}^2$. This gives a value of about 10^{-13}. In any case, however, the order of magnitude of the β-decay coupling constant is very small compared to unity and the fine-structure constant.

secrets in weak interactions. Who could have foreseen what an exciting role the neutrino was going to play in elementary-particle physics?

Left-Right Symmetry, Parity

In 1956, β decay was presented with a golden opportunity of performing a crucial test to determine the validity of the law of parity in weak interactions. It had been accepted for a long time previously that the laws of physics show complete symmetry between the left and the right; this is known as Mach's principle. No physical process will allow one to distinguish between a left- and a right-handed coordinate system. In other words, the fundamental laws of the physical system should be the same in either the original or the "space-inverted" coordinate system. The latter is obtained by reversing the sense of the three coordinate axes $\mathbf{r} \rightarrow -\mathbf{r}$, but retaining particle $\rightarrow$ particle and $t \rightarrow t$. Therefore, under space inversion a right-(left-)handed screw becomes a left-(right)-handed screw.

It is interesting to examine how various physical quantities behave under the space inversion.

Table 1-1 Transformation Properties of Physical Quantities under Space Inversion

	Definition	Under P Operation ($\mathbf{x} \rightarrow -\mathbf{x}$)
The momentum of a particle	$\mathbf{p} = m \dfrac{d\mathbf{x}}{dt}$;	$\mathbf{p} \rightarrow -\mathbf{p}$
The energy of a particle	$E = \frac{1}{2}m\left(\dfrac{d\mathbf{x}}{dt}\right)^2$	$E \rightarrow E$
The angular momentum of a particle	$\mathbf{J} = \mathbf{x} \times \mathbf{p}$	$\mathbf{J} \rightarrow \mathbf{J}$
The spin of a particle	transforms like $\mathbf{J}$	$\boldsymbol{\sigma} \rightarrow \boldsymbol{\sigma}$
The electric field		$\mathbf{E} \rightarrow -\mathbf{E}$
The magnetic field		$\mathbf{H} \rightarrow +\mathbf{H}$

Polar vectors $\mathbf{p}$ and $\mathbf{E}$ change sign under P operation, but axial vectors $\mathbf{J}$, $\boldsymbol{\sigma}$, and $\mathbf{H}$ do not change sign in space inversion.

It should be noted here that although the parity symmetry is a completely classical and geometrical concept, it is a discrete symmetry which is distinctly different from the rotational symmetry, the latter is continuous and can be obtained by compounding infinitesimal transformations. Therefore the parity operation has no useful constant of motion in classical physics. In quantum mechanics, however, the difference between the discrete and continuous symmetries disappears; the law of right-left symmetry then leads to the law of the conservation of parity.

The interesting sequence of events that developed this conservation law began by the experimental observations of Laporte (La-24) in 1924 of the energy levels in complex atoms, which can be classified into even and odd levels. In an electromagnetic transition in which one photon is emitted or absorbed, Laporte found that the levels always change from even to odd, or vice versa. This may be called "the law of parity change." Now we know that what Laporte called even levels are actually levels with parity $+1$ and odd levels are those with parity -1. If the photon emitted or absorbed in the usual atomic transitions is assumed to have an odd parity, then it is rather obvious that parity is conserved in these atomic transitions.

This empirical rule of Laporte's was given a significant interpretation by Wigner (Wi-27) in 1927, who said that the conservation of parity is actually a direct consequence of the reflection invariance or left-right symmetry. Soon this law of the conservation of parity, originally derived from electromagnetic interactions, was applied to nuclear reactions, meson interactions, β decays and strange-particle physics. It was found to be extremely useful. What was not realized then was the possibility that the conservation laws which are valid for strong or electromagnetic interactions may not hold exactly or may, in fact, be completely invalid for the weak interactions.

Actually, in 1952, Wick, Wightman, and Wigner (Wi-52) made a profound remark concerning reflection symmetry: "The disturbing possibility remains that *C* and *P* are both only approximate and *CP* is the only exact symmetry law." Nevertheless, the great majority of physicists did not question the validity of parity conservation until the work of Lee and Yang.

Violation of Parity Conservation in Weak Interactions

K-Meson Decay. In 1956, the problem of *K*-meson decay (Da-53) reached a critical stage in confounding the experts. All the physical properties of the primary particle in τ decay (3-pion final state) and θ

decay (2-pion final state) seemed to be identical; yet detailed analysis indicated opposite parities for the final states. How could the same particle decay now into an even-parity final state, then into an odd parity state? Could it be that the decay interaction did not conserve parity?

Lee and Yang (Le-56) took up the challenge. Their approach, after raising this question, was to make a systematic investigation of the experimental knowledge concerning parity conservation. They found impressive evidence for the validity of this law in the electromagnetic domain (atomic physics) and also in the strong interactions (nuclear physics). However, to their surprise they found that the vast accumulation of observations of weak interactions contained no data relevant to this question. No experiments had ever been designed specifically to test such an invariance principle in the radioactive decay of nuclei and elementary particles. So, the anxiety which began with a single, isolated puzzle was now applied to a broad and pressing question: Is parity conserved in all weak interactions?

The weak interactions are responsible for the slow decays of elementary particles, such as β decay, pion and muon decay, and strange-particle interactions. To use τ and θ particles themselves in these tests is impractical. However, the β decay of radioisotopes is perfectly suited for this experimentation.

Co^{60} *Experiment*. Wu, Ambler, Hayward, Hoppes, and Hudson (Wu-57) conducted the polarized-nuclei experiment. The essence of the polarized-nuclei experiment is to line up the spins of β-emitting nuclei along the same axis and then to determine whether the β particles were emitted preferentially in one direction or the other along the axis. The nuclear-orientation method used is based upon the magnetic hyperfine splitting in paramagnetic atoms. In order to reduce the thermal agitation which tends to disrupt the orderly orientation, the crystal is cooled down to a temperature of only 0.01°C above absolute zero (−273.17°C). The cooling is accomplished by the demagnetization method. Radioactive Co^{60} was selected for this test.

The result was that a large β asymmetry was observed. The time for disappearance of the β asymmetry coincides well with that of γ anisotropy and, therefore, with the nuclear depolarization. The sign of the asymmetry coefficient, α, is negative; that is, the emission of the β particle is more favored in the direction opposite to that of nuclear spin. This means that, from the standpoint of β emission, the nucleus of Co^{60}

has an intrinsically left-handed spin. Left can be distinguished from right, therefore, parity in β decay is not conserved, as shown by this experiment.

The asymmetrical distribution of β particles from polarized Co^{60} nuclei provided more than unequivocal proof of the violation of parity conservation. The large degree of asymmetry also gave evidence for the noninvariance of charge conjugation in weak interactions. The charge conjugation operator C changes a particle to its antiparticle, but leaves space and time unchanged. The long-accepted invariance of charge conjugation in weak interactions was, therefore, overthrown together with the parity laws.

π-μ-e Decay. Shortly after the first observation of nonconservation of parity and charge conjugation in β decay, these conclusions were confirmed by a similar test in the $\pi^{\pm} \rightarrow \mu^{\pm} \rightarrow e^{\pm}$ decays (Ga-57; Fri-57). Measurements indicated a maximum for e^+ emission in a direction opposite to the motion of the μ^+.

Two-Component Neutrino. The same Co^{60} experiment (Wu-57) which established nonconservation of parity and charge conjugation in β decay also prompted Lee and Yang (Le-57a) to consider an extremely simple and appealing theory of the neutrino. This possibility was proposed independently at about the same time by Landau (La-57) and Salam (Sa-57). The theory requires the spin of a neutrino to be always parallel to its momentum and the spin of an antineutrino to be always antiparallel to its momentum (or vice versa). The Dirac equation can then be expressed by a new wave function consisting of only two components instead of four. Hence the name "two-component theory." Incidentally, this theory also requires the rigorous masslessness of the particle, which is satisfying in view of what we know of the mass of neutrino from the slope of the upper end of the β spectrum. As will be clear from later developments, the success of this theory has greatly facilitated our understanding of many phenomena in weak interactions.

Polarization of Beta Particles. An important consequence of parity nonconservation in β decay suggests that β particles (as well as neutrinos) are longitudinally polarized. The activities of measuring the polarization of β particles started at the University of Illinois almost immediately after the first parity experiment and soon were in full swing in more than a dozen laboratories all over the world. The climax was reached around the middle of the summer of 1957. The results are startling and simple, and all agreed that β^- particles behave like left-handed screws and all β^+ particles behave like right-handed screws. At relativistic energies we have practically completely polarized electron or positron beams. An even more incredible fact is that some of the methods used to analyze the electron polarization were completely unknown prior to recent events. We have been working with polarized beams of β particles for the past sixty years, yet we were completely unaware of this fact because of the faultiness* of our left-right symmetry conception.

Evidence for V − A Interaction

Suddenly many doors swung open to lead to the determination of the β interactions.

β-ν Angular Correlations. Before the discovery of parity nonconservation in β decay, the *ST* combination had been the favorite choice based mostly on He^6 β-ν angular-correlation results. In fact, the β-ν angular correlation was the only means used to investigate the type of β interactions in those days. But this type of experiment was known to be difficult. Wu and Schwartzschild (Wu-58b) made a detailed examination of the old He^6 experiment and pointed out that the effective volume of the He^6 source in the hole of the pumping diaphragm was not correctly taken into account. Had this been done properly, the results of He^6 would not have implied the tensor interaction. However, in spite of its many limitations, the β-ν correlation is still an effective and

* It is interesting to note the following comments by Mott and Massey on the results of electron polarizations in *The Theory of Atomic Collisions*, Second Edition, p. 83, "Although it cannot yet be said that the relativistic theory of scattering of fast electrons by atomic nuclei has been confirmed by experiment, the most recent observations are in good agreement with its predictions." And, on page 84, "The internal consistency of all the experimental results using beta rays is not good and it is likely that the discrepancies will largely disappear when radioactive sources are replaced by artificial ones of controlled energy." This reference relates to work by Bleuler et al. (B1-42). There was also previous experimental work by Cox et al. (Co-28) which provided early (but at the time unrecognized) evidence for parity nonconservation. Unfortunately, the poor collimation of the β beam, the thick scatterers used, the instability of the detector, and the small asymmetry effect, $N_{270^\circ}/N_{90^\circ} = 1.03$ observed, apparently did not instill confidence and discouraged further pursuance of this subject.

powerful method for yielding information on the β interaction. The first sign of warning against the *ST* combination in the β interaction came in May of 1957 when Allen and his co-workers of the University of Illinois (He-57) published their β-ν correlation results on A^{35}, which decays mainly via the Fermi interaction. The results strongly supported the *V* interaction instead of *S*, as was once believed. Later, this group remeasured the β-ν correlation in He^6 with the same apparatus they used in the investigation of A^{35} at Argonne National Laboratory. The result favors *A* in He^6. *Thus the VA combination is strongly favored from* β-ν *correlation experiments.*

On the other hand, the findings of two completely different parity experiments also reached the same conclusion. One experiment was actually carried out to determine the helicity of the neutrino in electron-capture processes and the other one was the investigation of β decay of polarized neutrons.

Electron-Capture Process in Eu^{152*}. In an electron-capture process, a neutrino and the recoil nucleus are emitted in opposite directions

$$e^- + \mathrm{p} \rightarrow \mathrm{n} + \nu \tag{1-9}$$

If the capture process is followed by the emission of a γ ray and the spin and parity changes are favorable as shown in the following decay process,

$$A(0^-) \xrightarrow{e^- \text{ capture}} B^*(1^-) \xrightarrow{\gamma \text{ ray}} B(0^+)$$

then by applying the conservation laws of momentum and angular momentum we can deduce a simple correlation that the helicity of the downward γ ray will be the same as that of the upward neutrino. So the problem of determining the neutrino helicity becomes that of measuring the circular polarization of the γ ray. However, to select only those downward γ rays following the emission of the upward neutrinos, we must fulfill many conditions. First, the γ ray must have an energy comparable to that of the neutrino, and the lifetime of the excited level B^* must be very short ($\sim 10^{-14}$ sec) in order to permit the use of solid material. Even then we must detect only the resonantly scattered γ ray.

The requirements were indeed strict, but the radioisotope Eu^{152*} seemed perfect for this job. Goldhaber, Grodzins, and Sunyar (Goldh-58) knew of this radioisotope Eu^{152*} from their previous investigations, and it fulfills all the requirements stated above. By measuring the circular polarization of those γ rays from Eu^{152*} which are resonantly scattered by Sm, they found that the helicity of the γ ray is negative ($\mathscr{P} = -0.67 \pm 0.10$). From this result and the results of many other parity experiments, one concludes that the helicity of the neutrino in electron capture is negative and, therefore, the Gamow-Teller interaction in electron capture is dominantly A and not T.

Beta Decay of Polarized Neutrons. Meantime, at the Argonne National Laboratory a highly polarized neutron beam had been successfully completed subsequent to 1957. Burgy et al. (Bu-58) had been studying the angular distribution of electrons and neutrinos from the β decays of polarized neutrons. They concluded that the interaction in β^- decay is dominantly V and A with opposite phase relations—that is, $V - A$.

Look back at the history of the theory of β decay. It has been filled with surprises and excitement. Now, after a period of nearly sixty years of continuous investigation, the nonconservation of parity finally comes along. These two (classical β-decay theory and nonconservation of parity) joined forces in the formulation of a definite conclusion concerning the form of the β interaction.

(π-e) *Decay.* The great similarity in the strength of the coupling constants in β decay, μ decay, and μ capture suggests that the interaction forms of the three decay processes may also be similar. This possibility seemed to be ruled out during the time when β-decay coupling was thought to be ST and μ-decay coupling was deduced to be dominantly V and A from the negative sign of the asymmetry coefficient. However, now that the β-decay interaction is also known to be VA the situation is quite altered. This is particularly intriguing because this specific form (of V and A) had been prophesied independently by Sudarshan and Marshak (Su-58), by Feynmann and Gell-Mann (Fey-58), and also by Sakurai (Sa-58a). Many theorists have since discovered various aspects of beauty in the $V - A$ interaction.

An interesting confirmation of the $V - A$ theory was the discovery of $\pi^+ \rightarrow e^+ + \nu$ decay (Fa-58; Im-58) in the summer of 1958. Ever since the discovery of the π it has been known to decay in the mode $\pi \rightarrow \mu + \nu$. On the basis of simple statistical arguments, however, we would also have expected $\pi \rightarrow e + \nu$ decay to occur and, in fact, to predominate. However, it was possible to construct special forms of the β theory, in particular the form involving $V - A$ for which the electron mode would occur only once in about every ten thousand decays. Until 1958, however, the experimental results indicated a branching ratio much smaller than that. Nevertheless, in the summer of 1958 the $\pi \rightarrow e + \nu$ decay mode was finally observed; its occurrence was apparent in about one in every ten thousand decays. This removed the last apparent obstacle in the way of acceptance of the $V - A$ theory. Of course, this could have been discovered quite independently of any results of parity nonconservation. However, the discovery of parity nonconservation so stimulated interest in the whole field of weak interactions that it has perhaps had a direct contributing influence in solving the strange puzzle of the pion decay.

*The Conserved Vector Current Hypothesis.** Following the proposed universal $V - A$ Fermi interaction (see Chap. 7), it was found that, to a close approximation (2–3%), the vector coupling constants in β decay and μ decay are equal. This near-equality raised a question. Why does not the meson cloud of the nucleon introduce any renormalization effects on G_V which have no counterpart for G_μ? To avoid this apparent paradox, a conservation law for the β-decay vector current was postulated and is known as the "theory of the conserved vector current" (see Sec. 7-3). Evidences for the existence of such a conserved vector current have been reviewed recently (Wu-64).

The Question of Invariance under Time Reversal. With the observation of nonconservation of parity in weak interactions, the mirror image is not the same as the real object. Does this mean that there is an intrinsic distinction between left and right? This may not be so. Although C and P invariances are both violated, the laws of physics may still be invariant under the combined operation of CP, as predicted by the theorists (Wi-52; La-57; Ya-56). In that case, all particles are replaced by their antiparticles when mirror images are taken, and the left-right symmetry in space is retained. This is indeed a very comforting thought, and the full implications of this idea are yet to be understood. But how can we prove that we have CP invariance? From the theorem of CPT invariance of field theory, we have CP invariance; then there must also be invariance with respect to time reversal (T) also. At present, there are several experiments in progress

---

* To be more precise, the conserved vector current hypothesis should be called the isotriplet vector current hypothesis (Lee-65).

to decide the question of the invariance under time reversal. Definitely, no violations of the invariance of T have been detected so far, and the indication, especially from the study of the decay of polarized neutrons, is that T is conserved to a good approximation (within 8° out of 180°). On the other hand, recent experiments on decay of K° mesons (Ch-64; Ab-64) suggest that even CP invariance may hold only approximately.

1-5 THE FIFTH PERIOD

No sooner was the theory of β decay in the low-energy region found to be in good shape than people began questioning the validity of the treatment of the effective Lagrangian as a strict-point interaction in the high-energy region. It was shown that the breakdown of the local four-fermion interaction in the high-energy region must occur because of its violation of the so-called "unitary condition" (Le-60a) (see Sec. 7-3).

This difficulty may be avoided if an intermediate vector boson W mediates the weak interactions, so that one is no longer dealing with a local interaction. For instance, nuclear β decay can be generated through the coupling

$$\mathrm{n} + \bar{\mathrm{p}} \rightleftarrows W \rightleftarrows e + \bar{\nu}_e$$

The boson W moves a small but finite distance before its decay; thus the electron is created at a slightly different point from where the neutron disappeared.

Although the existence of an intermediate boson may preclude the difficulty of violating unitarity, it creates other difficulties. If $W^\pm$ exists, then the W cloud around the μ can shake off a photon, which leads to $\mu^\pm \to e^\pm + \gamma$. The question raised, then, is why this electromagnetic decay of muon ($\mu \to e + \gamma$) has never been seen.

The way out of this difficulty is to assume the existence of at least two kinds of neutrinos of the same helicity (Le-60a). The one which couples to the μ is called ν_μ, and the other which couples to e is named ν_e.

No matter how fantastic these theoretical deductions might appear at first, two kinds of neutrinos have actually been observed and verified (Da-62; Ce-63). The possible existence of an intermediate vector boson and its properties are being investigated. Thus we have crossed the threshold leading into another brand new and exciting period—the fifth period—in the development of β decay or, more generally, weak interactions. Now we are looking forward to learning more about the form factors of weak interactions. Furthermore, the massless and chargeless neutrino may also acquire an electromagnetic current distribution through its weak interaction with other charged particles. If and when they are detected, the electromagnetic form factors of these two elusive particles—the muon neutrino and electron neutrino—will really electrify the imagination!

CHAPTER 2

Simple Theory of Beta Decay: Allowed Spectra

In this chapter we discuss a simplified version of the theory of β decay and its application. Relativity is taken into account insofar as we use the correct relation between energy, momentum, and velocity for the light particles (leptons) involved in the process. This is, of course, necessary, for the massless neutrinos move with the velocity of light, and the electrons are usually emitted with the kinetic energy comparable to their rest energy. On the other hand, we do not take into account the spin or the relativistic quantum mechanical effects on the wave function of the leptons. As we shall see, it is possible to understand the general shape of allowed spectra with this simple theory.

2-1 FERMI FORMULATION OF BETA DECAY

A quantum mechanical theory of β decay was first given by Fermi who postulated that the β emission is analogous to the process of electromagnetic radiation. The latter process can be treated both classically and quantum mechanically, and it is of interest at this point to review briefly some of its highlights.

From a classical point of view, electromagnetic radiation is due to a time-dependent interaction between the radiation system (say, an atom) and its surrounding electromagnetic field. This is given by the well-known expression

$$H_\gamma = -\sum \frac{e_n}{m_n c} \mathbf{p}_n \cdot \mathbf{A}(\mathbf{r}_n, t) \tag{2-1}$$

summed over all particles n of the system. The symbols e_n, m_n, $\mathbf{r}_n$, $\mathbf{p}_n$ denote, respectively, charge, mass, position, and momentum of particles n, and $\mathbf{A}$ is the vector potential. This interaction leads to an exchange of energy between the system and the field.

Quantum mechanically, radiation involves absorption or emission of photons. For example, the transition in which a photon (γ) is emitted and the radiating system jumps from an excited state n^* to a ground state n may be represented as

$$n^* \rightarrow n + \gamma \tag{2-2}$$

In the quantum mechanical treatment of radiation, we use an interaction of the same form as Eq. 2-1 but regard A as a time-dependent operator which can create or annihilate photons

$$A(\gamma) = \psi_\gamma^*(\mathbf{r}) + \psi_\gamma(\mathbf{r}) \tag{2-3}$$

Here ψ_γ annihilates a photon whose wave function is, in fact, simply

$$\psi_\gamma(\mathbf{r}) = \text{const} \times \boldsymbol{\epsilon} e^{i\mathbf{k}\cdot\mathbf{r}} \tag{2-4}$$

where $\boldsymbol{\epsilon}$ is the polarization vector and $\mathbf{k}$ is the wave number of the quantum. On the other hand, ψ_γ^* creates a photon with polarization $\boldsymbol{\epsilon}$ and wave number $\mathbf{k}$.

Nuclear β decay may be regarded as similar to photon emission except that two particles, the electron and neutrino, are emitted instead of one, the photon. Actually, we shall adopt the point of view that the number of light particles is conserved in the β process. This is known as lepton conservation. Thus, we should say that a negatron and *anti*-neutrino, the latter being an *anti*particle, are emitted together. This can be represented as

$$Z^A \rightarrow (Z + 1)^A + e^- + \bar{\nu} \tag{2-5}$$

In positron decay, on the other hand, a positron and neutrino are emitted:

$$Z^A \rightarrow (Z - 1)^A + e^+ + \nu \tag{2-6}$$

This conserves the number of particles, for the positron is considered the antiparticle of the electron. As we shall see, there is strong evidence that the ν and $\bar{\nu}$ are actually different particles, and we shall adopt this point of view here. However, the word "neutrino" is used conventionally to denote either the neutrino (ν) or the antineutrino ($\bar{\nu}$), not necessarily only the neutrino (ν) unless it is otherwise specified.

Guided by the above argument, we can make a first guess for the Hamiltonian of the β interaction

$$H_\beta = g \sum_n [\psi_e^*(\mathbf{r}_n)\psi_{\bar{\nu}}^*(\mathbf{r}_n)Q_n^+ + \psi_e(\mathbf{r}_n)\psi_{\bar{\nu}}(\mathbf{r}_n)Q_n^-] \tag{2-7}$$

summed over all particles in the nucleus. Here $\psi_e^*(\mathbf{r}_n)$ and $\psi_{\bar{\nu}}^*(\mathbf{r}_n)$ are the wave functions of the created electron and antineutrino at the position of the nth nucleon; $\psi_e(\mathbf{r}_n)$ and $\psi_{\bar{\nu}}(\mathbf{r}_n)$ are the corresponding ones for the annihilated leptons. As in electromagnetic radiation, these lepton fields may be regarded as radiation fields. Q_n^+ is an operator which changes a neutron into a proton but leaves its wave function otherwise unchanged. The operator Q_n^- induces the reverse transition. The so-called coupling constant g, analogous to the electric charge e in the electromagnetic theory, specifies the strength of the β-decay interaction. Note that the β-decay interaction, like the electromagnetic interaction, is assumed to be *local*; that is, the process is postulated to occur only when the nucleons and the leptons are at the same place.

The analogy can be expressed by the relations

$$-\frac{e_n}{m_n c}\mathbf{p}_n \rightarrow gQ_n^+, \qquad \mathbf{A} = \psi_\gamma^*(\mathbf{r}) \rightarrow \psi_e^*(\mathbf{r}_n)\psi_{\bar{\nu}}^*(\mathbf{r}_n)$$

Now, since the neutrino is uncharged, it has very little interaction with anything. Its wave function, normalized to one particle per unit volume, is given by a plane wave

$$\psi_{\bar{\nu}} = \exp(i\mathbf{p}_{\bar{\nu}} \cdot \mathbf{r}/\hbar) \tag{2-8}$$

On the other hand, the emitted electron is subject to the Coulomb field of the residual nucleus and the atomic electrons. Consequently, its wave function ψ_e is not a plane wave. We will not consider this effect at present but will return to it in Sec. 2-3. Another assumption made here is that the de Broglie wavelength of each lepton is large compared to the size of the nucleus. This corresponds to the dipole approximation made in quantum electrodynamics and is always satisfied for nuclear β decay. For example, in a typical β transition in which the electron has a kinetic energy of 1 mev, its wavelength is about 10^{-10} cm, whereas the radius of even the heaviest nuclei is less than 10^{-12} cm. Thus, inside the nucleus both lepton wave functions can be represented with little error by the wave functions at the center of the nucleus $\psi_e(0)$ or $\psi_{\bar{\nu}}(0)$. Thus $\psi_e(0)\psi_{\bar{\nu}}(0)$ will be nearly 1.

For mathematical convenience, it is desirable to write the β process in a slightly more symmetrical form, namely

$$Z^A + \nu \rightarrow (Z+1)^A + e^- \tag{2-9}$$

When expressed in this form there are *two particles absorbed and two created.* This is possible according to the Dirac theory since both the electron and the neutrino have negative as well as positive energy state, as indicated in Fig. 2-1.

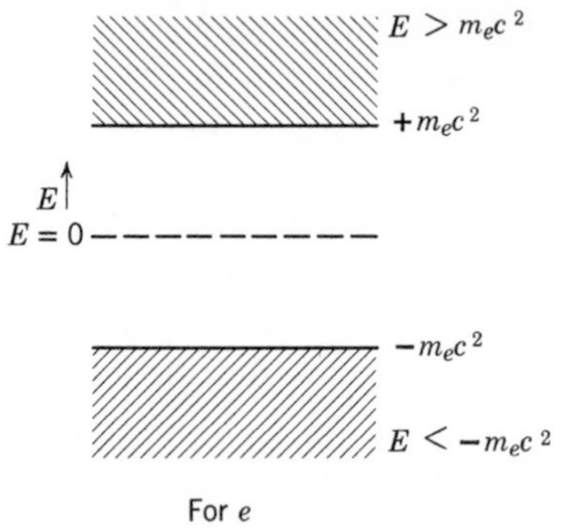

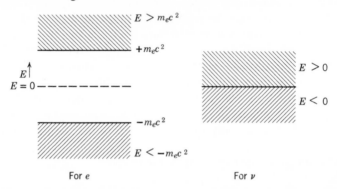

Fig. 2-1 Diagrams showing the positive and negative energy states of electron and neutrino according to the Dirac theory.

According to the Dirac theory (see Appendix II-4), negative energy states are normally completely filled with electrons, one in each state. When an electron is captured from a negative energy state, the resulting hole behaves precisely as an electron of positive charge, namely a positron. Thus, the capture of electrons from a negative energy state is equivalent to the emission of a positron. A more modern interpretation of positrons is that they are electrons moving backward in time; the results, however, are the same as for the Dirac interpretation (see Appendix II-4). In the same way, the capture of a neutrino from a negative energy state is equivalent to the emission of an antineutrino. If the antineutrino has energy E_ν and momentum $\mathbf{p}_\nu$, the corresponding neutrino must have been captured from a state of energy $-E_\nu$ and momentum $-\mathbf{p}_\nu$.

The corresponding β-decay Hamiltonian according to this symmetrical formulation can be written as

$$H_\beta = g \sum_n [\psi_e^*(\mathbf{r}_n)\psi_\nu(\mathbf{r}_n)Q_n^+ + \psi_e(\mathbf{r}_n)\psi_\nu^*(\mathbf{r}_n)Q_n^-] \tag{2-10}$$

2-2 BETA-SPECTRUM SHAPE FOR ALLOWED TRANSITIONS

Given the interaction, the decay probability of an electron with energy E per unit time is given by the well-known quantum mechanical expression

$$N(E)\,dE = \frac{2\pi}{\hbar}(H_{fi})^2\frac{dN_F}{dE_0} \tag{2-11}$$

where dN_F/dE_0 is the density of final states available to the system per unit range of total energy, and H_{fi} is the matrix element of the interaction H_β between initial (i) and final (f) states. According to the approximations made previously (Eq. 2-8), the matrix element of the interaction is given in full by

$$H_{fi} = g\int \psi_f^*\left(\sum_n Q_n^+\right)\psi_i\, d^3\mathbf{r}_1\, d^3\mathbf{r}_2 \cdots d^3\mathbf{r}_n \tag{2-12}$$

where ψ_i and ψ_f refer to the wave functions of the initial and final nucleus. In the case of neutron decay, we have $\psi_i = \psi_{\text{n}}$, $\psi_f = \psi_{\text{p}}$, but otherwise ψ_i and ψ_f denote states involving several nucleons. The integral appearing in this equation is conventionally denoted by the symbol $\int 1$. Its magnitude depends to some extent on the wave function of the nuclear states involved in the decay. It will be discussed more fully in Chap. 3. The other term containing the operator Q_n^- would change a proton into a neutron and, therefore, *cannot* contribute to β^- decay.

Next, consider the density of final states. In nuclear β decay, the vector momenta of the two leptons and the recoil nucleus must add up to 0, and their energies must add up to the total available energy. The maximum energy which the recoil can carry is usually negligible compared to the total decay energy E_0. On the other hand, there is no such restriction upon its momentum. In fact, if the nucleus is regarded as *infinitely* heavy, it can carry off any amount of momentum but practically no energy. Consequently, we may regard nuclear β decay as if it involved only *two* emitted particles—the leptons, which, between them, carry off all the available energy without any requirement of momentum conservation. Thus we have

$$E_e + E_{\bar{\nu}} = E_0 \tag{2-13}$$

The number of final states is then given by

$$dN_F = dN_e \, dN_{\bar{\nu}} \tag{2-14}$$

where dN_e denotes the number of states available to the electron and $dN_{\bar{\nu}}$ is the corresponding quantity for the antineutrino. To express the number of states in momentum space,

$$dN_e = \frac{4\pi p_e^{\,2}\, dp_e}{(2\pi\hbar)^3} \tag{2-15}$$

where $(2\pi\hbar)^3$ is the volume of phase space occupied by a single state of a particle.* The same thing applies to the antineutrino. Thus the density of final states per unit energy is

$$\frac{dN_F}{dE_0} = \frac{4\pi p_e^{\,2}\, dp_e}{(2\pi\hbar)^3} \frac{4\pi p_{\bar{\nu}}^{\,2}\, dp_{\bar{\nu}}}{(2\pi\hbar)^3} \frac{1}{dE_0} \tag{2-16}$$

If the rest mass of neutrino is zero, we can use

$$E_\nu = cp_\nu \qquad \text{and} \qquad E_\nu = E_0 - E_e \tag{2-17}$$

Furthermore, the neutrino momentum interval $dp_{\bar{\nu}}$ is to be taken per unit range of total energy E_0, whereas the β energy and momentum are held constant. That is,

$$dp_{\bar{\nu}} = \frac{dE_{\bar{\nu}}}{c} = \frac{dE_0}{c} \tag{2-18}$$

We can thus transform the expression for dN_F/dE_0 to

$$\frac{dN_F}{dE_0} = \frac{4\pi p_e^{\,2}\, dp_e}{(2\pi\hbar)^3} \frac{4\pi p_{\bar{\nu}}^{\,2}}{(2\pi\hbar)^3 c} = \frac{16\pi^2}{(2\pi)^6 \hbar^6 c^3} p_e^{\,2}(E_0 - E_e)^2 \, dp_e \tag{2-19}$$

in terms of distribution in momentum, or use the relation $c^2 p \, dp = E \, dE$ to express

$$\frac{dN_F}{dE_0} = \frac{1}{4\pi^4 \hbar^6 c^5} p_e E_e (E_0 - E_e)^2 \, dE_e \tag{2-20}$$

in terms of distribution in energy.

From Eq. 2-19 we can see that for small electron momentum the

* We assume a normalization of one particle per unit volume.

distribution is proportional to p^2. When the electron energy approaches the upper limit, the fractional variation of p^2 is small. Therefore the distribution is proportional to $(E_0 - E)^2$. In other words, the momentum distribution vanishes at both limits and has a maximum in the middle, as in Fig. 2-2*a* and *b*. However, the total number of electrons emitted per unit time with energies between E and $E + dE$ (the subscript e is omitted from now on) is then given by

$$N(E)\,dE = \frac{1}{2\pi^3 c^5 \hbar^7}\, g^2 \left| \int 1 \right|^2 pE(E_0 - E)^2\, dE \tag{2-21}$$

It is sometimes of interest to express the energy in units of the rest mass of the electron. Thus we will define a normalized energy

$$\epsilon = \frac{E}{mc^2} \tag{2-22}$$

Then the spectrum is given by

$$N(\epsilon)\,d\epsilon = \frac{mc^2}{\hbar}\frac{G^2}{2\pi^3} \left| \int 1 \right|^2 \epsilon\sqrt{\epsilon^2 - 1}\,(\epsilon_0 - \epsilon)^2\, d\epsilon \tag{2-23}$$

where G is a new coupling constant defined by

$$G = \frac{g}{mc^2}\left(\frac{mc}{\hbar}\right)^3 \tag{2-24}$$

This is identical with G_β defined in Chap. 1. Clearly, G is dimensionless, and both N and $mc^2/\hbar$ have the dimensions of an inverse time.

At this point it is of interest to consider some of the simplest features of the β spectrum.

From Eq. 2-23, if the total decay energy is much larger than the electron rest energy, the spectrum is approximately of the form

$$N(\epsilon)\,d\epsilon \sim \epsilon^2(\epsilon_0 - \epsilon)^2\, d\epsilon \tag{2-25}$$

In the other limit $\epsilon - 1 \ll 1$ we obtain

$$N(\epsilon)\,d\epsilon \sim \sqrt{(\epsilon - 1)}(\epsilon_0 - \epsilon)^2\, d\epsilon \tag{2-26}$$

(However, in the latter case, Coulomb corrections are of great importance and will change the spectrum shape considerably.) According

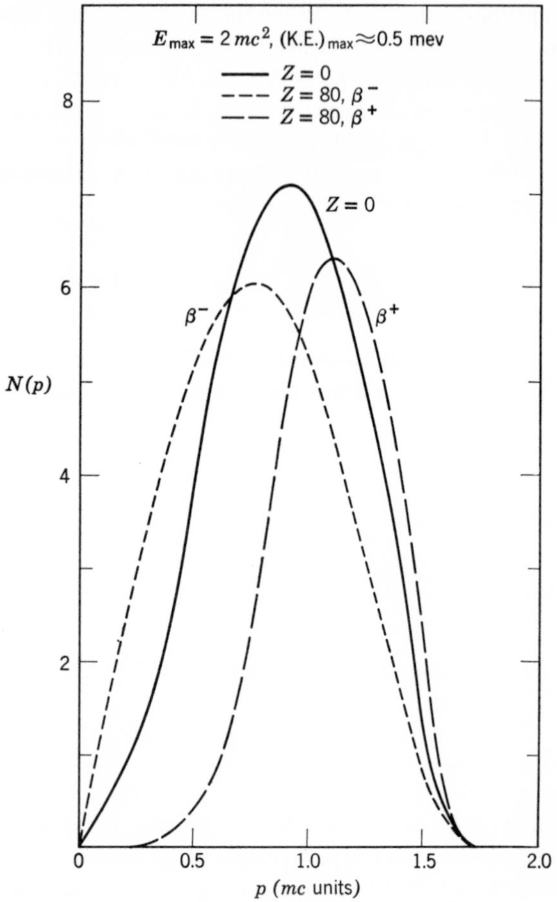

(*a*)

Fig. 2-2 The momentum distribution $N(p)\,dp$ for both β^- and β^+ spectrum with Coulomb correction of $Z = 80$ and $Z = 0$: (*a*) for $E_{max} = 2\,mc^2$, (*b*) for $E_{max} = 5\,mc^2$.

to the above, the ratio of the average electron kinetic energy to the maximum kinetic energy ranges from 1:3 for the low-energy limit to 1:2 for large decay energies.

The previous analysis also holds without essential change for positron decay, if we remember that positron creation can be regarded as absorption of an electron from a negative energy state. This process is governed by the second term of our basic Hamiltonian. Thus the

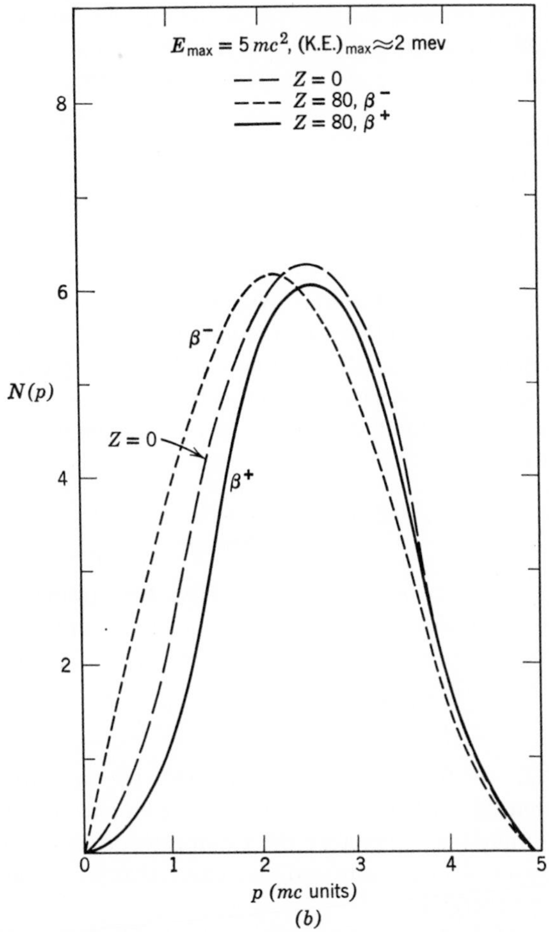

(b)

energy spectrum is given by the same expression as that for β^- decay, if we neglect Coulomb effects. However, as discussed in Chap. 1, the maximum positron energy is less than the total decay energy by $2\,mc^2 \sim 1.022$ mev (see Eq. 1-5).

2-3 EFFECT OF THE NUCLEAR COULOMB FIELD

So far we have assumed that the Coulomb force between the electron and the daughter nucleus can be neglected. Under such an assumption, the integral $\int |\psi_e|^2 \, dV_e$ over the interior of the nucleus can be approximated by $|\psi_e(0)|^2 \, V_N$ where $\psi_e(0)$ is the electron wave function evaluated at the center of the nucleus and V_N is the nuclear volume. It is obvious that the integral under the above assumption is an energy-independent factor, which has no effect on the energy distribution of the β spectrum. That is why the energy distribution of an allowed β spectrum with no Coulomb correction is solely determined by the statistical factor dN_F/dE_0 as in Eq. 2-21.

In reality, the Coulomb force on the electron must be taken into consideration, particularly for the low-energy β particles from high Z nuclei. Because of the Coulomb interaction, the factor $|\psi_e(0)|^2$ becomes energy dependent. Let us define the Coulomb correction factor $F(Z, E)$ as the ratio of the electron wave function evaluated at the center of the nucleus with Coulomb interaction to the electron wave function without it; that is,

$$F(Z, E) = \frac{|\psi_e(0)|_Z^2}{|\psi_e(0)|_{Z=0}^2} \tag{2-27}$$

By treating the electron nonrelativistically, the correction factor $F(Z, E)$ due to the nuclear Coulomb potential can be approximated by

$$F(Z, E) = \frac{2\pi\eta}{1 - e^{-2\pi\eta}} \tag{2-28}$$

where $\eta = \mp Ze^2/\hbar v$ for $\beta^\pm$ decays, v denotes the velocity of the electron far from the nucleus, and Z refers to the atomic number of the *final* (daughter) nucleus. Therefore the Coulomb correction enhances the probability of β^- emission and decreases that of β^+ emission, especially at low energies.

The influence of the Coulomb correction on the allowed momentum distribution for β^+ and β^- is illustrated in Fig. 2-2.

With a scintillation or proportional counter, the β spectrum is usually plotted according to its distribution in energy (Eq. 2-20). Figure 2-3 shows the theoretically calculated distributions in energy for allowed β^- and β^+ spectra with and without Coulomb correction. It is interesting to note that at energies close to the rest energy mc^2, the energy spectrum for no Coulomb field is proportional to p. However, if the Coulomb field is taken into account, the energy spectrum at low energies approaches a constant finite value for electrons and is proportional to $e^{-c/p}$ for positrons.

The Coulomb correction may be qualitatively interpreted as follows: The original energy distribution for β^- and β^+ at the moment of leaving the nucleus is the same and is represented by curve denoted by $Z = 0$. The Coulomb field of the nucleus accelerates the positrons and decelerates the electrons. Consequently, there are fewer positrons and more electrons in the low-energy regions of the respective spectra than there were for the original energy distribution.

A more accurate expression of the allowed β spectrum including the Coulomb correction is

$$N(E)\,dE = \frac{g_V^2}{2\pi^3}\,\mathrm{F}_0(\pm Z, E)pE(E_0 - E)^2 L_0\Big[\Big(\int 1\Big)^2 + \lambda^2\Big(\int \boldsymbol{\sigma}\Big)^2\Big] \tag{2-29}$$

where $L_0 = (2p^2\mathrm{F}_0)^{-1}(g_{-1}^2 + f_1^2)$

$$\lambda = -\frac{g_A}{g_V}$$

$$\mathrm{F}_0(\pm Z, E) = 4(2pR)^{2(\gamma-1)}e^{\pi y}\frac{|\Gamma(\gamma + iy)|^2}{[\Gamma(2\gamma + 1)]^2}$$

$$\gamma = \sqrt{1 - (\alpha Z)^2}, \quad \alpha = \frac{e^2}{\hbar c} = \frac{1}{137.03}, \quad y = \frac{\alpha Z E}{p}$$

The Coulomb correction term F_0 (Bh-62) enters into this expression twice; once it appears directly as $\mathrm{F}_0(\pm Z, E)$ and the other time through the symbol L_0. The Coulomb effect on L_0 is rather slight in all energy regions. However, the Coulomb correction on the Fermi function F_0 is important, particularly in the low-energy region. Here g_{-1} is the "large" radial function of an electron with angular momentum $\frac{1}{2}$ and parity $(-1)^1$, and f_1 is the corresponding "small" function for the same angular momentum and parity $(-1)^2$.

To calculate the Coulomb effects correctly we must formulate the electron radial functions by taking into account (a) the finite nuclear size effect, (b) the finite de Broglie wavelength effect, and (c) the electron screening effect.

The table which has been in common use for the F function was prepared in 1952 by the National Bureau of Standards (NBS-52). This table was calculated by assuming a point charge for the nucleus; the electronic radial functions are evaluated at the nuclear surface. Only the leading term in the expansion of the F function was retained.

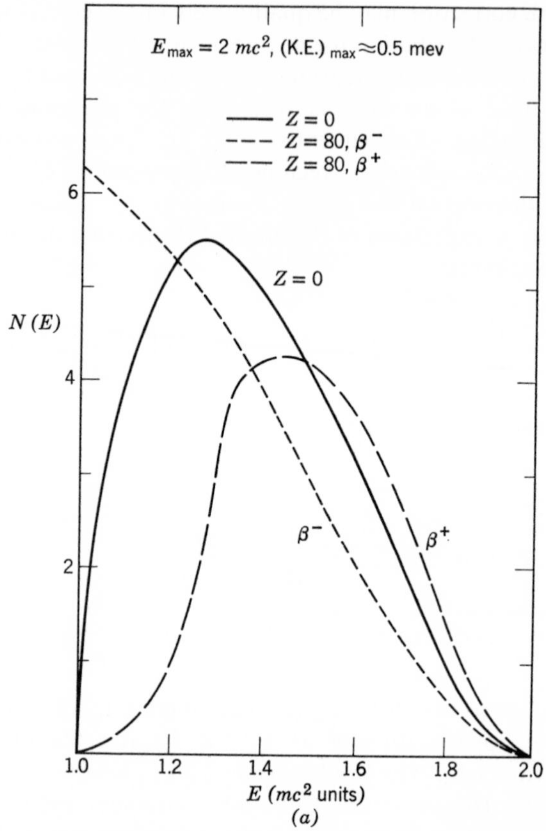

Fig. 2-3 The energy distribution $N(E)\,dE$ for both β^- and β^+ spectra with Coulomb correction of $Z = 80$ and $Z = 0$: (*a*) for $E_{max} = 2\,mc^2$, (*b*) for $E_{max} = 5\,mc^2$. Note that the energy spectrum of the β^- particles does not drop to zero but approaches a constant finite value toward $E = 1\,mc^2$.

In 1937, Rose (Ro-37) took account of the nuclear Coulomb field in terms of the electron Coulomb wave functions f_K and g_K, but only as it concerned a point nucleus. In 1951, Rose and Holmes (Ro-51a, b) calculated the electron wave functions for finite nuclear-size correction and prepared numerical tables for special functions L_i, M_i, and N_i. Yamada (Ya-53a, b) also studied the finite nuclear-size correction and noticed that this effect is particularly important when accidental cancellation among nuclear matrix elements occurs, such as in the case

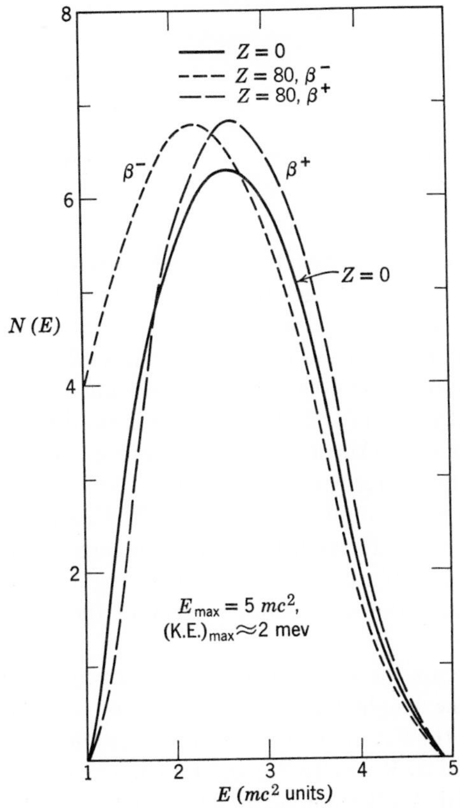

(b)

of RaE β spectrum (Ya-53c). Recently, Bühring (Bühr-63) has shown the importance of this effect on the interpretation of results from the first forbidden β transition. In 1953, Rose and his co-workers (Ro-53a, b) prepared tables for L_0, N_0, and the other spectral functions by including several higher terms in the power series of pR, thereby taking care of the finite de Broglie wavelength effect to a certain extent. This effect is important for the high-energy region.

Recently, Bhalla and Rose (Bh-62, 64) have prepared accurate electronic radial functions by considering the finite nuclear-size effects and the finite de Broglie wavelength effects simultaneously. The Fermi function is also tabulated. The Coulomb field of the daughter nucleus is represented by

$$V(r) = -\frac{\alpha Z}{r} \qquad \text{for } r > R$$

$$V(r) = -\frac{\alpha Z}{2r}\left(3 - \frac{r^2}{R^2}\right) \qquad \text{for } r < R$$

with $R = 1.2A^{1/3}f$.

The finite de Broglie wavelength effects are taken into account by expanding the confluent hypergeometric functions and retaining more than the leading term. The parameter in this series expansion is the product of the β momentum and the nuclear radius pR. Unfortunately, no electron screening effect was taken into account in the previously mentioned tables by Bhalla and Rose. There is another tabulation of the Fermi functions by Dzhelepov and Zyrianova (Dz-56). In these tables, both the finite nuclear-size effect and the electron screening effect are taken into account. Nevertheless, the corrections due to each effect are not separately listed; only the sum of both corrections is given. The finite de Broglie wavelength effect is taken care of by retaining the second-order term in the Fermi function expansion.

Now, let us discuss the electron screening correction. Because the Coulomb field of the daughter nucleus is screened by the orbital electron cloud, its effect on the Fermi function must be taken into account. This effect was estimated by Rose (Ro-36) and Longmire and Brown (Lo-49) by using a modified WKB method. It was calculated by Reitz (Re-50) by numerical integration of the Dirac equation using a Thomas-Fermi-Dirac model for the interaction between the electron and the residual ion. They showed that the correction reduces the nuclear Coulomb correction on electrons only slightly but is very important for positrons at low energies. In connection with the question of equality between g_V and g_μ, one must accurately calculate the ft values of the series $0^+ \rightarrow 0^+$ pure allowed Fermi transitions in order to determine g_V. The ft values from recent experimental results (Bardi-62; Ja-63; Fre-62; Fr-65) on O^{14}, Al^{26*}, Cl^{34}, Sc^{42}, V^{46}, Cr^{50}, and Co^{54}, by determining the nuclear Q values with high precision, have attained accuracies to 0.3 to 0.7%. Nevertheless, there is a large discrepancy between the electron screening correction calculated by Rose's approximation and the Reitz method (see Sec. 7-3).

2-4 THE KURIE PLOT

To facilitate the comparison between the experimental data to that of theoretically predicted distributions, Kurie (Ku-36) put forth a method of analysis based on the relation shown by Eq. 2-21; that is,

$$K(E) = \left[\frac{N(E)}{F(Z, E)pE}\right]^{1/2} \sim \text{const.} \times (E_0 - E) \qquad (2\text{-}30)$$

The quantities on the left-hand side are obtained from the measurements and from the tables of the Coulomb correction factor F. If the spectrum is of the allowed shape and if all the decays lead to one specific state of the final nucleus, a plot of $K(E)$ versus E should give a straight line with intercept on the energy axis at E_0. In fact, this provides a means of obtaining the total energy release in β^- decay. It is quite well established experimentally that the shape of the allowed β^- spectrum follows closely the predictions of the Fermi theory of β decay. However, since the mass of a β particle is small and the continuous energy distribution contains low-energy electrons as well as high-energy ones, the scattering and absorption effects easily distort the true shape of the spectrum and make it appear with a slight excess of the low-energy electrons. The great caution exerted since 1949 on the thinness and uniformity of the source preparation has eliminated practically all observed deviations in the low-energy region of the allowed spectrum. However, source preparation is not the only possible source of distortion; there are other problems, such as the scattering of β particles from the spectrometer walls and the baffle system, the energy dependence of the efficiency of the β detector, and the transmission and resolution properties of the β spectrometer. If a magnet with iron is used, its hysteresis and saturation properties must be checked.

Figures 2-4, 2-5, and 2-6 show the Kurie plots of the three simplest allowed β spectra—the neutron (Rob-51), H^3 (Cu-52), and He^6 (Sc-56). The neutron spectrum is taken with a coincidence arrangement between β and the recoil proton. The end point of 782 kev derived from the Kurie plot gives correctly the mass difference between neutron and hydrogen (Eq. 1-3). The H^3 spectrum is taken in a proportional counter; its Kurie plot is straight all the way down to 1 kev, the lowest β energy ever studied. The linearity of the He^6 Kurie plot extends to more than nine-tenths of its total range (0.25–3.50 mev). Many other

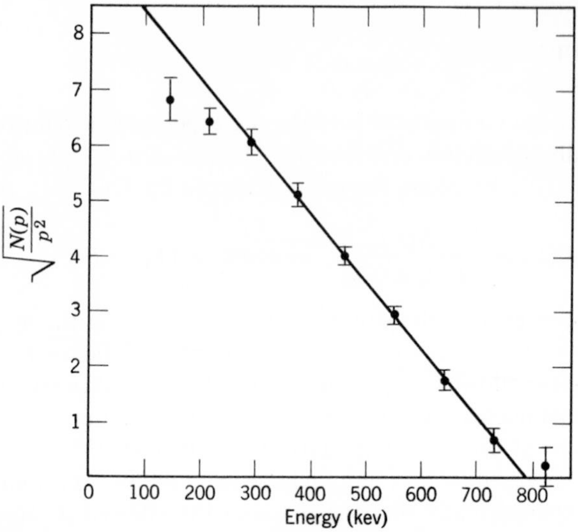

Fig. 2-4 The β spectrum of the neutron plotted as a Kurie plot. $N(p)$ is the number of coincidence per unit momentum interval between β particles and protons resulting from the neutron decay. From (Rob-51).

precision investigations of the allowed β spectra are all in good accord with the allowed shape. It is quite probable that some allowed β spectra of high Z or of exceptionally large ft values may exhibit a slight deviation of a few per cent from the straight Kurie plot at very low energies. These effects theoretically could be attributed to several

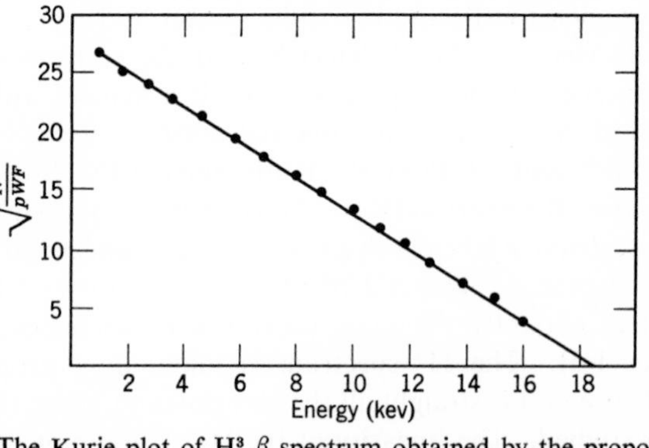

Fig. 2-5 The Kurie plot of H^3 β spectrum obtained by the proportional counter method showing the allowed form to below 1 kev. From (Cu-52).

possible causes, such as the finite nuclear-size correction, the finite de Broglie wavelength correction, and, for those transitions of exceptionally large *ft* values, the contributions from nuclear matrix elements of higher-order transitions. Nevertheless, these small deviations at the low-energy region can be differentiated easily from a nonallowed shape.

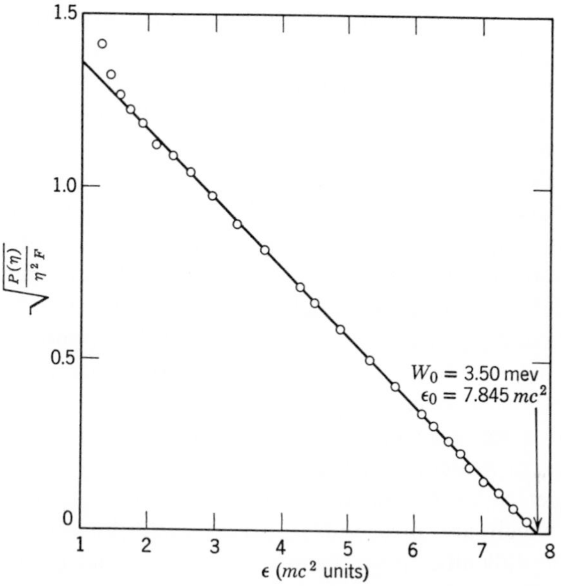

Fig. 2-6 The Kurie plot of He^6 β spectrum. The linear region extends from E_{max} = 3.5 mev down to 0.25 mev. From (Sc-56).

For certain types of β decay of very high energy, the upper-energy region may also show deviations from the linear plot according to the theory of conserved vector current. Such deviations have been reported in B^{12} and N^{12} (see Chap. 7).

2-5 THE REST MASS OF THE NEUTRINO

All the experimental evidence indicates that the rest mass of the neutrino is very small and may, in fact, be zero. Hence, for the sake of simplicity it is justifiable to neglect it in calculations of classical β decay. However, in the present theory of β decay and other weak interactions, the question about the rest mass of the neutrino assumes a rather important position. It is known that according to the two-component neutrino theory (see Sec. 4-3) the rest mass of the neutrino is expected to be identically zero. Second, it has recently been established (Da-62) that the neutrinos involved in β decay and in μ decay are two different particles. Naturally, it is extremely interesting to find out what properties and characteristics differentiate these two light neutral particles. Could it be that these two particles have different rest masses? Does the neutrino in β decay actually possess zero rest mass? If so, what is the evidence?

To obtain the neutrino rest mass by comparing the upper limits (E_{max}) of a β spectrum with the available β-decay energy is attractive in terms of its simplicity; however, it is not practical. Counting rates for β particles are always very small near the end of the spectrum. The only way to determine E_{max} accurately is by extrapolation of the linear Kurie plot. In doing so we unwittingly assume, at the beginning, a zero rest mass of the neutrino. This assumption makes extrapolation an unsuitable method for determining E_{max} (Ko-47).

There are two indirect methods of measuring neutrino masses. One is based on the measurement of nuclear recoil in β decay or K capture in order to determine the relation between the missing energy and momentum, which are presumably carried away by the neutrino. Because of the difficulties inherent in this method—that is, preparing a thin recoil surface and detecting and measuring the recoil spectrum—it is not easy to attain high precision. The other method is the investigation of the detailed shape of the beta spectrum in the vicinity of the upper limit. This method promises to give a more precise measurement of the neutrino rest mass.

The Relation between the Missing Energy and Momentum in Beta Decay

In this method we determine both the recoil momentum by the time-of-flight method and the momentum of β particles by magnetic deflection at specified angles to the recoil beam. The neutrino momentum, then, can be easily obtained by a simple momentum vector triangle. *In comparing the relation between the missing energy and momentum*, we gain information about the mass of the missing particle, the neutrino.

Sherwin (Sh-48, 51) was the first one to carry out such an investigation. He devoted a great deal of effort to preparing an approximate monolayer source of P^{32}. In plotting the missing energy against the missing momentum, a straight line passing through the origin was obtained. This was concluded to be $E = pc$ (within 10%), and consistent with zero rest mass. However, the scattering of the recoil ions was still quite bothersome, and Sherwin had to discard all the results that showed a smearing effect from the scattering. Therefore the validity of the results is still questionable.

Kofoed-Hansen (Ko-54b) and Snell and Pleasonton (Sn-55) used noble gas to circumvent the surface effect on the recoil ions. In their methods the principle is to measure either *the average recoil momentum* or *the average recoil energy*, since these recoil quantities are dependent on the mass of the missing particle. In Kofoed-Hansen's case the measured average recoil momentum (812 $\pm$ 8) kev/c from K capture in Ar^{37} was compared favorably with the known decay energy from reaction data (815 $\pm$ 2) kev. This result is consistent with the zero rest mass and yields an upper limit of the neutrino mass of < 8 kev/c^2. Snell and Pleasonton compared their measured *average recoil energy* (9.63 $\pm$ 0.06) ev from decay of Ar^{37} to the value (9.65 $\pm$ 0.05) ev, as calculated from Q values.and with an assumed zero neutrino mass. This agreement again favors the zero neutrino mass or sets an upper limit on the neutrino mass of < 6 kev/c^2.

The methods just discussed, although lacking in precision, illustrate the simple kinematic relations in β decay and the closeness with which the energy and momentum of the neutrino can be related by $E = pc$.

The Detailed Shape of the Beta Spectrum in the Vicinity of Its Upper Limit

It can be shown that the precise shape of the allowed β spectrum in the vicinity of its upper limit depends on the rest mass of the neutrino. Let us suppose that the rest mass of the neutrino were different from zero. The total neutrino energy E_ν would then be given by

$$E_\nu = (E_{\max} - E_e) + m_\nu c^2$$

where m_ν is the neutrino rest mass.

The Statistical Factor. The statistical factor $p_e E_e p_\nu E_\nu$ which determines the allowed electron-spectrum shape is now proportional to

$$p_e E_e[(E_{\max} - E_e) + m_\nu c^2]\{[(E_{\max} - E_e) + m_\nu c^2]^2 - m_\nu^2 c^4\}^{1/2} \quad (2\text{-}31)$$

Near the upper end point the factors p_e and E_e may be considered to be constant as $E_e \to E_{\max}$. The factor $E_{\max} - E_e + m_\nu c^2$, which is the total energy of the neutrino, may also be considered constant as long as $E_{\max} - E_e \ll m_\nu c^2$. However, the last term, which represents the momentum of the neutrino, may be rewritten as $[2m_\nu c^2(E_{\max} - E_e)]^{1/2}$.

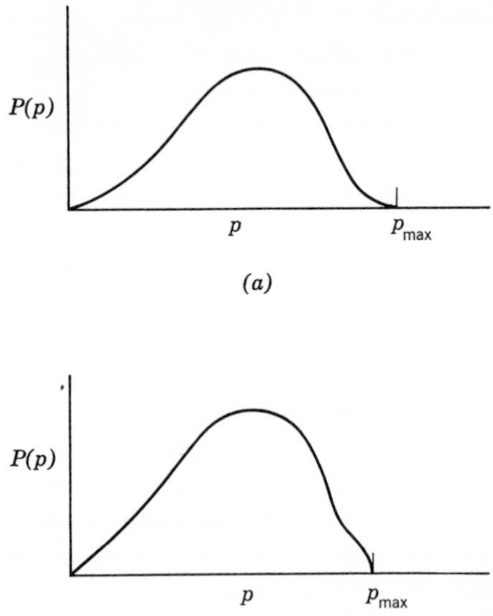

(b)

Fig. 2-7 Showing the dependence of the form of $P(p)$ near its maximum value on the rest mass of the neutrino m_ν: (a) for $m_\nu = 0$, (b) for $m_\nu \neq 0$.

This is the nonrelativistic expression of the momentum of the neutrino. At its upper limit, therefore, the energy spectrum would go to zero with a vertical tangent such as $(E_{\max} - E_e)^{1/2}$, as contrasted with the curve for a zero neutrino rest mass, which, as it approaches zero, would have a horizontal tangent such as $(E_{\max} - E_e)^2$ (see Fig. 2-7).

The general evidence based on the best-measured β spectra ruled out the vertical approach of the upper end of the spectrum to the energy axis. Nevertheless, to set an upper limit to the rest mass of the neutrino, the upper portion of the experimentally observed Kurie plot must be carefully compared with theoretically predicted ones of various assumed neutrino masses.

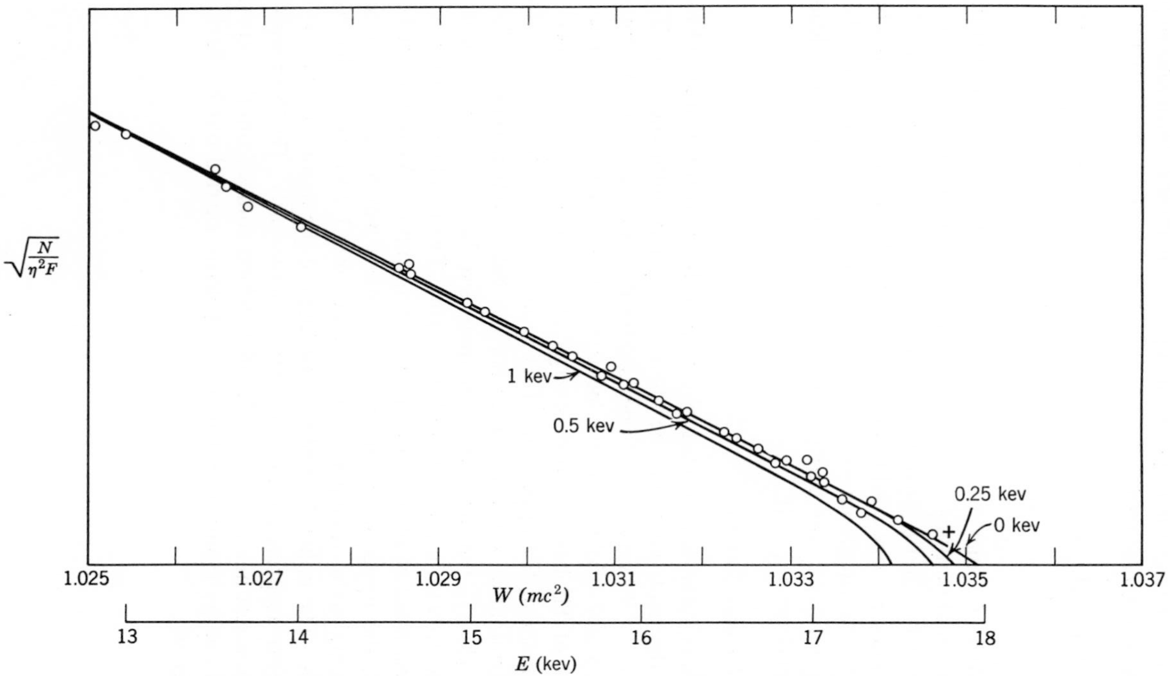

Fig. 2-8 An expanded Fermi plot of the end of the H^3 β^- spectrum obtained with a high-resolution magnetic spectrometer. The data are consistent with a neutrino rest mass of zero, and the upper limit is less than 250 ev. From (La-52).

The Relativistic Spinor Term. Actually, if the rest mass of the neutrino is not zero, the β spectrum depends on another term known as the *relativistic spinor term*:

$$P(E_e)\,dE_e \sim \underbrace{p_e E_e p_\nu E_\nu}_{\text{Statistical factor}} \underbrace{\left[1 + \frac{\alpha m_e^2 c^4}{E_e(E_{\max} - E_e + m_\nu c^2)}\right]}_{\text{The relativistic spinor term}} \qquad (2\text{-}32)$$

The coefficient α may vary between -1 and $+1$ according to (a) the definitive combinations of β interactions, and (b) the relative parities of the neutrino and e^- involved. In the preparity days the value of α was not known; one could only set an upper limit on m_ν for possible values of α varying from -1 to $+1$. This ambiguity is now removed (Sa-58a; En-57) by the parity nonconservation in β decay which leads to the conclusion $\alpha = 0$.

Experimental Results

The most suitable β spectra which could be used for evaluating the mass of the neutrino would be those of low maximum energies. The β spectrum of S^{35} was the first one used for this evaluation and an upper limit of 5 kev (Co-48) for the neutrino mass was obtained. The β spectrum of H^3 has an upper energy of 18.6 kev, so that a precise measurement of the upper end of its spectrum offers the best case for this determination. The H^3 spectrum has been studied very carefully (La-52; Ha-53), but the Kurie plot appears to be linear near the upper end point to within the experimental error. The results are consistent with a rest mass of zero for the β-decay neutrino ν_e. As is indicated in Fig. 2-8, the upper limit on the ν_e rest mass which can still fit the experimental data (taking $\alpha = 0$) is 250 ev, only 1/2000 of the electron rest mass. The upper limit of the rest mass of the muon neutrino ν_μ is not known as precisely as that of its counterpart. The best upper limit of the rest mass of ν_μ is < 3.5 mev, which comes from the experiment on energy-momentum balance in π decay carried out by Barkas et al. (Ba-56).

CHAPTER 3

Classical Beta Decay

In this chapter, we shall generalize the treatment of the β-decay process in order to take into account the spins of the elementary particles involved. The β-decay interaction can then have several possible forms besides the simple one discussed in Chap. 2. The number of such forms is, however, severely limited by the requirement that the interaction Hamiltonian be invariant under proper Lorentz transformations.

We will not take up the problem of parity nonconservation until Chap. 4. In the present chapter we shall treat the β interaction as invariant under space inversions; indeed, it was generally believed to be so until 1957. This "classical" version of the β-decay theory can still be used to interpret the results of many important experiments not directly involving parity nonconservation, such as β-decay lifetimes, electron-neutrino angular correlations, and shapes of allowed and forbidden spectra.*

3-1 THE POSSIBLE FORMS OF THE BETA INTERACTION

Let us look at the simple expression

$$\mathscr{H} = g(\psi_p{}^\dagger Q^+ \psi_n \psi_e{}^\dagger \psi_\nu + \text{h.c.}) \tag{3-1}$$

which represents the simplest possible form of the β-decay interaction.† If each of the nucleon and electron wave functions were functions of position only, this interaction which is a linear function of all the wave

---

* However, it is also possible to incorporate parity nonconservation into the theory from the very beginning and work in terms of helicities, that is, polarizations of the leptons. See, for example, Lipkin's *Beta Decay for Pedestrians* (Li-62).

† This quantity is a Hamiltonian density. It is related to the Hamiltonian H_β defined in Chap. 2 by $\mathscr{H} = \psi_p{}^\dagger H_\beta \psi_n$.

functions, would, in fact, be the only one possible. However, each of the particles involved also has a spin—an intrinsic angular momentum which has been measured to be $\frac{1}{2}\hbar$ for nucleons and electrons and is also strongly believed to be $\frac{1}{2}\hbar$ for a neutrino. Thus the wave function of each particle depends not only on position but also on the orientation of its intrinsic spin. In other words, the z component of the spin may be either $+\frac{1}{2}\hbar$ or $-\frac{1}{2}\hbar$. This increases the possible number of forms for the β interaction.

Now consider the effect of the spin, but for the moment treat all the particles nonrelativistically. Then the wave function of each particle is of the form

$$\psi = \begin{pmatrix} u^{(1)} \\ u^{(2)} \end{pmatrix} e^{ip\cdot x/\hbar} \tag{3-2}$$

where the symbols $\begin{pmatrix} u^{(1)} \\ u^{(2)} \end{pmatrix}$ denote, respectively, the probability amplitude of finding the particle with z component of spin, either plus or minus—that is, with the spin directed either up or down. The corresponding Hermitian conjugate* wave function $\psi^\dagger$ is given by

$$\psi^\dagger = (u^{(1)*}u^{(2)*})e^{-ip\cdot x/\hbar}$$

Now let us construct a product of electron and neutrino wave functions, a so-called bilinear combination of their wave functions, of the form $\psi_e{}^i\psi_\nu{}^j$. Since i and j may each take the values 1 and 2, we have altogether four independent ways of constructing such a combination. We may go one step further and see that there are sixteen different forms for the nonrelativistic β-decay interaction, namely,

$$g(\psi_{\mathrm{p}}^{\dagger(i)}Q^{+}\psi_{\mathrm{n}}^{(j)}\psi_e^{\dagger(k)}\psi_\nu^{(l)} + \text{h.c.}) \tag{3-3}$$

Invariance Requirements

If there were no further restrictions, any linear combination of these sixteen basic forms would be a possible form for the β-decay interaction. But now let us look at a particular one of these sixteen basic forms

$$\psi_{\mathrm{p}}^{\dagger(1)}Q^{+}\psi_{\mathrm{n}}^{(1)}\psi_e^{\dagger(1)}\psi_\nu^{(1)} \tag{3-4}$$

* The Hermitian conjugate wave function $\psi^\dagger$ is defined as a row matrix consisting of one row and N columns. The superscript † denotes the transposed conjugate—that is, the matrix where rows and columns are interchanged—and the complex conjugate of each element is taken: $\beta_{ln}^\dagger = \beta_{nl}^*$.

This form implies that the β-decay process can take place only if *all* four particles have the spin directed along the z axis. If we rotate our reference frame, then, in general, the form of the interaction will look different in the new reference frame. Put another way, an interaction of this form implies that a particular direction in space, in this case the z direction, is given special significance. But there are no reasons at all to believe that the laws of nature can single out any particular direction in space. In other words, as far as we know, our universe is isotropic. Of course, if we write down any interaction Hamiltonian with respect to some reference frame and then redefine the reference frame, say by rotation of the coordinate axes, the Hamiltonian expressed in a new coordinate system must have the same form as before. That is, in the nonrelativistic treatment (but not under Lorentz transformations), the Hamiltonian must be invariant with respect to rotations and reflections. This invariance requirement rules out such an interaction as the one just given.

In order to construct the invariant interaction forms, we write the four bilinear combinations of lepton wave functions a little differently than before, namely as

$$\psi_e^{\dagger}\psi_\nu, \quad \psi_e^{\dagger}\sigma_x\psi_\nu, \quad \psi_e^{\dagger}\sigma_y\psi_\nu, \quad \psi_e^{\dagger}\sigma_z\psi_\nu$$

where σ denotes Pauli spin matrices. It is shown in Eq. I-33 that the first combination is a scalar (S), whereas the last three transform under rotations as the three components of an axial vector (A). The only way to combine such terms in such a way as to obtain a scalar is to write either the product $S \cdot S$ or $A \cdot A$. Thus it is readily seen that there are only two linear combinations of the sixteen interaction forms which are invariant under rotation. These permitted forms are

$$(\psi_{\mathrm{p}}^{\dagger}Q^{+}\psi_{\mathrm{n}})(\psi_e^{\dagger}\psi_\nu) \tag{3-5}$$

$$\sum_{\mu}(\psi_{\mathrm{p}}^{\dagger}Q^{+}\sigma_\mu\psi_{\mathrm{n}})(\psi_e^{\dagger}\sigma_\mu\psi_\nu) \tag{3-6}$$

where σ_μ are the Pauli spin matrices.

Selection Rules

Fermi Interactions: $\Delta I = 0$; (no). The first form, the so-called Fermi interaction, is essentially the same as the one considered previously, except that the product $\psi_e^{\dagger}\psi_\nu$ now means

$$\psi_e^{\dagger(1)}\psi_\nu^{(1)} + \psi_e^{\dagger(2)}\psi_\nu^{(2)} \tag{3-7}$$

This form implies that the electron created and the neutrino destroyed have spins of the same direction; therefore no spin flip of the nucleons is required. It leads to selection rules for nuclear β decay as follows. The Hamiltonian density for general β^- decay can be written in a way slightly different from that used previously, namely

$$\mathscr{H} = g(\psi_f^\dagger \sum_n Q_n^+ \psi_i)(\psi_e^\dagger \psi_\nu) \tag{3-8}$$

where ψ_i and ψ_f denote initial and final nuclear states, and the operator Q^+ changes a neutron into a proton but does not flip the spin. In other words, i and f must have the same angular momentum. Thus one of the selection rules governing the spin change in Fermi transitions is $\Delta I = 0$. In addition there is a selection rule on the parity of the nuclear state involved. Let us neglect the dependence of ψ_e and ψ_ν on position; that is, we will make the long wavelength approximation. Now the nuclear wave functions have either even or odd parity. In other words, the wave functions will not change (or change signs) under space inversion ($\mathbf{r} \to -\mathbf{r}$). It is evident that since $\psi_e^\dagger \psi_\nu$ is independent of position, the matrix element of $\mathscr{H}$ vanishes unless the initial and final nuclear states have the same parity. Thus the Fermi transitions are subject to an additional selection rule—no change of parity, $\pi_i = \pi_f$, which is usually denoted by writing down a "no" in parentheses, (no).

Gamow-Teller Interaction: $\Delta I = 0;\ \pm 1$, (no $0 \to 0$); (no). Now consider the second possible nonrelativistic form for the β interaction first suggested by Gamow and Teller. This form can be written as

$$\mathscr{H} = g \sum_\mu (\psi_f^\dagger \sum_n Q_n^+ \sigma_\mu \psi_i)(\psi_e^\dagger \sigma_\mu \psi_\nu) \tag{3-9}$$

The three components of the axial vector $\psi_e^\dagger \sigma_\mu \psi_\nu$, namely

$$\psi_e^\dagger \sigma_x \psi_\nu \quad \psi_e^\dagger \sigma_y \psi_\nu \quad \psi_e^\dagger \sigma_z \psi_\nu$$

are defined in Appendix I (Eq. I-32). An alternative way of representing the interaction is

$$\mathscr{H} = g \sum_m (\psi_f^\dagger \sum_n Q_n^+ \sigma_m \psi_i)(\psi_e^\dagger \sigma_{-m} \psi_\nu)$$

where

$$\sigma_1 = \frac{1}{\sqrt{2}}(\sigma_x + i\sigma_y)$$

$$\sigma_0 = \sigma_z$$

$$\sigma_{-1} = \frac{1}{\sqrt{2}}(\sigma_x - i\sigma_y)$$

In this case the electron and antineutrino have parallel spins; that is, they carry away a total angular momentum of one unit of $\hbar$. This means that the nuclear spin can change by one unit of $\hbar$, $|\mathbf{I}_i - \mathbf{I}_f| = \hbar$. However, we can also have transitions in which $I_i = I_f$, $\Delta I = 0$. This is illustrated in Fig. 3-1. Here the direction of the nuclear spin, but not its magnitude, changes. On the other hand, transitions in which $I_i = I_f = 0$—that is, $0 \rightarrow 0$ transitions—are absolutely forbidden for Gamow-Teller interactions.

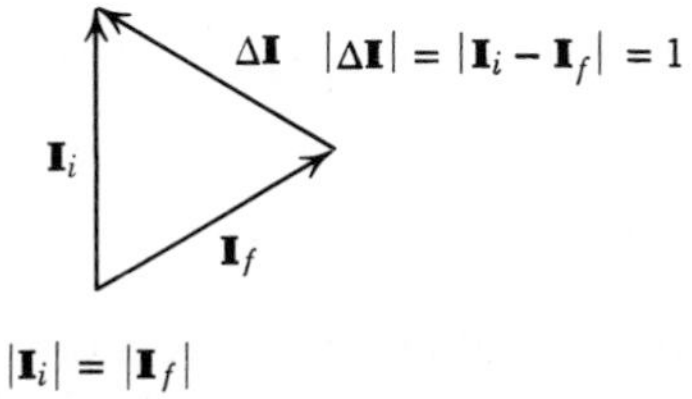

Fig. 3-1 A vector diagram illustrating the possible vector change of angular momentum in an allowed Gamow-Teller interaction. The direction of the nuclear spin changes but not its magnitude.

Therefore, for Gamow-Teller transitions the selection rules on angular momentum are $\Delta I = 0$ or ± 1, but not $0 \rightarrow 0$. It is also easy to see, since a spin operator $\boldsymbol{\sigma}$ has even parity, that the parity of the nucleus cannot change in the transition $\pi_i = \pi_f$ (Appendix I-1).

Altogether, according to the preceding arguments, the most general nonrelativistic form of the β-decay interaction is

$$\mathscr{H} = g_{\mathrm{F}}(\psi_{\mathrm{p}}{}^{\dagger}Q^{+}\psi_{\mathrm{n}})(\psi_{e}{}^{\dagger}\psi_{\nu}) + g_{\mathrm{GT}}\sum_{\mu}(\psi_{\mathrm{p}}{}^{\dagger}Q^{+}\sigma_{\mu}\psi_{\mathrm{n}})(\psi_{e}{}^{\dagger}\sigma_{\mu}\psi_{\nu}) + \text{h.c.} \tag{3-10}$$

where g_{F} and g_{GT} are coupling constants for Fermi and Gamow-Teller transitions. It is convenient to express all coupling constants in terms of a single one, and we can do this by writing

$$\begin{aligned} g_{\mathrm{F}} &= gC_{\mathrm{F}} \\ g_{\mathrm{GT}} &= gC_{\mathrm{GT}} \end{aligned} \tag{3-11}$$

where C_{F} and C_{GT} are taken to be dimensionless numbers. Then the number of electrons emitted per second is given by

$$N(E) = \frac{m^5c^4}{2\pi^3\hbar^7}\, g^2\mathrm{F}(\pm Z, E)\left(C_{\mathrm{F}}{}^2\left|\int 1\right|^2 + C_{\mathrm{GT}}^2\left|\int \boldsymbol{\sigma}\right|^2\right) \times pE(E_0 - E)^2\, dE \tag{3-12}$$

where the nuclear matrix elements $\int 1$ and $\int \boldsymbol{\sigma}$ are defined by

$$\left|\int 1\right| = \left\langle \int \psi_f^{\dagger} \left| \sum_n Q_n^{+} \right| \psi_i \right\rangle \tag{3-13}$$

$$\left|\int \sigma_\mu\right| = \left\langle \int \psi_f^{\dagger} \left| \left(\sum_n Q_n^{+}\sigma_\mu\right) \right| \psi_i \right\rangle$$

and

$$\left|\int \boldsymbol{\sigma}\right|^2 = \sum_\mu \left|\int \sigma_\mu\right|^2 \tag{3-14}$$

In evaluating $|\int \boldsymbol{\sigma}|^2$ we must sum over all possible orientations of angular momentum of the final state. Now, since the operator σ_μ can change I and m by one unit, we can have

$$m_f = m_i \quad \text{or} \quad m_f = m_i \pm 1 \tag{3-15}$$

However, because of rotational invariance the transition probability must be independent of m_i, the magnetic quantum number of the initial state. Finally, note from Eq. 3-12 that the spectrum shape is not at all altered by our taking spin into account. It is still the statistical shape derived in Chap. 2.

Relativistic Formulation

Now let us generalize our arguments and take into account the fact that the electrons involved in β decay are relativistic particles. The neutrino always moves with the velocity of light c and the velocity of an electron is usually an appreciable fraction of c. We can go even further and also treat the nucleons relativistically so as to handle all particles on the same footing. In the Fermi theory of β decay, each particle is assumed to obey the Dirac equation. The Dirac wave function for each particle has four components as opposed to two in the nonrelativistic case. The Dirac wave functions are discussed in Appendix II. There are, then, sixteen ways of forming bilinear combinations of the form

$$\psi_e^{\dagger(i)}\psi_\nu^{(j)}$$

and 256 linearly independent interaction forms which are products of the wave functions of all four particles,

$$\psi_{\mathrm{p}}^{\dagger(i)}Q^{+}\psi_{\mathrm{n}}^{(j)}\psi_e^{\dagger(k)}\psi_\nu^{(l)}$$

Relativistic Invariance Requirements. Again relativistic invariance requirements drastically reduce the number of permitted forms of the β interaction. In this case we require that the interaction Hamiltonian be unchanged not only under rotations but also under "pure" Lorentz transformations, which implies a transformation to a new reference frame moving at uniform velocity with respect to the old one.* In other words, all relativistic formulations require invariance under all *proper Lorentz transformations* (Appendix I-1). There is also the problem of how the Hamiltonian behaves under inversion of the coordinate system, or what is the same thing, under a mirror reflection with respect to an arbitrary plane, which is equivalent to changing all right-handed motion into left-handed motion and vice versa. In the nonrelativistic case this problem does not come up, since both of the two interaction forms which are invariant under rotations, 1·1 and $\boldsymbol{\sigma} \cdot \boldsymbol{\sigma}$, are also invariant under space inversion.† However, in the relativistic theory such is not the case. In fact, the results of the parity experiment prove that the β-decay interaction is not invariant under space inversion. We will return to this point in Chap. 4. Meanwhile, we will adopt a pre-1957 or "classical" point of view, which held that the β-decay interaction should be a *true* scalar—in other words, invariant under space inversion as well as under Lorentz transformation. Although this view is now known to be incorrect, it must be remembered that there was no a priori reason to believe in any asymmetry of the laws of nature with respect to handedness, such as is now required by parity nonconservation. The classical treatment can still be used to interpret the results of many important β-decay experiments such as electron-neutrino angular correlations, β-decay lifetimes, and energy spectra. Furthermore, in order to illustrate the beautiful and deductive manner in which the theory of β decay was progressively developed into its present status, it is essential to start with the old version and then modify it according to the necessities of the new experimental findings. Thus we will use the old version of the theory in the remainder of this chapter. It turns out that of the 256 independent possible forms for the β interaction

---

* Actually, it is the Lagrangian density $\mathscr{L}$ which must be invariant under Lorentz transformations. It is shown in standard books on field theory that this invariance leads to Lorentz invariant field equations. For the β interaction, $\mathscr{L}$ is a function of the wave functions themselves and not of their derivatives. Then the Hamiltonian density $\mathscr{H} = -\mathscr{L}$ so that the Hamiltonian density is also invariant. On the other hand, the energy is the 4-4 component of the energy momentum tensor and is not invariant.

† This conclusion holds only if (as assumed here), the interaction does not contain derivatives of the wave functions.

only five true scalars can be formed. One of these, the so-called scalar interaction, is of the form

$$\mathcal{H}_s = g_s(\tilde{\psi}_{\rm p}\, Q^+ \psi_{\rm n})(\tilde{\psi}_e \psi_\nu) = g_s(\psi_{\rm p}{}^\dagger Q^+ \beta \psi_{\rm n})(\psi_e{}^\dagger \beta \psi_\nu) \qquad \text{(3-16)}$$

This looks almost the same as in the nonrelativistic case except that the quantity $\tilde{\psi}$, the adjoint wave function, is defined slightly differently than in the nonrelativistic case, namely $\tilde{\psi} = \psi^\dagger \beta$, where $\psi^\dagger$ is the Hermitian conjugate of ψ, and β is a Dirac matrix (more details in Appendix II-2). The interaction is called a scalar interaction since both covariants $\tilde{\psi}_{\rm p}\psi_{\rm n}$ and $\tilde{\psi}_e\psi_\nu$ are *themselves* scalars.

The second possible form can be written as

$$\begin{aligned}\mathcal{H}_V &= g_V \sum_\mu (\tilde{\psi}_{\rm p}\, Q^+ \gamma_\mu \psi_{\rm n})(\tilde{\psi}_e \gamma_\mu \psi_\nu) \\ &= g_V(\psi_{\rm p}{}^\dagger Q^+ \psi_{\rm n})(\psi_e{}^\dagger \psi_\nu) - g_V(\psi_{\rm p}{}^\dagger Q^+ \boldsymbol{\alpha} \psi_{\rm n})(\psi_e{}^\dagger \boldsymbol{\alpha} \psi_\nu) \qquad \text{(3-17)}\end{aligned}$$

where γ_μ are the gamma matrices (discussed in Appendix II-2). This interaction was, in fact, the one proposed by Fermi in his original paper on the theory of β decay; it is called the vector interaction because each of the covariants $\tilde{\psi}_{\rm p}\gamma_\mu\psi_{\rm n}$ and $\tilde{\psi}_e\gamma_\mu\psi_\nu$ transforms as a four-vector. The product of these two covariants is, of course, a scalar, just as the scalar product of two vectors. The three other possible forms are the tensor interaction

$$\begin{aligned}\mathcal{H}_{\rm T} &= g_{\rm T} \sum_{\mu<\lambda} (\tilde{\psi}_{\rm p} Q^+ \gamma_\mu \gamma_\lambda \psi_{\rm n})(\tilde{\psi}_e \gamma_\mu \gamma_\lambda \psi_\nu) \\ &= g_{\rm T}(\psi_{\rm p}{}^\dagger Q^+ \beta \boldsymbol{\sigma} \psi_{\rm n})(\tilde{\psi}_e{}^\dagger \beta \boldsymbol{\sigma} \psi_\nu) + g_{\rm T}(\psi_{\rm p}{}^\dagger Q^+ \beta \boldsymbol{\alpha} \psi_{\rm n})(\psi_e{}^\dagger \beta \boldsymbol{\alpha} \psi_\nu) \qquad \text{(3-18)}\end{aligned}$$

the axial-vector interaction

$$\begin{aligned}\mathcal{H}_A &= g_A(\tilde{\psi}_{\rm p} Q^+ i\gamma_5 \gamma_\mu \psi_{\rm n})(\tilde{\psi}_e i\gamma_5 \gamma_\mu \psi_\nu) \\ &= g_A(\psi_{\rm p}{}^\dagger Q^+ \boldsymbol{\sigma} \psi_{\rm n})(\psi_e{}^\dagger \boldsymbol{\sigma} \psi_\nu) - g_A(\psi_{\rm p}{}^\dagger Q^+ \gamma_5 \psi_{\rm n})(\psi_e{}^\dagger \gamma_5 \psi_\nu) \qquad \text{(3-19)}\end{aligned}$$

and the pseudoscalar interaction.

$$\mathcal{H}_P = g_P(\tilde{\psi}_{\rm p} Q^+ \gamma_5 \psi_{\rm n})(\tilde{\psi}_e \gamma_5 \psi_\nu) = g_P(\psi_{\rm p}{}^\dagger Q^+ \beta \gamma_5 \psi_{\rm n})(\psi_e{}^\dagger \beta \gamma_5 \psi_\nu) \qquad \text{(3-20)}$$

In all cases the interaction is named after the way in which the nucleon covariant $(\psi_p{}^\dagger \boldsymbol{\sigma} \psi_{\rm n})$ *transforms. In the classical* β*-decay theory the lepton covariant* $(\psi_e{}^\dagger \boldsymbol{\sigma} \psi_\nu)$ *transforms in the same way. This is no longer true for parity nonconserving terms, as we shall see later.*

Treating Nucleons Nonrelativistically. In the case of nuclear β decay it is often a good approximation to treat at least the nucleons nonrelativistically—that is, to neglect all terms which are explicitly or implicitly proportional to the nucleon velocity v_{n} or higher powers of v_{n} and to set $\beta = 1$ in the nucleon covariant. However, we will still treat the leptons relativistically. The scalar interaction then reduces to

$$S: \qquad g_S(\psi_{\mathrm{p}}{}^{\dagger}Q^{+}\beta\psi_{\mathrm{n}})(\psi_e{}^{\dagger}\beta\psi_\nu) \tag{3-21}$$

This is almost the same as the nonrelativistic Fermi interaction. The only difference is in the appearance of the factor β in the lepton covariant. The vector interaction becomes

$$V: \qquad g_V(\psi_{\mathrm{p}}{}^{\dagger}Q^{+}\psi_{\mathrm{n}})(\psi_e{}^{\dagger}\psi_\nu) \tag{3-22}$$

Since $\langle\boldsymbol{\alpha}\rangle \simeq \langle v_n/c\rangle \sim 0.1$ for a typical nucleon in the nucleus, the terms involving $\langle\boldsymbol{\alpha}\rangle$ drop out in the nonrelativistic treatments, in the same way as in the original Fermi interaction. Both of these forms lead to the *Fermi selection rules* mentioned earlier:

$$\Delta I = 0, \qquad \pi_i = \pi_f \tag{3-23}$$

The tensor and axial-vector interactions reduce to the following:

$$T: \qquad g_{\mathrm{T}}\sum_{\mu}(\psi_{\mathrm{p}}{}^{\dagger}Q^{+}\sigma_\mu\psi_{\mathrm{n}})(\psi_e{}^{\dagger}\beta\sigma_\mu\psi_\nu) \tag{3-24}$$

$$A: \qquad g_A\sum_{\mu}(\psi_{\mathrm{p}}{}^{\dagger}Q^{+}\sigma_\mu\psi_{\mathrm{n}})(\psi_e{}^{\dagger}\sigma_\mu\psi_\nu) \tag{3-25}$$

This is merely a Gamow-Teller form with the selection rules

$$\Delta I = 0 \quad \text{or} \quad \pm 1, \qquad \text{no} \quad 0 \to 0, \qquad \pi_i = \pi_f \tag{3-26}$$

Again, the only difference between these forms is in the appearance of the matrix β in the tensor interaction. The pseudoscalar interaction cannot contribute at all in our case, for $\psi_{\mathrm{p}}{}^{\dagger}\gamma_5\psi_{\mathrm{n}}$ vanishes in the limit of low nucleon velocities.

Finally, we write down the energy spectrum of the electron according to our relativistic but classical treatment in the limit of zero nucleon velocity. We use the dimensionless coupling constants C_i defined by $g_i = gC_i$ (Eq. 3-11).

The energy distribution is

$$N(E)\,dE$$
$$= \frac{m^5c^4}{2\pi^3\hbar^2} g^2 F(\pm Z, E)\left[(C_S^2 + C_V^2)\left|\int 1\right|^2 + (C_T^2 + C_A^2)\left|\int \boldsymbol{\sigma}\right|^2\right.$$
$$\left.\pm \frac{2\,mc^2}{E}\left(C_S C_V\left|\int 1\right|^2 + C_T C_A\left|\int \boldsymbol{\sigma}\right|^2\right)\right] pE(E_0 - E)^2\,dE \quad (3\text{-}27)$$

where the plus or minus sign holds for β^- or β^+ decay, respectively. The derivation of this distribution is given in Appendix IV.

Fierz Interference Terms

The energy spectrum has a statistical shape unless both scalar *and* vector or both tensor *and* axial-vector interactions are present. In the latter case we would get characteristic deviations from the statistical spectrum shape called *Fierz interference terms* (the $1/E$ terms) (Fi-37). Careful analysis of observed β spectra has shown, however, that such Fierz terms must be either absent or very small.

The upper limit of the Fierz interference term in Gamow-Teller and Fermi types of interactions can be set as $b_{\mathrm{GT}} = -0.01 \pm 0.02$ (Sh-54) and $b_F = 0.00 \pm 0.10$ (Sherr-56), respectively. Kurie plots of allowed β spectra seem to be linear to a very good approximation (see Sec. 2-4). If we ignore such terms, our expression for the β spectrum reduces to the nonrelativistic form discussed previously, provided that we define

$$\begin{aligned} C_{\mathrm{F}}^2 &= C_S^2 + C_V^2 \\ C_{\mathrm{GT}}^2 &= C_T^2 + C_A^2 \end{aligned} \quad (3\text{-}28)$$

Furthermore, it can be shown that for two-component neutrinos the Fierz interference terms are identically zero.

3-2 *ft* VALUES

A striking feature of nuclear β decay is the great variations found in the half-lives. They range from less than a tenth of a second to 10^{16} years. However, even the shorter β-decay activities are very long-lived on a nuclear time scale. A typical nuclear time would be 10^{-21} sec. This is evidently due to the weakness of the β interaction and, therefore, the smallness of its coupling constants. The variation of the β-decay half-lives is due to *two* main causes.

First of all the different β decays may be classified into different groups depending on the amount of angular momentum carried off by the electron-neutrino pair, that is, by the angular momentum change of the nucleus, and also on whether or not the parity of the nucleus changes in the transition. Other things being equal, the transition probability is determined by the amplitude of the electron and neutrino wave function at the nucleus. This is largest if the two particles carry off no angular momentum—at least no *orbital* angular momentum—and if there is no parity change. Then we can obtain an allowed transition, and the Fermi or Gamow-Teller selection rules, $\Delta I = 0$ or $0, \pm 1$, are applicable, depending on whether the intrinsic spin of the electron and neutrino are antiparallel or parallel.

The second cause of the variation of β-decay half-lives is the available β-decay energy. The probability of decay depends on the phase space available for the leptons. This space increases very rapidly with the available energy. In addition, there is a significant effect of the nuclear Coulomb field on the wave function of the emitted electron. As a result, the β-decay half-life will depend on the atomic number of the nucleus involved. The energy and Coulomb effect are not, of course, directly connected with the details of the nuclear states. Therefore we should like to separate these effects out in order to study explicitly how the β-decay transition probability depends on *the wave functions of the nuclear states involved.* This can be accomplished by characterizing a β decay, not by its lifetime but rather by a so-called *comparative* half-life ft where f includes the effect of the energy and Coulomb field on the lifetime t. Thus two decays with the same nuclear structure but different energies and different nuclear charge will have different half-lives t but should have the same ft value.

To define f we start from the assumption that any β-decay spectrum has a statistical shape (see p. 26). This is, of course, not correct for some forbidden β spectra, but it will not seriously alter the picture discussed here. We also assume that there are no Fierz interference terms. Then the total probability of β decay per second may be obtained simply by integrating the β spectrum. The probability of β decays per second is given as follows:

$$w = \frac{m^5c^4}{\hbar^7}\frac{g^2}{2\pi^3}|M|^2 f = \frac{mc^2}{\hbar}\frac{G^2}{2\pi^3}|M|^2 f \tag{3-29}$$

The factor

$$|M|^2 = C_F^2 \left| \int 1 \right|^2 + |C_{GT}|^2 \left| \int \boldsymbol{\sigma} \right|^2$$

is a reduced transition rate which depends only on the relative strength of Fermi and Gamow-Teller interactions and on the magnitude of the nuclear matrix elements but is independent of the decay energy. G is the dimensionless quantity defined in Sec. 2-2 (Eq. 2-24). The quantity f is an integral over the electron spectrum (independent of the nuclear state or of the β-decay interaction) and is given by

$$f = \int_1^{E_0} F(Z, E)E(E^2 - 1)^{1/2}(E_0 - E)^2 \, dE \tag{3-30}$$

For allowed β transitions, we use the subscript zero f_0 to denote the zero order of forbiddenness. It is of interest to consider the limiting forms for f_0. For simplicity we assume there is no Coulomb field—that Z is equal to zero. In that case $F = 1$ and f_0 may be integrated explicitly:

$$f_0 = (E_0^2 - 1)^{1/2}\left(\frac{E_0^4}{30} - \frac{3E_0^2}{20} - \frac{2}{15}\right) + \frac{E_0}{4} \ln_e (E_0 + \sqrt{E_0^2 - 1})$$

In the limits, of small and large decay energies, we find

$$\begin{aligned} f_0 &= 0.216(E_0 - 1)^{7/2} && \text{if} \quad E_0 - 1 \ll 1 \\ f_0 &= \tfrac{1}{30} E_0^5 && \text{if} \quad E_0 \gg 1 \end{aligned} \tag{3-31}$$

A rapid method (Mo-51) of calculating the $\log f_0 t$ values for transitions is reproduced in Fig. 3-2. The values of f_0 can also be read from a set of graphs prepared by Feenberg and Trigg (Fe-50). A somewhat more accurate calculation of f_0 functions for superallowed β transitions was made by Moszkowski and Jantzen (Mo-55). However, there are additional corrections of a few per cent because of electron screening which must be taken into account in accurate calculations (cf. Sec. 7-3).

It is seen then that f varies rapidly with energy. Thus the variation of the comparative half-lives ft is expected to be much less than that of the half-lives themselves. Nevertheless, even the $f_0 t$ values vary considerably from nucleus to nucleus and for this reason it is more convenient to characterize the decay by the $\log f_0 t$ value.

Since the transition rate for β decay per second is

$$w = \frac{1}{t_{\text{av}}} = \frac{\ln 2}{t_{1/2}} \tag{3-32}$$

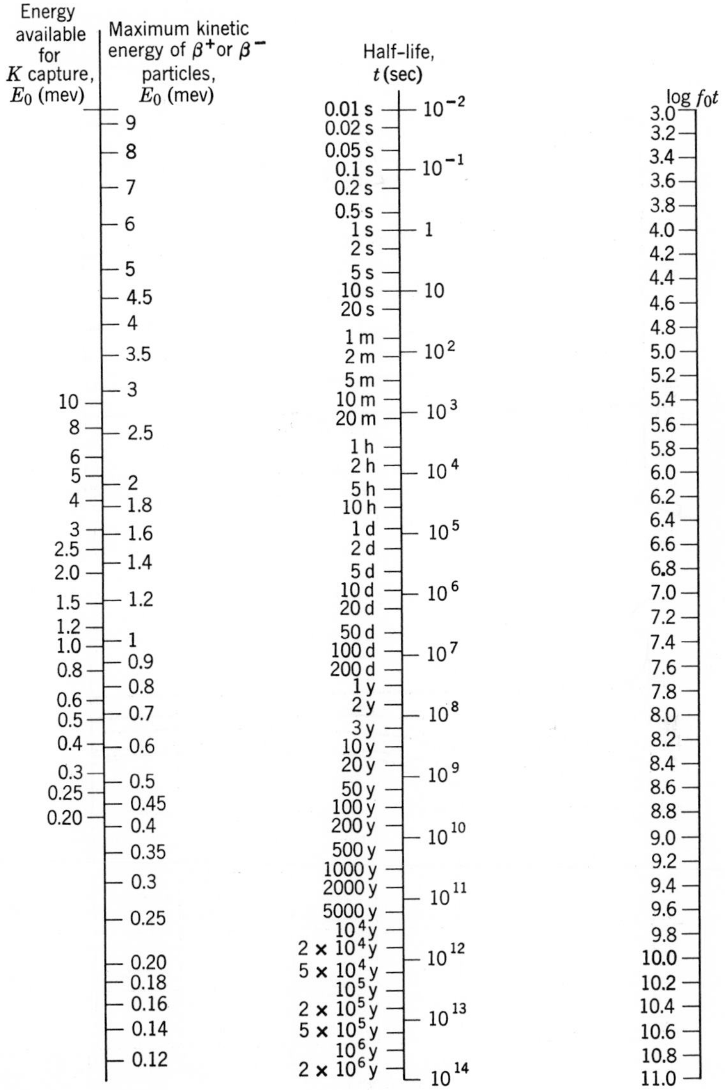

Energy available for K capture, E0 (mev)
Maximum kinetic energy of β+ or β− particles, E0 (mev)
Half-life, t (sec)
log f0t
10
8
6
5
4
3
2.5
2.0
1.5
1.2
1.0
0.8
0.6
0.5
0.4
0.3
0.25
0.20
9
8
7
6
5
4.5
4
3.5
3
2.5
2
1.8
1.6
1.4
1.2
1
0.9
0.8
0.7
0.6
0.5
0.45
0.4
0.35
0.3
0.25
0.20
0.18
0.16
0.14
0.12
0.01 s
0.02 s
0.05 s
0.1 s
0.2 s
0.5 s
1 s
2 s
5 s
10 s
20 s
1 m
2 m
5 m
10 m
20 m
1 h
2 h
5 h
10 h
1 d
2 d
5 d
10 d
20 d
50 d
100 d
200 d
1 y
2 y
3 y
10 y
20 y
50 y
100 y
200 y
500 y
1000 y
2000 y
5000 y
10^4 y
2 × 10^4 y
5 × 10^4 y
10^5 y
2 × 10^5 y
5 × 10^5 y
10^6 y
2 × 10^6 y
10^-2
10^-1
1
10
10^2
10^3
10^4
10^5
10^6
10^7
10^8
10^9
10^10
10^11
10^12
10^13
10^14
3.0
3.2
3.4
3.6
3.8
4.0
4.2
4.4
4.6
4.8
5.0
5.2
5.4
5.6
5.8
6.0
6.2
6.4
6.6
6.8
7.0
7.2
7.4
7.6
7.8
8.0
8.2
8.4
8.6
8.8
9.0
9.2
9.4
9.6
9.8
10.0
10.2
10.4
10.6
10.8
11.0

(a)

Fig. 3-2*a*

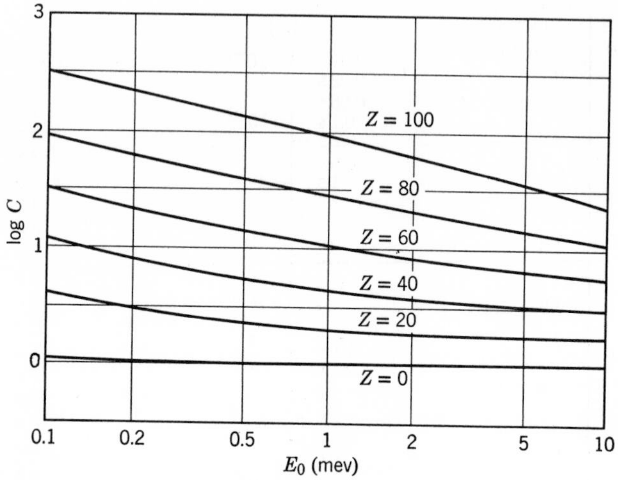

(b)

Fig. 3-2*b*

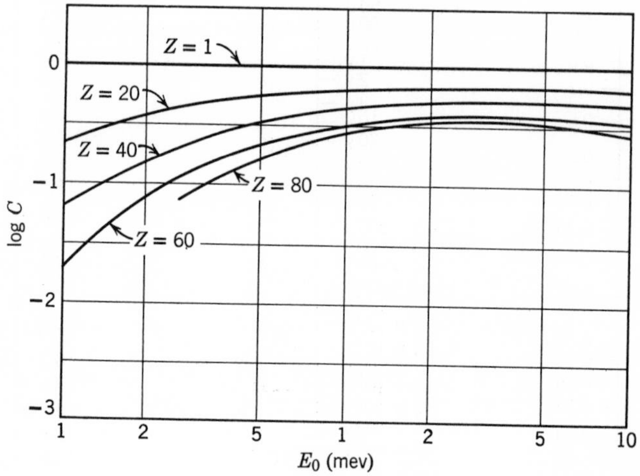

(c)

Fig. 3-2*c*

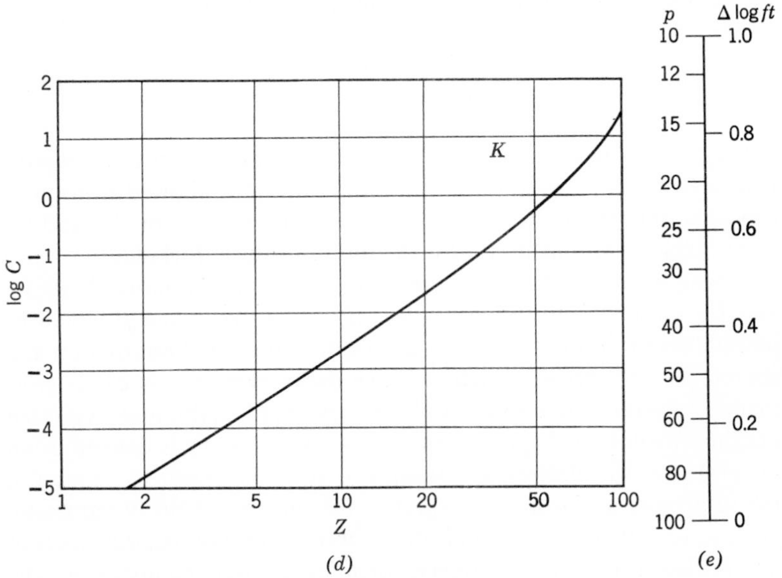

Fig. 3-2 Rapid method for calculating log *ft* values.

The parts of this figure permit the rapid calculation of log *ft* for a given type of decay, given energy, given half-life, etc. The notation is: E_0 for $\beta\pm$ emission is the maximum kinetic energy of the particles in mev; E_0 for *K*-electron capture is the disintegration energy in mev. When a β^+ emission and *K*-electron capture go from and to the same level, E_0 for *K* capture equals E_0 for β^+ emission plus 1.02 mev. *Z* is the atomic number of the initial nucleus, *t* is the total half-life, and *p* is the percentage of decay occurring in the mode under consideration. When no branching occurs, $p = 100$.

Procedure for obtaining log *ft*

1. First obtain log $f_0 t$, using part *a*. E_0 is read off the left-hand side of the E_0 column for *K*-electron capture and off the right-hand side for $\beta\pm$ emission. Put a straight edge over the given values of E_0 and *t* and note where it crosses the column of log $f_0 t$ values.

2. Then read off log *C* from parts *b*, *c*, and *d* for β^-, β^+, and *K*-electron capture, respectively.

3. Obtain $\Delta \log ft$ from part *e* if $p < 100$. When $p = 100$, $\Delta \log ft = 0$.

4. $\text{Log} ft = \log f_0 t + \log C + \Delta \log ft$.

Details concerning the construction, significance, and range of usefulness of these graphs are given in the original paper.

where $t_{1/2}$ refers to the partial half-life for the particular decay under consideration, the comparative half-life ft is given by

$$ft = \frac{\hbar}{mc^2}\frac{2\pi^3}{G^2}\frac{\ln 2}{|M|^2} = \frac{B}{|M|^2} \tag{3-33}$$

If the β-decay interaction is the same for all nuclei—in other words, if $B =$ constant—any variation in the ft value for allowed transitions can arise only from changes in the nuclear matrix elements $\int 1$ and $\int \boldsymbol{\sigma}$ from nucleus to nucleus. Furthermore, with a forbidden spectra involving a parity change or spin change of two or more, both $\int 1$ and $\int \boldsymbol{\sigma}$ must vanish. In this case, $|M|^2$ equals zero and ft would be infinite were it not for the presence of other so-called "retardation and source velocity terms" which can give decay even in this case. Normally, however, these terms will be very small. Although we often obtain nonallowed shapes for forbidden spectra and f is defined as an integral over the electron spectrum, it is still convenient to define f in the same way as for allowed spectra, for the size of the ft value still gives some rather accurate indications of the degree of forbiddenness of any nuclear transition. However, for more accurate comparisons, the shape factor must be taken into account in the calculation of ft values (see Sec. 3-3).

3-3 CLASSIFICATION OF BETA TRANSITIONS

A listing of β-decay transitions according to the ft value, as shown in Tables 3-1 and 3-2, presents three main groups of interest which overlap to some extent. The superallowed transitions have $\log ft = 3$ to 4. They occur exclusively in light nuclei. They are allowed, and, in fact, it is believed that the nuclear wave function of the initial and final state overlap so well that the matrix elements $\int 1$ and $\int \boldsymbol{\sigma}$ are of order unity. The superallowed transitions are discussed in more detail on pp. 60–63 and 66–71.

By studying such transitions we can obtain detailed information about nuclear wave functions and also about the nature of the β-decay interaction.

The allowed unfavored transitions have $\log ft$ values mostly between 4 and 6. These transitions occur mainly in medium and heavy nuclei.

There is independent evidence from the shell model (in many cases, at least) that the spin changes by zero or unity in these transitions, and that there is no parity change. Thus, in these allowed transitions, as compared to superallowed transitions, the relative smallness of the

Table 3-1 Classification of Beta Transitions According to *ft* Values

Type of Transition	Selection Rules	$\log f_0t$	$\log f_nt$	Remarks
Allowed:				
Superallowed	$\Delta I = 0, \pm 1$ (no)	3.5 ± 0.2		See Table 3-3
Allowed Unfavored	$\Delta I = 0, \pm 1$ (no)	5.7 ± 1.1		
Forbidden:				
First forbidden	$\Delta I = 0, \pm 1$ (yes)	7.5 ± 1.5		
Unique first forbidden	$\Delta I = \pm 2$ (yes)		8.5 ± 0.7	
Second forbidden	$\Delta I = \pm 2$ (no)	12.1 ± 1.0		Cl^{36}, Tc^{99}, I^{129}, Cs^{135}, Cs^{137}
Unique second forbidden	$\Delta I = \pm 3$ (no)		11.7 ± 0.9	B^{10}, Na^{22}
Third forbidden	$\Delta I = \pm 3$ (yes)	18.2 ± 0.6		Rb^{87}
Unique third forbidden	$\Delta I = \pm 4$ (yes)		15.2	K^{40}
Fourth forbidden	$\Delta I = \pm 4$ (no)	22.7		In^{115}

decay rate cannot be due to angular-momentum selection rules, but rather must be a reflection of a comparatively poor overlap between the wave functions of the initial and final nucleons. These points will be discussed later in a little more detail (see p. 74). The forbidden transitions have $\log ft$ usually larger than 6. In these transitions the parity and the spin changes are forbidden by the selection rules for allowed transitions, so that the allowed matrix elements $\int 1$ and $\int \boldsymbol{\sigma}$ must vanish. These transitions will be discussed later (see pp. 75–106).

Table 3-2 Distribution of Log ft Values for Allowed and Forbidden Beta Transitions (from Gle-63)

$\log f_0t$ or f_nt	Super-allowed*	Allowed	First Forbidden		Second Forbidden	
			Nonunique	Unique	Nonunique	Unique
2.8–3.2	6					
3.3–3.7	25†	1				
3.8–4.2	2	8				
4.3–4.7		57				
4.8–5.2		120	8			
5.3–5.7		99†	5			
5.8–6.2		74	24			
6.3–6.7		47	57			
6.8–7.2		25	40	1		
7.3–7.7		20	57†	1		
7.8–8.2		9	38	28		
8.3–8.7		5	25	35†		
8.8–9.2		9	21	10		
9.3–9.7			3	7	1	
9.8–10.2			5	2		
10.3–10.7		1	2	1	1	1
10.8–11.2			1	2	3	1
11.3–11.7			1		2	1†
11.8–12.2			5		4†	1
12.3–12.7			2		3	2
12.8–13.2					3	
≥13.3			1		3	
Total	33	475	295	87	20	6

* We include here also the $0^+ \leftrightarrow 1^+$ transitions in He^6, C^{10}, O^{14}, F^{18}, and Ne^{18}.
† Mean value.

Superallowed Transitions

Superallowed β transitions are those with log ft values of less than 4; they are entirely restricted to light nuclei. There are two main classes of superallowed transitions.

First, there are *mirror transitions in odd-even nuclei.* As an example we have such a transition as shown in Fig. 3-3. The ground states of the two nuclei involved differ only by the interchange of neutrons and protons, and, in particular, they have the same spin $I = \frac{5}{2}$. In fact, the energy difference involved in a mirror transition is due to the neutron-proton mass difference and to the larger Coulomb energy in the nucleus of larger Z. The ft values in this group range from about 1000 to 5000. The Fermi matrix element $\int 1$ equals unity; we simply turn a single proton into a neutron. On the other hand, the Gamow-Teller matrix element $\int \boldsymbol{\sigma}$ (which

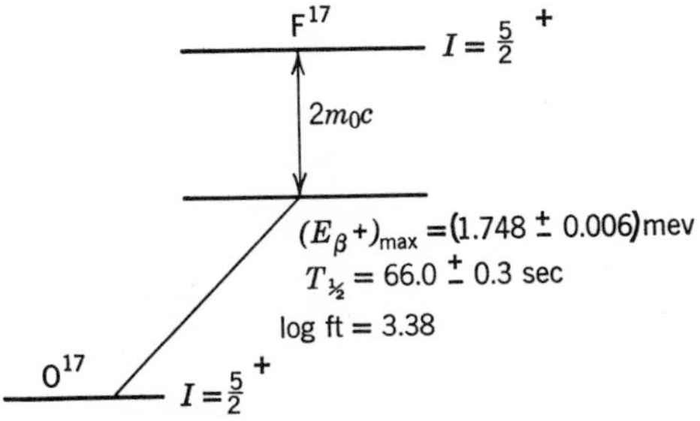

Fig. 3-3 Diagram of β^+ decay of F^{17}.

involves the flip of the spin) depends on the nuclear state in a more detailed manner, which we will discuss later.

Another kind of superallowed transition occurs in even A nuclei with $A = 4n + 2$. An example of such a transition is

$$_{8}O_{6}^{14} \rightarrow {}_{7}N_{7}^{14}$$

Its decay scheme is shown in Fig. 3-4.

The ground state of O^{14}, being even-even, is expected to have $I = 0$. The state to which it decays in N^{14} is also believed to be 0^+; it is, in fact, the analogous state of O^{14}. The ground state of C^{14} is the third member of the isobaric spin triplet of $T = 1$. The z components, T_z, of the isobaric spin of C^{14}, N^{14}, and O^{14} are -1, 0, and $+1$, respectively. In a sense, the 0^+ state of N^{14} is the same kind as that for O^{14} except that, although in O^{14} we have two protons, one of them has been changed into a neutron in N^{14}. For such a 0^+-to-0^+ transition, $\int \boldsymbol{\sigma}$ must vanish since the electron-neutrino pair cannot carry off an angular momentum of unity. On the other hand, $\int 1$ equals $\sqrt{2}$. This may be seen if we write the O^{14} wave function as pp and the N^{14} wave functions as $(\mathrm{np} + \mathrm{pn})/\sqrt{2}$. We treat both O^{14} and N^{14} as a two-particle system. Then

$$\int 1 = \langle \psi^{\dagger}_{N^{14}} \,|\, \sum Q^{-}(i) \,|\, \psi_{O^{14}} \rangle$$
$$= \left\langle \frac{\mathrm{n}(1)\mathrm{p}(2) + \mathrm{p}(1)\mathrm{n}(2)}{\sqrt{2}} \,|Q^{-}(1) + Q^{-}(2)|\, \mathrm{p}(1)\mathrm{p}(2) \right\rangle$$

Since $Q^{-}\mathrm{p} = \mathrm{n}$, we find $\int 1 = \sqrt{2}$ and therefore $|\int 1|^2 = 2$. This conclusion is unchanged even when we use many-particle wave functions

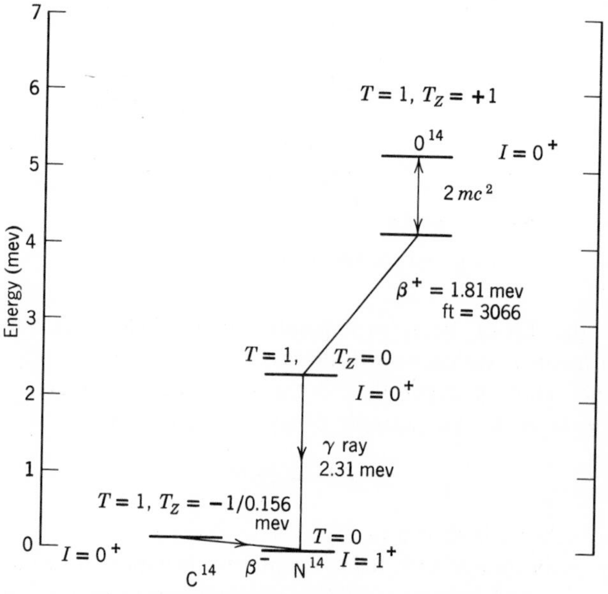

Fig. 3-4 The isobaric spin triplet of O^{14}, N^{14}, and C^{14}.

for the nuclei involved (as long as they are eigenfunctions of isobaric spin). The fact that $0 \rightarrow 0$ transitions occur at all proves the existence of a finite Fermi-type coupling constant g_F in β decay. In fact, since both ft and $\int 1$ are known for this case, we can deduce the absolute strength of the Fermi-type coupling constant g_F from the O^{14} lifetime. The result is

$$g_F = 1.415 \times 10^{-49} \text{ erg cm}^3$$

The dimensionless coupling constant equals

$$G_F \sim 3.0 \times 10^{-12} = 1.0 \times 10^{-5}\left(\frac{m_e}{m_p}\right)^2$$

See Sec. 7-3 for a more detailed discussion.

Like all other even-even nuclei, He^6 almost surely has an assignment 0^+ (Com-58); Li^6 has a measured spin of 1. Thus the spin changes by 1 unit. The Fermi matrix element $\int 1$ must, therefore, vanish. Only the Gamow-Teller interaction can contribute to this decay, which is shown in Fig. 3-5. The ft value 800 for this case is one of the smallest

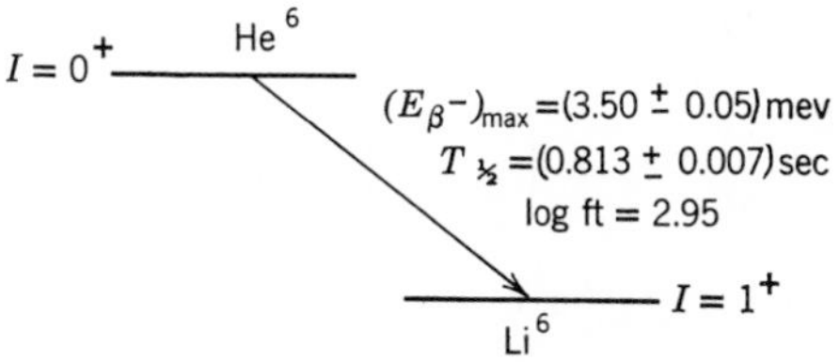

Fig. 3-5 Decay scheme of He^6.

for any known β transitions. The existence of decays of O^{14} and He^6 gives evidence that both the Fermi and Gamow-Teller interactions must contribute to β decay. Of course, we cannot tell from the study of ft values alone which kind of Fermi interaction (S or V) and Gamow-Teller interaction (T or A) occurs. If we knew the matrix element $\int \boldsymbol{\sigma}$ for He^6, we could directly deduce the relative coupling strength, assuming that the interaction is the same for all nuclei. Indeed, according to the simple L-S coupling model (believed to be a rather good approximation for the $A = 6$ nuclei), we obtain $|\int \boldsymbol{\sigma}|^2 = 6$. The empirical ft value then implies that

$$g_{GT} \sim 1.60 \times 10^{-49} \text{ erg cm}^3$$

that is, the coupling strength is slightly larger for Gamow-Teller transitions than for Fermi transitions. This estimate is, however, quite crude since $|\int \boldsymbol{\sigma}|^2$ depends on details of nuclear structure.

The Isobaric Spin Selection Rules in Beta Decay

In Fermi's original paper on the theory of β decay, he expressed the matrix element for the vector interaction (now known as Fermi interaction) by introducing, for the first time, the components of the isobaric spin operators $\tau_{\pm}$:*

$$\tau_{\pm}:\left|\int 1\right| = \left|\int \psi_f^{\dagger} \textstyle\sum_i \frac{1}{\sqrt{2}}\tau_{\pm}(i)\psi_i\, d\mathbf{r}\right| = \sqrt{2}\left|\int \psi_f^{\dagger} T_{\pm}\psi_i\, d\mathbf{r}\right| \quad (3\text{-}34)$$

where $\tau_{\pm} = \frac{1}{\sqrt{2}}(\tau_x \pm i\tau_y)$ is a linear combination of τ_x and τ_y.

Here τ_x, τ_y, and τ_z—analogous to the Pauli spin matrices σ_x, σ_y, σ_z—form the three components of the isobaric spin operator τ_i; $\tau_{\pm(i)}$ is for the ith nucleon and T_+ is the total isobaric spin operator $T = \frac{1}{2}\sum_i \tau(i)$. Their matrix representations are the same as those of the spin operators $S = \frac{1}{2}\sum_i \sigma(i)$:

$$\tau_x = \begin{pmatrix} 0 & 1 \\ 1 & 0 \end{pmatrix}, \quad \tau_y = \begin{pmatrix} 0 & -i \\ i & 0 \end{pmatrix}, \quad \text{and } \tau_z = \begin{pmatrix} 1 & 0 \\ 0 & -1 \end{pmatrix} \quad (3\text{-}35)$$

Therefore the operators $\tau_{\pm}$ have the matrix forms

$$\tau_+ = \sqrt{2}\begin{pmatrix} 0 & 1 \\ 0 & 0 \end{pmatrix} \quad \text{and} \quad \tau_- = \sqrt{2}\begin{pmatrix} 0 & 0 \\ 1 & 0 \end{pmatrix} \quad (3\text{-}36)$$

The isobaric spin functions for proton and neutron can be represented by

$$\pi(\text{proton}) = \begin{pmatrix} 1 \\ 0 \end{pmatrix} \quad \text{and} \quad \alpha(\text{neutron}) = \begin{pmatrix} 0 \\ 1 \end{pmatrix}$$

It is then clear that

$$\begin{aligned} \tau_+\psi_{\text{p}} &= 0 & \tau_-\psi_{\text{p}} &= \sqrt{2}\psi_{\text{n}} \\ \tau_+\psi_{\text{n}} &= \sqrt{2}\psi_{\text{p}} \quad \text{and} & \tau_-\psi_{\text{n}} &= 0 \end{aligned} \quad (3\text{-}37)$$

The physical interpretation of the operators $\tau_{\pm}$ is now obvious: τ_+ annihilates a proton state and transforms a neutron into a proton; τ_- annihilates a neutron state and converts a proton into a neutron. In terms of the Q operators defined in Chap. 2, $\tau_{\pm} = \sqrt{2}Q^{\pm}$.

The total isobaric spin operator $T_{\pm}$ which appears in the Fermi matrix element can only connect states of the same isobaric spin T; it increases (for the plus sign) and decreases (for the minus sign) the

* The sign of τ has been reversed here over Heisenberg's original definition. This is in accordance with the present convention in elementary-particle physics.

component T_z by one unit. This yields the isobaric spin selection rules for Fermi transitions in β decay as

$$\Delta T = \Delta I = 0, \qquad \Delta T_z = \pm 1 \text{ (no)} \tag{3-38}$$

For transitions in which T changes, the Fermi matrix element should vanish. This is expected to happen for all β transitions between low-lying states except those in mirror nuclei or nuclei with $N = Z$—in other words, for transitions in which at least one of the nuclei has $|N - Z| \geqslant 3$. Since for low-lying states we have

$$T = |T_z| = \left|\frac{N - Z}{2}\right| \tag{3-39}$$

T must change in the transition. There is evidence that, for such transitions, the Fermi matrix element is indeed very small. The matrix element $\int 1$ for Fermi transitions between states (α, T, T_z) and (α, T, T_z'), where α denotes all variables except those of isobaric spin, may be expressed by

$$\int 1 = \left(\alpha T T_z \left| \frac{\tau_\pm}{\sqrt{2}} \right| \alpha T T_z'\right) = [(T - T_z')(T + T_z' + 1)]^{1/2}$$

This expression may also be written as

$$\int 1 = [T(T + 1) - T_z T_z']^{1/2}$$

For example, in mirror transitions, $T = T_z = \frac{1}{2}$, $T_z' = -\frac{1}{2}$. Therefore

$$\int 1_{\text{mirror}} = 1$$

In the well-known $0^+ \rightarrow 0^+$ transitions, $T = 1$, $T_z = 1$, $T_z' = 0$. Therefore

$$\int 1_{0^+ \rightarrow 0^+} = \sqrt{2}$$

Since for the latter $|\int \boldsymbol{\sigma}|^2 = 0$, all such transitions would have the same ft value. This is indeed found to be a very good approximation (cf. Table 3-3).

Evidences for the strong hindrance of Fermi transitions because of the isobaric spin selection rules have often been observed. A striking

Table 3-3 Data on Superallowed Transitions

Nuclides	Spin	$t_{1/2}$ (sec)	$E_{\max}$ (kev)	ft (sec)	References
${}_0N^1 \to {}_1H^1$	$\frac{1}{2}$	11.7 ± 0.3 min	782 ± 1	1187 ± 35	(So-58)
${}_1H^3 \to {}_2He^3$	$\frac{1}{2}$	3.870×10^8	18.65 ± 0.2	1132 ± 40	(Jo-55) (Fri-58)
${}_4Be^7 \to {}_3Li^7$	$\frac{3}{2}$	53.38 ± 0.13 days	863 ± 2 (87.7%)	2300 ± 78	(Aj-59)
$\to {}_3Li^7$	$\frac{3}{2} \to \frac{1}{2}$		386 ± 2 (12.3%)	3600 ± 122	(Aj-59)
${}_6C^{11} \to {}_5B^{11}$	$\frac{3}{2}$	1224 ± 6	968 ± 8	4030 ± 150	(Aj-59)
${}_7N^{13} \to {}_6C^{13}$	$\frac{1}{2}$	603 ± 2	1202 ± 5	4700 ± 80	(Aj-59)
${}_8O^{15} \to {}_7N^{15}$	$\frac{1}{2}$	124.0 ± 0.5	1739 ± 2	4475 ± 30	(Aj-59)
${}_9F^{17} \to {}_8O^{17}$	$\frac{5}{2}$	66.0 ± 0.5	1748 ± 6	2380 ± 40	(Kis-59)
${}_{10}Ne^{19} \to {}_9F^{19}$	$\frac{1}{2}$	19.5 ± 1.0	2240 ± 10	1900 ± 100	(En-62)
${}_{11}Na^{21} \to {}_{10}Ne^{21}$	$(\frac{3}{2})$	22.8 ± 0.22	2508 ± 17	3500 ± 250	(En-62)
${}_{12}Mg^{23} \to {}_{11}Na^{23}$	$\frac{3}{2}$	12.04 ± 0.09	3056 ± 15	4480 ± 200	(En-62)
${}_{13}Al^{25} \to {}_{12}Mg^{25}$	$\frac{5}{2}$	7.23 ± 0.03	3239 ± 6	4280 ± 350	(En-62)
${}_{14}Si^{27} \to {}_{13}Al^{27}$	$\frac{5}{2}$	4.19 ± 0.05	3793 ± 8	4500 ± 100	(En-62)
${}_{15}P^{29} \to {}_{14}Si^{29}$	$(\frac{1}{2})$	4.23 ± 0.05	3926 ± 9	4740 ± 200	(En-62)
${}_{16}S^{31} \to {}_{15}P^{31}$	$\frac{1}{2}$	2.61 ± 0.03	4428 ± 17	4820 ± 250	(En-62)
${}_{17}Cl^{33} \to {}_{16}S^{33}$	$\frac{3}{2}$	2.53 ± 0.04	4553 ± 12	6000 ± 500	(En-62)
${}_{18}Ar^{35} \to {}_{17}Cl^{35}$	$\frac{3}{2}$	1.804 ± 0.012	4948 ± 30	5680 ± 400	(En-62)
${}_{19}K^{37} \to {}_{18}Ar^{37}$	$\frac{3}{2}$	1.23 ± 0.02	5128 ± 50	4250 ± 500	(En-62)
${}_{20}Ca^{39} \to {}_{19}K^{39}$	$\frac{3}{2}$	0.877 ± 0.006	5468 ± 40	4150 ± 300	(En-62)
${}_{21}Sc^{41} \to {}_{20}Ca^{41}$	$\frac{7}{2}$	0.87 ± 0.05	4940 ± 50	2560 ± 160	
${}_2He^6 \to {}_3Li^6$	$0 \to 1$	0.813 ± 0.007	3500 ± 20	808 ± 32	(Aj-59)
${}_6C^{10} \to {}_5B^{10*}$	$0 \to 1$	19.1 ± 0.8	2100 ± 100	1700 ± 150	(Aj-59)
${}_6C^{10} \to {}_5B^{10**}$	$0 \to 0$	1160 ± 150	1080 ± 100	5900 ± 2700	(Aj-59)
${}_8O^{14} \to {}_7N^{14}$	$0 \to 0$	71.36 ± 0.09	1812.6 ± 1.4	3066 ± 10	(Bardi-62)
${}_9F^{18} \to {}_8O^{18}$	$1 \to 0$	6660 ± 60	649 ± 9	4169 ± 158	(Aj-59)
${}_{10}Ne^{18} \to {}_9F^{18}$	$0 \to 1$	1.6 ± 0.2	3200 ± 200	794.4 ± 1.6	(Aj-59)
${}_{13}Al^{26*} \to {}_{12}Mg^{26}$	$0 \to 0$	6.374 ± 0.016	3208.0 ± 2.3	3015 ± 12	(Fre-62)
${}_{17}Cl^{34} \to {}_{16}S^{34}$	$0 \to 0$	1.565 ± 0.007	4460 ± 4.5	3055 ± 20	(Fr-63)
${}_{19}K^{38} \to {}_{18}Ar^{38}$	$0 \to 0$	0.946 ± 0.005	5030 ± 14	3140 ± 400	(En-62)
${}_{21}Sc^{42} \to {}_{20}Ca^{42}$	$0 \to 0$	0.6830 ± 0.0015	5409.0 ± 2.3	3077 ± 9	(Fr-65)
${}_{23}V^{46} \to {}_{22}Ti^{46}$	$0 \to 0$	0.4259 ± 0.0008	6032.1 ± 2.2	3088 ± 8	(Fr-65)
${}_{25}Mn^{50} \to {}_{24}Cr^{50}$	$0 \to 0$	0.2857 ± 0.0006	6609.0 ± 2.6	3082 ± 9	(Fr-65)
${}_{27}Co^{54} \to {}_{26}Fe^{54}$	$0 \to 0$	0.1937 ± 0.0010	7229 ± 5	2966 ± 18	(Fr-63)

case comes from the ground-to-ground β transition in

$$ {}_{31}Ga^{66}_{35} \to {}_{30}Zn^{66}_{36}(|\Delta T| = |2 - 3|). $$

The spins of both initial and final states are measured to be zero, and it is practically certain on the basis of the shell model that both states have even parity. The log ft value for this decay is 7.8, which implies that $|\int 1| \sim 10^{-2}$ for this case. Moreover, the recently developed β-γ (circularly polarized) angular-correlation method (Sec. 4-6) has provided an extremely sensitive way to detect the interference term between the Fermi and Gamow-Teller interaction and therefore a new means of determining the mixing ratio $\int 1/\int \boldsymbol{\sigma}$ in $\Delta T \neq 0$ β transitions.

Gamow-Teller Transitions. The matrix element for the Gamow-Teller transition is given by

$$\left|\int \boldsymbol{\sigma}_\mu\right| = \left|\int \psi_f{}^\dagger \sum_i \frac{1}{\sqrt{2}} \tau_\pm(i)\sigma_\mu(i)\psi_i \, dr\right| \tag{3-40}$$

The sum of the preceding expression cannot be expressed directly in terms of the total isobaric spin T. However, the operator $\sum_i \tau_\pm(i)\sigma_\mu(i)$ has essentially the same properties with respect to T as it does with

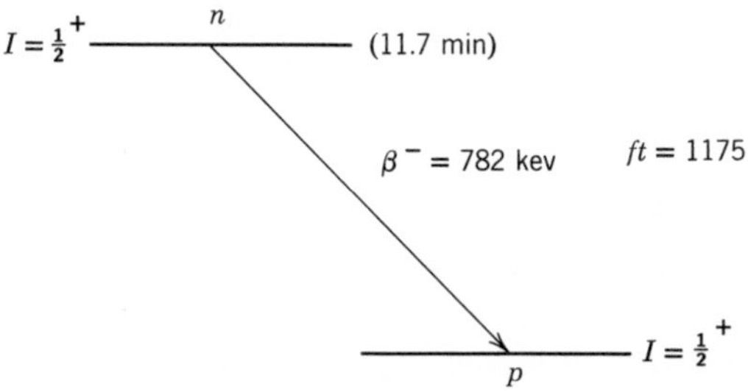

Fig. 3-6 Decay scheme of a neutron.

respect to the total spin S, that is, $\Delta T = 0$ or 1; more explicitly, $|\Delta \mathbf{T}| = 1$.

Now let us interpret the superallowed transition in a little more detail. According to the nonrelativistic theory just discussed, we have

$$|M|^2 = \left|\int 1\right|^2 + R\left|\int \boldsymbol{\sigma}\right|^2 = B/ft \tag{3-41}$$

where $R = g_{GT}{}^2/g_F{}^2$. Even if the β-decay interaction is the same for all nuclei, variations in $|M|^2$ and therefore in ft values are expected because $\int 1$ and $\int \boldsymbol{\sigma}$ are different from nucleus to nucleus. The study of the ft values of various nuclei can thus give information regarding the ratio of the β-decay coupling constants.

The simplest decay is that of a neutron itself (see Fig. 3-6). For this case we have $|\int 1|^2 = 1$ and $|\int \boldsymbol{\sigma}|^2 = 3$ and this prediction can be made uniquely since only a single particle is involved. The ft value deduced from the measurements is 1187 ± 35.* Thus we obtain the relation

$$(1 + 3R)1187 = B \tag{3-42}$$

---

* A more accurate calculation by Bühring and Schopper (Bü-65b) including radiative corrections (see Sec. 7-3) gives $ft = 1211 \pm 37$ for the neutron and 3111 ± 15 for O^{14}. This leads to a slightly smaller value of g_F than deduced above, 1.403×10^{-49} erg cm^3, but practically the same ratio g_{GT}/g_F, namely 1.175.

Now consider again the decay of O^{14}. The equation corresponding to Eq. 3-42 gives

$$B = 2 \times 3066 = 6132 \tag{3-43}$$

where 2 is the calculated value of $|\int 1|^2$ for a $0^+ \rightarrow 0^+$ transition. If we assume that the β-decay interaction is the same for the neutron and for O^{14}, we can solve the first equation for the ratio R and find $R = 1.39 \pm 0.04$. Thus the Fermi and Gamow-Teller coupling constants are of the same order of magnitude with the Gamow-Teller constant slightly larger, $g_{GT}/g_F = 1.18 \pm 0.02$, the same conclusion that was reached previously by a comparison of the He^6 and O^{14} decays.

The Mirror Transitions

Next let us look again at the mirror transitions. We shall interpret these on the basis of the single-particle model, a simplified version of the general nuclear shell model. In the single-particle model, all pairs of identical nucleons are assumed to couple to a ground state spin of 0. Into each single-particle state of given j we could put $2j + 1$ neutrons and the same number of protons. The levels fill up in order of increasing energy. Thus the angular momentum of the ground state of an odd A nucleus is predicted to be precisely the j of the last unpaired particle. The order of single-particle states deduced from both theory and nuclear systematics is indicated in Table 3-4. Levels on the same line seem to be close together in energy; those on different lines seem to be well separated, and the magic numbers indicate large gaps between some groups of levels.

According to the single-particle model, in a mirror transition the last nucleon does not change its state. It merely changes from a neutron to a proton (or vice versa). As shown in Appendix 5, the corresponding Gamow-Teller matrix elements are given by

$$\left|\int \boldsymbol{\sigma}\right|^2 = \frac{j+1}{j} \qquad \text{if} \quad j = l + \tfrac{1}{2} \tag{3-44}$$

$$\left|\int \boldsymbol{\sigma}\right|^2 = \frac{j}{j+1} \qquad \text{if} \quad j = l - \tfrac{1}{2} \tag{3-45}$$

For a more extensive discussion of the nuclear shell model, the reader is referred to Mayer and Jensen's *Elementary Theory of Nuclear Shell*

Structure (Ma-55), Feenberg's *Shell Theory of the Nucleus* (Fe-55) and the review article by Elliott and Lane (El-57). In this book we will use only the results expressed in Table 3-4.

The single-particle model is clearly the most applicable when we have a nucleus consisting of a closed shell plus or minus one particle. For example, consider again the mirror transition $F^{17} \rightarrow O^{17}$. Here we have one nucleon which changes from a neutron into a proton outside the O^{16}

Table 3-4 Order of Single-Particle States in the Nuclear Shell Model

Magic Numbers	Odd Number of Neutrons or Protons	Levels	Spins and Parities
(82)	65–81 (for neutrons only)	$s_{1/2}, d_{3/2}, h_{11/2}$	$\frac{1}{2}+, \frac{3}{2}+, \frac{11}{2}-$
	51–63	$d_{5/2}, g_{7/2}$	$\frac{5}{2}+, \frac{7}{2}+$
(50)	39–49	$p_{1/2}, g_{9/2}$	$\frac{1}{2}-, \frac{9}{2}+$
	29–37	$p_{3/2}, f_{5/2}$	$\frac{3}{2}-, \frac{5}{2}-$
(28)	21–27	$f_{7/2}$	$\frac{7}{2}-$
(20)	17–19	$d_{3/2}$	$\frac{3}{2}+$
	15	$s_{1/2}$	$\frac{1}{2}+$
	9–14	$d_{5/2}$	$\frac{5}{2}+$
(8)	7	$p_{1/2}$	$\frac{1}{2}-$
	3–5	$p_{3/2}$	$\frac{3}{2}-$
(2)	1	$s_{1/2}$	$\frac{1}{2}+$

core, which remains inert during the transformation. According to the single-particle model, the state of this participating nucleon is $d^{+}_{5/2}$, and according to the formula (3-44) we have $|\int \boldsymbol{\sigma}|^2 = \frac{7}{5}$. Another similar case is the decay of $O^{15} \rightarrow N^{15}$. Here we have one nucleon missing from a closed O^{16} shell, the missing nucleon being in a $p^{-}_{1/2}$ orbit. However, for our purposes, such a situation is the same as if there were a particle in this orbit rather than one missing. When we go from particles to holes, any matrix element either remains unchanged or merely changes sign. In any case, its square does not change. According to our formula, we have $|\int \boldsymbol{\sigma}|^2 = \frac{1}{3}$ for this case. The *ft* value for the F^{17} and O^{15} decays are 2380 and 4475, respectively. We can use these *ft* values together with that of O^{14} to get independent information about the ratio of Gamow-Teller to Fermi coupling constants. Using the single-particle values of $|\int \boldsymbol{\sigma}|^2$ we find that O^{14} and F^{17} together give

$$(1 + 7R/5) \times 2330 = 6130 \tag{3-46}$$

$$R = 1.18 \tag{3-47}$$

Once again, the Gamow-Teller constant is slightly larger than the Fermi constant but apparently not by as much as in the neutron decay. If we compare the decays of O^{14} and O^{15} in the same way, we obtain $R = 1.11$. Assuming that the experimental data are accurate enough and that our estimates of the nuclear matrix elements are correct,

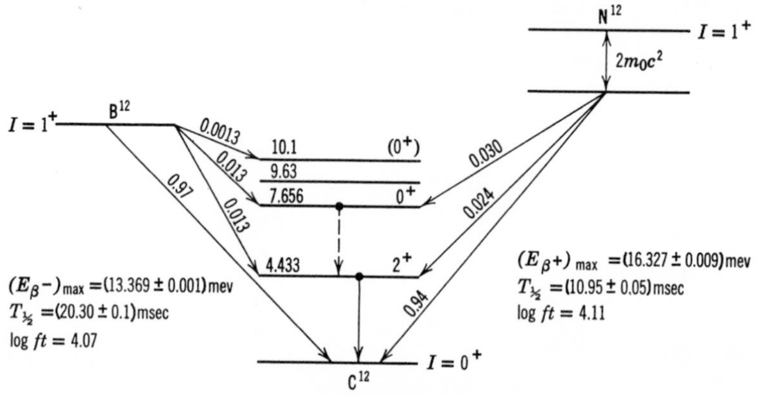

Fig. 3-7 Decay scheme of B^{12} and N^{12}.

the implication is that the β-decay coupling constants may be slightly different in the neutron and in heavier nuclei.

Of course, there is a whole series of positron decays from mirror nuclei, ranging from the $C^{11} \rightarrow B^{11}$ to $Sc^{41} \rightarrow Ca^{41}$. The ft values range from 1900 for Ne^{19} to about 6000 for the decays of Cl^{33} and Ar^{35}. The maximum possible value is expected to be about 6100, which would occur if $|\int \boldsymbol{\sigma}|^2 = 0$. A typical value is 4030 for the decay of C^{11}. If we know the form of the β interaction, we can use the measured ft values to deduce "empirical" values for the Gamow-Teller matrix element. Thus, for example, for Ar^{35} the matrix element for the Gamow-Teller interaction must be very small, whatever the detailed value of R. Considering the decay of C^{11}, and assuming that $R = 1.18$, we find that $|\int \boldsymbol{\sigma}|^2 = 0.37$. The ground-state spin of C^{11} is known to be $\frac{3}{2}$ in agreement with the single-particle shell model which predicts $p_{3/2}^-$. The single-particle model would have predicted $|\int \boldsymbol{\sigma}|^2 = \frac{5}{3}$ for this decay by use of Eq. (3-34). Thus the single-particle model fails badly in predicting the magnitude of the nuclear matrix element in this case. This also happens in other mirror transitions. Only in nuclei with a closed core $\pm$ one nucleon, as in the case of ${}_8O_7{}^{15}$ and ${}_9F_8{}^{17}$, does the single-particle model seem to work in this respect (even though it accurately predicts ground-state spins and parities much more extensively). On the other hand, $|\int \boldsymbol{\sigma}|^2$ can be calculated by using more realistic models of the nucleus where the interactions between several nucleons are taken into account. Such calculations (El–57) give $|\int \boldsymbol{\sigma}|^2$ much closer to the experimental values.

Finally let us consider the decay of B^{12}, as indicated in Fig. 3-7. The *ft* value of about 15,000 is somewhat larger than that for other superallowed transitions. In fact, this transition might be regarded as being on the boundary between superallowed and allowed transitions. However, since the nuclear spin changes by one unit ($1 \rightarrow 0$), the Fermi matrix element vanishes. For this case, then, the Gamow-Teller matrix element must be about $|\int \boldsymbol{\sigma}|^2 \sim \frac{1}{3}$, which is, in fact, a value larger than for some mirror transitions, such as Ar^{35}, where ($|\int \boldsymbol{\sigma}|^2 \leqslant \frac{1}{20}$). For a more detailed discussion on B^{12} and N^{12}, see Sec. 7-3.

Allowed Transitions

The group of allowed β spectra gives interesting information about nuclear structure in two ways. First, by virtue of being allowed (as suggested by the allowed spectrum shape and by a log *ft* value of less than 6), we can tell that the decay involves no parity change and $\Delta I = 0$, or ± 1. If the spin and parity of either the initial or final state are known, we are given information about the properties of the other states. On the other hand, the magnitude of the log *ft* value also gives direct information about nuclear structure. Consider, for example, the transition in which I changes by one unit. Here only the Gamow-Teller interaction can contribute.

From the previous discussion we can say that

$$\left|\int \boldsymbol{\sigma}\right|^2 \sim (5000/ft) \tag{3-48}$$

Thus for a transition in which log *ft* is 5, we conclude that $|\int \boldsymbol{\sigma}|$ is only about 0.2. Similarly, the Fermi matrix element $\int 1$ in this group of allowed transitions is also reduced as compared to that of superallowed transitions. Consider, for example, the decay of $S^{35} \rightarrow Cl^{35}$, as indicated in Fig. 3-8.

The spin of both S^{35} and Cl^{35} has been measured to be $\frac{3}{2}$ and, according to the single-particle version of the shell model, both states should have $d_{3/2}$ assignments. This is a straightforward allowed transition, but the log ft = 5.0. Another interesting case is the decay of Co^{60}, which

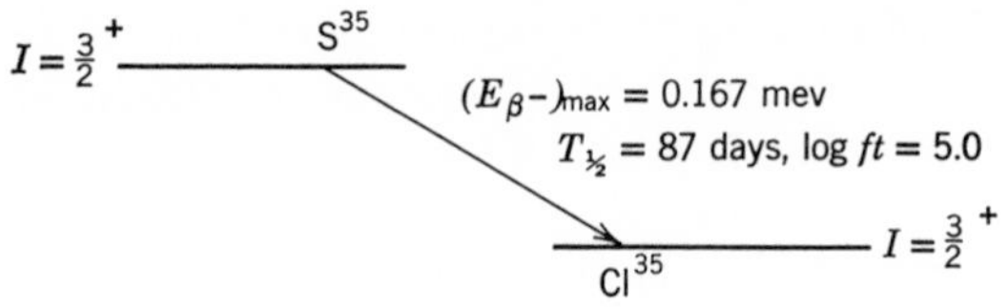

Fig. 3-8 Decay scheme of S^{35}.

we will meet again in the discussion of parity nonconservation (see Fig. 3-9). This figure shows a pure Gamow-Teller transition. The spin of Co^{60} has been measured as five. It decays into a state whose spin is believed to be four; and both states are of even parity. The spin and parity assignments are based partially on experimental measurements. They are also strongly suggested theoretically and from a study of

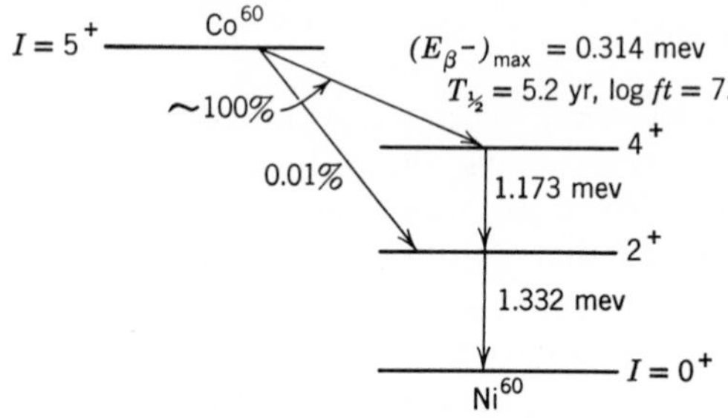

Fig. 3-9 Decay scheme of Co^{60}.

nuclear systematics. The log ft value is rather high for an allowed transition, but not unreasonable. Evidently, $|\int \boldsymbol{\sigma}|$ is unusually small for this case.

A very interesting *unfavored* allowed transition is the decay of C^{14} (see Fig. 3-10), which has become famous for its application to radiocarbon dating in archeology, geology, etc. In this case the Gamow-Teller matrix element must be exceptionally small, $|\int \boldsymbol{\sigma}|^2 \sim 5 \times 10^{-6}$.

In fact, calculations using shell-model wave functions (Vi-57) (considering, of course, several particles) actually can account quite well for this very small value of $\int \boldsymbol{\sigma}$.

A simple application of β decay to the nuclear shell model is provided in the decay scheme of Zn^{69} shown in Fig. 3-11.

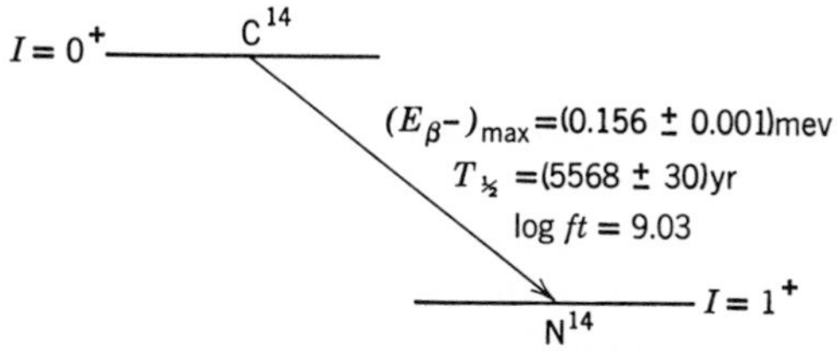

Fig. 3-10 Decay scheme of C^{14}.

The log ft value for this β decay classifies it as an allowed one. The ground-state spin of Ga^{69} is known to be $\frac{3}{2}$, and the shell model gives it a $\frac{3}{2}^-$ assignment. Thus the ground state of Zn must be $\frac{1}{2}^-$, $\frac{3}{2}^-$, or $\frac{5}{2}^-$. In fact, the single-particle shell model predicts $p_{1/2}$ or $g_{9/2}$ for 39 neutrons, either $\frac{1}{2}^-$ or $\frac{9}{2}^+$. Clearly, everything fits if we assume an assignment $\frac{1}{2}^-$.

An excited state of Zn is also known. This state is evidently the $\frac{9}{2}^+$ state. It decays to the ground state of Zn by emission of γ radiation

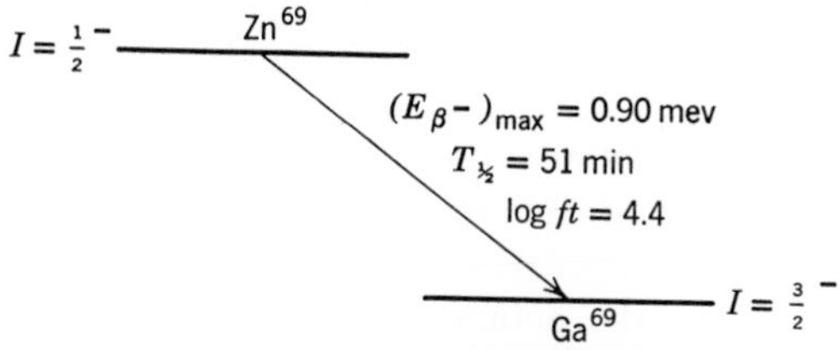

Fig. 3-11 Decay scheme of Zn^{69}.

whose properties are known to be characteristic of $M4$, $\Delta I = 4$ (change of parity). Thus both the β and γ decays are consistent with expectations from this single-particle shell model.

In general, the reduction in the nuclear matrix element which occurs for unfavored transitions results because the single-particle model is not quite realistic enough. Although ground-state spins are, in general, correctly explained by this model, transition probabilities usually depend more sensitively on details of the wave functions.

One essential feature of allowed unfavored transitions is the lack of overlap between initial and final state. Consider, for example, a three-particle configuration containing two neutrons and one proton. Since one of the neutrons can have spin up and the other spin down, all three particles can be in the same spatial state without violating the Pauli exclusion principle. The mutual interactions, being attractive, tend to favor the maximum overlap in the spatial wave functions; thus in the absence of spin-orbit coupling the ground state will have maximum spatial symmetry—that is, the wave function is unchanged upon exchange of particle coordinates. Suppose that after decaying this state has only one neutron and two protons, that is, its "mirror." Clearly, the spatial wave functions can be the same in the two states, and we obtain a superallowed mirror transition.

On the other hand, suppose that the decay results in a state with three neutrons. In the latter, at least two of the neutrons must have the same direction of spin, and thus the spatial wave function cannot be completely symmetric without violating the exclusion principle. Indeed, the spatial wave function turns out to be orthogonal to the symmetric one (Wi-39). Thus in the decay $n^2p \to n^3$ we must not only change a proton into a neutron but also lower the spatial symmetry of the wave function. Since the allowed β-decay operators Q^+ and $\boldsymbol{\sigma} Q^+$ involve only spin and charge, and not spatial coordinates, they cannot change any spatial wave functions. Consequently, the matrix elements $\int 1$ and $\int \boldsymbol{\sigma}$ vanish (even if the angular-momentum and parity selection rules are satisfied).

The preceding remarks are true quite generally for any transitions between states of different isobaric spin, provided there is no spin-orbit coupling.

Actually, owing to the action of spin-orbit coupling, the spatial wave functions will no longer be completely orthogonal, and, therefore, some transitions can occur. However, as we know empirically, unfavored transitions have comparative decay rates more than order of magnitude smaller than superallowed transitions.

Although the picture just given qualitatively explains the unfavored transitions, our knowledge of nuclear wave functions is not yet sufficient to make accurate theoretical calculations of ft values feasible except in a few special cases. Such calculations were recently made for nuclei with $20 \leqslant N, Z \leqslant 28$, where the odd nucleon is in an $f_{7/2}$ orbit, and reasonable agreement with experimental data was found (Ba-63).

More generally, considerable advances in calculating overall trends of ft values for allowed transitions have been made recently, based on the shell model with pairing correlations, the "quasi-particle model" (Ki-60; Sa-63; Kis-63; Fu-63).

Forbidden Beta Transitions

The previous remarks regarding β spectra apply only to those allowed transitions which involve a spin change of 0 or 1 and no change of parity. In such cases the nuclear matrix elements $\int 1$ and $\int \boldsymbol{\sigma}$ can be nonzero, and the electron and neutrino each carry off no *orbital* angular momentum. Therefore, their wave functions at the nucleus are nonzero. This can be seen from the expression of the wave function $\psi_e(r)$ for a free electron emitted with orbital angular momentum l_e, which is proportional to $(p_e r_e)^{l_e}$ for a small distance r_e from the center of the nucleus. Thus $\psi_e(0)$ is different from zero only when $l_e = 0$; that is, the function is finite at $r = 0$ only when electrons are emitted with zero orbital angular momentum. The same considerations hold for the neutrino wave function.

Now consider the case where the parity of the nucleus changes or the change of spin is greater than 1. In that case the nuclear matrix elements $\int 1$ and $\int \boldsymbol{\sigma}$ must vanish. Thus the β transition cannot occur to this order of approximation. Such transitions are known as "forbidden transitions." However, when we consider that the electron wave function is not completely constant over the volume of the nucleus and also take into account the finite velocity of the nucleons, such transitions can occur; however, the transition probability is greatly reduced compared with allowed transitions of the same energy.

In all except the last part of this section, we shall consider the so-called "first forbidden" transitions, the lowest-order nonallowed kind in which the electron-neutrino pair carries an orbital angular momentum $1\hbar$. A comprehensive discussion of these transitions, including an extensive bibliography, can be found in a review paper by Weidenmüller (We-61).

Several Terms Contributing to Forbidden Transitions

Retardation Terms. The electron or neutrino may carry off orbital angular momentum. This gives rise to so-called retardation terms which correspond to the higher-order terms in a multipole expansion. In the

Fermi matrix element $\int 1$, the spatial part of the bilinear product $\psi_e{}^\dagger\psi_\nu$ becomes

$$e^{-i(\mathbf{p}+\mathbf{q})\cdot r} \tag{3-49}$$

Thus the nuclear matrix element is

$$\int \psi_f{}^\dagger e^{-i(\mathbf{p}+\mathbf{q})\cdot\mathbf{r}}\psi_i\, d^3\mathbf{r} \tag{3-50}$$

where i and f refer to initial and final states of the nucleus. An expansion in powers of r gives

$$\int \psi_f{}^\dagger\psi_i\, d^3\mathbf{r} - i(\mathbf{p}+\mathbf{q})\int \psi_f{}^\dagger\mathbf{r}\psi_i\, d^3\mathbf{r} = \int 1 - i(\mathbf{p}+\mathbf{q})\cdot\int \mathbf{r} \tag{3-51}$$

The first term in this expansion vanishes, and the second term corresponds to the dipole matrix element $\int \mathbf{r}$. Then, ψ_i and ψ_f must have opposite parity and $\Delta I = 0$ or ± 1. (If they have the same parity, contributions to the matrix element from each pair of points $\mathbf{r}$ and $-\mathbf{r}$ cancel, and $\int \mathbf{r}$ must vanish.)

In the expression for the spectrum there will then be an additional factor

$$(\mathbf{p}+\mathbf{q})^2 \sim p^2 + q^2 \sim (\epsilon^2 - 1) + (\epsilon_0 - \epsilon)^2 \tag{3-52}$$

in addition, of course, to the allowed statistical factor. (The cross term $2\mathbf{p}\cdot\mathbf{q}$ vanishes when averaged over angles between electrons and neutrinos.) Thus we obtain a characteristic nonallowed shape. (We will see later, however, that the Coulomb field restores the allowed shape for most transitions with $\Delta I = 0, 1$ (yes).) The transition probability for a decay of this type would be smaller than that for an allowed transition by a factor which is approximately

$$\text{Ratio} \sim (\epsilon_0{}^2 - 1)R^2/10 \tag{3-53}$$

where R is the radius of the nucleus and is expressed in units of the electron Compton wavelength $\hbar/mc \sim 3.8 \times 10^{-11}$ cm. For typical cases, this ratio is approximately 10^{-4} to 10^{-3}. For example, for a decay of energy 1.5 mev and A $\sim$ 100, we have $\epsilon_0 \sim 4$, $R \sim 0.015$, Ratio $\sim 3 \times 10^{-4}$. Physically, the reduction in the transition probability, compared to that of an allowed transition, arises because the electron and neutrino, at least one of which must carry off orbital angular momentum, are kept away from the nucleus by the centrifugal force; hence their wave functions at the nucleus are greatly reduced.

So far we have considered the vector interaction only. Now let us apply the same consideration to the axial-vector interaction, which, as we have seen, can be written in the form

$$\int \boldsymbol{\sigma} \cdot \int \boldsymbol{\sigma} - \int \gamma_5 \cdot \int \gamma_5 \tag{3-54}$$

The term $\int \boldsymbol{\sigma} \cdot \int \boldsymbol{\sigma}$ gives rise to several retardation matrix elements which contain the product of two vectors such as $\boldsymbol{\sigma}$ and $\mathbf{r}$. The nine independent components $\sigma_i x_j$ can be grouped into three matrix elements: the scalar product $\boldsymbol{\sigma} \cdot \mathbf{r}$, the vector product $\boldsymbol{\sigma} \times \mathbf{r}$, and the symmetrical tensor of zero trace

$$B_{ij} = \int (\sigma_i x_j + \sigma_j x_i - \tfrac{2}{3}\, \delta_{ij} \sigma \cdot r) \tag{3-55}$$

The matrix element $\int \boldsymbol{\sigma} \cdot \mathbf{r}$ behaves as a pseudoscalar, that is, $\Delta I = 0$ (yes); the $\int \boldsymbol{\sigma} \times \mathbf{r}$ obeys the polar-vector selection rules $\Delta I = 0, \pm 1$ (yes); but there is no $0 \rightarrow 0$ transition. The matrix element B_{ij} has completely different selection rules. *The vector change of angular momentum* $|I_f - I_i|$ *must be* 2. Thus the selection rules are $\Delta I = 0, 1, 2$, $\pi_f = -\pi_i$, but no $0 \rightarrow 0$, $\frac{1}{2} \rightarrow \frac{1}{2}$ or $1 \leftrightarrow 0$ transitions can occur. Therefore, when $|\Delta I| = 2$ and $\pi_f \neq \pi_i$, the transition can occur only by virtue of the B_{ij} matrix element, and the spectrum shape is uniquely determined by the shape factor of this matrix element. This type of β spectrum, in which the change of angular momentum is one unit higher than the order of its forbiddenness $\Delta I = n + 1$, is generally known as a *unique forbidden transition*. The other matrix elements $\int \gamma_5$ can only connect states of the same angular momentum and of opposite parity. For a scalar interaction, the retardation term is $\int \beta \mathbf{r}$, but the presence of β in the matrix element has no effect on selection rules. Therefore it is the same as that of $\int \mathbf{r}$. The terms in tensor interactions $\int \beta \boldsymbol{\sigma} \cdot \mathbf{r}$, $\int \beta \boldsymbol{\sigma} \times \mathbf{r}$, and $\beta \mathrm{B}_{ij}$ should have similar selection rules as those for the axial vector interaction.

Source Velocity Effects. There are also other terms which can give rise to forbidden transitions. For example, the vector interaction Hamiltonian contains the relativistic terms $\int \boldsymbol{\alpha} \cdot \int \boldsymbol{\alpha}$. This term is essentially of the form $\int (v_{\mathrm{n}}/c) \cdot \int (v_{\mathrm{n}}/c)$ where v_{n} is the velocity of a nucleon inside of the nucleus (approximately equal to one-tenth of the velocity of light c); it gives the same selection rules as the dipole term $\Delta I = 0, 1$, considered previously. This time, if the electron has $v_e \sim c$, the lepton covariant $\psi_e^\dagger\psi_\nu$ is approximately unity. Thus the matrix element for the transition is approximately the same as the nuclear matrix element,

$$\int \psi_f^\dagger \frac{v_n}{c} \psi_i \sim 0.1 \int \psi_f^\dagger \psi_i \tag{3-56}$$

for a typical transition. *In this case we still obtain a β spectrum of allowed shape and a transition probability of the order of* 1% *of the allowed value.* The matrix elements produced by the source velocity effects are $\int \boldsymbol{\alpha}$ *for vector* and $\int \gamma_5$ *for axial vector.*

Table 3-5 First Forbidden Matrix Elements

Retardation Term		Source Velocity		Selection Rules
V	A	V	A	
	$\int \boldsymbol{\sigma} \cdot \mathbf{r}$		$\int \gamma_5$	$\Delta I = 0$ (yes)
$\int \mathbf{r}$	$\int \boldsymbol{\sigma} \times \mathbf{r}$	$\int \boldsymbol{\alpha}$		$\Delta I = 1$ (yes) No $0 \leftrightarrow 0$
	$\int B_{ij} = \int (\sigma_i x_j + \sigma_j x_i - \frac{2}{3}\delta_{ij}\boldsymbol{\sigma} \cdot \mathbf{r})$			$\Delta I = 2$ (yes) No $\begin{pmatrix} 0 \leftrightarrow 0 \\ 0 \leftrightarrow 1 \\ \frac{1}{2} \leftrightarrow \frac{1}{2} \end{pmatrix}$

In summary, the first forbidden matrix elements for V and A interactions and their respective selection rules are listed in Table 3-5.

Effect of the Nuclear Coulomb Field—The Quasi-allowed (ξ) *Approximation.* The nuclear Coulomb field increases the negatron wave function near the nucleus, thus increasing the transition probability in the same way as for allowed transitions. There is, however, another effect which is a consequence of the Coulomb field in conjunction with relativity. Consider an electron in a state of given j. The possible values of l are $j + \frac{1}{2}$ and $j - \frac{1}{2}$. For example, a $j = \frac{1}{2}$ electron can be either in an $s_{1/2}$ or a $p_{1/2}$ state.

The magnitude of the electron wave function at some average distance R from the center of the nucleus should be 1 for the $l = 0$ state—that is,

$s_{1/2}$—and kR for the $l = 1$ state—that is, $p_{1/2}$ and $p_{3/2}$—where k = wave number = $p/\hbar$. Detailed calculations taking relativity and the Coulomb field into account show that these conclusions hold for the $s_{1/2}$ and $p_{3/2}$ states (and generally for $j = l + \frac{1}{2}$), but that for an electron in the $p_{1/2}$ state we have $\psi(\mathrm{R}) \sim \alpha Z$ rather than kR if $\alpha Z \gg kR$ (α is the fine-structure constant $e^2/\hbar c$). This condition is equivalent to $Ze^2/R \gg E_0 = pc$; that is, the decay energy is small compared to the Coulomb barrier energy at the nuclear radius which is satisfied for most forbidden spectra.

The strong effect of the Coulomb field on the $p_{1/2}$ state (and, more generally, on states with $j = l - \frac{1}{2}$) can be understood as follows: Because of relativity and the Coulomb field, there is a coupling between the spin and orbital momentum. Thus the electron which might basically be, say, in a $p_{1/2}$ state will actually spend a small part of its time in the other state of the same j, that is, $s_{1/2}$.

Now suppose the probability amplitude for being in an s state is f ($f \approx \alpha Z$). Then we have

$$\psi_{p_{1/2}}(R) = \psi_p(R) + f\psi_s(R) = kR + f \tag{3-57a}$$

Evidently ψ is greatly increased if $f > kR$, even though f may be much smaller than one. On the other hand, for an electron in the $s_{1/2}$ state, this correction is much smaller since

$$\psi_{s_{1/2}}(R) = \psi_s(R) + f\psi_p(R) = 1 + fkR \approx 1 \tag{3-57b}$$

The mixing effect can be neglected. However, the transition amplitude of an electron in the $p_{1/2}$ state is increased considerably because of the mixing of $s_{1/2}$ into this $p_{1/2}$ state. It should be multiplied by $\alpha Z/kR$. This means that the spectrum correction factor can now be given by the energy independent factor $(\alpha Z)^2$ rather than by $(p^2 + q^2)R^2$. For transitions of the form $\Delta I = 0, 1$ (yes), it is always possible for the electron to be emitted in a $p_{1/2}$ state with the neutrino in an $s_{1/2}$ state, and these transitions can be expected to have an allowed spectrum shape. *The approximation $\alpha Z/E_0R = \xi \gg 1$ required to give this kind of spectrum is known as the ξ approximation or "quasi-allowed" approximation.*

On the other hand, for transitions with $\Delta I = 2$ (yes), it is not possible for the electron to be emitted in a $p_{1/2}$ state. The only way to satisfy the selection rules is to have the two leptons in $s_{1/2}$ and $p_{3/2}$ states, respectively, in which case the Coulomb effect does not alter our earlier conclusions. Only the matrix element B_{ij} can give a finite contribution, and we obtain the unique first forbidden nonallowed shape characterized by the correction factor $p^2 + q^2$, except for a relatively small additional Coulomb correction.

Although transitions with $\Delta I = 0, 1$ (yes) are expected to have nearly allowed shapes in most cases, exceptions can occur under at least three conditions.

1. For light nuclei with a large decay energy—that is, if the condition $\alpha Z \gg E_0 R$ is no longer satisfied.
2. If various energy-independent terms which contribute to the transition amplitude should happen to cancel, leaving only the smaller energy-dependent terms. (This seems to occur for RaE, as we shall see presently, and to a lesser extent for some other decays as well.)
3. If additional approximate selection rules due to nuclear structure should reduce the magnitudes of the $\Delta I = 0, 1$ matrix elements, leaving only B_{ij} to dominate the spectrum. (This seems to happen to some extent for the decay of Sb^{124}.) (See p. 126 for a more detailed discussion.)

First Forbidden Spectra

From the foregoing argument, we can conclude that first forbidden spectra fall into two main groups, those in which $\Delta I = 0$ or ± 1 with mainly allowed shapes, and those with $\Delta I = \pm 2$ with nonallowed shapes. Many spectra of the first kind, for example, Pr^{144}, Ce^{141}, Pm^{147}, and Au^{198}, have been carefully measured and were found, as expected,* to have shapes quite close to allowed. There are only a few exceptions known so far.

Let us now consider the first group—$\Delta I = 0, \pm 1$; change of parity. As we have seen, the lifetime would be approximately 1,000 times that for allowed transitions; therefore, $\log ft \sim 6$ to 8. Transitions of this type occur mainly for heavy nuclei with more than 82 neutrons. For such heavy nuclei, according to the shell model, the neutron and

* Actually, even for these spectra, we would generally expect Fierz-type deviations from allowed shapes if either the *SA* or *VT* combinations occur in the β interaction. Such deviations were looked for but not found (Ma-52). The absence of Fierz interference effects in allowed and first forbidden spectra limits the possible combination in the β-decay interaction to *ST* and *VA* (apart from a possible pseudoscalar term). These remarks do not, of course, take into account parity-violating terms in the interaction. Thus the Fierz interference terms vanish in the two-component neutrino theory.

proton orbits usually have opposite parity. Thus the parity is expected to change in the transition. As a simple example let us consider the decay ${}_{58}Ce^{141}_{83} \rightarrow {}_{59}Pr^{141}_{82}$ illustrated in Fig. 3-12. The Kurie plot of the β spectrum for this transition is known to be nearly linear. The spins of both initial and final states have been measured. The single-particle shell model assignments are $f^{-}_{7/2}$ for $N = 83$ and $d^{+}_{5/2}$ for $Z = 59$ which is

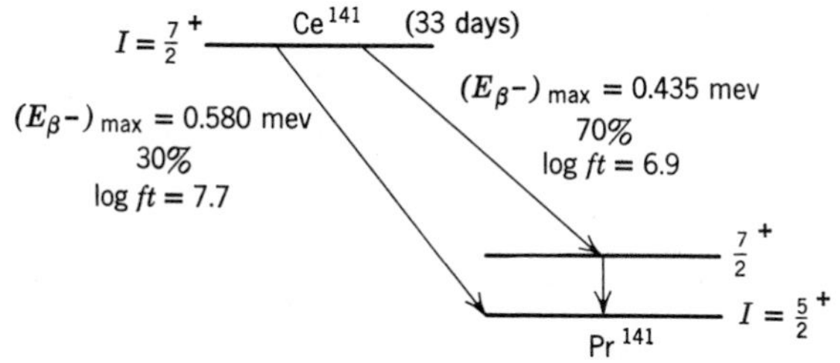

Fig. 3-12 Decay scheme of Ce[141].

consistent with the measurements. The log ft value for the 574-kev transition is 7.7, which is reasonable for transitions of this kind. The transitions to the $\frac{7}{2}^{+}$ state has log $ft \sim 6.9$, which is also reasonable.

Beta Decay of Nonspherical Nuclei

Next we shall consider the nonspherical or deformed nuclei (Boh-53; Al-56; Mo-57) which occur for $6 < A < 10$, $19 < A < 30$, $150 < A < 190$, and $A > 220$. We shall discuss some examples from the group $150 < A < 190$, for which most (but by no means all) β decays are of the "forbidden" class. The reason is that the last neutron and proton are generally (but not always) in states of opposite parity, and thus the β decays involve a change of parity.

For deformed nuclei, the simple version of the single-particle shell model previously discussed is not applicable. On the other hand, the low-lying states are grouped into rotational bands.

These nuclei are believed to have axial symmetry and reflection symmetry, that is, to be somewhat "football-shaped," as indicated in Fig. 3-13. For a static nucleus of this shape, the component of angular momentum K along the symmetry axis is conserved. However, in order to satisfy the Heisenberg uncertainty principle

$$\Delta I \, \Delta\theta \geqslant \hbar \tag{3-58}$$

the symmetry axis cannot "sit idly in space" but must precess—that is, rotate—about the angular-momentum axis. For a given value of K

the possible total angular momenta are

$$I = K, \quad K + 1, \quad K + 2 \cdots \tag{3-59}$$

except that for $K = 0$ the reflection symmetry requires that I be even

$$I = 0, 2, 4, \ldots \tag{3-60}$$

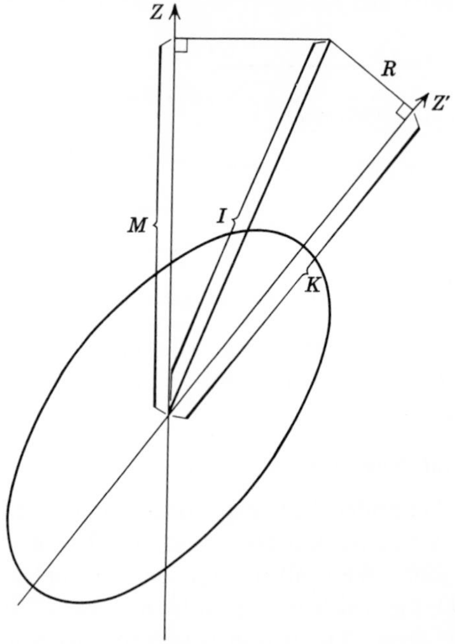

Fig. 3-13 Coupling scheme for deformed nuclei.

The energy associated with this rotation is

$$E_I = \frac{\hbar^2}{2\mathscr{I}} [I(I + 1) - K(K + 1)] \tag{3-61}$$

where $\mathscr{I}$ is a moment of inertia.

In order to obtain K, we can regard the nucleons as moving independently in the average nuclear potential, except that the potential is now not spherical, as in the simple shell model, but spheroidal. Whereas in the spherical shell model each level is characterized by an angular momentum j and has a degeneracy $2j + 1$, in the spheroidal case only the component of angular momentum K along the symmetry axis is a good quantum number. For a given orbit K there is another orbit with $-K$,

$$\psi_{-K} = \psi_K{}^* \tag{3-62}$$

which occurs at the same energy, that is, each level is only twofold degenerate. The K value of each level is understood to represent $|K|$, that is, to include both the K and $-K$ orbits. The structure and class of single-particle levels in a spheroidal potential have been studied extensively, especially by S. G. Nilsson (Ni-55) and B. R. Mottelson and S. G. Nilsson (Mot-59).

In the spherical shell model, pairs of equivalent nucleons tend to couple to a resultant $J = 0$. Similarly, in deformed nuclei, the K values for a pair of nucleons in a given orbit cancel. Indeed, because of the short-range interactions between nucleons, such configurations, in which the two nucleons overlap perfectly, are energetically formed. Thus for even-even nuclei the ground-state band has $K = 0$, $I = 0$, 2, 4, and other bands occur only at energies of about 1 mev, whereas for low states of odd A nuclei the K values are associated with the K of the last odd nucleon.

There are important special selection rules for β decay associated with deformed nuclei (Al-55). Thus for an allowed or first forbidden (nonunique) transition not only $|\Delta I|$ but also $|\Delta K|$ is smaller than or equal to one. A transition for which $|\Delta I| = 1$ but $|\Delta K| \geqslant 2$ will be hindered. A drastic example of this hindrance is provided by the decay of the Lu^{176} ground state illustrated in Fig. 3-14 where the first

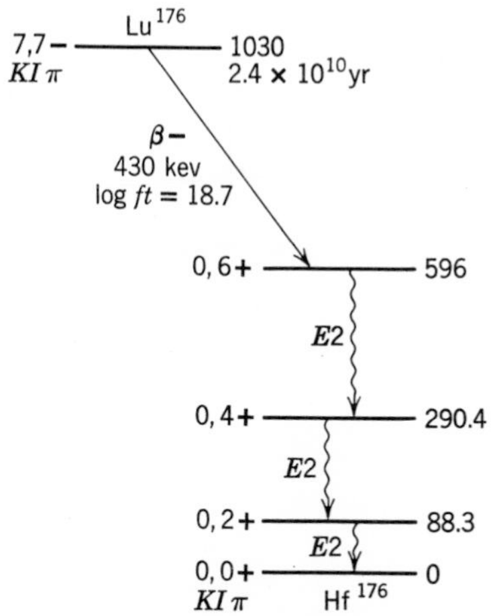

Fig. 3-14 Decay scheme of the long-lived Lu^{176}. From (Ga-62).

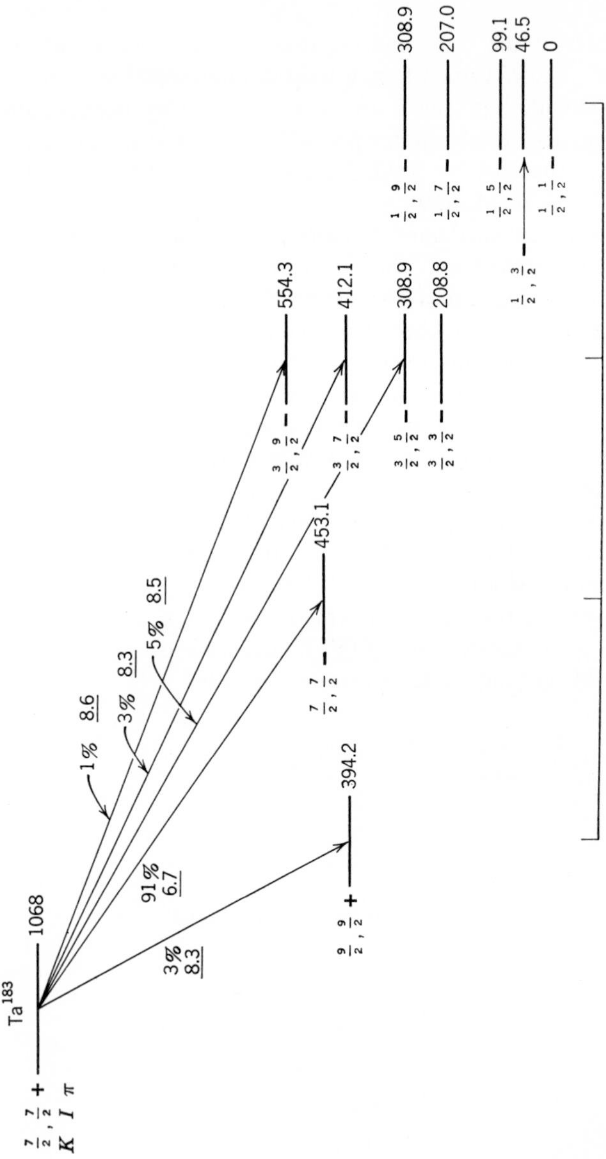

Fig. 3-15 Decay scheme of Ta^{183}. From nuclear data sheets.

forbidden decay has an ft value about 10^{12} as large as normally expected. This is reasonable because we have six orders of K forbiddenness.

Even in other cases there is a considerable increase of the log ft value compared to the usual range of values 6 to 8 for first forbidden transitions. For example, in the β decay of Ta^{183} (cf. Fig. 3-15) no decay to the $I = \frac{5}{2}, \frac{7}{2}$, or $\frac{9}{2}$ states of the $K = \frac{1}{2}$ band is observed at all, even

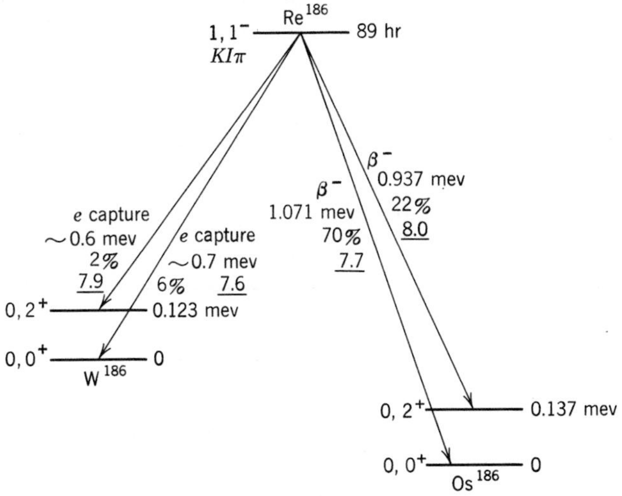

Fig. 3-16 Decay scheme of Re^{186}. From (Ga-62).

though they involve $|\Delta I| \leqslant 1$ and are, in fact, favored energetically over the other β branches.

Incidentally, the level order for the $K = \frac{1}{2}$ band is seen to deviate from the simple rotational law (Eq. 3-61). This is due to the so-called decoupling effect (Boh-53; Mos-57) which occurs for $K = \frac{1}{2}$ bands. It is a consequence of Coriolis interaction between the degenerate $K = \frac{1}{2}$ and $K = -\frac{1}{2}$ orbits.

For transitions in which K selection rules are satisfied, there are simple relations among nuclear matrix elements and, therefore, among ft values. Consider, for example, the decay of the ground state Re^{186} as indicated in Fig. 3-16. Both β^+ and β^- decay can occur, leading in each case to the two lowest states $K = 0$, $I = 0$, 2 of the final nucleus. These two states have the same basic structure and differ only in the amount of rotation. According to the rotational model, we can show that the ft values should be related by single geometric factors. More specifically, the model predicts

$$\frac{ft)_{1\to 2}}{(ft)_{1\to 0}} = \left[\frac{C(I_i\lambda I_f\,;\,K_i\ K_f - K_i\ K_f)}{C(I_i\lambda I_f';\,K_i\ K_f - K_i\ K_f)}\right]^2 = \left[\frac{C(110;\,1\ -1\ 0)}{C(112;\,1\ -1\ 0)}\right]^2 = 2 \tag{3-63}$$

where C is a Clebsch-Gordon coefficient. The ratio is in very good agreement with the experimental value, not only for Re^{186} but also in similar cases such as Tm^{170}.

Decays of Nuclei near Pb^{208}. One group of first forbidden transitions, which occurs between nuclei near the double magic nucleus ${}_{82}Pb^{208}_{126}$, has

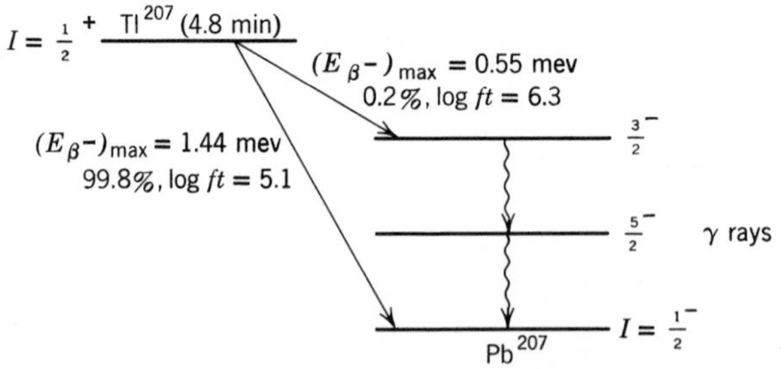

Fig. 3-17 Decay scheme of Tl^{207}.

unusually small log ft values. A simple example is the decay of Tl^{207} (Fig. 3-17). The spin and parity assignments given in the figure are consistent with shell-model predictions and with systematics of neighboring nuclei. Thus it is very likely that the parity changes in this transition. Nevertheless, the log ft value is characteristic of an allowed transition. A probable explanation of this point is that here we have a forbidden transition with an exceptionally large nuclear matrix element, somewhat analogous to the superallowed transitions discussed previously. After all, in most forbidden transitions we have not only the retardation effect discussed in this section but also the unfavored effect mentioned in connection with most allowed transitions. However, in the decays near Pb^{208}, apparently only the retardation effects appear, and the wave functions of initial and final nucleus are very similar.

Beta Spectrum of RaE

In some forbidden spectra with $\Delta I = 0, \pm 1$, the spectrum shape is considerably different from allowed. Evidently in such cases the various large energy-independent terms, discussed earlier, tend to cancel; then the smaller but energy-dependent terms dominate. One classic example of this is provided by the decay of RaE(Bi^{210}) (see Fig. 3-18a) whose spectrum is known to have an anomalous shape (see Fig. 3-18b).

It is unfortunate that RaE, being a natural radioactive isotope, was one of the first spectra studied. The fact that it exhibited a nonallowed shape delayed the development of β-decay theory considerably. In the absence of additional information, this spectrum shape appeared to contradict the simple Fermi theory and stimulated alternative formulations, such as the Konopinski-Uhlenbeck modification (Ko-35).* Only after several allowed spectra, with the simple statistical shape predicted by the Fermi theory, were identified did it become clear that it was the RaE spectrum which was anomalous. For a time it was supposed to be second forbidden, for, as we shall see later, it is possible to obtain a variety of nonallowed shapes for high forbidden spectra.

After the development of the nuclear shell model, some progress began to be made in understanding this decay. ${}_{83}RaE^{210}_{127}$ has 83 protons and 127 neutrons, that is, a double magic core of ${}_{82}Pb^{208}_{126}$ and an extra proton and neutron. The shell model predicts that the extra proton is in the orbits $h_{9/2}, f_{7/2}$, or $p_{3/2}$, and that the extra neutron is in the orbits $i_{11/2}, g_{9/2}$, or $d_{5/2}$. Therefore, it is quite certain that the parity of RaE is odd. The β transition must involve a parity change, since the parity of the final even-even nucleus ${}_{84}Po^{210}_{126}$(RaF) must be even.

This necessity ruled out the possibility of a second forbidden transition since no change in parity could be involved. The possibility that the spectrum was unique first forbidden—that is, $2^- \rightarrow 0^+$—was also ruled out, because of the observed shape.

Another possibility considered was that the spectrum might not be simple but rather contain several components. This possibility was discarded, however, after a very careful but futile search (Boe-53) for

---

* In the K–U modification, the β interactions between the electron-neutrino field and the nucleus were assumed to be dependent on the momentum of the two light particles and therefore contained derivatives of the electron and neutrino wave functions.

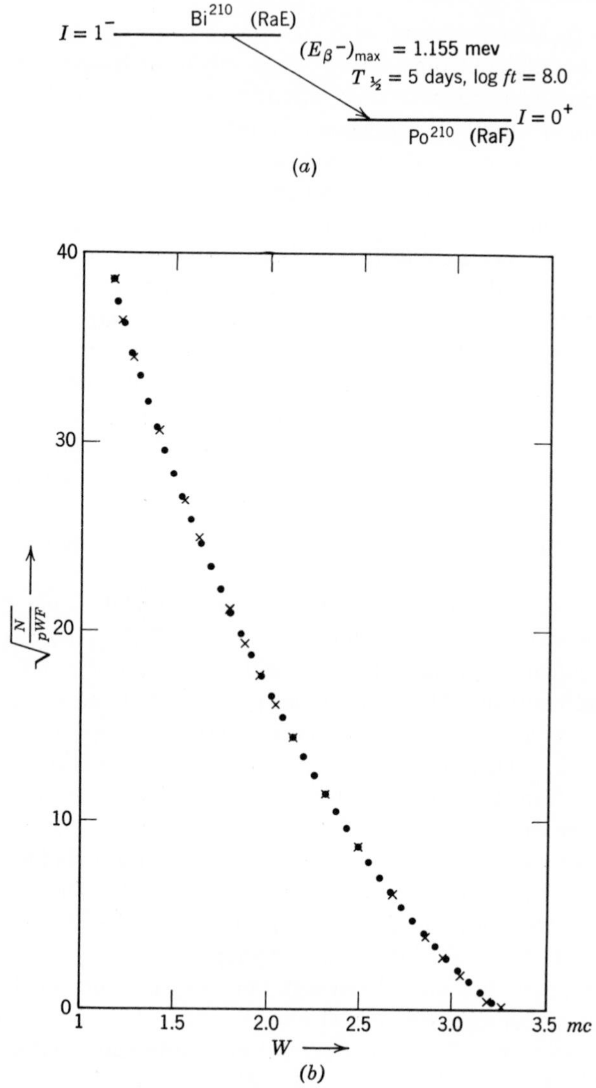

Fig. 3-18 (*a*) Decay scheme of RaE. (*b*) Kurie plot of RaE β spectrum. (*c*) The required shape factors.

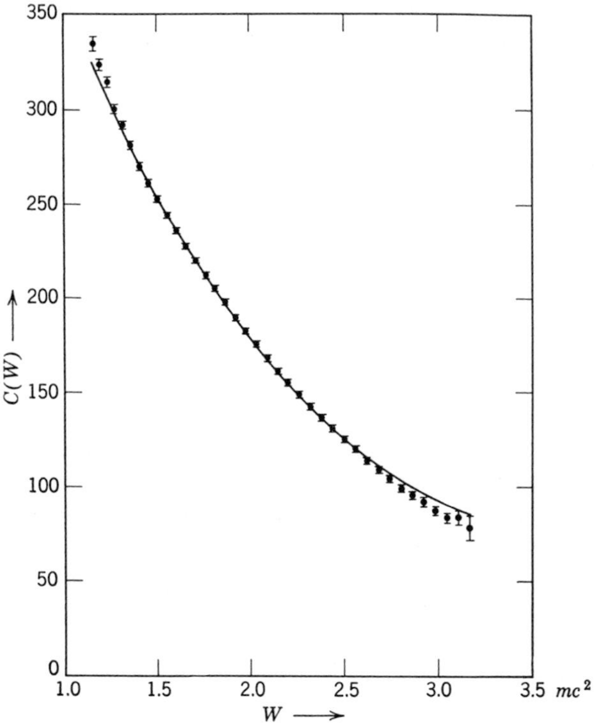

(c)

γ rays and internal-conversion electrons. Only the theoretically expected characteristic X rays near the region of 80 kev, produced by ionization of the atom through β decay, were found to be superimposed on the continuous background of the internal bremsstrahlung.

It had to be concluded that the transition involves spin and parity change of $\Delta I = 0$ or ± 1 (yes). As we have seen, such spectra normally have allowed shapes. However, the expression for the transition amplitude is a sum of several terms, and if the large energy-independent terms should happen to cancel each other, the smaller nonallowed terms may become relatively important. At that time, Petschek and Marshak (Pe-52) investigated the possibility of fitting the RaE spectrum with various linear combinations of interactions. They found that the only way to obtain a fit to the data was by assuming a $0 \rightarrow 0$ (yes) transition with tensor and pseudoscalar interaction. In particular, they could not fit the spectrum on the assumption of a spin one for RaE, regardless of the interaction assumed.

There was a certain amount of additional evidence for this picture at the time. The magnetic moment of RaE was measured in 1953 and found to be very small ($|\mu| < 0.35$ nuclear magnetons, not inconsistent with 0), pointing toward a spin of zero (for which μ *must* equal 0). It seemed unlikely, a priori, that the magnetic moment would be so small if the spin were one. Moreover, although the form of the β interaction was not yet known, the results of β-ν angular-correlation experiments of He^6 pointed *at the time* toward the tensor rather than the axial-vector interaction. Indeed, there were theoretical arguments which supported the assumption of an *STP* combination (Sec 7-1). A scalar interaction would not contribute to a $0 \rightarrow 0$ (yes) transition.

Although all the evidence seemed to be internally consistent, more detailed analysis showed that the amount of pseudoscalar interaction required to cancel the tensor terms would have to be much larger than theoretically expected; that is, $C_P/C_T \sim 150$ (Ah-52) would be needed. Theoretically, at that time the β interaction was widely believed to be of the form $S \pm T + P$ [see Sec. 7-1 (Pe-53; Ko-53)] for which $C_P/C_T \simeq 1$. This, in turn, led various authors to question the whole treatment of the pseudoscalar interaction. However, by modifying the theoretical treatment, it was possible to remove this difficulty, at least in part (Rud-53).

Beginning in 1954, the whole question of RaE was reopened (Ya-53c). First of all, a direct spin measurement (Sm-54) showed the spin of RaE to be one rather than zero. Secondly, certain effects not considered by Petschek and Marshak in their shape analysis were found to alter the theoretical fits considerably. Their calculations had been based on the assumption that the nuclear radius is small. In particular, the variation of the lepton wave function inside the region of the nucleus itself had been neglected; in addition, the nuclear radius was regarded as small compared to the de Broglie wavelength of the electrons. Although the finite-size corrections are small for allowed spectra, they become quite important in a case such as RaE where a near-cancellation of the leading terms occurs. Indeed, a fit could no longer be obtained for $0 \rightarrow 0$ (yes) (*STP*), but, instead, good agreement with data was found with $1 \rightarrow 0$ (yes) and either of the combinations *ST* or *VA*. This development removed the theoretical difficulty associated with the pseudoscalar interaction, for this term no longer contributed to the spectrum.*

The establishment in 1958 of the VA interaction combination as the correct combination further clarified the picture. For this interaction the leading terms in the spectrum can be expressed as follows,

$$N(E) = |M|^2 N_{\text{allowed}}(E) \tag{3-64}$$

where the total matrix element is given by (We-61)

$$M = \left(C_V i\xi \int \mathbf{r} - C_V \int \boldsymbol{\alpha} + C_A \xi \int \boldsymbol{\sigma} \times \mathbf{r}\right) \tag{3-65a}$$

$$= C_V i\xi \int \mathbf{r}\left(1 - \frac{B}{\xi} + \frac{C_A}{C_V}\frac{1}{A}\right) \tag{3-65b}$$

with $\xi = \alpha Z/2R \sim 15$ Rae, $B = \int \boldsymbol{\alpha}/i\int \mathbf{r}$, $A = i\int \mathbf{r}/\int \boldsymbol{\sigma} \times \mathbf{r}$. The notation adopted here agrees with that of Konopinski-Uhlenbeck (Ko-41), Morita (Mo-58), and Weidenmüller (We-61) but differs slightly from that used by some other authors.

Table 3-6 Notation for First Forbidden $\Delta I = 1$ Beta-Decay Matrix Elements

This Book	Kotani (Kot-59), Lipnik and Sunier (Li-64)	Fujita (Fu-62)
$\int \mathbf{r}$	$\int \mathbf{r}$	$R\langle \mathbf{r} \rangle$
$\int \boldsymbol{\alpha}$	$-\int \boldsymbol{\alpha}$	$-\langle \boldsymbol{\alpha} \rangle$
$\int \boldsymbol{\sigma} \times \mathbf{r}$	$\int \boldsymbol{\sigma} \times \mathbf{r}$	$-R\langle \boldsymbol{\sigma} \times \mathbf{r} \rangle$

Theoretical Evaluation of B. As we shall point out, the ratio B does not depend very strongly on details concerning nuclear structure.

* Actually, it is very difficult to establish experimentally the magnitude of the pseudoscalar coupling in β decay, for even a large coupling strength gives only a small correction to spectrum shape and electron polarization. Bhalla and Rose (Bh-60) have made a very careful analysis of the decay of Pr^{144} (first forbidden $0^- \to 0^+$) to which only the A and P interactions can contribute. No evidence of a correction attributable to pseudoscalar interaction was found, but specifically it can only be concluded that $|g_P/g_A| \leqslant 90$.

First of all, we may reduce the relativistic matrix elements to nonrelativistic (Ah-52) form, which gives

$$\int \boldsymbol{\alpha} = -\frac{\int \mathbf{p}}{m_{\mathrm{p}}c} \tag{3-65f}$$

Then

$$B = \frac{i\int \mathbf{p}}{m_{\mathrm{p}}c\int \mathbf{r}} \tag{3-65g}$$

Let us first *treat the nucleons as free*, with Hamiltonian

$$H_0 = \frac{\mathbf{p}^2}{2m_{\mathrm{p}}} \tag{3-65h}$$

and neglect any effect of nuclear forces. Then, of course, we have

$$\int \mathbf{p} = -\frac{im_{\mathrm{p}}}{\hbar}\int [\mathbf{r}, H_0] = \frac{-im_{\mathrm{p}}}{\hbar}(E_i - E_f)\int \mathbf{r} = -im_{\mathrm{p}}\omega\int \mathbf{r} \tag{3-65i}$$

where the brackets denote commutator and

$$B = \frac{E_i - E_f}{\hbar c} = \frac{\omega}{c} \tag{3-65j}$$

independent of the actual value of the matrix element $\int \mathbf{r}$. Now, of course, *the nucleons are not free*—that is, the nuclear Hamiltonian also contains interaction terms. Therefore this argument is not necessarily valid. Suppose, first of all, that the interactions are functions of interparticle spacings alone and are independent of nuclear charge. The interactions then commute with the operator $\mathbf{r}$; thus our Eq. 3-65i would still hold with H now representing the total Hamiltonian. Actually, the interactions are neither charge-independent nor functions of coordinates alone. The noncommutivity of the interactions with $\mathbf{r}$ implies that Eq. 3-65i breaks down. Thus the commutator (the time derivative of $\mathbf{r}$) is no longer simply proportional to $\mathbf{p}$.

Siegert's Theorem. A similar problem also occurs in the theory of electromagnetic radiation and, in particular, for electric dipole radiation. The interaction of a classical current distribution j with an electric dipole radiation field is given by

$$U_{\mathrm{E1}} = -\int \mathbf{j}\cdot\mathbf{A}\,d\mathbf{r} = -\int \mathbf{j}\cdot\boldsymbol{\epsilon}\,d\mathbf{r} \tag{3-66}$$

in the long wavelength approximation, where $\boldsymbol{\epsilon}$ refers to the polarization vector. Integrating by parts we find

$$U_{E1} = -\int \mathbf{j} \cdot \nabla(\mathbf{r} \cdot \boldsymbol{\epsilon})\, d\mathbf{r} = \int (\nabla \cdot \mathbf{j})(\mathbf{r} \cdot \boldsymbol{\epsilon})\, d\mathbf{r} \tag{3-67}$$

Although U_{E1} as written above involves the current distribution, it can be expressed directly in terms of the electric charge distribution ρ. Thus with the help of the equation of charge conservation

$$\frac{\partial \rho}{\partial t} + \nabla \cdot \mathbf{j} = 0 \tag{3-68}$$

we obtain

$$U_{E1} = -\int \frac{\partial \rho}{\partial t}(\mathbf{r} \cdot \boldsymbol{\epsilon})\, d\mathbf{r} = i\omega \int \rho(\mathbf{r} \cdot \boldsymbol{\epsilon})\, d\mathbf{r} \tag{3-69}$$

The foregoing argument then holds even if there are interactions between the particles making up the charge distributions. *As Siegert (Si-37) pointed out, the argument holds provided the interactions can be expressed in terms of nucleon coordinates alone rather than of the mesons which transmit the interaction.* This will be valid if the nucleon velocities are much smaller than those of the exchanged mesons. Siegert's theorem holds also for higher-order electric multipole radiation (Sa-53). However, the interaction with magnetic radiation depends in an essential way on the current distribution and cannot be expressed in terms of the charge distributions alone.

The foregoing argument implies that the interaction Hamiltonian can be written as

$$H_{E1} = i\omega \sum_i (e_i \mathbf{r}_i) \cdot \boldsymbol{\epsilon} \tag{3-70}$$

Of course for noninteracting particles this holds as

$$H_{E1} = -\frac{\sum e_i \mathbf{p}_i}{m_p} \cdot \boldsymbol{\epsilon} = i\omega \sum (e_i \mathbf{r}_i) \cdot \boldsymbol{\epsilon} \tag{3-71}$$

However, in the presence of interactions the simple relation between $\mathbf{p}$ and r no longer holds. In this case, the terms involving $\mathbf{p}$ account for the electric dipole transitions of the nucleons alone, whereas the remainder is accounted for by the interaction of the exchanged mesons with the radiation field.

The Application of Siegert's Theorem to the First Forbidden Beta Decay. A similar situation occurs also for the first forbidden β decay with the $\Delta I = 1$, the analogue of electric dipole radiation.

The β-decay matrix element $\int \boldsymbol{\alpha}$ or $\int \mathbf{p}$ corresponds to only a part of the decay amplitude. Assuming the validity of a conserved vector current for β decay, we should use instead $\int \dot{\mathbf{r}}$. Again, the two results agree for free nucleons, but not necessarily in the presence of interactions. The difference represents the β decay of exchanged mesons which are present by virtue of the nuclear interactions. Thus our form for B should hold for an arbitrary charge-independent interaction.

However, we still have to take into account the fact that a part of the nuclear Hamiltonian is charge-dependent. Of most importance here is the Coulomb interaction, which gives different energy in the initial and final state (the nuclear charge changes by one unit). We must also take into account the neutron-proton mass difference.

Altogether we can write

$$H = H_0 + H_1 \tag{3-76}$$

where H_0 denotes the part of the Hamiltonian which is charge-independent (although it may involve complicated meson exchanges), and H_1 contains the Coulomb effect and neutron-proton mass difference according to the foregoing argument; we can then write

$$B = \frac{1}{i\hbar} \frac{\int [\mathbf{r}, H_0]}{\int \mathbf{r}} \tag{3-77}$$

We shall treat H_1 as a constant. Then for the initial state we have

$$H_0 \psi_i = E_i' \psi_i \tag{3-78}$$

where

$$E_i' = E_i - \frac{3}{5} \frac{Z(Z-1)e^2}{R} - (m_{\mathrm{p}} Z + m_{\mathrm{n}} N) \tag{3-79}$$

(The charge distribution is assumed to be uniform of radius R.) For the final state we have

$$E_f' = E_f - \frac{3}{5} \frac{Z(Z+1)e^2}{R} - [m_{\mathrm{p}}(Z+1) + m_{\mathrm{n}}(N-1)] \tag{3-80}$$

Thus

$$B = \frac{1}{\hbar c}(E_i' - E_f') = \frac{1}{\hbar c}\left[\frac{6}{5}\frac{Ze^2}{R} - (m_{\mathrm{n}} - m_{\mathrm{p}}) + E_i - E_f\right] \tag{3-81}$$

and under our approximation B is exactly proportional to the energy difference which would result if charge-dependent effects were subtracted out. For actual β decays, the Coulomb term is quite dominant.

Thus we find approximately

$$B = \Lambda\xi \tag{3-82}$$

where

$$\xi = \frac{\alpha Z}{2R} \sim 15 \quad \text{for RaE} \tag{3-83}$$

and

$$\Lambda = 2.4 \tag{3-84}$$

Earlier estimates by Pursey (Pu-51) and Ahrens and Feenberg (Ah-52), who did not postulate a conserved vector current, gave somewhat smaller values of $\Lambda = 2.0$ and 1.0, respectively. In addition, Rose and Osborn (Ro-54) estimated that $\Lambda \sim 2$.

Using Fujita's value and the experimental ratio of coupling constants ($C_A/C_V = -1.2$), we find that the quantity in parentheses in Eq. 3-65b becomes $1 - 2.4 - (1.2/A)$. Thus to obtain the required cancellation of matrix elements it is necessary that $A \sim -0.8$.

A more accurate theoretical analysis of the RaE decay has been made by Fujita (Fu-62), who found it possible to fit both the spectrum shape and the incomplete polarization* ($P \sim -0.75$ v/c) of the β rays, provided that $-1.3 \leqslant A \leqslant -0.4$. A more recent analysis by Deutsch and Lipnik (De-65) yields less satisfactory fits, but if we assume the validity of the conserved vector theory, the data imply that $A \sim -1$.

The quantity A depends on details of nuclear structure and, in particular (as can be seen from the occurrence of the operator $\int \boldsymbol{\sigma}$ in the denominator but not in the numerator), on the detailed coupling between spin and orbital motion. Thus, if the foregoing interpretation of the RaE spectrum is correct, one possibility suggested by the shell model and the known spin $\frac{9}{2}$ of ${}_{83}\mathrm{Bi}^{209}_{126}$ is to assume that RaE has the proton and neutron in $h_{9/2}$ and $i_{11/2}$ orbits, respectively, outside the ${}_{82}\mathrm{Pb}^{208}_{126}$ core, and that in ${}_{84}\mathrm{Po}^{210}_{126}$ both extra protons are in the $h_{9/2}$ orbit. Calculations by Newby and Konopinski (Ne-59) and by Banerjee and Zeh (Ba-60), who assumed a contact interaction between the extra particles, indeed gave rise to wave functions close to these simple forms. However, their theoretical value of A was approximately $+1.0$, far from the experimental value and, indeed, of the wrong sign.

---

* Although electrons from almost all β decays have maximum polarization ($-$v/c) (cf. Sec. 4-5), there is less longitudinal polarization in a special case such as RaE, where the leading (energy-independent) terms in the spectrum cancel.

Spector and Blin-Stoyle (Sp-62a) have considered the effect of finite range of the nuclear forces. Increasing the range from zero to a reasonable value has little effect on the Po^{210} wave function but changes the RaE wave function drastically, so that it is now predicted to be mainly of the form $h_{9/2}g_{9/2}$. With this new wave function they find that $A \sim 0.27$; therefore the disagreement between theory and experiment is cut in half.

More recently, Kim and Rasmussen (Kim-63) have taken into account the presence of tensor forces. In this way they are able to account approximately for the value of A (they obtain $A \sim -0.63$) and also explain why the ground state of RaE has spin 1^-. (For central forces we would have expected a ground-state spin zero.) The remaining discrepancy can perhaps be removed by considering the excitation of the Pb^{208} core in the decay (Sp-62b).

Altogether, it now appears that the decay of RaE is finally understood, after almost 40 years. Still, we should not be complacent. When we consider the past history of RaE, it is quite possible that further surprises await us in the study of this fascinating nucleus.

The Unique Forbidden Spectra

The energy distribution of the β spectra from the transitions with $\Delta I = n + 1$ (where n is the order of forbiddenness) was theoretically predicted to be unique, for only one nuclear matrix element ($B_{ij\ldots n}$) fails to vanish for it. Furthermore, it could be realized only through the Gamow-Teller interaction. The eventual observation of abundant examples of unique first forbidden spectra together with representative cases of the unique second and third forbidden spectra gave convincing evidence that the approach to the theory of forbidden β decay was correct. It provides additional confirmation for the existence of the Gamow-Teller interaction; the well-known argument concerning the β decay of the He^6 as a superallowed transition also requires the existence of a Gamow-Teller interaction.

When the Coulomb effect on the electron is neglected, the unique shape factors for various degrees of forbiddenness can be simplified to (see Eq. 3-52)

$$\begin{aligned}
\Delta I &= 2 \text{ (yes)} \quad a_1 = p^2 + q^2 \\
\Delta I &= 3 \text{ (no)} \quad a_2 = p^4 + \tfrac{10}{3}p^2q^2 + q^4 \qquad (3\text{-}85)\\
\Delta I &= 4 \text{ (yes)} \quad a_3 = p^6 + 7p^4q^2 + 7p^2q^4 + q^6
\end{aligned}$$

The energy dependence of these factors strongly emphasizes the contribution of high-energy β particles; therefore the energy distribution of the unique β spectra is readily distinguishable from an allowed one. To illustrate the characteristics of each of these factors,

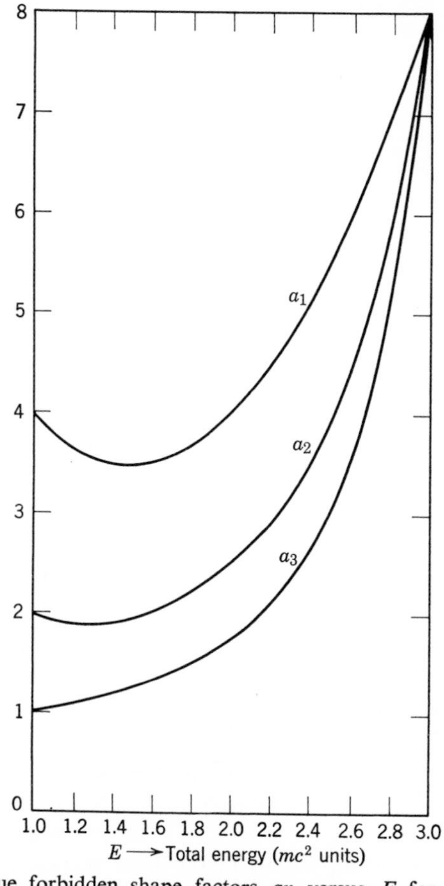

Fig. 3-19 Unique forbidden shape factors an versus E for $E_0 = 3\ mc^2$. The approximate forms for a_1, a_2, a_3 are given in the text.

a_1, a_2, and a_3 are plotted versus energy for a β transition of maximum total energy $E_0 = 3\ mc^2$, as shown in Fig. 3-19. All three factors decrease rapidly with decreasing energy at the high-energy end. The rate of decrease becomes smaller in the low-energy region. For a_1 the factor reaches a minimum at an energy equal to $E_0/2$ if $E_0 \gg 2\ mc^2$.

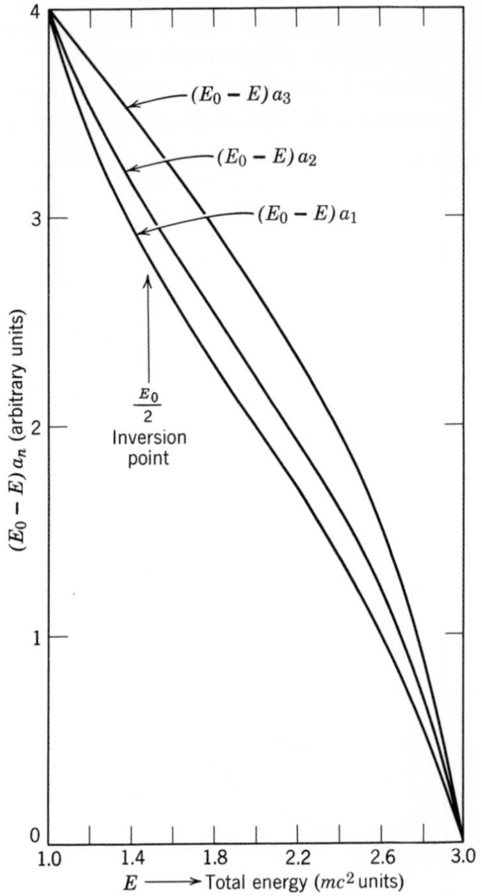

Fig. 3-20 Uncorrected Kurie plots for unique first, second, and third forbidden transitions for $E_0 = 3\ mc^2$.

Then the curve swings up again below that energy. Such an effect makes the uncorrected Kurie plot bulge upward at high energy and also curve upward at low energy, thereby producing an inversion point at $E_0/2$ (Fig. 3-20). For comparison, the momentum distributions of an allowed spectrum and of the unique forbidden ones are exhibited in Fig. 3-21 (for simplicity, no Coulomb effect is taken into account). A pronounced shift to the high-energy end for the unique forbidden spectra can be easily seen.

Although the existence of the unique forbidden spectra was theoretically predicted as early as 1941, its confirmation was not reported until 1949. Langer and Price (La-496) found that the β spectrum of Y^{91} distinctly deviated from the allowed shape. According to its comparative half-life ($f_0t = 5 \times 10^8$) this transition should be classified as second forbidden. But from shell-model considerations, the transition should

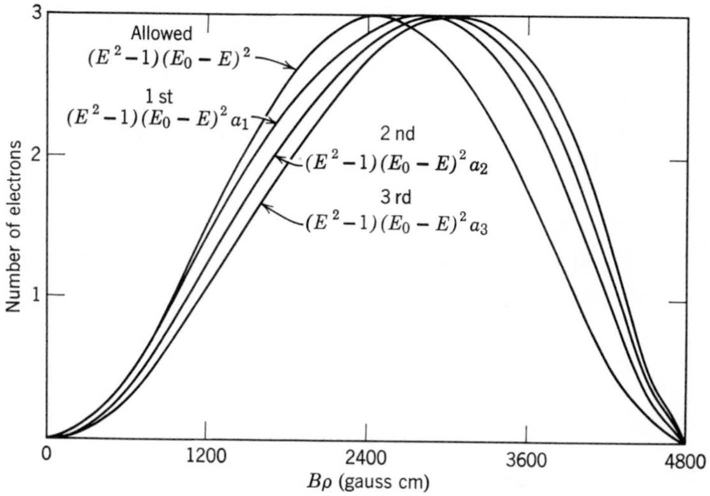

Fig. 3-21 Momentum distributions of allowed, unique first, second, and third forbidden spectra with $Z = 0$ for $E_0 = 3\ mc^2$.

involve a total momentum change of two units and a parity change of ${}_{39}Y^{91}(p_{1/2}\text{ odd}) \rightarrow {}_{40}Zr^{91}(d_{5/2}\text{ even})$. Therefore it is a unique first forbidden transition [$\Delta I = 2$ (yes)]. When the Kurie plot was divided by the corresponding unique shape factor $(a_1)^{1/2}$, all the curvatures were removed and an exceedingly straight line resulted (see Fig. 3-22).

In deriving Eq. 3-85 for the unique shape factors a_n, the Coulomb effect on the electron is neglected. The unique shape factors a_n are relatively insensitive to the Coulomb forces as contrasted with most types of forbidden spectra where the Coulomb effect on the shape factor is quite considerable. However, the inadequacy of the simplified formula for the factors a_n was detected for Tl^{204} where Z is equal to 81. Figure 3-23 shows the three Kurie plots of Tl^{204} β spectrum.

The bottom one is the uncorrected Kurie plot ($a_1 = 1$). The middle curve is corrected by the shape factor a_1 of the low Z approximation (Eq. 3-85). The linear plot starts to deviate upward around 350 kev. The top curve is corrected by the exact shape factor. It linearizes the plot all the way down to 100 kev. The deviation observed below 100 kev could be due to finite source thickness.

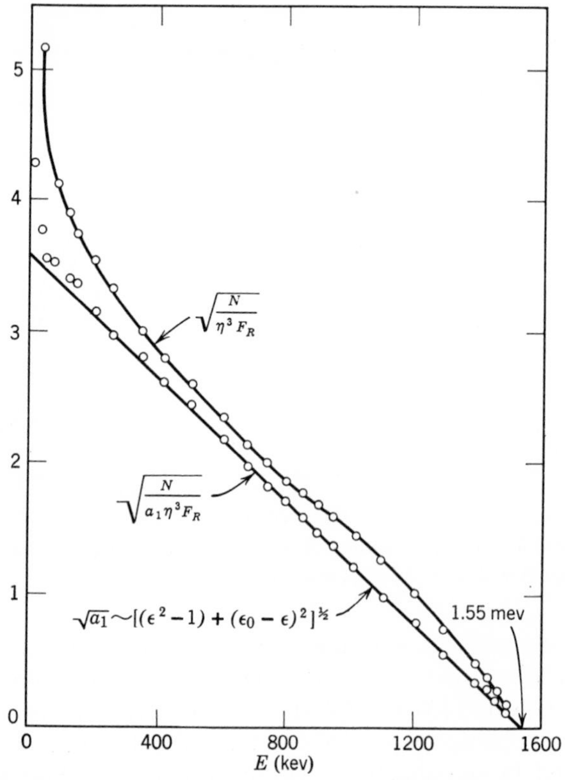

Fig. 3-22 The Kurie plot of Y^{91} using the unique first forbidden correction factor a_1. From (Wu-50).

Only a few examples of unique forbidden shape spectra larger than or equal to 2 have been identified to date. The best-known examples are the Be^{10} (Fig. 3-24) and Na^{22} spectra (second forbidden), and K^{40} (Fig. 3-25) (third forbidden); Be^{10} is an even-even nucleus and is assumed to have zero spin, whereas the spin of B^{10}, the product nucleus,

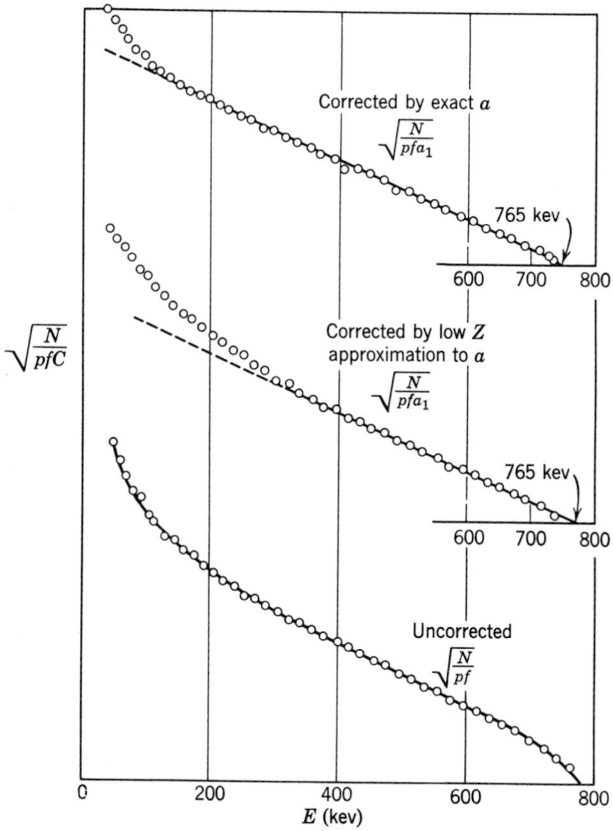

Fig. 3-23 The Kurie plots of the Tl^{204} β spectrum. The lower curve is the uncorrected Kurie plot ($a_1 = 1$). The middle curve is corrected by the shape factor a_1 of the low Z approximation. The top curve is corrected by the exact shape factor. From (Wu-50).

has been found to be three. Thus the spin change involved in the transition is three. Furthermore, the shell model of the nucleus predicts no parity change for the transition. Thus $\Delta I = 3$ (no). A similar situation occurs in the Na^{22} decay. These are the conditions for the unique second forbidden transition given by the Gamow-Teller selection rules.

For K^{40}, the spin change is four units. The parity should change according to the shell-model prediction. Therefore K^{40} represents a

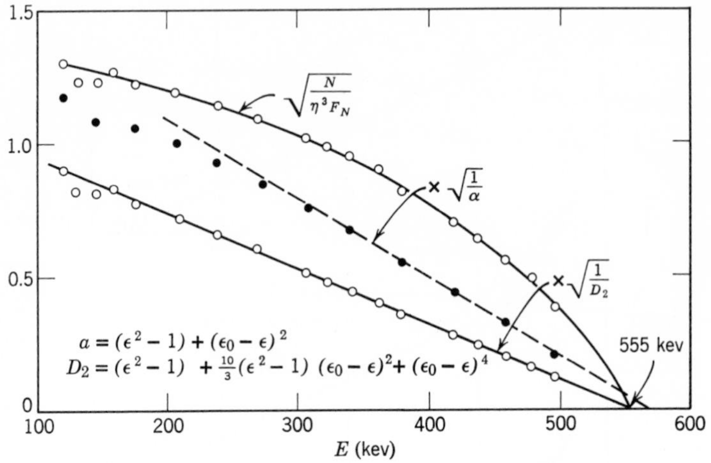

Fig. 3-24 Kurie plots of the Be^{10} β spectrum. From (Wu-50).

$$a = (\epsilon^2 - 1) + (\epsilon_0 - \epsilon)^2$$
$$D_2 = (\epsilon^2 - 1) + \tfrac{10}{3}(\epsilon^2 - 1)(\epsilon_0 - \epsilon)^2 + (\epsilon_0 - \epsilon)^4$$

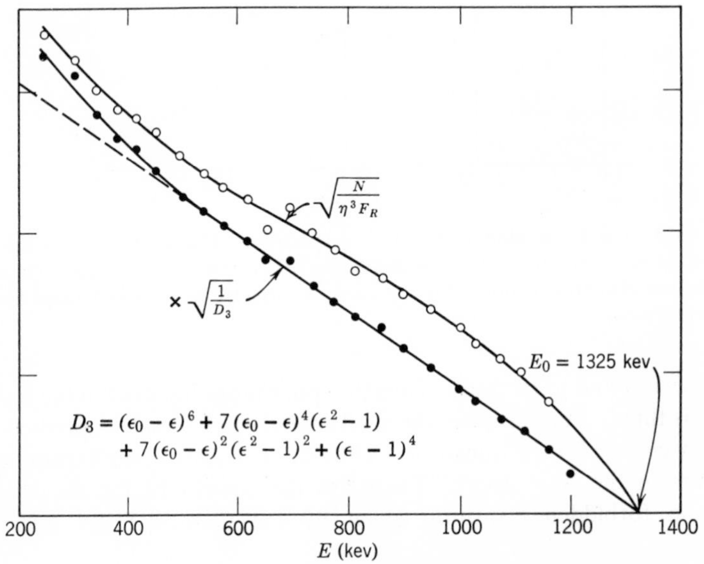

Fig. 3-25 Kurie plots of the K^{40} β spectrum. From (Wu-50).

$$D_3 = (\epsilon_0 - \epsilon)^6 + 7(\epsilon_0 - \epsilon)^4(\epsilon^2 - 1)$$
$$+ 7(\epsilon_0 - \epsilon)^2(\epsilon^2 - 1)^2 + (\epsilon - 1)^4$$

unique third forbidden transition. Unfortunately, K^{40} has a half-life of 2.7×10^9 years, and the natural abundance of K^{40} is only 0.016%. To obtain an undistorted spectrum of K^{40}, a highly enriched K^{40} source must be used. Some KCl enriched to approximately 10% in K^{40} was prepared by electromagnetic separation at Oak Ridge under the supervision of C. P. Keim. Feldman and Wu (Fel-50; Fe-52) prepared uniform sources of 2.5 mg/cm² and investigated its β spectrum in the solenoid spectrometer of a momentum resolution of 9%. The uncorrected Kurie plot is definitely forbidden. The unique third forbidden shape factor $a_3 = p^6 + 7p^4q^2 + 7p^2q^4 + q^6$ provides a good fit to the data from the end point (1325 ± 15) kev down to 500 kev with the deviation increasing toward lower energies. The deviation is readily explained by the excessive thickness of the source. These results are in general agreement with thick-source (~2.5 mg/cm²) spectrum measurements of K^{40} reported by other laboratories.

Half-Lives of the Unique Transitions

The comparative half-life of a β decay is defined as the product of the observed half-life t multiplied by a function f_n where f_n is given by

$$f_n = \int_1^{E_0} a_n F_0(E, \pm Z) pE(E_0 - E)^2 \, dE \qquad (3\text{-}86)$$

The a_n inside the integral is the shape factor defined in Eq. 3.85. For allowed transitions

$$a_0 = 1 \qquad (3\text{-}87)$$

The integral thus obtained is usually denoted by $f_0(Z, E_0)$. We expect the values of $f_0 t$ for allowed transitions to be relatively constant for a given class of nuclei. The numerical values of $f_0(Z, E_0)$ for various values of Z and E_0 have been calculated and presented by a set of formulas and curves by various authors (Sec. 3-2). For a forbidden spectrum, the shape factor a_n is energy-dependent. To evaluate f_n, we must first know the exact formula for the shape factor which fits the observed spectrum and then substitute it for a_n and carry out the integration. In general, it is easier to evaluate it by numerical integration for any particular case. However, for unique forbidden transitions of $Z = 0$, the shape factors are simple and exact. Davidson (Da-51) has shown that f_n can be expressed for $Z = 0$ in terms of $\bar{C}_n f_0$ where $\bar{C}_n$ is given approximately by

$$12\bar{C}_1(E_0) = \tfrac{6}{10}(E_0^2 - 1) - \tfrac{1}{5}(E_0 - 1)$$

First forbidden (3-88a)

$$5.6^3\bar{C}_2(E_0) = \tfrac{3}{7}(E_0^2 - 1)^2 - \tfrac{26}{105}(E_0^2 - 1)(E_0 - 1) - \tfrac{2}{105}(E_0 - 1)^2$$

Second forbidden (3-88b)

$$70.72^2\bar{C}_3(E_0) = \tfrac{1}{3}(E_0^2 - 1)^3 - \tfrac{9}{35}(E_0^2 - 1)^2(E_0 - 1) - \tfrac{2}{35}(E_0^2 - 1)(E_0 - 1)^2 + \tfrac{8}{105}(E_0 - 1)^3$$

Third forbidden (3-88c)

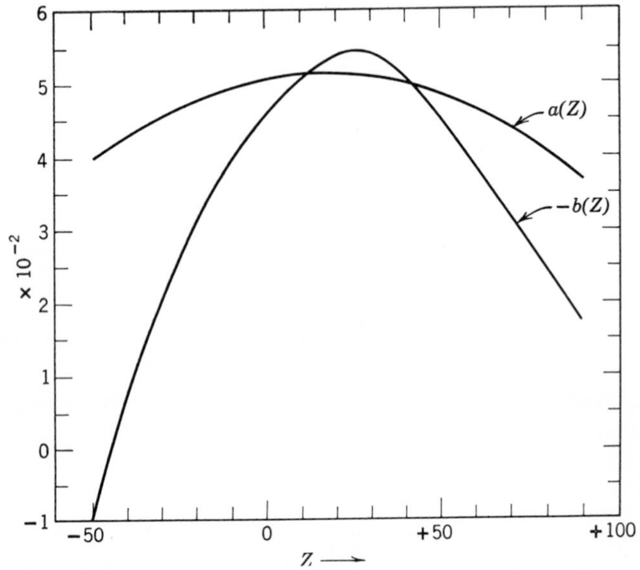

Fig. 3-26 The coefficients $a(Z)$ and $-b(Z)$ plotted against Z, where $f_1/f_0 = a(Z) \times (E_0^2 - 1) + b(Z)(E_0 - 1)$. See (Da-51).

For any value of Z, Davidson derived the following expression for f_1:

$$f_1 = f_0[a(Z)(E_0^2 - 1) + b(Z)(E_0 - 1)] \qquad (3\text{-}89)$$

The functions $a(Z)$ and $b(Z)$ are average values determined empirically and are plotted against Z, as shown in Fig. 3-26.

Using Feenberg and Trigg's (Fe-50) curve for f_0 and the formula and curves of Davidson, we obtain the log f_1t value for the unique first forbidden transitions.

The log $f_n t$ values of the unique first forbidden transitions are all between 7–9, whereas the log $f_0 t$ values of the first forbidden parity unfavored transitions are between 6–8. The ratio of the $(ft)_n$ values between the various degrees of forbiddenness are in accord with theoretical predictions.

Second- and Higher-Order Forbidden Transitions with $\Delta I = n$ (*Order of Forbiddenness*)

Second- and higher-order forbidden transitions with $\Delta I = n$ give rise to nonallowed but also nonunique spectral shapes. In this case several nuclear matrix elements are involved, and the corresponding

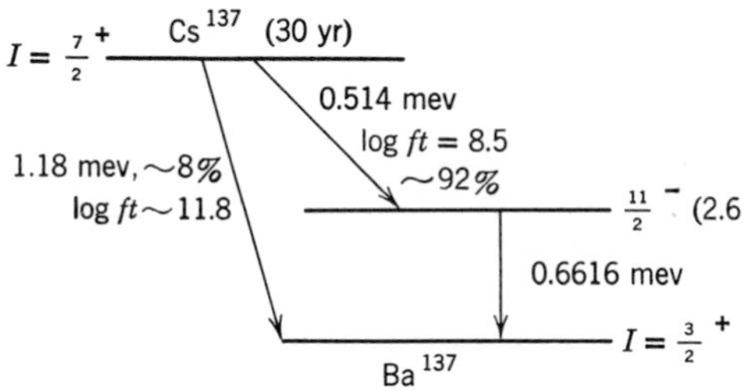

Fig. 3-27 Decay scheme of Cs^{137}.

spectrum terms may have different shapes. In particular, for second forbidden spectra, the predicted spectrum shape (under the same assumption that would give an allowed shape for a first forbidden spectra) is of the form $p^2 + \lambda q^2$ (Pe-53). The parameter λ depends on the detailed nuclear structure and the assumed form of the β interaction. Thus, in principle, from this type of spectrum we can obtain information about the nuclear matrix element and also about the form of the β interaction itself—for example, to test the idea that the interaction is indeed close to $V - A$. In practice, however, such information is very difficult to obtain; so far it has not been possible to draw very definite conclusions.

One well-understood example of a second forbidden spectrum is provided by the decay of Cs^{137}, as indicated in Fig. 3-27. This decay is thoroughly investigated. The spins of all the ground states involved have been measured. The spin and parity assignments of both the ground states and the excited state are, it can be said with confidence, certain. The γ transition between the Ba^{137} states is characteristic of an $M4$ transition with $\Delta I = 4$ and change of parity. Thus the ground-to-ground β transition is second forbidden, and its spectrum shape is, in fact, close to the form $p^2 + \lambda q^2$ with $\lambda \geqslant 10$. The single-particle model gives $\lambda \approx 10^2$ for this case. The β decay to the excited state of Ba^{137} is of the unique first forbidden class. All this information has been checked, and it provides a confirmation both of shell-model predictions and of the β-decay theory.

Finally, one of the longest-life β activities is that of In^{115} whose decay scheme is shown in Fig. 3-28. Both the spin of In^{115} and that of Sn^{115} have been measured, and this transition is evidently of the form $\Delta I = 4$

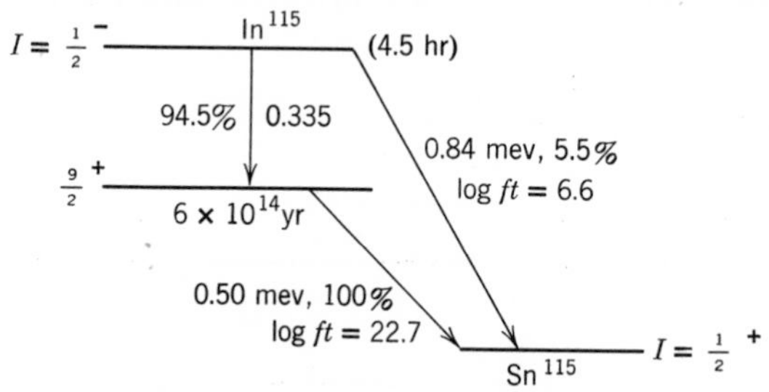

Fig. 3-28 Decay scheme of In^{115}.

(with no change of parity according to the shell model). Actually, this isotope of indium occurs naturally, because its β-decay lifetime is about 10^5 times as large as the age of the earth.

3-4 THE ELECTRON-NEUTRINO ANGULAR CORRELATION

We can obtain valuable information about the β-decay interaction by studying the angular correlation between the electron and neutrino emitted in allowed β decay. The angular correlation is given by

$$W(\theta) = 1 + a(v/c)\cos\theta \tag{3-90}$$

where θ = angle between electron and neutrino and

$$a = \frac{(-|C_S|^2 + |C_V|^2)\left|\int 1\right|^2 + \frac{1}{3}(|C_T|^2 - |C_A|^2)\left|\int \boldsymbol{\sigma}\right|^2}{(|C_S|^2 + |C_V|^2)\left|\int 1\right|^2 + (|C_T|^2 + |C_A|^2)\left|\int \boldsymbol{\sigma}\right|^2} \tag{3-91}$$

For each single interaction, the values of a are

	S	V	T	A
a	-1	$+1$	$+\frac{1}{3}$	$-\frac{1}{3}$

The foregoing expression for $W(\theta)$ is derived in Appendix IV. For parity nonconservation in β decay, this expression remains unchanged except that we must replace

$$|C_i|^2 \quad \text{by} \quad (|C_i|^2 + |C_i'|^2)$$

This replacement will be discussed in subsequent chapters.

Experimental Methods

Experimentally, measurements of β-neutrino angular correlations are very difficult. In the first place, we cannot detect the neutrino directly. Rather we must study the electrons and the recoil ions. However, the recoil energy is usually very small. Let ϕ be the angle between electron and recoil ions. It is related to θ (the angle between β and ν) by

$$\sin\phi = (q/r)\sin\theta \tag{3-92}$$

where q is the neutrino momentum and r is the momentum of the recoil ion. Furthermore, the r and E_r (recoil kinetic energy) can be expressed in terms of p (electron momentum), q (neutrino momentum), and θ by

$$r = (p^2 + q^2 + 2pq\cos\theta)^{1/2} \tag{3-93}$$

$$E_r = \frac{r^2}{2M} = \frac{533}{A}\,[E(E + 1.02) + (E_0 - E)^2 + 2(E_0 - E)\sqrt{E(E + 1.02)}\cos\theta] \tag{3-94}$$

where E and E_0 are the energy and the maximum energy of the electron. Therefore, there are various experimental possibilities for approaching this problem. The several distributions (Ko-54a) which we could investigate between any two of the three variables E, ϕ, r are (a) $W(E, r)$, (b) $W(E, \phi)$, and (c) $W(r, \phi)$.

$W(E, r)$—The Distribution of Electron Energies and Recoil Momenta at Constant ϕ. For a constant angle ϕ between the directions of the recoil and electron, the relation between E and r is determined. Figure 3-29 shows the permitted area in the E, r plane for $E_0 = 8$. This method was not pursued to any extent except in the early work on

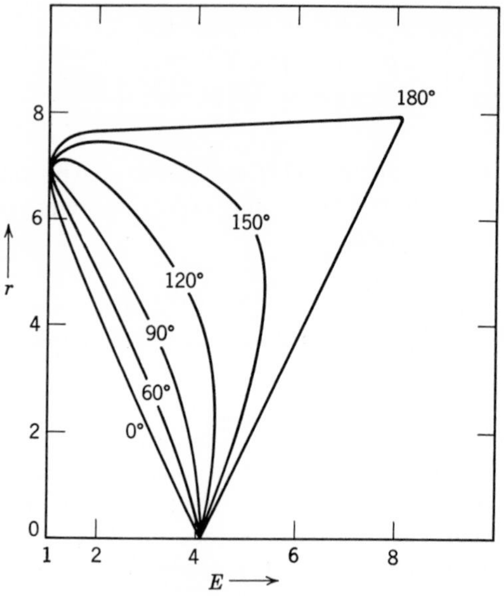

Fig. 3-29 The permitted area in E, r plane for $E_0 = 8$. From (Ko-54a).

Cl^{38} (Cr-38) when the drop counting method in a cloud-chamber investigation was used. No attempts were made to determine the coefficient a of Eq. 3-90.

$W(E, \phi)$—The Beta-Energy and the Beta-Recoil Ion Angular Distribution. For β-energy and β-recoil ion angular distribution, if $p > q$, there are, in general, two angles θ for fixed values of p and q and two corresponding values of r (see Fig. 3-30). For both of these, however,

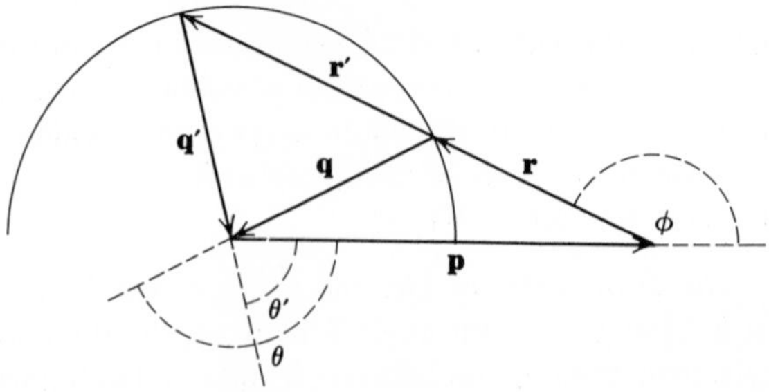

Fig. 3-30 Momentum triangle for $E_0 = 8$, $E = 5$, and $Q = 3$. Showing two possible values of θ and r. From (Ko-54a).

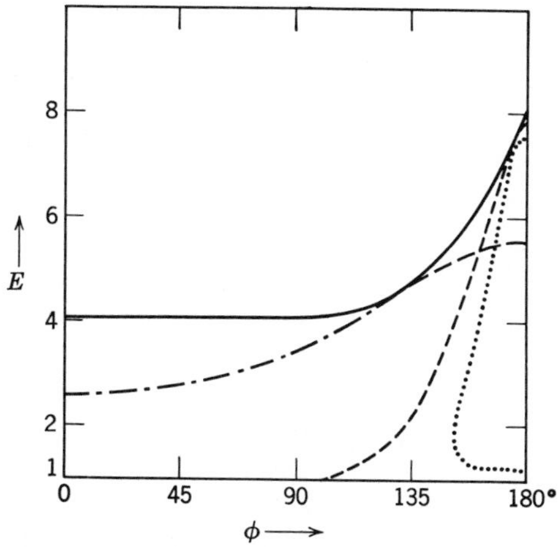

Fig. 3-31 The permitted area in the E, ϕ plane for $E_0 = 8$. From (Ko-54a).

$\phi > \pi/2$. For each value of $p > q$, there is a minimum angle, given by $\sin \phi = q/p$, at which the recoil ion can appear. The permitted area in the E, ϕ plane is below the solid curve in Fig. 3-31, drawn for an example in which $E_0 = 8$. Experiments to measure the distribution $W(E, \phi)$ can be performed either by keeping E constant and measuring the distribution in ϕ, or by keeping ϕ constant and measuring the distribution of E. The β-energy distribution for $E_0 = 8$ and $\phi = \pi$ is shown in Fig. 3-32. The difference between the distribution for axial vector $a = -\frac{1}{3}$ and tensor $a = +\frac{1}{3}$ is rather small. In contrast, the angular correlation $W(\phi)$ at a constant value of E shows considerably greater sensitivity to the coefficient a. Figure 3-33 shows the theoretical curves of $W(\phi)$ for different values of E. Thus, theoretically, the measurement of $W(\phi)$ is a more sensitive way of determining a. Rustad and Ruby (Rus-53) investigated the β-ν angular correlation in He^6 by the latter method. It must be cautioned here that the detection efficiency of the β detector at various angles with respect to the recoil detector must be thoroughly examined in order to avoid erroneous interpretation (Wu-58). In the Rustad-Ruby experiment, overlooking this effect resulted in the faulty conclusion of tensor dominance in Gamow-Teller interaction from He^6 result.

$W(r, \phi)$—The Recoil Momentum (r) and the Beta-Recoil Ion Angular Distribution. Practically all recoil experiments (but not the one by

Rustad and Ruby) are carried out by measuring the energy spectrum of the recoil ions. The energy spectra for recoil ions with values of $a = +1, -1$, and 0 are shown in Fig. 3-34. The difference between the distributions for $a = +1$ and -1 is very marked indeed.

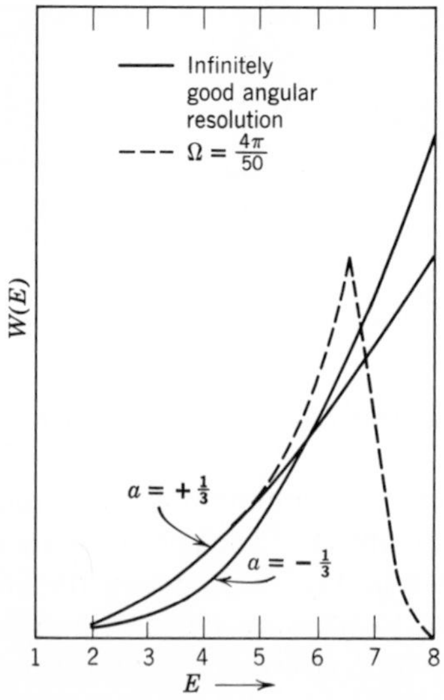

Fig. 3-32 Beta-energy distribution for constant ϕ for $E_0 = 8$, $\phi = \pi$. From (Ko-54a).

Interpretation of Results

From the study of *ft* values we know that both the Fermi and Gamow-Teller interactions contribute to β decay, but we do not know whether the Fermi interaction is *S* or *V*, and whether the Gamow-Teller interaction is *T* or *A*. The absence of Fierz interference indicates that the interaction must be a combination of *ST*, *VT*, *SA*, or *VA*. In principle, we could tell whether the Fermi interaction is *S* or *V* by studying the β-ν correlation in a $0^+ \rightarrow 0^+$ transition where the Gamow-Teller matrix elements vanish. In such a case, a must be either $+1$ for vector interaction or -1 for scalar interaction, as shown in Eq. 3-91. However, although the angular correlations for these two possibilities would be extremely different, no β decays of $0^+ \rightarrow 0^+$ transitions are suitable for such investigations, because we must be sure that the recoil ion is in an atomic state and does not form a molecular ion with other atoms. For example, in the famous $0^+ \rightarrow 0^+$ transition of O^{14}, the high affinity of oxygen atoms to form O_2 or other oxides makes a monoatomic form very unlikely. For this reason, β-ν correlation investigations have been carried out only for neutrons and noble gases such as He^6, Ne^{19}, Ne^{23}, and Ar^{35}. Nevertheless, they provide us with all the information we need. First of all, we can obtain information about the nature of the Gamow-Teller interaction by a study of the $He^6[0^+ \rightarrow 1^+ \text{(no)}]$ decay. In this decay the Fermi matrix element vanishes and a is either $\frac{1}{3}$ for a tensor or $-\frac{1}{3}$ for axial-vector interaction. The early experimental results indicated that a is close to

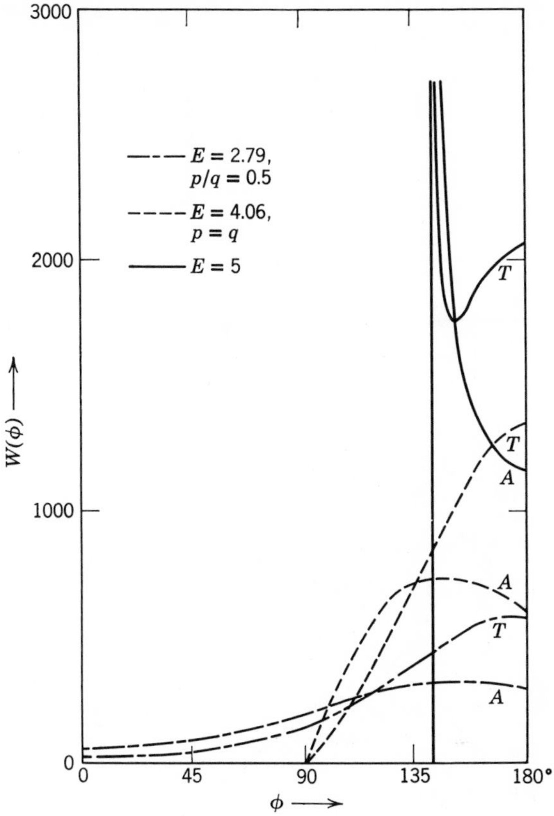

Fig. 3-33 Relative angular correlations for T and A interactions for $E_0 = 8\ mc^2$ From (Ko-54a).

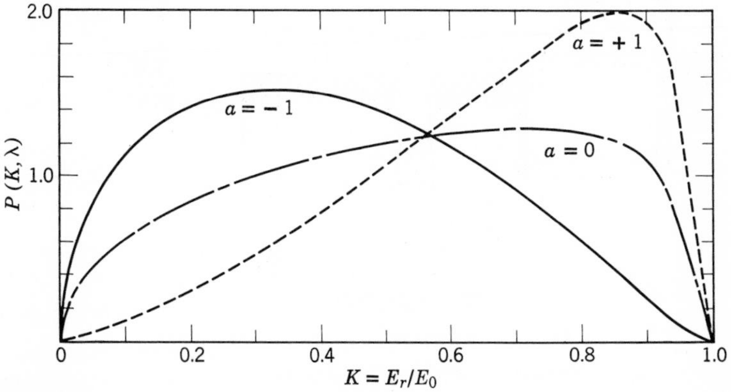

Fig. 3-34 The energy spectra for recoil ion with values of $a = +1$, -1, and 0. The difference between the distributions of $a = +1$ and $a = -1$ is very marked as shown.

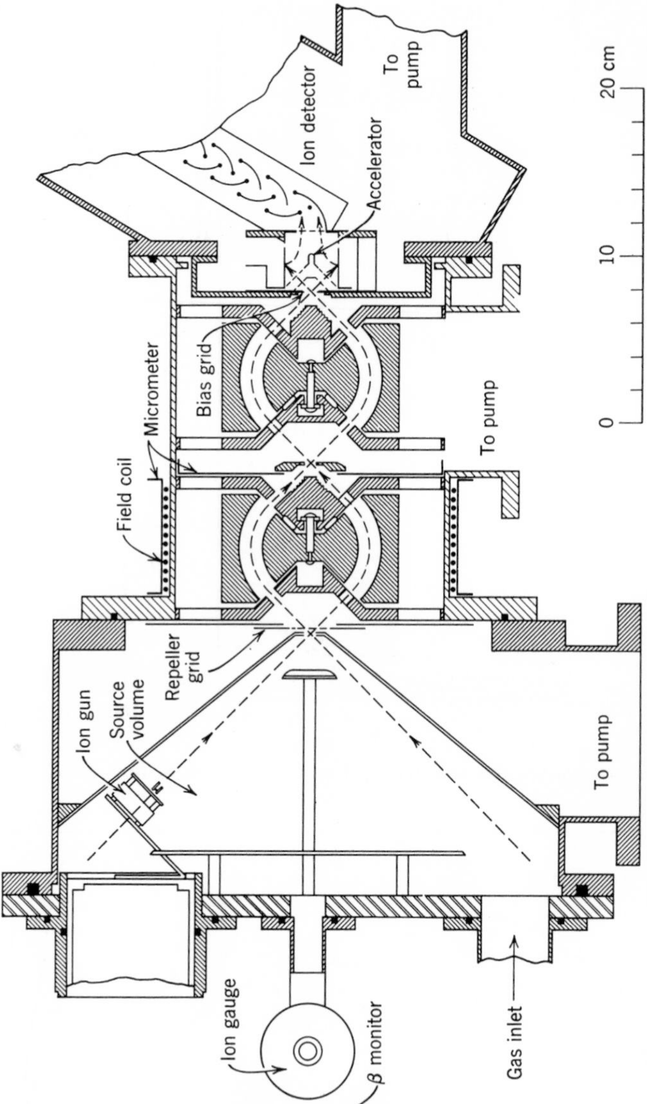

Fig. 3-35 A schematic diagram of the apparatus used by Hermannsfeldt et al. (He-58) to measure the electron-neutrino angular correlation in the β decay of Ar^{35} and He^{6}.

$+\frac{1}{3}$, favoring a tensor interaction. However, more recent experiments (He-58; Al-59), whose arrangements are shown in Fig. 3-35, prove conclusively that the coefficient a in Gamow-Teller interaction is negative, being in fact close to the expected value of $-\frac{1}{3}$ for the axial-vector form (see Fig. 3-36*a*). This result has been confirmed by the Oak Ridge group (Jo-63) with a more refined setup. The result is $a = -0.334 \pm 0.003$.

We can obtain additional information about the β-decay interaction by studying other allowed transitions where both matrix elements $\int 1$ and $\int \boldsymbol{\sigma}$ are nonzero. First of all, regardless of the form of the interaction, the correlation coefficient a must be between -1 and $+1$. In addition, however, a value of a larger than $+\frac{1}{3}$ can occur only if the vector interaction dominates. It is found experimentally (He-57; Al-59) in the decay of Ar^{35} that $a \sim +0.97 \pm 0.14$ (see Fig. 3-36*a*). We have already seen from the study of ft values that the Gamow-Teller matrix element seems to be very small in this decay. Thus this decay provides a sensitive test for distinguishing between S and V interaction in β decay, almost as convincing as $0^+ \rightarrow 0^+$ transitions would have been. The measured value of a clearly favors the vector interaction (He-57). Combining the results from Ar^{35} and He^6 we conclude that the β-decay interaction is a mixture of V and A. Furthermore, if the Fermi and Gamow-Teller coupling constants were about equal, it is clear that the coefficient a would nearly vanish for the neutron decay, and we would have practically no β-ν angular correlation at all. The experimental results are summarized in Fig. 3-36*a* and *b*.

3-5 BETA-GAMMA ANGULAR CORRELATIONS*

Radiations from unpolarized or unaligned nuclei (such as β radiation or γ radiation) have an isotropic angular distribution since no direction in space can be distinguished from any other. If, however, the nuclei are polarized, then, in general, the angular distribution of the radiation intensity is anisotropic; it depends on the angle between the radiation and the direction of polarization of the nucleus.

* This section was prepared in cooperation with Dr. Masato Morita.

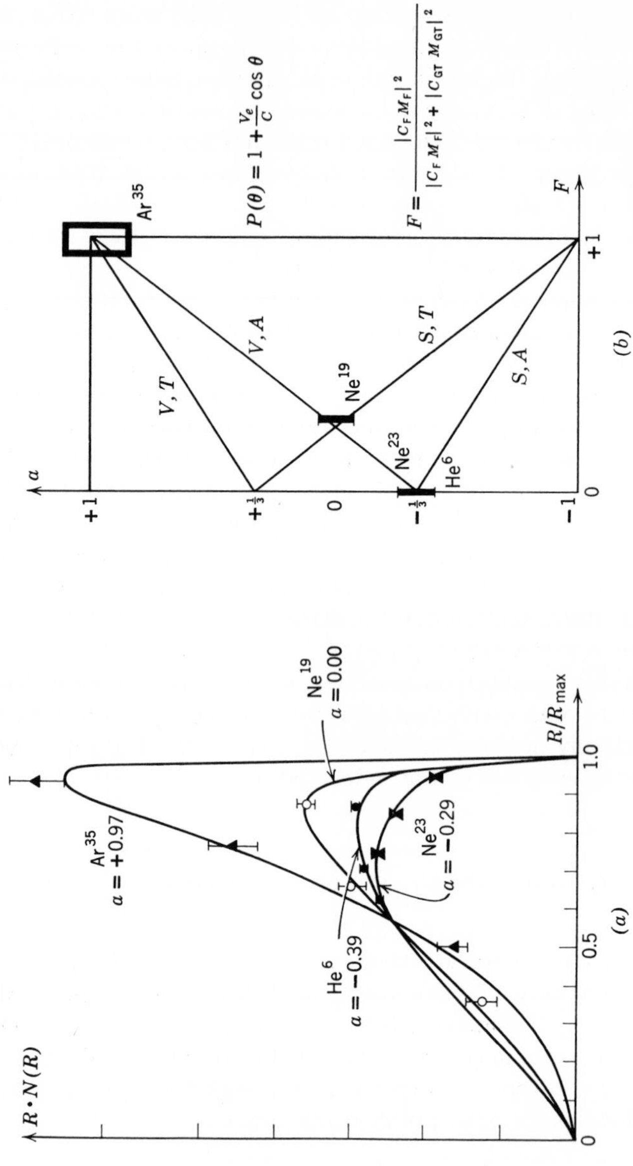

Fig. 3-36 (*a*) Recoil spectra of He^{6}, Ar^{35}, Ne^{19}, and Ne^{23}, (*b*) a versus $F = \dfrac{|C_F M_F|^2}{|C_F M_F|^2 + |C_{GT} M_{GT}|^2}$.

As a simple example of the angular distribution of radiation from polarized nuclei, consider the decay of a nucleus of spin one which is totally polarized in the direction of the positive z axis (see Fig. 3-37). Suppose that it decays to a state of spin zero. Suppose also that we only detect γ rays of helicity $+1$—that is, γ rays whose spin and linear momentum are parallel. Qualitatively we can see that such γ rays tend

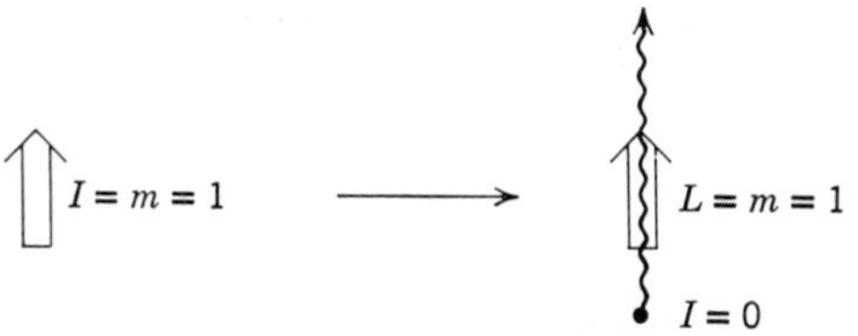

Fig. 3-37 Angular distributions of γ ray from polarized nuclei. Polarized nuclei with spin one decay into the daughter nuclei with spin zero. The emitted dipole γ rays with helicity $+1$ are mostly coming out in a direction parallel to the initial spin direction. This is the consequence of the conservation of magnetic quantum number.

to be emitted preferentially with their spin in the direction of nuclear spin and, hence, preferentially with their linear momentum in the direction of nuclear spin. An exact calculation gives

$$W(\theta) = (1 + \cos\theta)^2 \tag{3-96}$$

for the angular distribution of the γ rays. This distribution has a maximum at $\theta = 0°$ and a minimum at $\theta = 180°$. The situation is similar for β rays, but this case will be discussed below.

As we shall explain in detail later, angular distributions of radiations are dependent on the nuclear spins involved, the nuclear matrix elements, and so on. This means that from experimental data on angular distributions of radiations from oriented nuclei we can gain insights into nuclear structure.

The interpretation of β-γ correlation results is not *always* unique. In fact, it is a very involved analysis because of the existence of several nuclear matrix elements besides the possibility of a mixed multipole γ ray. Furthermore, possible interferences can occur between matrix elements of the same rank as well as of different ranks. In addition, to interpret the experimental results properly we must use the detailed electron wave functions with finite nuclear size and screening effect corrections. We must also include the higher-order matrix elements.

An example of such detailed analysis performed with the help of a computer can be found in a paper by Simms (Si-65). In this section we shall merely outline the general principle and procedure involved in β-γ correlation and will not give a detailed analysis.

There are several methods of effecting nuclear orientation, such as low-temperature technique, optical pumping method, etc. Apart from these, there is a simple method to select preferentially an ensemble of nuclei with a certain nuclear orientation from an ensemble of unoriented

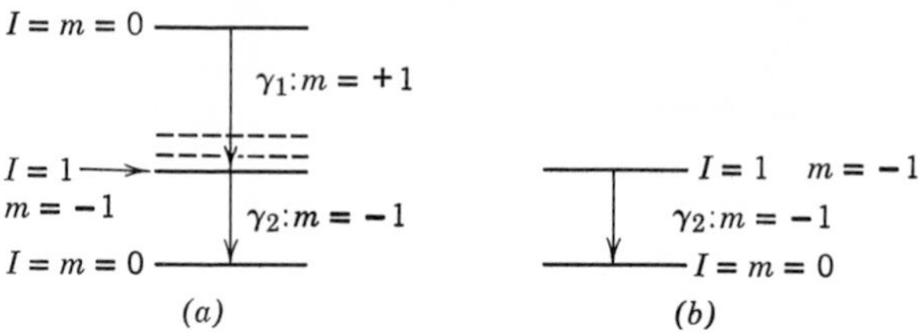

Fig. 3-38 Decay scheme. (*a*) Two dipole γ rays are successively emitted from the initial state of spin zero; the state decays to the intermediate state of spin one and, subsequently, to the final state of spin zero. If we measure the directions and polarizations for both γ_1 and γ_2 in coincidence, and the γ_1 has helicity $+1$, only one magnetic sublevel with $m = -1$ in the intermediate state is excited, as far as this observation is concerned. Here the direction of the emission of γ_1 is the quantization axis. The γ_2 has necessarily $m = -1$. It is easily seen that the γ_2 has the same property as that of the γ ray from polarized nuclei shown in part *b*.

nuclei—by using two different detectors in a coincidence measurement of two radiations which are successively emitted in a cascade transition. Since the coincidence counting rate of the two γ rays depends on the relative angle of the directions of the emission of the two radiations, we call this phenomenon the angular correlation. In this section we first explain how the nuclear orientation is achieved in the angular-correlation experiments and then give theoretical formulas for analyzing the experimental data.

It is well known that each magnetic substate m of a nuclear state I is polarized to a degree m/I. Since all magnetic substates of this nuclear state I are equally populated under normal conditions, there is no average direction of orientation. This is the case of unoriented nuclei. If we can select from a group of randomly oriented atomic nuclei an ensemble of nuclei in a state of a definite magnetic quantum number m, this ensemble is effectively polarized. Now suppose, for example, that we have two successive γ transitions which are both dipole radiations (see Fig. 3-38). The initial state is assumed to be spin zero, which is necessarily an unoriented state. The spins of the intermediate and the final states are one and zero, respectively. We choose the upward direction of emission of the first γ ray as the quantization axis. When the nucleus in the initial state emits a γ ray with helicity $+1$, the intermediate state is excited in $m = -1$; but no other substates of the intermediate state are excited in the ensemble of atomic nuclei with which we are concerned. Since the degree of the nuclear polarization is m/I, the excited state after emission of the first γ ray is completely *polarized* along the minus z direction (that is, along the direction opposite

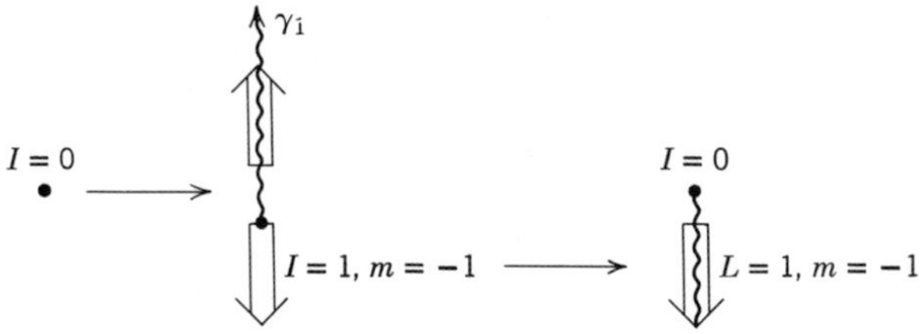

Fig. 3-39 Angular correlations of two γ rays. As is shown in Fig. 3-38, two dipole γ rays are emitted in the decay scheme $0 \to 1 \to 0$. We assume that both γ rays have helicity $+1$. From the conservation of magnetic quantum number, the two γ rays are preferentially coming out antiparallel.

to the emission of the first γ ray). The second γ ray emitted from this level, in coincidence with the first γ ray, has an angular distribution characteristic of that from polarized nuclei. We know that the γ ray with helicity $+1$ comes out parallel to the direction of nuclear polarization in a $1 \to 0$ transition (see Fig. 3-37). Therefore the second γ ray is emitted downward as in Fig. 3-39, if this γ ray has helicity $+1$. As a result, two dipole radiations are preferentially emitted in the opposite directions, if both γ rays have helicity $+1$ and the decay scheme is $0 \to 1 \to 0$. If the first γ ray is unpolarized—that is, if the direction of emission is measured but not its helicity—substates with both $m = +1$ and -1 are excited in the intermediate level, so that this level is *aligned* (not polarized) in the direction of the z axis. Then γ rays in both the parallel and antiparallel z directions are preferentially emitted. Both the foregoing cases are generally called the *γ-γ angular correlations.* Because the angle between the directions of the two γ rays is a relative one, this discussion holds just as well if we choose the direction of emission for the second γ ray to be the z axis.

It is easily understood that a similar consideration holds for the β-γ *angular correlation*, if one of the γ rays is replaced by a β ray (see Fig. 3-40). That is, we consider the total angular momentum of the electron-anti-neutrino system, rather than that of the γ ray. Under such conditions the β ray has an angular distribution which is expressed in terms of even powers of cos θ with respect to the γ ray. We call this the *β-γ directional correlation.* On the other hand, if we measure not only the direction of emission but also the circular polarization of the γ ray, the intermediate state is polarized. In this case, the angular correlation has *odd* as well as *even* powers of cos θ. We call this the *β circularly polarized γ correlation.* The two are generally called the *β-γ angular correlations.*

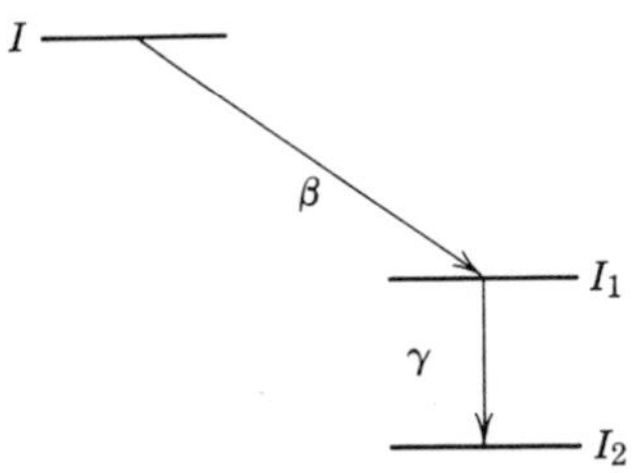

Fig. 3-40 Beta-gamma cascade transitions.

We have just discussed the fact that the alignment or polarization of the intermediate state in cascade transitions is essential in the problem of the angular correlations. However, the polarization or alignment of the intermediate nuclear state can be perturbed by interactions of nuclear moments with the internal electromagnetic fields as well as with the external. Therefore the degree of spin orientation in the intermediate state diminishes with time after the emission of the first radiation. To obtain the true angular correlation, the second radiation has to come out before the intermediate state loses any significant amount of its nuclear orientation. The rate of reduction of nuclear orientation is usually given by the relaxation time T. In this chapter we assume that $T \gg \tau_{1/2}$, $\tau_{1/2}$ being the half-life of the intermediate state, so that there is no effect from relaxation on the angular correlations. The half-life of the intermediate state is generally required to be shorter than 10^{-10} sec.

Historically, the first attempt to calculate β-γ angular correlations was made by Falkoff and Uhlenbeck (Fa-50). This work was significant because it served to stimulate further studies. But it omitted two important considerations: the effect of the nuclear Coulomb field on the emitted electrons and the interference among the matrix elements of different ranks. The first practical and most comprehensive formulas were given by Morita and his co-workers (Ya-52; Mo-53, 55, 56; Ya-55). Since at the time these studies were written parity conservation was postulated in the theory of β decay, only the β-γ directional angular correlation had been studied. (If parity is strictly conserved, β circularly polarized γ angular-correlation experiments give the same results as the β-γ directional angular-correlation experiments.) The formulas have been derived up to the second forbidden transitions and include all cross terms among the five relativistic invariants in the β interaction.

Shortly after the discovery of the parity nonconservation, the β circularly polarized γ correlations for allowed and first forbidden transitions were investigated. Alder, Stech, and Winther (Ald-57) gave formulas for the *STP* interaction with some restrictions, and Morita and Morita (Mor-57; Mo-58) worked out formulas for the *STPVA* interaction. Recently, these formulas have been excellently reviewed by other authors (Kot-59; We-61; Fra-64), and the formulas have been arranged so that the major characteristics of the experimental observables were easily seen. However, in a more recent paper, Bühring (Bühr-63) gave formulas which include *additional* matrix elements of two types. One type is due to the finite nuclear-size correction, and the other type is the third forbidden matrix elements from the usual multipole expansion. Formulas are stated so that the electron wave functions of Bhalla and Rose can be used to calculate numerical parameters. However, the screening of the nuclear charge by the atomic electrons was not included in the tables of Bhalla and Rose (Bh-64). Formulas for the parameters which include the screening effect have been prepared by Bühring (Bü-65a).

Since 1949, many β-γ directional-correlation experiments have been carried out. In the early 1950's the data were less accurate. In the last several years, however, the techniques have been greatly improved, and many accurate data are now being accumulated in various laboratories. At present, anisotropic directional correlations have been observed for Cl^{38}, K^{42}, As^{76}, Rb^{84}, Rb^{86}, Sb^{122}, Sb^{124}, I^{126}, Eu^{152}, Eu^{154}, Ho^{166}, Tm^{170}, Re^{186}, and Au^{198}. Experiments on the β circularly polarized γ correlation have also been done in recent years in connection with parity nonconservation (see Sec. 4-8).

Angular-Correlation Functions

The angular-correlation functions are written as $W(\theta, \tau)$. Here θ is the angle between directions of the emission for β and γ rays and τ is the circular polarization of γ ray. The $W(\theta, \tau)$ is expressed in a power series of $\cos^n \theta$ or in a series of Legendre polynomials $P_n(\cos \theta)$, n being zero or a positive integral. The maximum value of n is the minimum of the three integers $(2k + 1)$, $2L_1$, and $2I_1$. Here k, L_1, I_1 are, respectively, the forbiddenness of the β decay, the multipolarity of the γ ray, and the spin of the intermediate state. Except for the restrictions due to L_1 and I_1, the angular correlations are given in the following forms:

Beta Circularly Polarized Gamma Correlation. For the allowed transitions,

$$W(\theta, \tau) = 1 + \tau\left(\frac{v}{c}\right)A \cos \theta \tag{3-97}$$

For the first forbidden transitions,

$$W(\theta, \tau) = (1 + a \cos^2 \theta) + \tau\left(\frac{v}{c}\right) \cos \theta(b + c \cos^2 \theta) \tag{3-98}$$

or $$W(\theta, \tau) \sim 1 + \tau\left(\frac{v}{c}\right)A \cos \theta$$

with $$A = \frac{b + c \cos^2 \theta}{1 + a \cos^2 \theta} \tag{3-99}$$

Here $\tau = +1(-1)$ for the right- (left-) handed circularly polarized γ rays; v is the electron velocity. It is noticed that $W(\theta, \tau)$ is the same for both electric and magnetic radiations of the same order. The values of A, a, b, and c depend on the spins of the nuclear states, the multipolarity of γ ray, the energies of the electron and neutrino, and the various nuclear matrix elements involved in the β decay.

Beta-Gamma Directional Correlation. The directional angular-correlation function is obtained from Eqs. 3-97 and 3-98 with $\tau = 0$. For allowed transitions;

$$W(\theta) = \text{constant} \tag{3-100}$$

That is, we have an isotropic distribution. For first forbidden transitions,

$$W(\theta) = 1 + a \cos^2 \theta \tag{3-101}$$

where $$a = \frac{W(180°) - W(90°)}{W(90°)} \tag{3-102}$$

The degree of circular polarization $\mathscr{P}_\gamma$ of the γ ray in coincidence with the β ray is given by

$$\mathscr{P}_\gamma = \frac{v}{c} A \cos \theta = \frac{W(\theta, +1) - W(\theta, -1)}{W(\theta, +1) + W(\theta, -1)} \tag{3-103}$$

The quantities a and A are called the *anisotropy* and *asymmetry*, respectively. If the intermediate state has spin zero or one-half, a is zero; that is, the directional correlation is isotropic. A is also zero if the intermediate state has spin zero.

Besides a and $\mathscr{P}_\gamma$, we can measure the ft value for the β-ray transition and the shape correction factor for the β-ray spectrum. From all these data, we should be able to evaluate magnitudes of nuclear matrix elements involved in the β decay concerned. These values thus provide very useful information for understanding the nuclear structure.

In the next two sections we give the formulas for β-γ angular correlations in allowed and first forbidden transitions. The decay scheme is $I \xrightarrow{\beta} I_1 \xrightarrow{\gamma} I_2$ (see Fig. 3-40, p. 118. Here I, I_1, and I_2 are the nuclear spins of the initial, intermediate, and final states, respectively. In the derivation of these formulas, we have assumed the VA theory, a two-component neutrino ($C_V = C_V'$, $C_A = C_A'$), and time-reversal invariance for β decay (C_V/C_A = rèal). Formulas without these restrictions have been given in the literature (Mor-57; Mo-58).

Allowed Transitions

For the allowed β transitions, the β-γ directional correlation is isotropic and the shape correction factor is energy-independent.*

In Sec. 4-8 we discuss the β circularly polarized correlation for a pure multipole γ ray.

First Forbidden Transitions

For the first forbidden transitions there are, in general, six nuclear matrix elements (see p. 78), neglecting finite-size corrections and higher-order matrix elements (Bühr-63):

$$\begin{aligned} &\text{for} \quad L=0, \quad \int \gamma_5 \quad \text{and} \quad \int \boldsymbol{\sigma} \cdot \mathbf{r} \\ &\text{for} \quad L=1, \quad \int \mathbf{r}, \int \boldsymbol{\alpha}, \quad \text{and} \quad \int \boldsymbol{\sigma} \times \mathbf{r} \qquad (3\text{-}104) \\ &\text{for} \quad L=2, \quad \int B_{ij} \end{aligned}$$

* There is a small anisotropy of the β-γ directional correlation and a small energy dependence of the shape correction factor. These are due to contributions of the second forbidden transition and of an additional term which comes from the hypothesis of the conserved vector current (Ge-58; Mo-59). They are negligible except in a few cases, such as β decays of Li^8, B^8, N^{12}, B^{12}, and F^{20}.

Here L is the rank of the nuclear matrix elements which satisfies the selection rule

$$|I - I_1| \leqslant L \leqslant I + I_1$$

with I and I_1 being the initial and final spins, respectively. Since the angular correlations are dependent only on the relative magnitudes of the nuclear matrix elements among themselves, we may express the angular correlation in terms of five parameters. These parameters can all be chosen to be real, because time-reversal invariance is assumed to be valid. We introduce the five nuclear parameters in the following manner (for $\beta^{\mp}$ decay):

$$r = \frac{\int \gamma_5 \mp (\alpha Z/2R) \int \boldsymbol{\sigma} \cdot \mathbf{r}}{\int \boldsymbol{\sigma} \times \mathbf{r}} \tag{3-105}$$

$$s = \frac{\pm(\alpha Z/2R) C_A \int \boldsymbol{\sigma} \times \mathbf{r} + i(\alpha Z/2R) C_V \int \mathbf{r} \mp C_V \int \boldsymbol{\alpha}}{C_A \int \boldsymbol{\sigma} \times \mathbf{r}} \tag{3-106}$$

$$iw = \frac{\int \boldsymbol{\sigma} \cdot \mathbf{r}}{\int \boldsymbol{\sigma} \times \mathbf{r}} \tag{3-107}$$

$$ix = \mp \frac{C_V \int \mathbf{r}}{C_A \int \boldsymbol{\sigma} \times \mathbf{r}} \tag{3-108}$$

$$iz = \frac{\int B_{ij}}{\int \boldsymbol{\sigma} \times \mathbf{r}} \tag{3-109}$$

For β^- decay, the numerator of Eq. 3.106 is just the quantity M defined by Eq. 3.65a. The r and s, which are linear combinations of several nuclear matrix elements, have been introduced for the purpose of simplifying the expression of β-γ correlations. This can be done only *if the point-charge approximation for the nucleus is valid.* The advantage of this approximation (Ko-41) is that all Coulomb factors $\alpha Z/2R$ in the theoretical formulas are absorbed into the definitions of r and s.

In the definitions of parameters, Z is always positive and C_V/C_A is negative for the $V - A$ theory. The changes of signs produced by the charge conjugation are properly taken into account by the double sign in the foregoing expressions where the upper (lower) sign refers to the negatron (positron) (cf. p. 342).

Now we shall study the details of the formulas for the β-γ angular correlations. The β-γ directional correlation is given of the form

$$W|\theta| = 1 + \epsilon P_2(\cos\theta) \tag{3-110}$$

with

$$\epsilon = \frac{p^2}{E}\frac{l + mE}{C(E)} \tag{3-111}$$

with p and E denoting momentum and energy of electrons in mc and mc^2, respectively. Here $C(E)$ is the spectrum shape factor which has an energy dependence

$$C(E) = a + bE^{-1} + cE + dE^2 \tag{3-112}$$

The β circularly polarized γ angular correlation is

$$W(\theta, \tau) = 1 + \tau\frac{p}{E}A\cos\theta \tag{3-113}$$

with

$$A = \frac{f + gE + hE^2 + e(E^2 - 1)(\frac{5}{2}\cos^2\theta - \frac{1}{2})}{C(E)[1 + \epsilon p_2(\cos\theta)]} \tag{3-114}$$

In the foregoing, all of a, b, c, d, e, f, g, h, l, and m are *energy-independent*. They are functions of the nuclear parameters r, s, w, x, and z. Moreover, e, f, g, h, l, and m are dependent on the nuclear spins involved in the β-γ cascade transitions. In most of the nonunique transitions, $C(E)$ has almost no energy dependence. However, we can find, for example, f, g, h, l, and m experimentally by measuring the energy dependence of β-γ angular correlations; and through f, g, h, l, and m we can find the five nuclear parameters. The only remaining unknown is the magnitude of $\int \boldsymbol{\sigma} \times \mathbf{r}$, which can be found from the half-life for β decay $t_{1/2}$:*

$$\left|\int \boldsymbol{\sigma} \times \mathbf{r}\right|^2 \int_1^{E_0} C(E)F(Z, E)pEq^2\,dE = \frac{2\pi^3 \log_e 2}{C_A^2 t_{1/2}}\frac{2I_1 + 1}{2I_2 + 1} \tag{3-115}$$

Theoretically, the magnitudes of all six matrix elements can be separately determined if we have the complete information on the β-γ directional correlations, β circularly polarized γ correlations, β-ray spectra, and the half-life of β decay. Particularly for a unique first

---

* Our convention for nuclear matrix elements differs from that of Konopinski-Uhlenbeck by a factor $(2I_1 + 1)/(2I_2 + 1)$.

forbidden transition with $I - I_1 = \pm 2$, the β-γ angular correlations are given uniquely.

Although the general formulas are rather involved, the actual analysis can be simplified, depending on the dominating terms. In general, there are three factors which greatly affect the correlations. These factors are the large Coulomb energy terms, the cancellation effect, and the selection rules. We shall now discuss each of these separately.

The Case of Large Coulomb Energy (*the Quasi-allowed* (ξ) *Approximation*). In the β decay of medium and heavy nuclei, the maximum energy of the electron is considerably smaller than one-half the Coulomb energy (measured at nuclear radius R); that is, $\alpha Z/2R \gg E_0$. In β-decay theory, $\alpha Z/2R$ is commonly abbreviated by ξ; hence it is called the ξ approximation (cf. p. 79). Under such conditions we can put $r \gg 1$ or w, and $s \gg 1$ or x, if there is no cancellation among the matrix elements. The B_{ij} term is simply omitted because it contains no $\alpha Z/2R$ term. Therefore all formulas under the ξ approximation can be expressed by only the square terms of r and s. Consequently, all formulas reduce to those for the allowed transitions. In other words,

1. The shape correction factor is energy independent.
2. The β-γ directional correlation is nearly isotropic. As a matter of fact, the anisotropy a is of the order of $2RE_0/\alpha Z$ and it is proportional to p^2/E.
3. The β circularly polarized γ correlation has the same form for $\beta^{\mp}$ decay as for allowed transitions, if we replace λ by a real number λ_1:

$$\lambda_1 = \frac{-C_A \int \gamma_5 \pm i(\alpha Z/2R)C_A \int \boldsymbol{\sigma} \cdot \mathbf{r}}{\pm(\alpha Z/2R)C_A / \int \boldsymbol{\sigma} \times \mathbf{r} + i(\alpha Z/2R)C_V \int \mathbf{r} \mp C_V \int \boldsymbol{\alpha}} \quad \text{if} \quad I_1 = I$$

$$= 0 \quad \text{if} \quad I_1 = I \pm 1 \qquad (3\text{-}116)$$

An example of a nucleus which obeys the ξ approximation is Au^{198}.

Cancellation Effect. If there is certain cancellation among the matrix elements in the numerator of Eqs. 3-105 and 3-106 so that the Coulomb terms no longer dominate, we have to use more detailed expressions for the angular correlation. Generally, we expect a strong energy dependence for the spectrum shape factor and β-γ angular correlation in such cases. The forbidden shape of the RaE spectrum (cf. p. 87) is a good example of this cancellation effect, but in this case the β decay proceeds to the ground state and is not followed by a γ ray.

Selection Rule Effect. Sometimes nuclear selection rules predict that certain nuclear matrix elements occurring in the β decay of a nucleus will be forbidden or prevented from occurring. In first forbidden β decay these selection rules usually tend to reduce or eliminate the Coulomb-dependant terms. As an example, consider a unique first forbidden transition—that is, a transition in which $|I - I_1| = 2$, where I and I_1 are the initial and final spins of the nucleus respectively. From the selection rule given on p. 78, we see that only the $L = 2$ matrix element can appear. That is, all other matrix elements except the $\int B_{ij}$ matrix element vanish. In particular, all the terms which involve the Coulomb factor ξ will be zero. The spectrum shape for a transition where only the $\int B_{ij}$ term is present is the so called α type. This type of spectrum is strongly energy dependent, being proportional to $p^2 + q^2$ (see Eq. 3.85).

In addition to the example just mentioned involving the overall change of nuclear spin, there are other selection rules arising from nuclear-model considerations. These selection rules do not hold strictly and are only good when the assumed nuclear model is a a good approximation. One example of a nuclear-model selection rule is the Δj selection rule which applies to the j-j coupling shell model of the nucleus. The Δj selection rule states that $|j_{\mathrm{p}} - j_{\mathrm{n}}| \leqslant L \leqslant j_{\mathrm{p}} + j_{\mathrm{n}}$ where j_{p} and j_{n} are the spins of the proton and neutron relevant to the β decay—that is, the initial and final spins of the nucleon undergoing β decay. Another nuclear-model selection rule is the ΔK selection rule (p. 83) which applies to rotational nuclei. This selection rule states that $|K_i - K_f| \leqslant L \leqslant K_i + K_f$, where K_i and K_f refer to the rotational quantum number K of the initial and final states, respectively.

Since the nuclear-model selection rules are not strictly obeyed, the nuclear matrix elements corresponding to L values of $L \leqslant |I_{\mathrm{p}} - I_{\mathrm{n}}| = \Delta I$ or $L \leqslant |K_i - K_f| = \Delta K$ are not identically zero. However, if the assumed nuclear model is a good approximation, these matrix elements will be small compared to the others. Often the $\int B_{ij}$ matrix element is the only one permitted by nuclear-model selection rules, and we are led to believe that the element $\int B_{ij}$ is large compared to the $L = I$ and

$L = 0$ matrix elements. In such cases we may be able to adopt *the modified B_{ij} approximation*. This approximation supposes that the matrix element B_{ij} is of the order ξ times larger than the matrix elements $\int \mathbf{r}$, $\int \boldsymbol{\sigma} \times \mathbf{r}$, and $\int \boldsymbol{\sigma} \cdot \mathbf{r}$. Theoretical considerations also lead us to believe that, in general, the matrix elements $\int \gamma_5$ and $\int \boldsymbol{\alpha}$ will have orders of magnitude $\int \boldsymbol{\alpha} \sim \xi \int \mathbf{r}$ and $\int \gamma_5 \sim i\xi \int \boldsymbol{\sigma} \cdot \mathbf{r}$. The explanation of this is given by Ahrens and Feenberg (Ah-52). We then have in Eqs. 3-105 to 3-109 r, s, $iz \gg iw$, ix. In the modified B_{ij} approximation we can express the angular correlation in terms of only two real parameters x and y where

$$x = r/z \tag{3-117}$$

$$y = s/z \tag{3-118}$$

We shall return to the B_{ij} approximation later, but first let us discuss some specific nuclei which serve to illustrate the effects just mentioned. Note that the modified B_{ij} approximation, in which B_{ij}, $\xi \int \mathbf{r}$, etc., are assumed to be of the same order of magnitude, is intermediate between (a) the pure B_{ij} approximation where $B_{ij} \gg \xi \int \mathbf{r}$ and (b) the ξ approximation for which $B_{ij} \ll \xi \int \mathbf{r}$.

Typical Examples. As typical examples of the foregoing three cases, we shall discuss the β decays of Au^{198}, Sb^{124}, and Rb^{86}.

Au^{198}—ξ APPROXIMATION. Ninety-nine per cent of the β decay proceeds through the decay scheme $2^- \xrightarrow{\beta} 2^+ \xrightarrow{\gamma} 0^+$. In this β decay, $\alpha Z/2R \sim 16$ and $E_0 = 2.9$, so that the ξ approximation is expected to be valid. In fact, experiments show that the anisotropy is about 3% at E_0, the spectrum has statistical shape within $\pm 5\%$, and the β circularly polarized γ correlation is proportional to p/E. Since the ξ approximation is valid, the nuclear parameters s and r are dominant. We can determine s and r, but it is impossible to determine the nuclear matrix elements separately.

Sb^{124}—SELECTION-RULE EFFECT. In the decay scheme $3^- \xrightarrow{\beta} 2^+ \xrightarrow{\gamma} 0^+$, the maximum energy of the β ray is 2.3 mev. The ft value is large and $\log ft$ is 10.2. The spectrum shows definite deviation from the allowed shape and the β-γ directional correlation shows a large anisotropy, $|\epsilon| \cong 40\%$. Since the latter has no $P_4(\cos\theta)$ term, this decay is a first forbidden transition. The four nuclear matrix elements can be found from the data of $\log ft$, spectrum shape factor, β-γ directional correlation, and β circularly polarized γ correlation. According to a recent analysis by Mitra (Mit-63),

$$\frac{\int B_{ij}}{R} = (1.0 \pm 0.2) \times 10^{-2}$$

$$\frac{\int \mathbf{r}}{R} = (7.5 \pm 6.4) \times 10^{-4}$$

$$\frac{i\int \boldsymbol{\sigma} \times \mathbf{r}}{R} = (15.5 \pm 5.9) \times 10^{-4}$$

$$-i \int \boldsymbol{\alpha} = (7.0 \pm 2.1) \times 10^{-4}$$

In the normal case, $\int r/R$ and $i \int \boldsymbol{\sigma} \times \mathbf{r}/R$ are of the order of unity, and $\int B_{ij}/R$ and $-i \int \boldsymbol{\alpha}$ are of the order of 0.1. In the foregoing values, the matrix elements with $L = 1$ are strongly suppressed; $\int B_{ij}$ is also suppressed, but to a much smaller degree than the $L = 1$ matrix elements. This case clearly demonstrates the selection rule effect. According to theoretical calculations by Kisslinger and Wu (Ki-64), very small values of the matrix elements would be expected in this transition, and there is generally some suppression for β transitions leading to the first excited 2+ state of an even-even nucleus, if this final nucleus has both neutrons and protons outside closed shells.

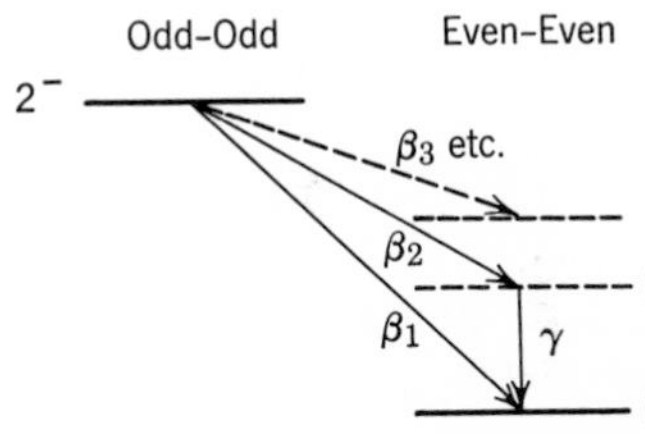

Fig. 3-41 Decay scheme of typical odd-odd nucleus with 2^- ground state. The initial state (odd-odd nucleus) 2^- decays into the ground state 0^+ and the excited state 2^+ by emitting β_1 and β_2, respectively. It may also decay into the higher excited states.

Rb^{86} and Rb^{84} (Si-65)—STRUCTURE OF THE 2^+ STATES IN EVEN-EVEN NUCLEI. The decays of Rb^{86} and Rb^{84} are examples of a particular kind of decay scheme, $2^- \xrightarrow{\beta} 2^+ \xrightarrow{\gamma} 0^+$, as shown in Fig. 3-41. This decay scheme plays an important role in the study of first forbidden transitions. The 2^- ground state of the odd-odd nucleus can decay either to the 0^+ ground state or the 2^+ first excited state of the even-even nucleus. We denote the transitions by the subscript 0, 2, respectively. In the β_1 transition there is only a single nonvanishing matrix element $(B_{ij})_1$

involved. In the β_2 transition all six possible first forbidden matrix elements can occur.

The study of the β-γ angular correlation in Rb^{86} can shed some light on the properties of the 2^+ state in Sr^{86} and offers a test of various simple nuclear models. Thus, according to the simple shell model, in the ${}_{37}Rb^{86}_{49}$ ground state the odd proton and neutron are, respectively, in

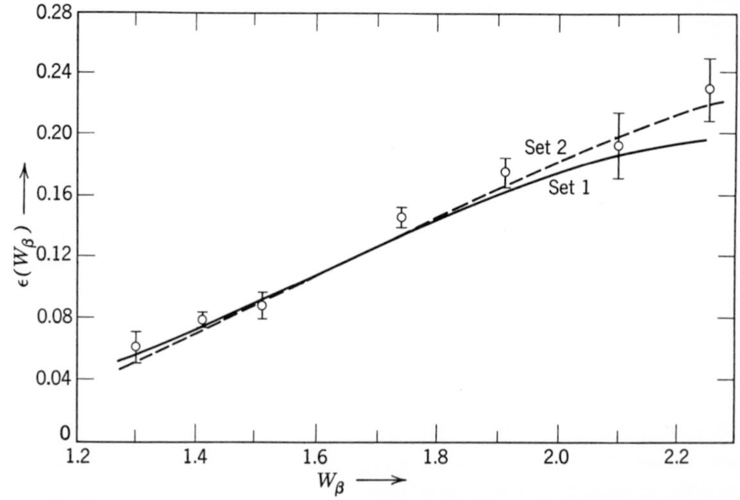

Fig. 3-42 Rb^{86} β–γ directional-correlation parameter as a function of β energy. From (Si-65).

$f_{5/2}$ and $g_{9/2}$ orbits. In the β decay to the Sr^{86} ground state the $g_{9/2}$ neutron changes into an $f_{5/2}$ proton, requiring an angular-momentum change of $2\hbar$ both for the nucleus as a whole and for the jumping nucleon. Thus we obtain a B_{ij} shape for β_1. In the other transition, β_2, no change of angular momentum is required. However, if the 2^+ state in Sr^{86} is basically of the same kind as the ground state—for example, if it involves the $g_{9/2}$ neutrons coupling to form a 2^+ state (rather than 0^+, as in the ground state)—the β_2 transition will still require $\Delta j = 2$ for the jumping nucleon, and this spectrum will also have a B_{ij} shape. The same conclusion would hold if Sr^{86} were a nonspherical rotating nucleus, in which case the 2^+ state would have basically the same structure as the ground state (already briefly mentioned, pp. 85-86). Indeed, Rb^{86} has an unusually large directional correlation (Fig. 3-42) and circular polarization (Fig. 3-43), and the

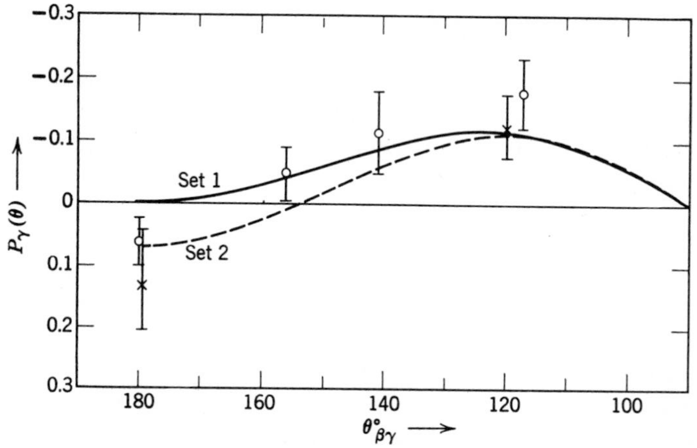

Fig. 3-43 Rb^{86} β–γ circular polarization as a function of angle. Integral pulse height selection was used for the β detector. ×, Simms et al.; ○, Boehm and Rogers. From (Bo-63; Si-65).

relative magnitudes of the nuclear matrix elements do not agree with the ξ approximation.

Recently, Eichler (Ei-63) has made detailed calculations using a model which is more realistic for nuclei in this region, a shell model with pairing interactions and quadrupole surface oscillations along the lines considered by Kisslinger and Sorenson (Ki-60). With this model Eichler is able to account satisfactorily for the empirical results in Rb^{86}. Experimentally, the β_2 decay of Rb^{86} fits neither the B_{ij} nor the ξ

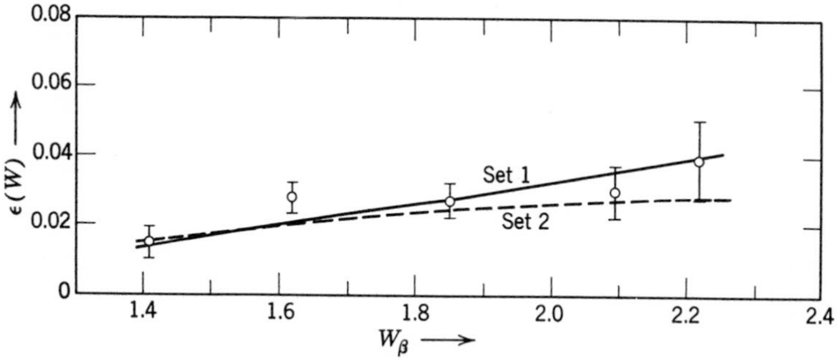

Fig. 3-44 Rb^{84} β–γ directional-correlation parameters as a function of β energy. From (Bo-63).

approximation. Neither of the simple models already mentioned gives a realistic description of the 2^+ state in Sr^{86}.

On the other hand, the decay of Rb^{84} is very similar to that of Rb^{86} but has very different characteristics. The direction correlation parameter ϵ is small (Fig. 3-44), and the circular-polarization measurements (Bo-63) are not as extensive as desired. The very small β-γ angular correlation and nearly allowed spectrum shape would imply that the nucleus of Rb^{84} obeys the ξ approximation. However, a detailed analysis of the experimental results of Rb^{84} by Simms shows that there are two sets of solutions. In one set the B_{ij} matrix element dominates, and the agreement with the C.V.C. theory is good. In fact, the matrix elements for Rb^{84} and Rb^{86} are similar. In another set the matrix elements from change of nuclear spin by one unit are comparable to B_{ij}, and the absolute magnitude of the C.V.C. ratio is 50% too small. It would be very difficult, however, to distinguish experimentally between these two sets. Thus it should be stressed that the possibility of selection rule effects must be extensively investigated in spite of the superficial agreement with the ξ approximation at first glance.

CHAPTER 4

Parity Nonconservation in Beta Decay

4-1 SIGNIFICANCE OF PARITY NONCONSERVATION

In the old β theory the Hamiltonian was formulated in such a way that it was invariant not only under the proper Lorentz transformations but also under space inversion P and time reversal T. In 1956 when Lee and Yang (Le-56) started to examine the possible implications of parity nonconservation in β decay, they introduced a more general Hamiltonian density which includes a pseudoscalar as well as the original scalar term:

$$\mathscr{H} = g\Big[\sum_i C_i(\tilde{\psi}_p \hat{O}_i Q^+ \psi_n)(\tilde{\psi}_e \hat{O}_i \psi_\nu) + \sum_i C_i'(\tilde{\psi}_p \hat{O}_i Q^+ \psi_n)(\tilde{\psi}_e \hat{O}_i \gamma_5 \psi_\nu) + \text{h.c.}\Big]$$

where $i = S, V, T, A$, and P, and h.c. denotes Hermitean conjugate.

We call C_i the parity-conserving coupling constant and C_i' the parity-nonconserving coupling constant (in units of g). Actually, whether C_i or C_i' is the parity-conserving term depends on the relative parity of the neutrino with respect to the electron. In classical β decay it was conventionally assumed that the neutrino and the electron had the same parity; then $C_i \neq 0$ and $C_i' = 0$. This was known as "even" coupling. Otherwise, if the neutrino and e^- were of opposite parity, then $C_i = 0$ and $C_i' \neq 0$ were called "odd" coupling. There is no way to distinguish between C_i and C_i' without measuring the spin of the neutrino (Ya-50).

Parity Conservation and Neutrino Helicity

Since Lee and Yang's original paper on the possible nonconservation of parity in β decay, readers have been accustomed to the notation of

C_i and C_i' for even and odd β coupling constants. However, in the first parity experiment it was clear that the violation of parity being searched for actually attains a maximum; therefore the hypothesis of the two-component neutrino came to the fore. Under such circumstances the physical significance of C_i and C_i' is best understood if we define the coupling constants in terms of the helicities of the neutrinos:

$$C_i^R \equiv C_i - C_i' \quad \text{and} \quad C_i^L \equiv C_i + C_i'$$

where C_i^{R*} and C_i^{L*} are the amplitudes for creating right-handed (that is, positive-helicity) neutrinos and left-handed (i.e., negative-helicity) neutrinos, respectively, in β^+ decay, and C_i^R and C_i^L are the amplitudes for creating left-handed antineutrinos and right-handed antineutrinos in β^- decay.

If there is space inversion (P) invariance, left cannot be distinguished from the right. We should have an equal number of left-handed and right-handed neutrinos or antineutrinos. Then $|C_i^R| = |C_i^L|$ and either C_i or C_i' must be identically equal to zero.

Searching for Pseudoscalar Quantities

We have mentioned that in order to detect noninvariance in parity, a pseudoscalar term as well as the scalar term must be introduced into the β Hamiltonian $\mathscr{H}_\beta$. Thus we have the parity-nonconserving coupling constants C_i' as well as the parity-conserving constants C_i. However, in the old β experiments the quantities which are measured are

$$\mathbf{p}_e \text{ and } \mathbf{p}_\nu = -\mathbf{p}_e - \mathbf{p}_{\text{recoil ion}}$$

It is obvious that no pseudoscalars can be formed from these two polar vectors. In measuring the scalar quantities, the only changes necessary from the old expressions, which contain only the C_i, to the new ones, which contain both C_i and C_i', are made by replacing

$$C_i^2 \rightarrow |C_i|^2 + |C_i'|^2 \tag{4-1}$$

and

$$2C_iC_j \rightarrow 2\,\text{Re}\,(C_iC_j^* + C_i'C_j'^*) \tag{4-2}$$

Hence terms of the form $C_iC_j'^*$, which come from the interference between the parity-conserving and the parity-nonconserving parts (that is, whether or not both C_i and $C_i' \neq 0$), cannot possibly be detected. This is why, with the voluminous experimental information on β decay

—that is, the shape of the β spectra, the ft values, the β-ν angular correlations and the β-γ angular correlations—no light was ever shed on the question of the conservation of parity in β decay.

Lee and Yang (Le-56) suggested that in order to test the parity conservation in β decay, we must measure a pseudoscalar formed from the experimentally measured quantities. For example, if a spin $\boldsymbol{\sigma}$ and a momentum $\mathbf{p}$ are measured, or if three momenta $\mathbf{p}_1$, $\mathbf{p}_2$, and $\mathbf{p}_3$ are measured, the existence of pseudoscalar terms such as $<\boldsymbol{\sigma}\cdot\mathbf{p}>$ or $<\mathbf{p}_1\cdot(\mathbf{p}_2\times\mathbf{p}_3)>$ directly violates the invariance of space inversion and, therefore, parity conservation.

This theorem can be proved by the following simple example. Let $\mathbf{I}$ be a unit vector in the spin direction of a particle or a nucleus, and let $\mathbf{p}$ be the unit momentum vector. If parity conservation is valid, the expectation value of the pseudoscalar quantity $(\mathbf{I}\cdot\mathbf{p})$ must be zero. The expectation value of $(\mathbf{I}\cdot\mathbf{p})$ is given by

$$\langle(\mathbf{I}\cdot\mathbf{p})\rangle = \int d\mathbf{r}\psi^*(\mathbf{r})[\mathbf{I}(\mathbf{r})\cdot\mathbf{p}(\mathbf{r})]\psi(\mathbf{r})$$

where $\psi(\mathbf{r})$ is the eigenfunction describing the interaction. By reversing the sign of $\mathbf{r}$, the expectation value changes to

$$\langle(\mathbf{I}\cdot\mathbf{p})\rangle = \int d\mathbf{r}\psi^*(-\mathbf{r})[\mathbf{I}(-\mathbf{r})\cdot\mathbf{p}(-\mathbf{r})]\psi(-\mathbf{r})$$

If parity invariance is valid, then by definition of the parity operation P

$$P\psi(\mathbf{r}) = \psi(-\mathbf{r}) = \pm\psi(\mathbf{r})$$

The second equation of the expectation value becomes

$$\begin{aligned}\langle(\mathbf{I}\cdot\mathbf{p})\rangle &= \int d\mathbf{r}\psi^*(\mathbf{r})[\mathbf{I}(-\mathbf{r})\cdot\mathbf{p}(-\mathbf{r})]\psi(\mathbf{r})\\ &= -\int d\mathbf{r}\psi^*(\mathbf{r})[\mathbf{I}(\mathbf{r})\cdot\mathbf{p}(\mathbf{r})]\psi(\mathbf{r}) = -<(\mathbf{I}\cdot\mathbf{p})>\end{aligned}$$

Therefore $<(\mathbf{I}\cdot\mathbf{p})> = 0$; in other words, if parity invariance is valid, the expectation value of a pseudoscalar quantity must be identically zero.

Essentially, there are three possible ways of detecting and measuring such quantities: (a) β asymmetry from polarized nuclei; (b) longitudinal polarization of β particles; and (c) β-γ circular polarization. We will discuss first the polarized Co^{60} experiment, an example of method (a); later in this chapter we will also treat the other two methods.

4-2 THE POLARIZED Co^{60} EXPERIMENT

The essence of the polarized nuclei experiment (Wu-57) is to line up the spins of β-emitting nuclei along the same axis and then to determine whether the β particles were emitted preferentially in one direction or the other along the axis. The property by which atomic nuclei can be oriented is the magnetic moment.

When the nuclear magnetic moment μ interacts with a large magnetic field, the degeneracy of the $2I + 1$ spatial orientations is removed. Because of the smallness of μ, the magnetic field required to align these tiny magnets, even for $T \sim 0.01°K$, is prohibitively high, about 10^5 gauss. Fortunately, strong magnetic fields do exist in the vicinity of the atomic nucleus of paramagnetic ions, such as Ni, Fe, Co, and some rare earths produced by the unfilled holes in the inner electron shells. The magnetic moments of such ions are about a thousand times larger than those of nuclei. Thus paramagnetic ions can be lined up in moderately strong magnetic fields (hundreds of oersteds), and their tremendous fields at the nucleus, in turn, orient the nuclear moments. This ingenious method of nuclear orientation was independently proposed by Rose (Ro-48) and Gorter (Go-48). In order to reduce the thermal agitation which tends to disrupt the orderly orientation, the radioactive nuclei were introduced into the cerium-magnesium-nitrate crystal $[2Ce(NO_3)_3 \cdot 3Mg(NO_3)_2 \cdot 24H_2O]$, which was cooled down by the adiabatic demagnetization method to a temperature of 0.01°C above absolute zero.

The paramagnetic radioactive Co^{60} which decays by pure Gamow-Teller interaction $[\Delta I = 5 - 4 = 1 \text{ (no)}]$ was selected for this test. Its decay scheme is shown in Fig. 3-9, p. 72.

To study the β distribution from polarized nuclei in the present problem, two major difficulties had to be overcome. The β detector had to be placed inside the demagnetization cryostat at approximately 1°K, and the radioactive nuclei had to be located in a thin surface layer (<0.1 mm) and polarized. The β detector was a thin anthracene crystal located inside the vacuum chamber about 2 cm above the Co^{60} source. The scintillations were transmitted through a glass window and a lucite light pipe 4 feet long to a photomultiplier which was located at the top of the cryostat (at room temperature).

The amount of polarization of Co^{60} was determined by measuring simultaneously the anisotropy of its γ radiation:

$$\gamma = \frac{W(\pi/2) - W(0)}{W(\pi/2)} \tag{4-3}$$

The schematic diagram of the experimental arrangements is shown in Fig. 4-1.

A large β asymmetry was observed. In Fig. 4-2 the anisotropy and β asymmetry versus time were plotted both up and down for the polarizing field. The time for the disappearance of the β asymmetry coincided well with that of the γ anisotropy. The sign of the asymmetry coefficient was found to be negative; that is, the emission of β particles is more favored in the direction opposite to that of the nuclear spin. This means that, viewed from the position of the emitted β particles, the nuclei Co^{60} appear to rotate clockwise. Left can be distinguished from right. Therefore parity is *not* always conserved, as shown by this experiment.

In the electron angular distribution (see Appendix VI for its derivation)

$$I(\theta) = 1 + A\frac{\langle I_z\rangle}{I}\frac{v}{c}\cos\theta \tag{4-4}$$

With θ as the angle between the nuclear spin and electron momentum direction, the measured asymmetry parameter A is nearly equal to -1.* This value implies that the parity interference effects are about as large as they can be. Thus this first experiment on parity not only revealed that parity is not conserved in β decay but also pointed to something more drastic and significant. Many important deductions can be directly derived from the observed asymmetry parameter ($A \sim -1$) in the polarized Co^{60} β-decay experiment. If we write down the expression A for the β decay of Co^{60}, which is a pure Gamow-Teller

* The actual observed asymmetry is ~25% (see Fig. 4-2),

$$\frac{W(0) - W(\pi)}{W(0) + W(\pi)} = -0.25 = A\frac{\langle I_z\rangle}{I}\frac{v}{c} \quad \text{where } \frac{\langle I_z\rangle}{I} = 0.65$$

calculated from γ anisotropy; $v/c \cong 0.6$ from pulse height selection. Furthermore, the back scattering of the electrons from the CeMg nitrate crystal was carefully studied in a magnetic spectrometer and was found to be 30–35%. Therefore $A \cong -0.25 \times (0.65 \times 0.60)^{-1} \times \frac{3}{2} \cong -1$.

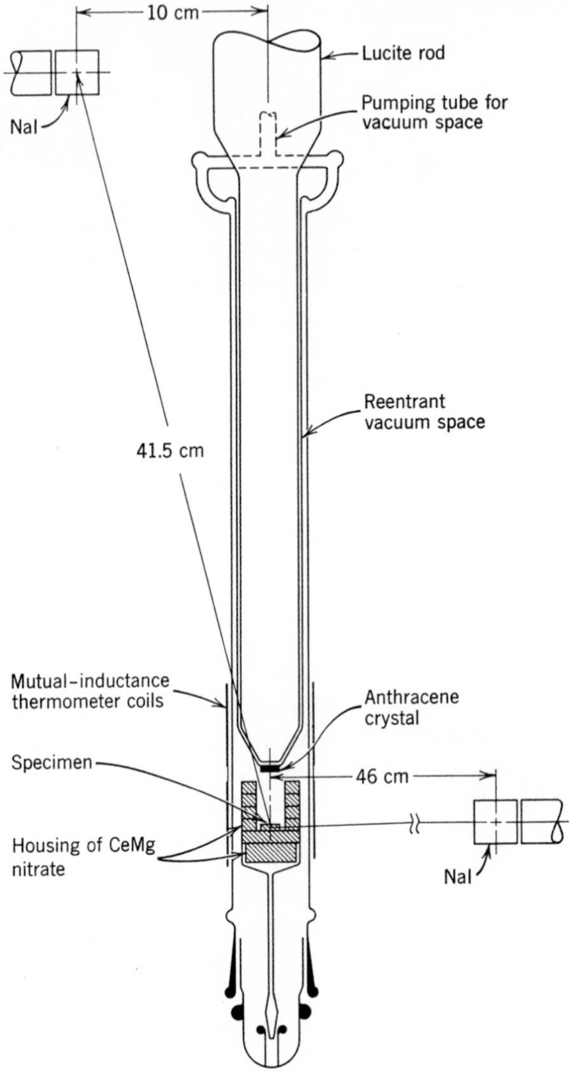

Fig. 4-1 A schematic diagram showing the demagnetization cryostat used in the measurement of the angular distribution of the electrons from the β decay of oriented Co^{60} nuclei. The Co^{60} nuclei were polarized parallel to the axis of the cylindrical cryostat. The electrons were detected by an anthracene scintillation counter. Two NaI γ-ray scintillation counters are also shown. From (Wu-57).

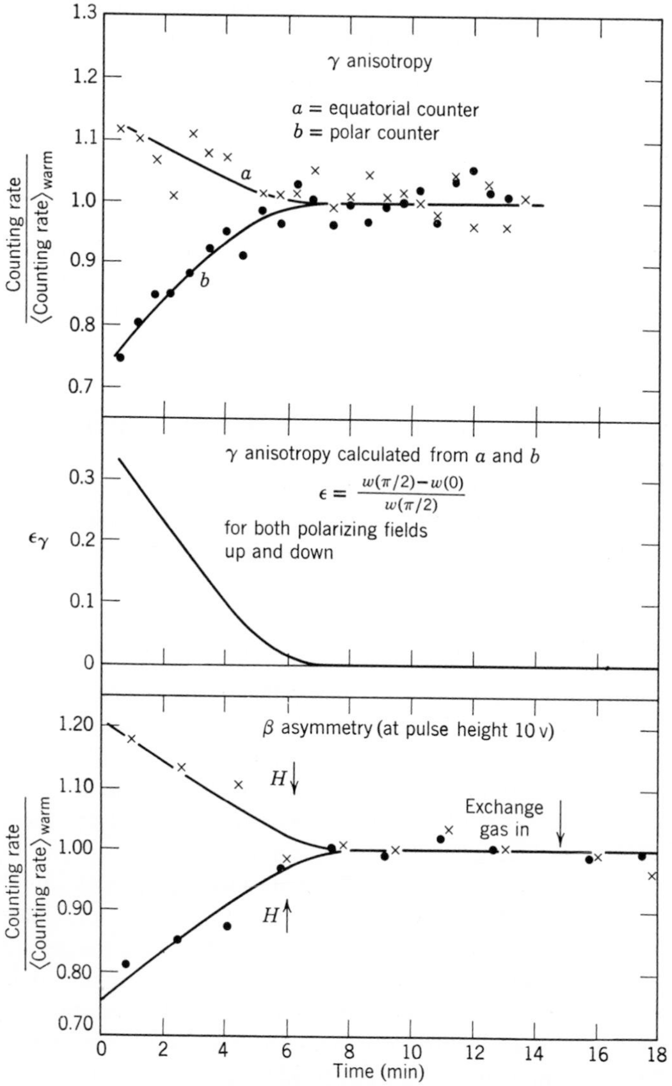

Fig. 4-2 Results of β asymmetry and γ anisotropy from polarized Co^{60} experiment. The disappearance of the β asymmetry coincides exactly with the time of disappearance of γ anisotropy. The measured asymmetry indicates that the emission of electrons is preferred in the direction opposite to that of the nuclear spin. From (Wu-57).

transition (and assumed to be axial-vector in accordance with the results of β-ν angular-correlation experiments), we find

$$A = -2\frac{\mathrm{Re}\,(C_A{}^*C_A{}')}{|C_A|^2 + |C_A{}'|^2} \cong -1 \tag{4-5}$$

Thus our observed asymmetry implies that†

$$C_A \approx C_A{}' \tag{4-6}$$

As we shall see later, the results of the first Co^{60} experiment imply *not only that parity invariance is violated, but also that charge conjugation is not invariant* ($C_i/C_i{}'$ is not purely imaginary). Furthermore, it pointed to something even more drastically significant.

4-3 THE TWO-COMPONENT THEORY OF THE NEUTRINO

From $C_A = C_A{}'$, we have the total neutrino operator $(1 + \gamma_5)\psi_\nu$. It is well known that the term $(1 \pm \gamma_5)/2$ affects the wave function as a projection operator for the longitudinal polarization, where

$$\tfrac{1}{2}(1 + \gamma_5)\,\psi_\nu = \psi_\nu{}^L \quad \text{for left polarization} \tag{4-7}$$

and

$$\tfrac{1}{2}(1 - \gamma_5)\,\omega_\nu = \psi_\nu{}^R \quad \text{for right polarization} \tag{4-8}$$

This is particularly the case with mass-zero particles, because $\psi_\nu{}^R$ can be uncoupled from $\psi_\nu{}^L$, each of which is an eigenstate of the Hamiltonian; therefore the complete polarization of either right-handed or left-handed helicity is implied. A simple and appealing two-component theory of the neutrino was independently proposed by Landau (La-57), Salam (Sa-57), and Lee and Yang (Le-57a), in 1957. In the conventional neutrino theory there are four components in the neutrino wave function, two for the positive energy state (designated as neutrino ν) with right and left polarizations, and two for the negative energy state (designated as antineutrino $\bar{\nu}$), also with right and left polarization. The existence of only one completely polarized state each for the neutrino and antineutrino reduces Dirac's neutrino wave function from four components to two (cf. p. 323); hence, the name.

It is interesting to recall that in 1929 Weyl (We-29) proposed the mathematical possibilities of such a two-component massless relativistic

† At the time the Co^{60} experiment was performed, it was not known whether the Gamow-Teller interaction was tensor or axial-vector. For a tensor interaction we would have $C_T{}' = -C_T$.

particle of spin one-half. It was rejected by Pauli (Pa-33a) because it violated the law of parity.*

Masslessness of the Neutrino

For the axial-vector interaction the neutrino operator is

$$(1 + \gamma_5)\psi_\nu \tag{4-9}$$

By applying the relation

$$(1 + \gamma_5) = (1 + \gamma_5)\gamma_5 \tag{4-10}$$

it follows that the Hamiltonian term is invariant under the replacements of the neutrino wave function ψ_ν by

$$\psi_\nu \to \gamma_5\psi_\nu \quad \text{for } A \text{ interaction} \tag{4-11}$$

Nevertheless, this substitution rigorously requires that the mass of the neutrino be equal to zero in the Dirac equation for *a free neutrino*:

$$\left(\sum_\mu \gamma_\mu \frac{\delta}{\delta x_\mu} + m_\nu\right)\psi_\nu = 0 \tag{4-12}$$

Substitute

$$\psi_\nu \to \gamma_5\psi_\nu, \qquad \left(\sum_\mu \gamma_\mu \frac{\delta}{\delta x_\mu} + m_\nu\right)\gamma_5\psi_\nu = 0 \tag{4-13}$$

or multiply Eq. 4-12 by γ_5 to obtain

$$\left(\sum_\mu \gamma_\mu \frac{\delta}{\delta x_\mu} - m_\nu\right)\gamma_5\psi_\nu = 0 \tag{4-14}$$

The change of the relative sign between the two terms in these equations is due to the anticommuting relation between γ_5 and γ_μ. Therefore, to have both the free neutrino and the interaction Hamiltonian invariant under the substitution $\psi \to \pm\gamma_5\psi_\nu$, *the mass of neutrino* (m_ν) *must be equal to zero.*

That the masslessness of the neutrino is necessary for the definite helicity of the neutrino is physically quite obvious. So far, the experimental evidence of the mass of the neutrino indeed indicates its vanishing smallness to less than 250 ev (see Sec. 2-5). It is interesting to note (Le-65) that if we give up lepton conservation, a wave function can be constructed for two-component neutrinos with finite rest mass. Conversely then, the two-component theory requires zero rest mass only in conjunction with lepton conservation.

* See, however, the remarks by Touschek in *Rend. Scuola. Intern. Fis.* "*Enrico Fermi*" **XI**, 40 (1960).

Helicity of the Neutrino

In writing down the Dirac equation of a *massless* neutrino ($m_\nu = 0$), we need only three anticommuting Hermitian matrices because of the absence of the mass term; the neutrino can be represented by a two-component spinor function,

$$i \frac{\delta}{\delta t} \psi_\nu = - i \boldsymbol{\alpha} \cdot \boldsymbol{\nabla} \psi_\nu \tag{4-15}$$

However, $\boldsymbol{\alpha}$ can be expressed by $\boldsymbol{\alpha} = -\gamma_5 \boldsymbol{\sigma} = -\boldsymbol{\sigma}\gamma_5$ where $\boldsymbol{\sigma}$ denotes the three 2×2 Pauli matrices. Therefore

$$i \frac{\delta}{\delta t} \psi_\nu = + i \boldsymbol{\sigma} \cdot \boldsymbol{\nabla} \gamma_5 \psi_\nu \tag{4-16}$$

For a massless neutrino we can make the substitution $\psi_\nu = \pm \gamma_5 \psi_\nu$ with $+(-)$ for $A(T)$ interaction. Then we obtain

$$i \frac{\delta}{\delta t} \psi_\nu = \pm i \boldsymbol{\sigma} \cdot \boldsymbol{\nabla} \psi_\nu \tag{4-17}$$

By Fourier transformation the foregoing expression becomes

$$H\psi_\nu = \mp(\boldsymbol{\sigma} \cdot \mathbf{p})\psi_\nu \quad \begin{matrix} -\text{ for } A \text{ interaction} \\ +\text{ for } T \text{ interaction} \end{matrix} \tag{4-18}$$

where H is the Hamiltonian operator, or

$$E = \mp(\boldsymbol{\sigma} \cdot \mathbf{p}) \tag{4-19}$$

where E is the eigenvalue of the energy state.

The helicity $\mathfrak{H}$ is defined as

$$\mathfrak{H} = \frac{\boldsymbol{\sigma} \cdot \mathbf{p}}{|\mathbf{p}|} = \begin{matrix} +1 \text{ for right-handed screw motion} \\ -1 \text{ for left-handed screw motion} \end{matrix} \tag{4-20}$$

The physical implication of Eq. 4-19 means that for a definite momentum p the particle has two distinct states. *These two distinct positive and negative energy states exhibit opposite helicities.* For an axial-vector interaction, then, the Co^{60} experiment predicts E and $\mathfrak{H}$ for the neutrino to be

$$E = -(\boldsymbol{\sigma} \cdot \mathbf{p}) \tag{4-21}$$

or

$$\mathfrak{H} = -\frac{(\boldsymbol{\sigma} \cdot \mathbf{p})}{|\mathbf{p}|} \tag{4-22}$$

In other words the *neutrino has negative helicity* and the *antineutrino has positive helicity*. This is indeed what was confirmed in the neutrino helicity experiment.

4-4 INVARIANCE UNDER TIME REVERSAL AND CHARGE CONJUGATION

Since the β interaction is not invariant under space inversion, it might now be wondered whether or not it is invariant under the other two fundamental inversion operations, namely, time reversal T and charge conjugation C.

Time Reversal

Time reversal is defined as $t \rightarrow -t$, but particle $\rightarrow$ particle and $\mathbf{r} \rightarrow \mathbf{r}$. Therefore this operation involves classical concepts. In classical theory the motion of a dynamical system possesses the property of time reversibility, expressed by the equation of motion

$$m \frac{d^2\mathbf{r}(t)}{dt^2} = -\nabla V(\mathbf{r})$$

where the potential V is independent of time and $\mathbf{r}$ derivatives. If $\mathbf{r}(t)$ is a possible trajectory, then $\mathbf{r}(-t)$ is one also, as we can see from

$$m \frac{d^2\mathbf{r}(-t)}{d(-t)^2} = m \frac{d^2\mathbf{r}(-t)}{dt^2} = -\nabla V$$

From the classical point of view, it is easy to see that under time reversal T the transformations of the following quantities defined in the introduction (see p. 11) are

$$\begin{array}{ccc} \mathbf{p} \rightarrow -\mathbf{p} & & \mathbf{r} \rightarrow \mathbf{r} \\ \mathbf{J} \rightarrow -\mathbf{J} & \text{and} & \mathbf{E} \rightarrow \mathbf{E} \\ \boldsymbol{\sigma} \rightarrow -\boldsymbol{\sigma} & & \epsilon \rightarrow \epsilon \\ \mathbf{H} \rightarrow -\mathbf{H} & & \end{array}$$

In quantum theory (nonrelativistic quantum mechanics and relativistic field theory), although the mathematical formulation of the T operation is more complicated (see Appendices I and III), the transformations generated for these quantities are the same as in the classical theory. The invariance under time reversal implies, therefore, that for every state of motion of a system, the law of physics permits a corresponding reversed state of motion, in which all the particles traverse the original path backward, with reversed velocities and spins. In fact, the principle of detailed balance for collision processes is a direct consequence of the T invariance.

How can we test for T invariance in β decay? We have seen that both $\mathbf{p}$ and $\boldsymbol{\sigma}$ change signs under time reversal. Thus *odd* functions of $\boldsymbol{\sigma}$ and $\mathbf{p}$ such as

$$\boldsymbol{\sigma}\cdot(\mathbf{p}_1\times\mathbf{p}_2)\quad \mathbf{p}_1\cdot(\mathbf{p}_2\times\mathbf{p}_3)\quad\text{and}\quad \boldsymbol{\sigma}_1\cdot(\boldsymbol{\sigma}_2\times\boldsymbol{\sigma}_3)$$

change signs under time reversal. We might think that the experimental detection of such a quantity implies noninvariance under time reversal. However, this is *true only* when there are no strong interactions between various decay products in the final states. If there is a strong interaction between particles, for instance, a certain phase difference exists between the s and p waves, and under time reversal this phase difference reverses sign. Such a term, $\boldsymbol{\sigma}\cdot(\mathbf{p}_1\times\mathbf{p}_2)$, has been observed in the polarization of protons perpendicular to the scattering plane in p-p scattering even though time reversal is known to be conserved in the strong interactions. The nonvanishing of this odd function is actually due to the strong interactions between the protons in the final state. In β decay the only interaction in the final state is the electromagnetic interaction between the outgoing electron and the nucleus. For neutron decay, neglecting the electromagnetic interaction in the final state introduces only a small error of the order of $\frac{1}{137}$, but for heavier nuclei the correction, which is of order αZ, can be appreciable.

The underlying principle of proof of the T invariance is the measuring of the relative phases between the coupling constants C_i. If T is invariant, the C_i are all real and vice versa, as shown by the following argument.

We have shown in Appendices I and III that the time reversal operator T cannot be represented by a unitary operator U_T, as in operation C or P, but rather by

$$T = U_T \times \text{complex conjugation}$$

Now the most general β Hamiltonian density $\mathscr{H}_\beta$, is a linear combination of various interaction terms $\mathscr{H}_i$:

$$\mathscr{H}_\beta = \sum_i C_i \mathscr{H}_i$$

Under time reversal each individual interaction Hamiltonian $\mathscr{H}_i$ is multiplied by a phase factor but is otherwise unchanged. If we allow all such phase factors to be included in C_i^*, the total Hamiltonian $\mathscr{H}_\beta$ under time reversal can be written as

$$T\mathscr{H}_\beta T^{-1} = \sum_i C_i^* \mathscr{H}_i$$

For invariance under time reversal

$$T\mathscr{H}_\beta T^{-1} = \mathscr{H}_\beta$$

we must have

$$C_i = C_i^*$$

which implies that the coupling constants C_i must be real.

Charge Conjugation

The charge conjugation operation C is defined as:

$$\text{particle} \leftrightarrows \text{antiparticle}, \ \mathbf{r} \rightarrow \mathbf{r}, \ \mathbf{t} \rightarrow \mathbf{t}$$

The invariance of charge conjugation is not a simple geometrical one such as the left-right symmetry in parity operation. It has its origin in the algebraic property of the complex numbers in the relativistic quantum theory and is essentially a symmetry between *matter and antimatter*. Since the Dirac theory of relativistic quantum mechanics had been constructed in such a way as to treat particles and antiparticles on an equal footing, this theory implies that for every particle there exists a distinct antiparticle with the same mass and spin but with an opposite charge and baryon or lepton number. The invariance under charge conjugation therefore states that for every state of a system of particles there is a corresponding state identical in all respects except for the interchange particle → antiparticle.

To test the validity of the charge conjugation C in β decay, we must carry out experiments with antiparticles as well as with particles and measure certain correlations to see whether they are invariant. For example, to test the validity of the charge conjugation by the polarized Co^{60} experiment, we must repeat the same investigation with anticobalt and measure the asymmetry of the decay positrons to see whether it is the same as in the normal Co^{60}. Naturally, this is beyond our reach.

However, it has been mentioned that the first Co^{60} experiment also proves that the charge conjugation is violated in β decay.

A direct proof of the noninvariance of the charge conjugation can be found in the $\pi^{\pm} \rightarrow \mu^{\pm} \rightarrow e^{\pm}$ decay chain. The polarization of μ^+ and e^+ from π^+ is found to be opposite to that of μ^- and e^- from π^-. This is an unequivocal proof of the violation of charge conjugation.

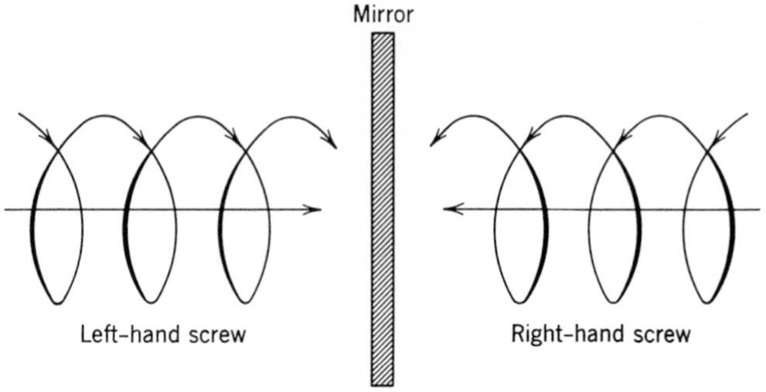

Fig. 4-3 Two neutrinos in mirror reflection.

For invariance under charge conjugation, the amplitude of emitting right-handed antineutrinos in β^- decay ($A \rightarrow B + e^- + \bar{\nu}$) should equal that of right-handed neutrinos in β^+ decay ($\bar{A} \rightarrow \bar{B} + e^+ + \nu$), because in charge conjugation we only change matter to antimatter; we do *nothing else*. The spin and momentum remain the same and so does the helicity. Using the argument given on p. 342, it follows that

$$|C_i^L| = |C_i^{R*}|$$

or equivalently $C_i/C_i' =$ pure imaginary.

The two-component theory of the neutrino violates both space inversion P and charge conjugation C invariance. A left-handed neutrino looks into a mirror and finds a right-handed neutrino, but according to the two-component theory of the neutrino, there is no such possible state (see Fig. 4-3). The charge conjugate of a left-handed neutrino is a left-handed antineutrino. However, the only allowed antineutrino state is right-handed. Thus the charge conjugate of the neutrino state is not an allowed state. This is a clear-cut violation of invariance under charge conjugation.

Furthermore, it can be seen that the much-used Fierz interference terms between S and V, expressed as $C_S C_V^* + C_S' C_V'^*$, and between A and T, expressed as $C_T C_A^* + C_T' C_A'^*$, now automatically vanish because the neutrino or antineutrino associated with S and T or V and A has opposite helicity; therefore no interference occurs. For the same reason the combinations V and T or S and A will not result in interference between Fermi and Gamow-Teller terms.

The CPT Theorem, CP Invariance

Finally, if we apply the combined operation of CPT so that the signs of all four space-time coordinates are reversed and each particle is changed into its corresponding antiparticle, we obtain an operation of singular simplicity which commutes with every proper homogeneous Lorentz transformation. Therefore, if a local Lagrangian theory is invariant under the proper Lorentz transformation, it is also invariant under the product of CPT (and its permutation), although the theory may not be *separately* invariant under each one of the three operations C, P, and T.

The CPT theorem implies that any particle and its antiparticle must have the same rest mass and lifetime. This conclusion is in agreement with all known results. Thus the experimental lifetimes of μ^+ and μ^- are equal to within 0.1% or less.

This theorem was first recognized by Lüders (Lu-54, 57). Thus in relativistic field theory it is possible to write interactions which violate either C, P or T invariance, or a combination of two of these, such as CP. However, to write an interaction which violates the combined operation of CPT, we must conceive of a theory which is radically different from any of the present schemes. Earlier, Schwinger (Sc-53; Schw-57) had used something resembling CPT to deduce the spin-statistics connection. Later Pauli (Pa-55) discussed the subject at great length and showed that the so-called strong reflection (SR) follows from the proper Lorentz invariance and the spin-statistics connection. Hence this theorem has often been referred to as the Schwinger-Lüders-Pauli theorem. From the CPT invariance theorem, if P is not conserved in the weak interactions, then at least one of the other invariances C or T should not be conserved. From the polarized Co^{60} experiment and the π-μ-e decays, we learned that the charge conjugation as well as parity is not conserved in these weak interactions. Of particular interest, then, is whether the invariance under time reversal is still intact. If the operation of time reversal T is invariant, then from the CPT theorem *the combined operation CP* is invariant. The invariance of this combined operation CP was examined by Landau (La-57), Wick (Wi-52), and Yang (Ya-56) even before the nonconservation of parity in weak interaction was discovered. From the CP combined invariance we replace all particles by their anti-particles in taking a mirror image, and the right-left asymmetry in space is retained. This is indeed a very comforting thought. In 1964, however, careful investigations of decay of the K_2 mesons (Ch-64, Ab-64) indicated strongly that the CP invariance is also violated (but only by less than 1%). In contrast, the violation of C and P invariance

Table 4-1 Relations among Coupling Constants Implied by Invariance under P, T, and C*

Invariant Operators	Noninvariant Operators	Requirements for the Coupling Constants
C, P, T	None	$C_i = \text{real},\ C_i' = 0;\ C_i^R = C_i^L$
C or PT	P and T	$C_i = \text{real},\ C_i' = \text{imag};\ C_i^R = C_i^{L*},$ $C_i^R \neq C_i^L$
T or CP	C and P	$C_i = \text{real},\ C_i' = \text{real};\ C_i^R = C_i^{R*},$ $C_i^L = C_i^{L*} \neq C_i^R$

* Of course, all coupling constants could be multiplied by a common phase factor $e^{i\alpha}$ without any change in physical results. All measurable quantities depend on products of the form $(C_i^*$ or $C_i'^*) \times (C_j$ or $C_j')$ which are unchanged under this transformation. Thus, if all C_i and C_i' are pure imaginary, the interaction is still invariant under time reversal and corresponds to $e^{i\alpha} = i$.

separately is the maximum possible. At the present moment there are several speculations (Le-65, Pr-65) about the cause of this observed violation of CP invariance in K_2^0 decays.* Further experimental investigations are under way to test these proposed explanations.

It is interesting to see that if parity is not conserved, we have both C_i and $C_i' \neq 0$. Meanwhile, if the time reversal is intact, both C_i and C_i' are real. Then it is evident that the charge conjugation cannot be invariant because C_i/C_i' must be pure imaginary. This conclusion can also be arrived at from the application of the CPT theorem.

Our discussion may be summarized by the results in Table 4-1.

---

* Assuming the CPT theorem holds, this would imply a slight breakdown of time reversal symmetry.

Number of Independent Coupling Constants

To allow for the possibility of the noninvariance of $\mathscr{H}$ under time reversal, the 10 coupling constants ($5C_i$ and $5C_i'$) must be taken to be complex, and there are 18 real parameters to be determined.* Pauli (Pau-57) and others (En-57; Ka-57) have also pointed out that if lepton conservation does not hold—that is, if the neutrino ν as well as the antineutrino $\bar{\nu}$ are emitted in β^- decay—then we are faced with

Table 4-2 Number of Coupling Constants for Various Forms of the Beta-Decay Interaction

	Old Theory	Two-Component Neutrino	Parity Nonconserving	No Parity, No Time-Reversal Invariance	Most General Form
Parity conservation	Yes	No	No	No	No
Two-component neutrino	No	Yes	No	No	No
Time reversal	Yes	Yes	Yes	No	No
Lepton conservation	Yes	Yes	Yes	Yes	No
Number of coupling coefficients	5	5	10	20	40
Independent coefficients	5	5	9	18	35

20 complex numbers. However, the number of real parameters which can be experimentally determined is only 35 (Le-57b). Fortunately, experimental evidence seems to support both the invariance under time reversal and the lepton conservation. Hence the number of coupling constants to be determined is reduced to nine. If we also accept the two-component neutrino, the number of coupling constants is back to five, as in the old theory.

The number of independent coupling constants under various assumptions are listed in Table 4-2.

---

* All measurable quantities depend on products of the form $C_i^{R*} \times C_j^R$ and $C_i^{L*} \times C_j^L$ (no interference between processes in which right-handed and left-handed neutrinos are emitted). Thus all the coupling constants can be multiplied by a common phase factor $e^{i\alpha}$(α = real) without any change in physical results. Indeed, we may have two independent phase factors $e^{i\alpha_L}$ and $e^{i\alpha_R}$ for right-and left-handed neutrinos, respectively. Thus the number of independent coupling constants is 18 rather than 20.

4-5 THE CONSERVATION OF LEPTONIC AND MUONIC NUMBERS

Nuclear β decay can be written as

$$\mathrm{p} + e^{-} \leftrightarrow \mathrm{n} + \nu$$

wherein one lepton is absorbed and one is created. This expression suggests that for a proper assignment of particle and antiparticle, the number of leptons in the decay process is always conserved. The law of lepton conservation was suggested by Konopinski and Mahmoud (Ko-53) in order to explain the nonoccurrence of certain decay processes,

Table 4-3 Leptonic and Muonic Numbers

Leptonic Number	Muonic Number
$l = +1$ for e^{-}, ν_e	$m = +1$ for μ^{-}, ν_μ
$l = -1$ for e^{+}, $\bar{\nu}_e$	$m = -1$ for μ^{+}, $\bar{\nu}_\mu$
$l = 0$ for all others (including μ, ν_μ, etc.)	$m = 0$ for all others (including e, ν_e, etc.)

and interest in it was renewed after the overthrow of the law of parity in weak interactions (Wu-57; Le-57a). The law states that if a leptonic number is assigned to each lepton, the sum of leptonic numbers must be conserved in all reactions.

The two-component theory alone does not rule out the possibility that in π^{+} decay sometimes a neutrino and sometimes an antineutrino is emitted. However, experimental results on the helicity of muons emitted from pion decay indicate that the decay of the π^{+} is always of the form $\pi^{+} \rightarrow \mu^{+} + \nu$, not $\pi^{+} \rightarrow \mu^{+} + \bar{\nu}$. Thus, if we regard each e^{-}, μ^{-}, and ν as a particle (lepton) to which we assign a leptonic number $l = +1$, and regard each e^{+}, μ^{+}, and $\bar{\nu}$ as an antilepton with $l = -1$ (π, γ, K, and all heavy particles will have $l = 0$), the number of leptons in observed decays is conserved.

The recent discovery (Da-62) that the neutrino associated with $\pi \rightarrow \mu$ decay is different from the neutrino in nuclear β decay—that is, $\nu_\mu \neq \nu_e$—implies that π-μ decay is of the form $\pi^{+} \rightarrow \mu^{+} + \nu_\mu$, whereas $\pi^{+} \rightarrow \mu^{+} + \nu_e$ is forbidden.

These developments (cf. p. 292) suggest a second conservation law which may be called the conservation of muonic number m (Table 4-3).

The algebraic sum of l or m is conserved in all reactions. Any linear combination of the leptonic number l and the muonic number m is also conserved. For example,

$$\begin{array}{ccc} \mu^- & \rightarrow & e^- + \bar{\nu}_e + \nu_\mu \\ m = +1 & & l = +1, l = -1, m = +1 \end{array}$$

is allowed, and

$$\begin{array}{ccc} \mu^- & \rightarrow & e^- + \gamma \\ m = +1 & & l = +1 \end{array}$$

is forbidden.

Actually, the present experimental results do not really prove that these conservation laws hold, but neither do they refute their validity. If these laws hold generally, and it seems very likely that they will, then it may have far-reaching significance. The absence of certain inverse β processes (see Sec. 5-3) and of neutrinoless double β decay (see Sec. 5-2) also strongly suggests the validity of lepton conservation.

4-6 POLARIZATION OF ELECTRONS AND NEUTRINOS IN BETA DECAY

Since parity is not conserved, the expectation value of the pseudoscalar quantity $\langle \boldsymbol{\sigma}_e \cdot \mathbf{p}_e \rangle$ formed from the measured spin and momentum vector of the electron may not be zero. That is, if the electron momentum vector $\mathbf{p}_e$ serves as the quantization axis for the electron spin orientation $\pm\frac{1}{2}$, an excess of either of these two orientations may be formed and is described as a right- or left-handed longitudinal polarization, respectively. As a matter of fact, from the observed asymmetry of the electron angular distribution of polarized Co^{60} nuclei, the left-handed longitudinal polarization of the electron can be easily deduced. The β decay of Co^{60} involves a pure Gamow-Teller interaction in which one unit of angular momentum in the direction of its initial spin $\mathbf{5} \rightarrow \mathbf{4}$ must be carried away by the emitted electrons and antineutrinos. Since electrons are observed to be emitted predominantly in a direction opposite to the spin of Co^{60}, most of the electrons must have their spins directed opposite to their momentum vectors; hence we have a left-handed longitudinal polarization for both A and T interactions, as illustrated in Fig. 4-4.

The experimental results on the longitudinal polarization of β

particles are startling and simple.* The conclusion which is generally agreed upon is that the β^- particles emitted in radioactive decay exhibit negative helicity (σ_e and p_e antiparallel), and the β^+ particles exhibit positive helicity (σ_e and p_e parallel). For relativistic energies ($v/c \cong 1$) we have almost completely polarized electron and positron beams.

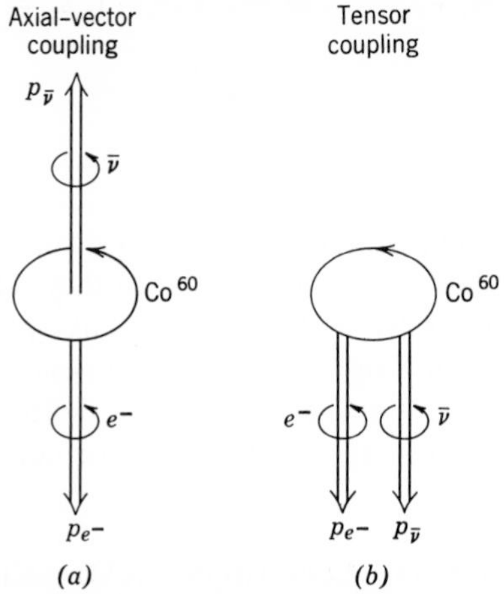

Fig. 4-4 A simple vector diagram illustrating the relative helicity relations of leptons in Co^{60} β decay (*a*) for axial-vector coupling and (*b*) for tensor coupling. In (*a*) $\mathscr{H}_{e^-} = -1$, $\mathscr{H}_{\bar{\nu}} = +1$; in (*b*) $\mathscr{H}_{e^-} = -1$, $\mathscr{H}_{\bar{\nu}} = -1$.

These results are again in agreement with the predictions of the two-component neutrino theory.

General Formulation of the Electron Polarization

Consider the general Hamiltonian density

$$(\tilde{\psi}_{\text{p}}\hat{O}_i Q^+ \psi_{\text{n}})[\tilde{\psi}_e \hat{O}_i(1 \pm \gamma_5)\psi_\nu] + \text{h.c.} \tag{4-23}$$

$\tilde{\psi}_e$ in the lepton covariant term can be expressed by $\psi_e^{\dagger}\gamma_4$; therefore we have

$$\psi_e^{\dagger}\gamma_4\hat{O}_i(1 \pm \gamma_5)\psi_\nu \tag{4-24}$$

In this expression, apply the plus for V, A and minus for S, T, P. The signs for V and S are only assumed for this derivation because there are no polarized nuclear experiments to guide us. On the other

* Some inconclusive evidence for polarization of beta particles was found many years ago. See footnote on p. 15.

hand, the measured helicity of the electrons will yield information on the correlation of the β interaction and the neutrino helicity. However, $\gamma_5\hat{O}_i = -\hat{O}_i\gamma_5$ where $\hat{O}_i$ applies for V, A; $\gamma_5\hat{O}_i = \hat{O}_i\gamma_5$ where $\hat{O}_i$ applies for S, T, P. In addition,

$$\gamma_4\gamma_5 = -\gamma_5\gamma_4 \tag{4-25}$$

Therefore

$$\psi_e^{\dagger}\gamma_4\hat{O}_i(1 \pm \gamma_5)\psi_\nu = \psi_e^{\dagger}(1 + \gamma_5)\gamma_4\hat{O}_i\psi_\nu \tag{4-26}$$

Note here that it is $1 + \gamma_5$ *for all five types of interactions.* To write down its Hermitian conjugate, we have

$$\psi_\nu^{\dagger}\gamma_4\hat{O}_i(1 + \gamma_5)\psi_e \tag{4-27}$$

For relativistic energies $E_e \gg mc^2$, the electron is effectively massless; the $\frac{1}{2}(1 + \gamma_5)$ is a projection operator used to effect complete left longitudinal polarization. Thus we have left-handed electrons for all five interactions.

If $(v/c)_e < 1$, the assumption that $m = 0$ is not valid. In this case, the right and left parts of the electron wave function are not uncoupled. In other words, $(1 + \gamma_5)\psi_e$ is no longer the eigenstate of the Hamiltonian, and the complete longitudinal polarization based on $m = 0$ no longer holds. In fact, the polarization of the electron vanishes at zero velocity. Using the conventional method of projecting the final states of the electron on the eigenstates of $\boldsymbol{\sigma}_e \cdot \mathbf{p}_e$ and evaluating the various traces, we obtain a simple expression for the $\beta^{\pm}$ polarization (for its derivation, see p. 340),

$$\mathscr{P} = \frac{\langle \boldsymbol{\sigma}_e \cdot \mathbf{p}_e \rangle}{|p_e|} = -\frac{v}{c}\frac{E}{|E|} \tag{4-28}$$

where the energy state E is positive for β^- and negative for β^+ particles. The general expression for a linear combination of β interactions involving C_i and C_i' is

$$\mathscr{P}_{\beta^{\mp}} = \pm\frac{v}{c}\frac{2\,\mathrm{Re}\,[(C_S C_S'^{*} - C_V C_V'^{*})|M_F{}^2| + (C_T C_T'^{*} - C_A C_A'^{*})\,|M_{GT}|^2]}{(|C_S|^2 + |C_V|^2 + |C_S'|^2 + |C_V'|^2)\,|M_F|^2 + (|C_T|^2 + |C_A|^2 + |C_A'|^2 + |C_T'|^2)\,|M_{GT}|^2} \tag{4-29}$$

If we assign $C_S = -C_S'$, $C_T = -C_T'$ (for left-handed antineutrino), or $C_V = C_V'$, $C_A = C_A'$ (for right-handed antineutrino), then

$$\mathscr{P}_{\beta^{\mp}} = \mp v/c$$

The Measurement of the Polarization of the $\beta^{\pm}$ *Particle**

The first to observe this longitudinal polarization from β decay was the Frauenfelder group (Frau-57a). They used a Co^{60} source and the Mott scattering method and obtained $\mathscr{P} \sim -v/c$ which is in good agreement with the observed electron asymmetry from the polarized Co^{60} experiment.

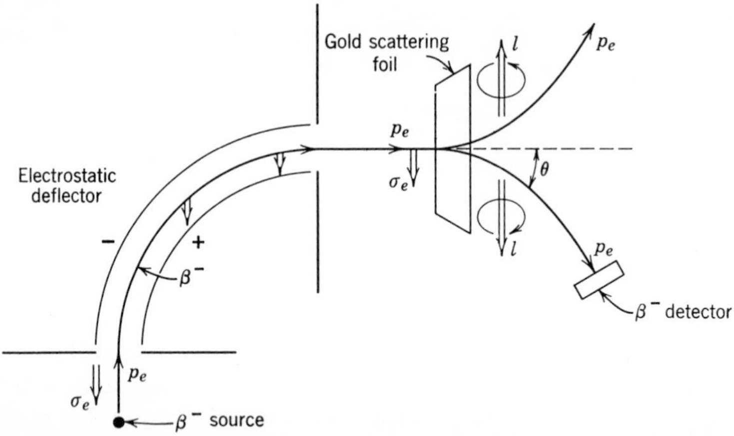

Fig. 4-5 The left half of the diagram illustrates the function of an electrostatic deflector which transforms the longitudinally polarized electron to transversely polarized one. Electrons with downward spins, incident on the scatterer, are preferentially scattered to the left as viewed along the beam. It can be seen from the diagram that when the spin and orbital momenta are in opposite direction, the magnetic interaction reinforces the attractive force of the nucleus for the electron.

There are three major methods being used for the determination of electron polarization:

1. Coulomb scattering from heavy nuclei (Mott scattering).
2. Free electron-electron scattering (Møller or Bhabha scattering).
3. Circular polarization of forward bremsstrahlung.

Coulomb Scattering. When a transversely polarized electron $\boldsymbol{\sigma}_e \perp \mathbf{p}_e$ is scattered by a nucleus, its scattering cross section depends also on the relative orientation of the spin $\boldsymbol{\sigma}_e$ and the direction of the orbital angular momentum $\mathbf{l}$, as shown in Fig. 4-5, because of the interaction

---

* (To-56; Pa-59; Gro-59; Fa-59.) Those whose prime interests are not in the experimental details may skip this section entirely.

between the magnetic moment of the electron and the magnetic field which the moving electron experiences in the nuclear Coulomb field.

The basic physical idea underlying Mott scattering can be easily understood by describing the scattering in the electron rest system. In Fig. 4-6*b*, the scattered electron approaching σ_2 (scatterer) feels an effective magnetic nucleus σ_2 moving toward the electron. We can easily see that the magnetic interaction for electrons that pass to the right (R) of the nucleus is in the same direction as the electric one, whereas for those that pass to the left (L) of the nucleus, the magnetic and electric interactions are in opposite directions. Since passing to the right implies scattering into the plane of the figure, and passing to the left implies scattering out of the plane, it follows that electrons with spin down, that is, with the magnetic moment pointing up, approaching a nucleus of positive charge straight ahead are predominantly scattered to the left. (Fig. 4-5).

To apply this method to measuring the longitudinal polarization of electrons, we must convert the longitudinally polarized electron to a transversely polarized electron by one of the following methods: (a) a static electric field (**E**); (b) an electromagnetic cross field (**E** and **H**); or (c) double scattering.

THE STATIC ELECTRIC FIELD. The static electric-field method was originally proposed by Tolhoek and De Groot (To-56). If we neglect relativistic considerations, its principle of action for the conversion of longitudinal polarization to transverse polarization is rather simple. The spin is not affected by electrostatic forces and remains in its original direction, whereas the momentum vector of the electron changes direction continuously. Thus the direction of motion is eventually turned at a right angle to the spin direction of the electron (see Fig. 4-5). However, for relativistic cases, the spin of the electron also turns in the field and in the same direction as that of momentum. To make the spin and the momentum vector transverse to each other again, the momentum vector must be continuously changed through an angle much greater than $\pi/2$ as in the nonrelativistic case, and the equation for the necessary amount of turning of the momentum vector of the relativistic electron is

$$\frac{\pi/2}{1 - E_{\text{kin}}/E} \tag{4-30}$$

where $E = E_{\text{kin}} + m_0c^2$. For $E_{\text{kin}} \cong 1$ mev, the deflection required is

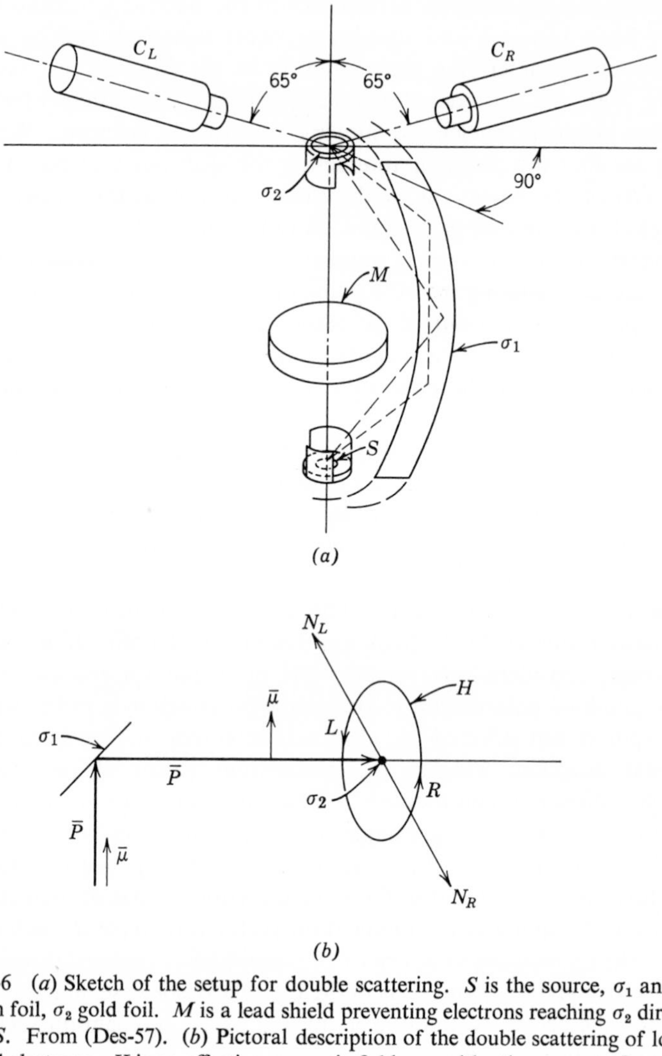

Fig. 4-6 (*a*) Sketch of the setup for double scattering. S is the source, σ_1 an aluminum foil, σ_2 gold foil. M is a lead shield preventing electrons reaching σ_2 directly from S. From (Des-57). (*b*) Pictoral description of the double scattering of longitudinal electrons. H is an effective magnetic field caused by the current of positive nuclei of σ_2 moving toward the electron (in its rest frame). For more details see (Des-57).

$\pi/2 \times 3 = \frac{3}{2}\pi$ which is three times greater than that required by the nonrelativistic electrons.

E AND **H** CROSS FIELD. The electron beam is arranged to travel at right angles to both fields which are themselves at right angles. The ratio $|\mathbf{E}|/|\mathbf{H}| = \beta = v/c$ is chosen so that electrons of a particular energy, corresponding to β, pass through undeflected, whereas the absolute values of the fields are such that the electron spins are rotated through certain angles in traversing the region. In a number of ways, this system is more flexible than that based on deflection in a pure electrostatic field. However, the stray magnetic field on the scattered electrons is rather bothersome and should not be lightly overlooked. Furthermore, the focusing property varies greatly with the amount of spin rotation; therefore we cannot actually utilize the flexibility of the conversion of the longitudinal polarization to any degree of transverse polarization that seems to be offered. The cross-field device used by Cavanagh and his co-workers (Ca-57) as a spin twister is shown in Fig. 4-7. The β energy was preselected by means of a magnetic lens which does not alter the polarization, because $\boldsymbol{\sigma}_e \cdot \mathbf{p}_e$ is a constant of the motion in an electrostatic field-free region ($\mathbf{E} = 0$). Their results on Co^{60} and Au^{198} showed full $-v/c$ electron polarization.

DOUBLE SCATTERING. The third method is to use the double scattering as reported by De Shalit (Des-57) et al. The longitudinal polarization of an electron becomes transverse after a 90° scattering to the extent that the original spin direction is unchanged after scattering. The apparatus used by De Shalit et al. is shown in Fig. 4-7. The first scatterer, which is a thin aluminum foil in the form of an arc of a circle, actually served as a polarization transformer (from longitudinal to transverse). The source and the second scatterer are located at the two ends of the diameter. Thus the total scattering angle is 90° for a large range of emission angles at the source. The observed asymmetry at the second scatterer of gold foil at an angle of 75° (for electrons with energy greater than 900 kev from P^{32}) is 5%. This was interpreted by the authors as compatible with 100% polarization of the initial beam. Moreover, the sign of the polarization is unambiguously determined to be negative.

INTERPRETATION OF THE OBSERVED LEFT-RIGHT ASYMMETRY. In the Mott scattering measurements, the observed asymmetry is generally defined as

$$\delta = \frac{N(\Phi) - N(\Phi + \pi)}{N(\Phi) + N(\Phi + \pi)} = \mathfrak{H}_e a(\theta) \sin \Phi \tag{4-31}$$

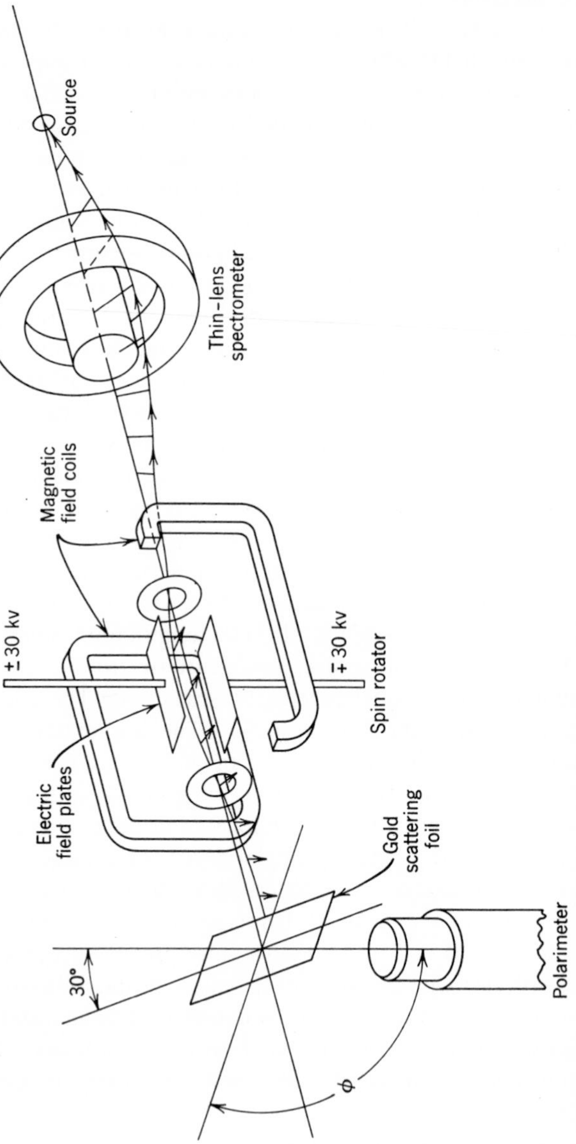

Fig. 4-7 Mott scattering from gold foil for electron polarization measurement, with the *E-H* cross fields acting as spin rotator, the thin-lens spectrometer as electron energy selector. From (Ca-57).

where $N(\Phi)$ is the counting rate at azimuthal angle Φ, $\mathfrak{H}_e$ is the helicity of the electron, and $a(\theta)$ is the right-left asymmetry factor. The right-left asymmetry factor $a(\theta)$ in 90° single scattering of transversely polarized positrons and electrons by $Z = 80$ is shown in Fig. 4-8 (Ba-40; Ma-43; Sherm-56). It can be seen that the expected asymmetry for electrons is large and that its maximum occurs for electrons at around 160 kev. However, the asymmetry effect is much smaller for the positrons because the Coulomb repulsion prevents the close approach of positrons to the nucleus. The Mott scattering method is

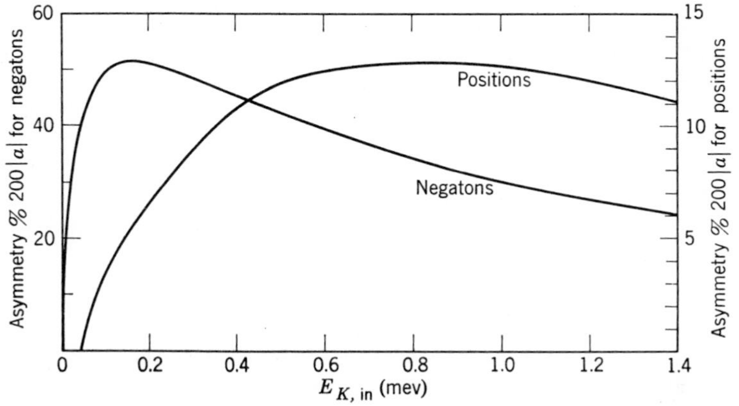

Fig. 4-8 Right-left asymmetry $a(\theta)$ as a function of the kinetic energy of the transversely polarized electrons and positrons scattered through 90° by Hg nuclei. From (Ba-40, Ma-43).

extremely sensitive to instrumental asymmetries. Cavanagh (Ca-57) and Greenberg (Gre-60) have independently investigated various possible errors and have found that the effects are rather striking. These instrumental errors are:

1. Nonuniformities in the beam striking the scatterer as well as beam displacement from the instrument axis. These errors are not completely accounted for by taking Au to Al ratios.
2. The effect of plural scattering must be carefully investigated and accounted for.
3. Depolarization arising from scattering in the source and source backing will lead to a reduction in the observed asymmetry.

Because of these possible systematic errors, the polarization experiments may be deceptively simple, but to attain any degree of reliability, thorough checks must be carried out in order to prevent erroneous conclusions.

The results of polarization determination by Mott scattering are summarized in Table 4-4 and strongly support the $\mathscr{P}_{\beta^\mp} = \mp v/c$ prediction.

Table 4-4 Results of Mott Scattering

Nuclides	Spin Rotator	v/c	$\mathscr{P}_{\beta^\mp}$	Reference
Co^{60}	Cylindrical **E** field	0.47–0.49	$(-0.16) - (-0.40) \pm 0.07$	(Frau-57a)
	Crossed **E** and **H**	0.60	-0.65 ± 0.13 -0.59 ± 0.065	(Ca-57)
	Cylindrical **E** field	0.58 0.64 0.70	-0.49 ± 0.012 -0.60 ± 0.012 -0.70 ± 0.014	(Bi-59)
	Cylindrical **E**	0.695	-0.715 ± 0.035	(Gre-60)
P^{32}	Spherical **E**	0.6 mev	$-(0.990 \pm 0.009)v/c$	(Br-62)

Free Electron-Electron Scattering. The basic idea is very simple. Electron-electron scattering is spin-dependent. The theory of electron-electron scattering was first investigated by Møller (Mø-32), and that of positron-electron scattering was studied by Bhabha (Bh-36). The main differences in these two scatterings are the indistinguishability of the two particles for e^--e^- scattering and possible virtual pair production for e^+-e^- scattering. After the nonconservation of parity in β decay became known, these two scatterings for the longitudinally polarized electrons and positrons were further formulated by Bincer (Bi-57) and Ford and Mullim (Fo-57). For electron-electron scattering, Bincer found that, in the Born approximation (assuming free electrons), the ratio of the two cross sections $\Phi_{\uparrow\uparrow}$ (spins in parallel) and $\Phi_{\uparrow\downarrow}$ (spins in antiparallel) is

$$\frac{\Phi_{\uparrow\uparrow}}{\Phi_{\uparrow\downarrow}} = \frac{\gamma^2(1 + 6X + X^2) - 2\gamma(1 - X) + 1 - X^2}{8\gamma^2 - 2\gamma(4 - 5X + X^2) + 4 - 6X + 2X^2} \tag{4-32}$$

where γ is the total energy in units of mc^2, $X \equiv (1 - 2W)^2$, and W is the energy transfer.

It can be seen from Fig. 4-9 that the spin dependence of the cross section is most pronounced for symmetric scattering—that is, where both electrons after scattering possess equal energies. The difficulty of discriminating against the overwhelming Coulomb scattering can be overcome by using a fast coincidence technique together with energy and angular selections. Any magnetic foils with a narrow rectangular **B-H** curve such as Supermendur steel, Delta-Max, etc., could be used as a scattering target. This method was first applied to the measurement of the polarization of β^- particles from P^{32} and Pr^{144} by Frauenfelder

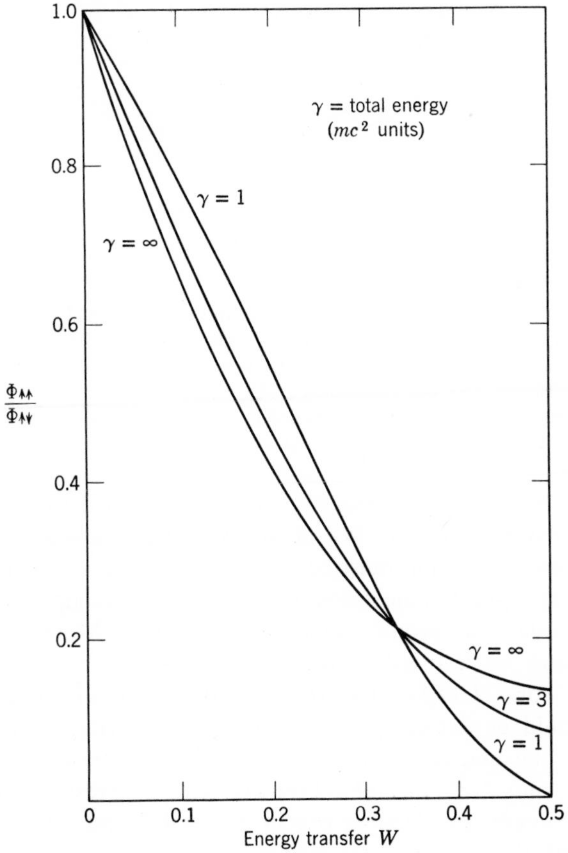

(a)

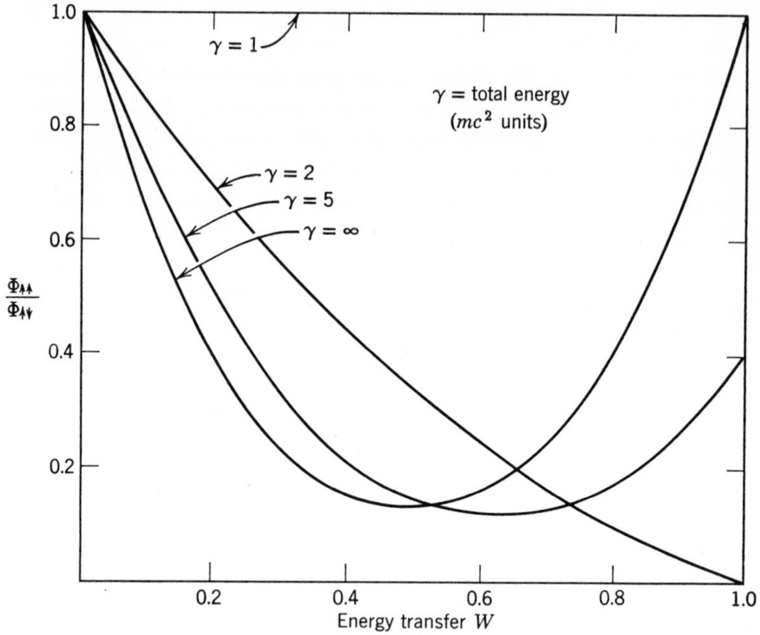

(*b*)

Fig. 4-9 (*a*) The ratio $\Phi_{\uparrow\uparrow}/\Phi_{\uparrow\downarrow}$ for e^-–e^- scattering: γ is the total energy of the incident electron in units of mc^2 in the laboratory frame, and W is the relative kinetic energy transfer. The numbers on the abscissa can be interpreted as either W or $1 - W$. From (Bi-57). (*b*) The ratio of $\Phi_{\uparrow\uparrow}/\Phi_{\uparrow\downarrow}$ for e^+–e^- scattering (γ and W refer to the position in the laboratory frame and have the same meaning as in part *a*). From (Bi-57).

et al. (Frau-57b). Their experimental setup is sketched in Fig. 4-10. Subsequent investigations by Wu et al. (Wu-58a) showed that precautions in energy selection must be taken to discriminate against true time-coincident Compton electrons (caused by the accompanying γ's) which could otherwise produce false Møller events. More elaborate energy selection by a thin-lens magnetic spectrometer was used in more recent work (Ul-61). Theoretically, the maximum amount of effect that could be detected is nearly 15%, but, owing to the non-saturation of the magnetic foil and the inclination between the foil and the beam, only 7–8% effect has been detected. The results from this type of experiment are summarized in Table 4-5 and again are in agreement with the $\mathscr{P}_{\beta\mp} = \mp v/c$ prediction.

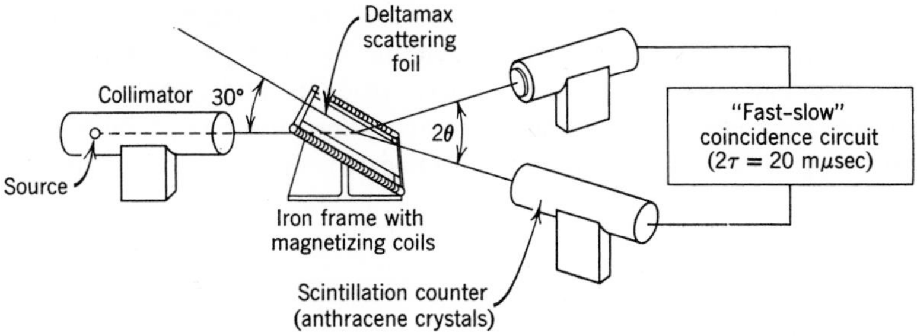

Fig. 4-10 Schematic diagram for $e^- - e^-$ Møller scattering setup. From (Fr-57).

Circular Polarization of Forward Bremsstrahlung.* The longitudinal polarization of the β^- and β^+ rays happens to give rise to a circular polarization both of the bremsstrahlung (electromagnetic radiation

Table 4-5 Polarization of β^- Particles by Møller Scattering

Nuclides	Energy Selection in mev	δ*	$\mathscr{P}/(v/c)$	Reference
$P^{32}(1^+ \to 0^+)\beta^-$	>0.15	+0.06 ± 0.007	−1.0 ± 0.11	(Frau-57b)
	>0.4	+0.069 ± 0.010	−1.0 ± 0.16	(Frau-57b)
	>0.15	+0.051 ± 0.003	−0.91 ± 0.08	(Gei-58)
	0.66–0.99		−1.00 ± 0.02	(Ul-61)
$Y^{90}(2^- \to 0^+)\beta^-$	0.6–0.9	+0.0742 ± 0.010	−0.99 ± 0.14	(Wu-57)
			−0.84 ± 0.08	(Ko-58)
	>0.15	+0.047 ± 0.003		(Gei-58)
$Au^{198}(2^- \to 2^+)\beta^-$	0.3–0.5	+0.0665 ± 0.0133	−1.02 ± 0.19	(Wu-57)
				(Ko-58)
	>0.15	+0.050 ± 0.009	−0.89 ± 0.17	(Gei-58)
	460–810		−0.98 ± 0.03	(Ul-61)
$RaE(1^- \to 0^+)\beta^-$	>0.15	+0.036 ± 0.0005	−0.64 ± 0.10	(Gei-58)
	520–950		−0.75 ± 0.03	(Ul-61)
$Ga^{68}\beta^+$	1030–1300		+0.99 ± 0.09	(Ul-61)

$$* \delta \equiv \frac{2(n_{\uparrow\uparrow} - n_{\uparrow\downarrow})}{(n_{\uparrow\uparrow} + n_{\uparrow\downarrow})}$$

* For the determination of circular polarization, refer to Sec. 4-8.

caused by acceleration or deceleration of charged particles) and of the annihilation radiation in flight which the charged particles produce. This was first observed by Goldhaber, Grodzins, and Sunyar (Go-57), and the theoretical calculations were first done by McVoy (Mc-57) and extended by Fronsdal and Uberall (Fro-58). The degree of circular

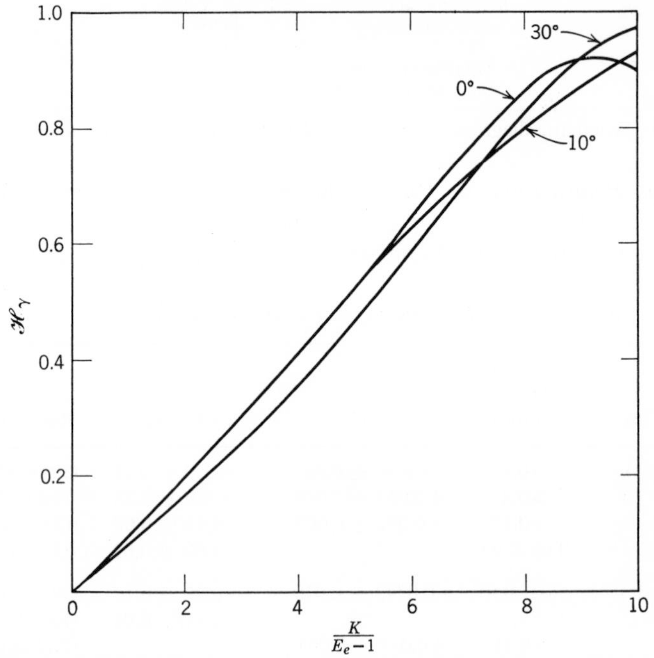

Fig. 4-11 Circular polarization $\mathscr{H}_\gamma$ of the bremsstrahlung from 100% longitudinally polarized electrons with initial total electron energy $E_e = 6$ ($\approx$ 2.5 mev) versus fractional photon energy $K(E_e - 1)$; 0°, 10°, and 30° are the photon emission angles with respect to the incident direction of the electron. From (Fro-58).

polarization of the bremsstrahlung approaches that of the longitudinal polarization of relativistic β rays for high-energy transfers in the forward direction. The maximum circular polarization is given by

$$\mathscr{P}_{\max}(\gamma) = \left(1 - \frac{1}{2E_0^{\ 2}} \mathscr{P}_e\right) \tag{4-33}$$

where E_0 is the kinetic energy of the electron in units of mc^2 and $\mathscr{P}_e$ is the longitudinal polarization of the electron. Even for 1-mev electrons

$E_0 \cong 2$, then $\mathscr{P}_{max}(\gamma) \cong 0.88$, and the helicity transfer is, therefore, rather high. Furthermore, for high-energy electrons the circular polarization of the bremsstrahlung which they produce is almost independent of the angle of emission, as shown by Fronsdal and Uberall (Fro-58) in Fig. 4-11.

The experimental arrangement of Goldhaber et al. (Go-57) is shown in Fig. 4-12. A Y^{90} source (in equilibrium with Sr^{90}), covered front and

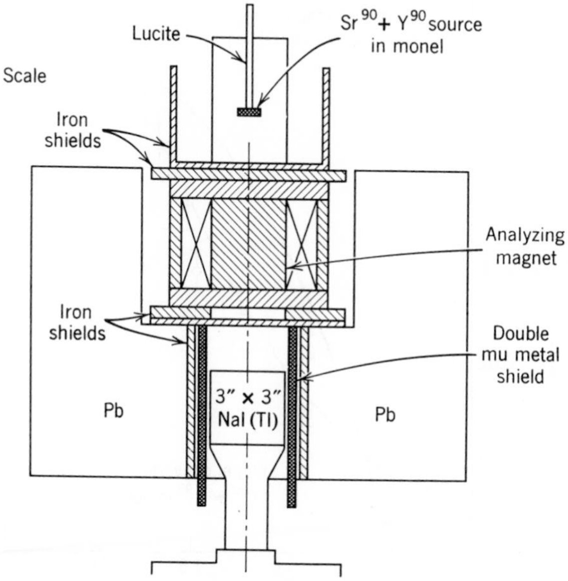

Fig. 4-12 Experimental setup for measuring the circular polarization of the bremsstrahlung. From (Go-57).

back with 100 mg/cm² of Monel ($Z_{eff} \sim 28$) was placed above a 5-in.-long magnetized iron cylinder (20,000 gauss), below which was a 3 × 3-in. NaI (Tl) scintillation counter. The circular polarization was measured as a function of the energy of the bremsstrahlung radiation. The measured asymmetric effect was 7% at 1.8 mev, that is,

$$\delta = \frac{2(N_- - N_+)}{(N_- + N_+)} = -0.07 \pm 0.005 \tag{4-34}$$

where N_+ denotes the counting rate when the magnetic field is in the direction of bremsstrahlung, and N_- when the field is opposite to the bremsstrahlung direction. The negative sign indicates clearly that the circular polarization of the bremsstrahlung and, therefore, the helicity of the β^- particle are negative. The measured asymmetric effect versus energy of the bremsstrahlung is shown in Fig. 4-13. To calculate the absolute value of circular polarization from the observed asymmetric effect, we must know the magnetic-field distribution in the iron path

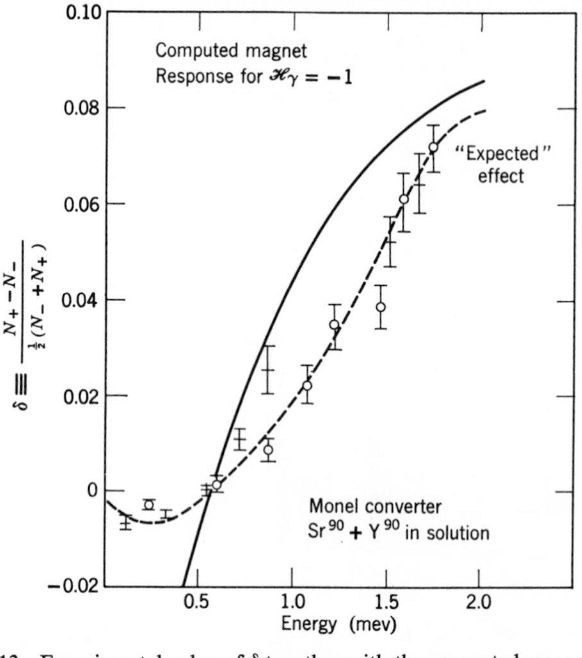

Fig. 4-13 Experimental value of δ together with the computed magnet response for $\mathscr{H}_\gamma = -1$ (solid curve) and as modified by the curve of Fig. 4-11 (dashed curve). From (Go-57).

precisely, which is rather difficult. Boehm and Wapstra (Bo-58) and Schopper and Galster (Sc-58) also used a forward Compton scattering on magnetized iron in a ring geometry to study the circular polarization of the bremsstrahlung. They found that the electrons from P^{32}, Tm^{170}, and Y^{90} have polarization $\mathscr{P}_e/(v/c) \cong -1$.

The Measurement of Longitudinal Polarization of Positrons. The principle which is used in measuring the helicity of positrons is the spin dependence of the annihilation process.

There are three groups, as follows: (a) circular polarization of the annihilation-in-flight quanta; (b) cross section of annihilation with polarized electrons; and (c) positronium formation.

CIRCULAR POLARIZATION OF THE ANNIHILATION-IN-FLIGHT QUANTA. Page (Pag-57a) developed the theory of annihilation of positrons in flight, including the annihilation of helical positrons with unpolarized electrons, even before a beam of polarized positrons was thought to be possible—that is, before the discovery of nonconservation of parity in β decay. His calculated results for the helicity of the most energetic photon in the annihilation of a helical positron of kinetic energy E_{β^+} are shown in Fig. 4-14. It is clear that the helicity of the energetic photon is high even for very low-energy positrons. If we select only the very forward photons, the helicity is essentially 100% at energies greater than 1 mev. Deutsch, Bauer, Gittelman, Grodzins, and Sunyar (Deu-57) have measured the helicity of the annihilation-in-flight quanta to determine the helicity of 2.5–3.0-mev positrons from $0^+ \rightarrow 0^+$ pure Fermi) β transitions. The experimental arrangement is shown in Fig. 4-15. The thin-lens spectrometer is used to select the energy of the positrons and to shield the polarimeter from the γ radiation coming from the source. Two decays were investigated:

$$\mathrm{Ga}^{66}\,(0^+) \xrightarrow[4.1\text{ mev}]{\beta^+} \mathrm{Zn}^{66}\,(0^+)$$

and

$$\mathrm{Cl}^{34}\,(0^+) \xrightarrow[4.5\text{ mev}]{\beta^+} \mathrm{S}^{34}\,(0^+)$$

The intensity change, $\delta = 2(N_- - N_+)/(N_- + N_+)$, as a function of photon energy is shown in Fig. 4-16 for 3-mev Ga^{66} positrons. Whereas N_+ represents the counting rate when the magnetic field of the polarimeter is in the direction of the positron momentum, N_- represents the opposite. The helicity of the photon measured is nearly unity $(+95 \pm 14)\%$. The error quoted is a result of the uncertainty of polarimeter efficiency. Results are shown in Table 4-6.

Boehm, Novey, Bames, and Stech (Bo-57b) studied the helicity of positrons from the mirror transition $\mathrm{N}^{13} \xrightarrow[1.25\text{ mev}]{\beta^+} \mathrm{C}^{13}$ by the annihilation-in-flight method. In the mirror transitions the ratio of the nuclear matrix elements for Fermi and Gamow-Teller interactions can be calculated. Their results strongly support the concept that the positron helicities from Fermi and Gamow-Teller interactions are the same.

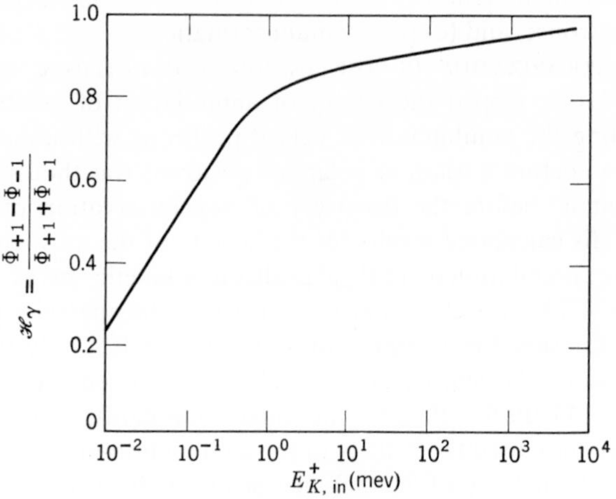

(*a*)

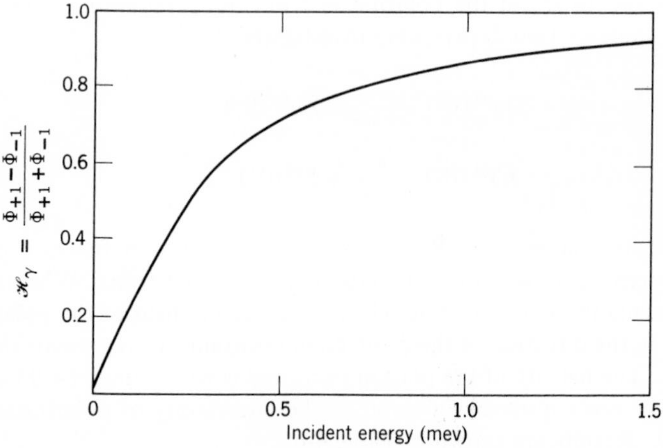

(*b*)

Fig. 4-14 (*a*) Helicity of the most energetic photon from annihilation of helical positrons; $\mathscr{H}_{\beta+} = +1$. From (Pag-57a). (*b*) Helicity of outgoing particle (photon or electron) from one-quantum annihilation and photon-electron effect; $\mathscr{H}_{\text{incident}} = +1$. From (Mc-57).

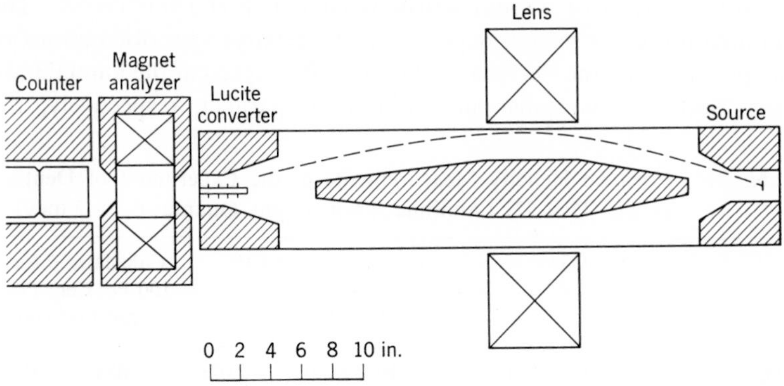

Fig. 4-15 Experimental setup for determining the helicity of annihilation-in-flight quanta. From (Deu-57).

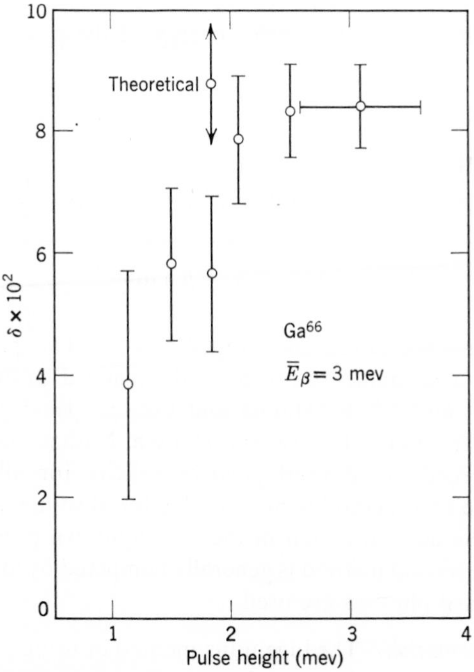

Fig. 4-16 Effect of field direction on the transmission of annihilation radiation from Ga^{66} through the analyzer. From (Deu-57).

CROSS SECTION OF ANNIHILATION WITH POLARIZED ELECTRONS. The annihilation cross section depends on the relative spin orientations of the positron and the electron. If $\Phi_{\uparrow\uparrow}$ and $\Phi_{\uparrow\downarrow}$ represent the annihilation cross sections for spins parallel and antiparallel, respectively, the

Table 4-6 Positron Helicity Measurements in the Experiment of Deutsch et al. (Deu-57) (Annihilation-in-Flight Quanta $E_\gamma > 2$ mev)

	δ for Ga^{66}		δ for Cl^{34}	Calculated δ for 100 Per Cent Polarized Positrons
	$E_{\beta^+} = 3$ mev	$E_{\beta^+} = 2.6$ mev	$E_{\beta^+} = 3$ mev	
Thick analyzer	$\delta = +0.084 \pm 0.005$	$+0.088 \pm 0.010$	$+0.056 \pm 0.021$	$+0.088 \pm 0.010$
Thin analyzer	$\delta = +0.049 \pm 0.009$		$+0.054 \pm 0.013$	$+0.044 \pm 0.015$

theoretical asymmetric effect δ versus energy of the positron is given by (Pag-57a):

$$\delta = \frac{\Phi_{\uparrow\uparrow} - \Phi_{\uparrow\downarrow}}{\Phi_{\uparrow\uparrow} + \Phi_{\uparrow\downarrow}}$$

$$= \frac{2\beta(-\beta^4 + \beta^2 - 3) + (\beta^6 + \beta^4 - 3\beta^2 + 3)\ln\dfrac{1+\beta}{1-\beta}}{2\beta^3(\beta^2 - 2) + \beta^2(3 - \beta^4)\ln\dfrac{1+\beta}{1-\beta}} \qquad (4\text{-}35)$$

The energy dependence of δ is shown in Fig. 4-17. This principle has been applied in measurements for both thermalized positrons from Ga^{64}, Na^{22}, Ga^{66}, and N^{13} by Hanna and Preston (Ha-57) and high-energy positrons from Ga^{66} by Frankel, Hausen, Nathan, and Temmer (Fra-57). Both methods showed positive helicity for all positrons investigated. The first method is not suitable for absolute quantitative analysis unless the depolarization in the slowing-down process is well understood. The second method is generally hampered by low counting rate if only forward photons are used.

Positronium Formation. The ingenious method of using positronium formation to determine the helicity of the positrons was first thought of and carried out by Page and Heinberg (Pag-57b). The principles involved are directly connected with the positronium formation in a magnetic field.

In the absence of a magnetic field, the wave functions characterizing the $m = 0$ substates of the singlet and the triplet states are expressed by

$$J = 0, \quad m = 0: \quad \frac{1}{\sqrt{2}}[\alpha_- \beta_+ - \beta_- \alpha_+]$$

$$J = 1, \quad m = 0: \quad \frac{1}{\sqrt{2}}[\alpha_- \beta_+ + \beta_- \alpha_+]$$

where α represents spin pointing up (↑), and β spin pointing down (↓).

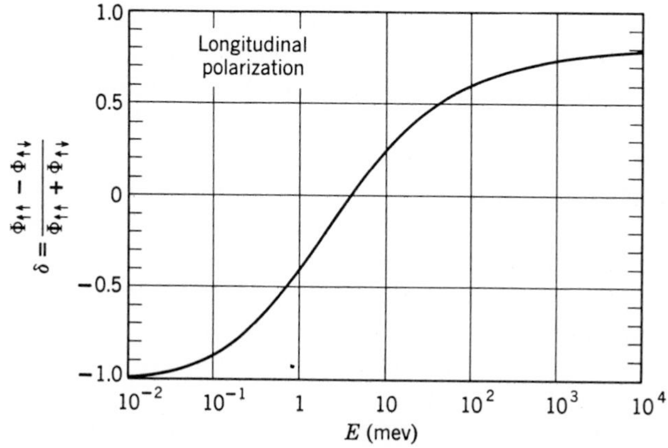

Fig. 4-17 Comparison of total annihilation cross section for spins parallel *versus* spins antiparallel when the particles are polarized along the line of collision. Kinetic energy E refers to one of the particles, the other being at rest (Pag-57a).

The plus and minus signs are for positrons and electrons, respectively. In the presence of a magnetic field H in the upward direction, the state functions are, respectively,

$$J = 0, \quad m = 0: \quad \frac{1}{\sqrt{2}}[(\alpha_- \beta_+ - \beta_- \alpha_+) - a(\alpha_- \beta_+ + \beta_- \alpha_+)]$$

$$= \frac{1}{\sqrt{2}}[(1 - a)\alpha_- \beta_+ - (1 + a)\beta_- \alpha_+]$$

$$J = 1, \quad m = 0: \quad \frac{1}{\sqrt{2}}[(\alpha_- \beta_+ + \beta_- \alpha_+) + a(\alpha_- \beta_+ - \beta_- \alpha_+)]$$

$$= \frac{1}{\sqrt{2}}[(1 + a)\alpha_- \beta_+ + (1 - a)\beta_- \alpha_+]$$

where $a = 2y/(1 + y^2)$; $y = \dfrac{[(1+\chi^2)^{1/2} - 1]}{\chi}$; and $\chi = 4\mu(\mathbf{H})/\Delta W$; μ is the electron magnetic moment, and ΔW is the singlet and triplet splitting at $\mathbf{H} = 0$. The relative spin population (up and down of the positrons in the triplet and singlet state) is

$$\frac{1 \mp a}{1 \pm a} \quad \text{(the upper sign for triplet)}$$

In other words, a positron that is initially completely polarized opposite to the field **H** is preferentially captured into the triplet state. For an unpolarized positron beam, the positronium formed is not polarized.

How do we determine the population in these two substates—that is, the $J = 1$, $m = 0$, and the $J = 0$, $m = 0$? The singlet state is known to decay with the emission of two oppositely directed photons and its lifetime is approximately 10^{-10} sec. The triplet state usually decays with three coplanar photons and lives some thousand times longer when there are no "spin-flip" or exchange processes present. However, in a magnetic field, l is a good quantum number. The $J = 1$, $m = 0$ substate of $^3S_1$ can therefore mix with the singlet level $^1S_0$ and thus quenches the three-photon process, causing more positrons to decay by two-photon emission. At 10,000 gauss, the lifetime of the two-photon annihilation of the $^3S_1$ state is approximately 3×10^{-9} sec and accounts for 15% of the total two-photon yield. Therefore the lifetime measurement is one of the possible ways to differentiate the pseudosinglet from the pseudotriplet. This method was suggested by Lundby (Lu-60) and Telegdi (see Gro-59) but has not yet been applied to positronium formation in a magnetic field in gases.

Nevertheless, Page and Heinberg (Pag-57b) successfully carried out the first experiment of this type by using a different method to distinguish the two-photon annihilation events of pseudotriplet from those of pseudosinglet. Their method required strict angular correlation at 180°; positronium atoms in the pseudosinglet state, being only about 10^{-10} sec old at annihilation, retained enough of the kinetic energy at formation to yield a broad angular correlation, whereas the pseudotriplet state, being on the average 30 times older at annihilation, lost most of the motion by the time it underwent two-photon annihilation and yielded a narrow component. This behavior is best illustrated in Fig. 4-18.

Page and Heinberg's first positronium experiment (Pag-57b), which used positrons from Na^{22} in argon and various gas mixtures, showed definitely that β^+ particles in the approximate range $0.7 < v/c < 0.8$ exhibit positive helicity with respect to the "average" direction of emission. To obtain quantitative results, we must estimate the depolarization and back-scattering effects on the helicity of the positron just before its capture; such an estimate is rather involved. The positronium experiment was recently reviewed by Dick et al. (Dick-64) who directly

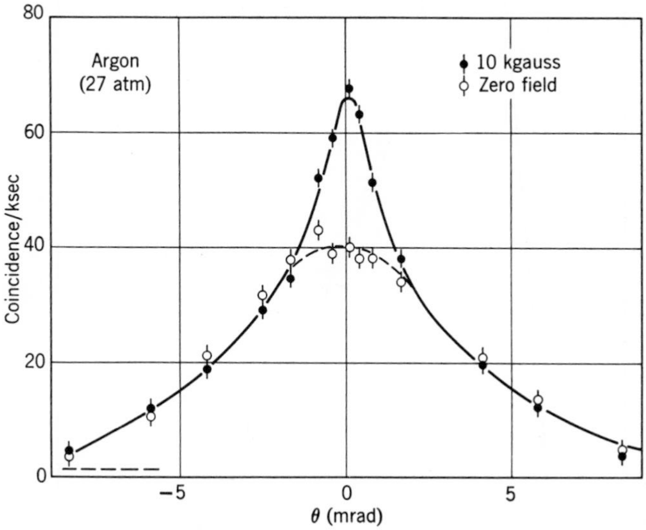

Fig. 4-18 Angular correlation of two-photon annihilation in argon for 0- and 10,000-gauss fields. From (Pag-57c).

measured the different time dependences of the two-photon annihilation in amorphous media. It is known that the time distribution of the two-photon annihilation of positrons in most amorphous media can be resolved into two mean lives [most recent elaborate analyses yield three mean lives (Sp-64; Su-64)]: (a) a fast component $\Gamma_f \sim (1 - 2) \times 10^{-10}$ sec; and (b) a slow component $\Gamma_s \sim (10 - 20)\Gamma_f$.

The fast component is attributed to a superposition of the direct annihilation of positrons and of the annihilation of $^1S_0$ positronium, whereas the slow component is attributed to the "pick-up" annihilation of the positron (by the electrons in the medium) in an originally $^3S_1$ positronium atom. The populations of these two pseudosinglet and pseudotriplet states are modified in a magnetic field and depend on the magnitude of the field and the relative direction of the spin of the

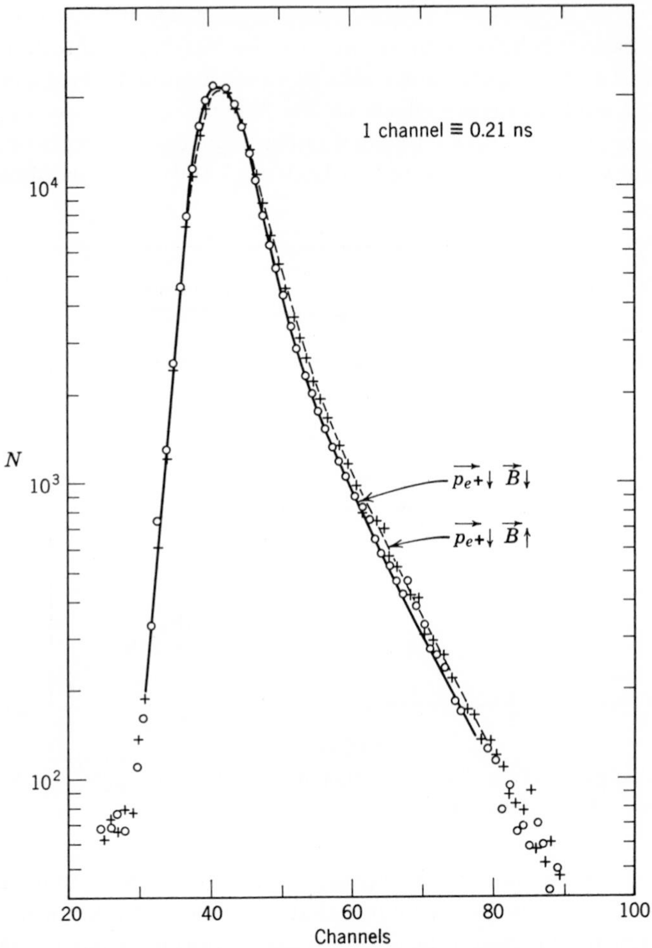

Fig. 4-19 The time distributions of the two-quantum annihilation of positrons from Na^{22} in a plastic scintillator; $B = 18.5$ kgauss. From (Dick-64).

positron and the direction of the field (see Fig. 4-19). For detailed analysis, please see the original paper of Dick et al. (Dick-64). In the measurement of the polarization of positrons from Na^{22}, they obtained an effective polarization,

$$\mathscr{P}_{\text{eff}} = \frac{v}{c}\frac{\langle \boldsymbol{\sigma} \cdot \mathbf{p} \rangle}{|\mathbf{p}|} \sim 0.8 \times 0.6 = 0.48$$

which is in accord with theory. However, they also measured the $\mathcal{P}_{\text{eff}}$ for positrons from B^8 and μ^+ decays. When the results from B^8 and μ^+ are normalized by the results from Na^{22}, they found that the helicity of e^+ from B^8 is in agreement with theoretical calculations, but the positrons from μ^+ decay coming from the maximum of the spectrum possess a polarization of only $(28 \pm 16)\%$, in contradiction to the theory of universal $V - A$ Fermi interaction. The foregoing result, therefore, called for further extensive investigations on the helicity of positrons from μ^+ decay by various methods. For the results of these latest measurements see p. 225.

The Measurement of the Helicity of the Neutrino

When electrons are captured through the conservation of momentum, the neutrino and the recoil nucleus are emitted in opposite directions:

$$e^- + \mathrm{p} \rightarrow \mathrm{n} + \nu \tag{4-36}$$

According to the foregoing argument, the neutrinos will be right-handed (positive helicity) for S, T, and P interactions, and left-handed (negative) if the interaction is a combination of V and A. If the capture process is followed by the emission of a γ ray, and the spin and parity changes are favorable, as shown in the following decay process,

$$A(0^-) \xrightarrow{e^-\text{ capture}} B^*(1^-) \xrightarrow{\gamma\text{ ray}} B(0^+) \tag{4-37}$$

then, in the capture process $e_K(\frac{1}{2}) + A(0) \rightarrow B^*(1) + \nu(\frac{1}{2})$, the conservation angular momentum requires that the spin of B^* be opposite that of the neutrino (only the capture of s electrons is considered). Therefore the nucleus B^* has the same handedness as the neutrino (see Fig. 4-20). Now let $B^*(1^-)$ de-excite to the ground state $B(0^+)$ with the emission of a γ ray; then the helicity of the downward γ ray will be the same as that of the upward neutrino, as shown in Fig. 4-20, and the problem of determining the neutrino helicity becomes one of measuring the circular polarization of the γ ray emitted opposite to the neutrino momentum. To select only the γ rays that follow the emission of a neutrino in the opposite direction, the nuclear resonance scattering may be used. It can easily be shown that in both emission and absorption processes of γ radiation, the nucleus recoils and, therefore, takes up the total amount of recoil energy equal to $2 \times E_0^2/2Mc^2 = E_0^2/Mc^2$; thus the γ-ray energy available for excitation when it is absorbed is only $E_0(1 - E_0/Mc^2)$. In order to make the resonance possible, extra energy equal to the energy lost in recoil must be supplied to the emitted γ rays. One of the methods by which to compensate for this energy loss is to utilize the recoil caused by the radiation previously emitted; in this case it would be the recoil caused by the emission of neutrinos in the K-capture process. Of course, the lifetime of the excited state must be extremely short so that de-excitation occurs

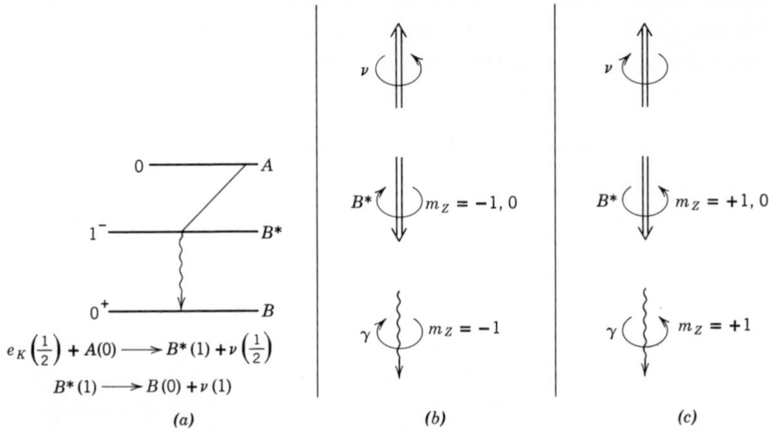

Fig. 4-20 Showing that gamma rays emitted opposite to the neutrino direction in K capture have the same helicity as the neutrino in $0 \rightarrow 1^- \rightarrow 0^+$ transition. (*a*) Decay scheme, (*b*) neutrino with positive helicity $\mathscr{H}_\nu = +1$, (*c*) neutrino with negative helicity $\mathscr{H}_\nu = -1$.

before the nucleus slows down. If this condition is fulfilled, the Doppler shift of the γ energy caused by the recoil of the nucleus will be

$$\Delta E = E_0 \times \frac{v_R}{c} \cos\theta \tag{4-38}$$

where v_R is the recoil velocity of the nucleus and is equal to E_ν/Mc. E_ν is the neutrino energy, and θ is the angle between the direction of the recoil and the γ ray. Therefore the excitation energy which can be transferred to the nucleus B is

$$E_\gamma = E_0 + E_0 \frac{E_\nu}{Mc^2}\cos\theta - \frac{E_0^{\,2}}{Mc^2} \tag{4-39}$$

The condition for resonance absorption is then $E_\nu \cos\theta = E_0$. When the neutrino has the same energy as the γ ray, the resonant condition is fulfilled only for those γ rays emitted opposite to the neutrino. Thus, by measuring the circular polarization of the gamma rays that cause resonant scattering, we can determine the helicity of the neutrino.

The nucleus used by Goldhaber, Grodzins, and Sunyar (Goldh-58) was $Eu^{152m}(0^-)$. One branch of its decay scheme closely approximates the requirements set forth in the hypothetical example just given. This

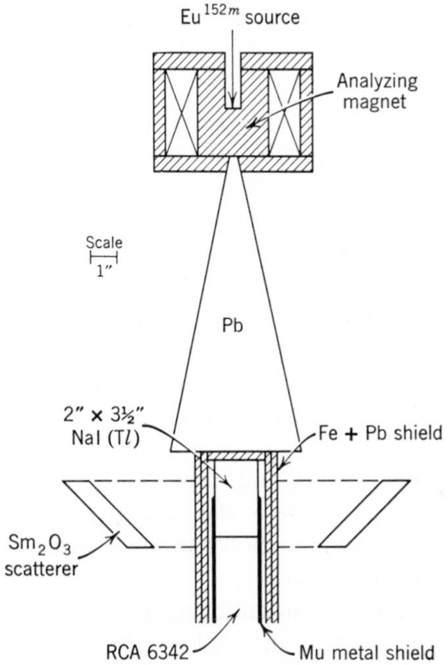

Fig. 4-21 Schematic diagram of the experimental setup of neutrino helicity determination. From (Goldh-58).

interesting decay branch is

$$Eu^{152m}(0^-) \xrightarrow[K \text{ capture}]{E_\nu = 900 \pm 10 \text{ kev}} Sm^{152*}(1^-) \quad [\tau = (7 \pm 2) \times 10^{-14} \text{ sec}]$$

$$\xrightarrow[E(1)\gamma \text{ ray}]{E_\gamma = 961 \text{ kev}} Sm^{152}(0^+) \qquad (4\text{-}40)$$

The lifetime of the (1^-) state is short enough $[\tau = (7 \pm 2) \times 10^{-14}$ sec] to expect that the γ ray retains a memory of the nuclear recoil resulting from neutrino emission.

The experimental arrangement is shown in Fig. 4-21. The circular polarization of the γ rays was analyzed by transmission through

3 ± 0.3 mean free paths ($= 6.4$ cm) of fully magnetized iron. The ring scatterer was 1700 g of Sm_2O_3 which could be alternated with a lead scatterer containing an equivalent number of electrons. The change in the counting rate of resonantly scattered γ rays could then be determined when the magnetic field was reversed. The observed change in counting rates is

$$\delta = \frac{2(N_- - N_+)}{N_- + N_+} = -2.1\%$$

where N_+ and N_- denote the counting rates with the field in the direction of γ emission and opposite to it, respectively. The circular polarization calculated from this observed effect is $(67 \pm 15)\%$ which compares favorably with the theoretically expected 84%. The most important information gained is that the helicity of the γ ray is negative. Hence the neutrino emitted in K capture has an excess of negative helicity, and the axial-vector interaction A, rather than the tensor interaction T, dominates in the Gamow-Teller β interaction. This is in good agreement with the conclusion obtained from the investigation of the β-ν angular correlations of He^6 and Ar^{35} decay.

The possibilities of obtaining the neutrino helicity by performing similar investigations of mixed and forbidden transitions are restricted by our lack of exact knowledge of the mixing ratios of Gamow-Teller to Fermi interactions and the relative value of various nuclear matrix elements in forbidden transitions.

The study of the helicity of the antineutrino in β^- decay is complicated by the simultaneous emission of a helical electron. Treiman (Tr-58), Morita, Morita, and Yamada (Mo-58), and Bincer (Bi-58) investigated the problem theoretically and concluded that for a pure Gamow-Teller transition the helicity of the resonantly scattered γ rays should be approximately zero for axial-vector interaction, but it can be appreciable for tensor interaction. So far, no experiments on the helicity of the antineutrino similar to those on the neutrino have been reported.

4-7 BETA DECAY OF POLARIZED NEUTRONS

The decay of a neutron is the simplest kind of nuclear β^- process. It involves a β^- transition between two free nucleons, and its nuclear matrix elements can therefore be calculated exactly. The investigation of this process should give us direct information about the β-decay interactions. Extensive studies of the decay of polarized neutrons were successfully carried out by Burgy et al. (Bu-58) at Argonne National Laboratory and also by Clark et al. (Cl-58) at the laboratories at Chalk River, Ontario, Canada. The theoretical discussion of this process, assuming $V - A$ interaction for β decay, is given in Appendix IV. In this section we shall give a simple description of the experiments and their physical interpretation.

The experiments can be divided into two groups.

1. One group consists of measurements of the angular distribution of electrons and also that of antineutrinos with respect to the spin of the polarized neutrons $W[\theta(\mathbf{I}_n \cdot \mathbf{p}_e)]$ and $W[\theta(\mathbf{I}_n \cdot \mathbf{p}_{\bar{\nu}})]$. The quantitative results of these experiments can be used to decide on the proper combinations of the β interactions in neutron decay and, hence, nuclear β decay in general.
2. The other group involves measurements of the simultaneous electron-antineutrino distribution with respect to the neutron spin. This second investigation is directly related to the question of time reversal.

The experimental arrangement is shown in Fig. 4-22. A beam of polarized thermal neutrons (87% polarized) was obtained by reflection at a small grazing angle (~8 min) from a 95% Co and 5% Fe mirror (12 cm high by 120 cm long) which is magnetized perpendicular to the beam direction. Neutron decays are observed by coincidences between a β detector and a proton detector in order to distinguish them from background events.

Angular Distributions of Leptons with Respect to Neutron Spin

The Electron Distribution $W[\theta(\mathbf{I}_n \cdot \mathbf{p}_e)]$. The vertical cross section through the vacuum tank showing the arrangements of the neutrons is given in Fig. 4-23. Measurements were made with neutrons polarized toward and away from the electron detector and with and without a steel sheet 0.02 cm thick, placed at the entrance to the vacuum chamber. This sheet completely depolarizes the beam of thermal neutrons and thus gives a null measurement for both field directions.

These measurements affected the asymmetry so that approximately 20% more electrons were emitted opposite to the spin direction than

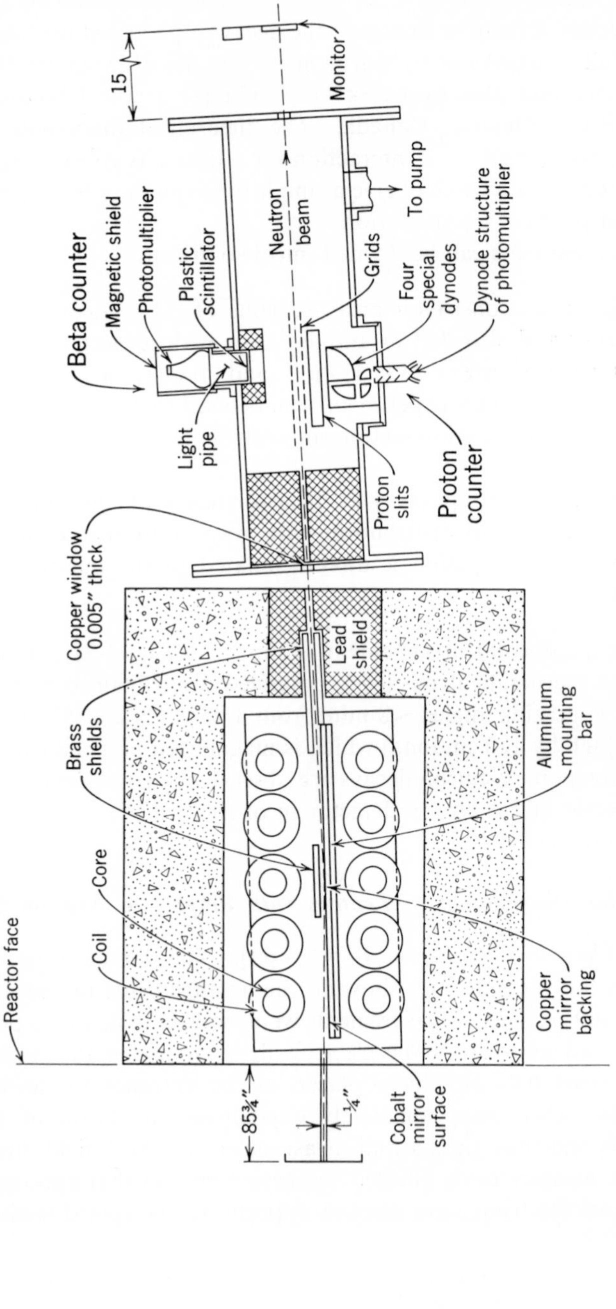

Fig. 4-22 Experimental arrangements of polarized neutron beam.

along the spin direction. The theoretical distribution can be expressed by

$$W[\theta(\mathbf{I}_n \cdot \mathbf{p}_e)] = 1 + A\frac{v}{c}\cos\theta(\mathbf{I}_n \cdot \mathbf{p}_e) \tag{4-41}$$

where A is the asymmetry parameter and is equal to the observed $A = -0.11 \pm 0.02$.

The Antineutrino Distribution $W[\theta(\mathbf{I}_n \cdot \mathbf{p}_{\bar{\nu}})]$. Since it is impossible to detect the antineutrino by itself directly, the direction of the recoil

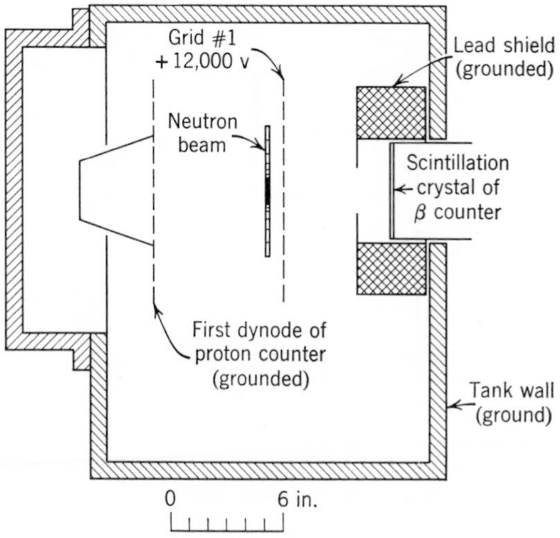

Fig. 4-23 Detection arrangement for experiment on electron distribution with respect to neutron spin $W[\theta(\mathbf{I}_n \cdot \mathbf{p}_e)]$. From (Bu-58).

proton is determined instead. The arrangement used is shown schematically in Fig. 4-24. The neutron spins point vertically up or down. The electrons are detected to the right, as before. The collimator requires that the recoiling protons have a downward component of velocity in order to pass through, as in the case of antineutrino emission into the upper hemisphere. Measurements are made with both directions of neutron spin and with and without the depolarizing shown in the $\theta(\mathbf{I}_n \cdot \mathbf{p}_e)$ experiment. The observed antineutrino angular distribution can be expressed by

$$W[\theta(\mathbf{I}_n \cdot \mathbf{p}_{\bar{\nu}})] = 1 + B\frac{v}{c}\cos\theta(\mathbf{I}_n \cdot \mathbf{p}_{\bar{\nu}}) \tag{4-42}$$

where B is the asymmetry parameter, expressed in terms of the coupling constants. The observed $B = +0.88 \pm 0.15$.

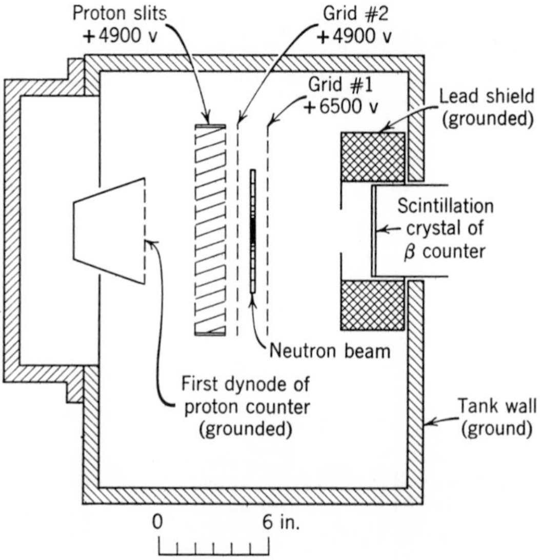

Fig. 4-24 Detector arrangement for experiment on antineutrino distribution with respect to neutron spin $W[\theta(\mathbf{I}_n \cdot \mathbf{p}_{\bar{\nu}})]$. From (Bu-58).

Testing for Time-Reversal Symmetry

The object of the experiments to be discussed next is to test for the time-reversal symmetry of the β-decay process. The principle of the experiments can best be illustrated with the aid of Fig. 4-25*a*. It is known that to an observer using "reversed" time the direction of spin of the neutron as well as the directions of the momentum of the emitted particles will appear reversed. Thus the "time-reversed" situation would be the one depicted in Fig. 4-25*b*. If we measure simultaneously the directions of emission of the electron and of the antineutrino with respect to the neutron spin, and find that the probabilities of emission in these two situations (see Figs. 4-25*a* and *b*) are identical, then we will have exact symmetry under time reversal; that is, the expectation value of the term $\langle \mathbf{I}_n \cdot \mathbf{p}_e \times \mathbf{p}_{\bar{\nu}} \rangle$ is identically equal to zero. (The expression for the coefficient of $\langle \mathbf{I}_n \cdot \mathbf{p}_e \times \mathbf{p}_{\bar{\nu}} \rangle$ was derived by Jackson, Treiman, and Wyld (Ja-57) and is given by

$$\int 1 \cdot \int \boldsymbol{\sigma} \, \mathrm{Im}\,(C_S C_T^* + C_S' C_T'^* - C_V C_A^* - C_V' C_A'^*) \qquad (4\text{-}43)$$

which vanishes if C_i, C_i' are real—that is, if time-reversal invariance holds.) The actual experimental comparison of these two situations may be simplified by rotating Fig. 4-25*b* 180° about the spin axis, so

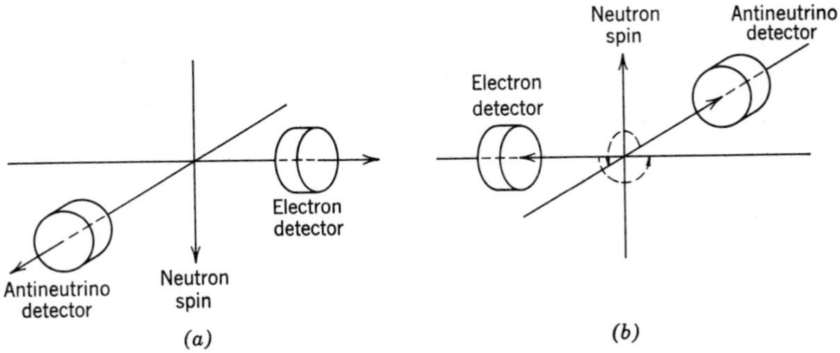

Fig. 4-25 Diagram of the three-vector experiment to examine the symmetry under time reversal. Parts *a* and *b* show the time-reversed experiments. The rotation about the spin axis indicated by the dashed lines in part *b* brings the electron and antineutrino detectors into positions as shown in part *a*. From (Bu-58).

that the two respective detectors resume their original positions as in Fig. 4-25*a*. Then we have only to invert the direction of the neutron spin in order to give an effective time reversal.

The experimental setup is the same as in Fig. 4-24, except that the collimater and proton detector are rotated by 90° about an axis through the β detector. The proton detectors are then selectively sensitive to recoils produced by antineutrinos emitted in (or out of) the plane of the paper, which is the desired situation. Hence measurements with two opposite neutron-spin orientations indicate time-reversal symmetry. So far, the results of these measurements indicate no breakdown of the symmetry. They yield the relative phase angle between C_A and C_V equal to 0° or 180° (±8°). For time-reversal symmetry the relative phase angle should indeed be either zero (for $V + A$) or 180° (for $V - A$). The uncertainty of ±8° is entirely statistical. Therefore, until proved otherwise, we may assume that time-reversal invariance still holds.*

Let us now interpret the significance of the electron and neutrino angular distributions. We already know from e-ν angular-correlation experiments that the β interaction involves the linear combination VA, and from electron polarization it follows that the even and odd couplings are equal in sign and magnitude; that is, $C_i' = C_i$. Furthermore, from time-reversal invariance established in the experiment just discussed, it follows that the β interaction must be of the form $V - \lambda A$ with

	$S+T$		$S-T$		$V+A$		$V-A$		
	$\bar{\nu}_L$	$\bar{\nu}_R$	$\bar{\nu}_L$	$\bar{\nu}_R$	$\bar{\nu}_L$	$\bar{\nu}_R$	$\bar{\nu}_L$	$\bar{\nu}_R$	Experimental
A	-1	$+1$	-0.09	0.09	$+1$	-1	0.09	-0.09	-0.11 ± 0.02
B	-0.09	0.09	-1	$+1$	-0.09	0.09	-1	$+1$	0.88 ± 0.15

Fig. 4-26 Predicted values for A and B. From (Bu-60).

λ real. The angular distributions for an arbitrary VA combination have been worked out in Appendix VI. We find for the coefficients A and B,

$$A = \frac{2\lambda(1 - \lambda)}{1 + 3\lambda^2} \tag{4-44}$$

$$B = \frac{2\lambda(1 + \lambda)}{1 + 3\lambda^2} \tag{4-45}$$

For a $V - A$ interaction ($\lambda = 1$) we find $A = 0$, $B = +1$, whereas for a $V + A$ combination ($\lambda = -1$), $A = -1$, and $B = 0$. The results of the experiment are obviously much closer to the predictions for the $V - A$ interaction.

Next suppose that λ is slightly different from 1; that is,

$$\lambda = 1 + \epsilon \tag{4-46}$$

Then we obtain

$$A = -\tfrac{1}{2}\epsilon + \tfrac{1}{4}\epsilon^2 \cdots \tag{4-47}$$

$$B = 1 - \tfrac{1}{4}\,\epsilon^2 \cdots \tag{4-48}$$

The experimental result $A = -0.11$ implies that $\epsilon = 0.24$; that is, $\lambda = 1.24$, which is in good agreement with the ratio $|\lambda| = 1.18$ deduced from the comparison of neutron and O^{14} half-lives (see p. 68). This in turn should give $B = 0.99$, which, although disagreeing with the experimental mean value, is well within the quoted experimental error.

* See, however, the remarks on p. 146 concerning $K_2{}^0 \to 2\pi$ decay.

Incidentally, the neutron experiment gives a very nice *independent* test of the right-handedness of the antineutrino—that $C_i' = C_i$. Suppose we assume only (say, on the basis of a comparison of ft values for mirror nuclei) that the Gamow-Teller coupling is larger than the Fermi coupling. But let the interaction be either ST or VA, with the sign of the ratio either plus or minus and with the antineutrinos either right- or left-handed. There are then eight possible combinations. As shown in Fig. 4-26 for $|\lambda| = 1.2$, only one of the eight combinations—namely, $V - 1.2A$ with $\bar{\nu}_R$—is in agreement with the experimental results.

4-8 BETA-GAMMA (CIRCULARLY POLARIZED) CORRELATION EXPERIMENT

It can be deduced from the observed β asymmetry of polarized nuclei that the β decay should leave the nucleus partly polarized with respect to the direction in which the β particle is detected. It is also well known that a γ ray emitted by polarized nuclei will be circularly polarized; therefore, if a γ ray is emitted immediately after β decay, it should have circular polarization proportional to the cosine of the angle between the β particle and γ ray. However, since there is no β asymmetry to be expected in a pure Fermi interaction, no such correlation exists in a pure Fermi interaction.

A simple example will illustrate the consequences just stated. Suppose an unpolarized nucleus A, with spin zero, decays by Gamow-Teller interactions to one of the excited states of its daughter nucleus B^*. The spin of the excited state B^* is 1. By conservation of angular momentum we have

$$A(0) \rightarrow B^*(1) + e^-(\tfrac{1}{2}) + \bar{\nu}(\tfrac{1}{2}) \rightarrow B(0) + \gamma(1) + e^-(\tfrac{1}{2}) + \bar{\nu}(\tfrac{1}{2})$$

This is illustrated in Fig. 4-27.

In other words, the direction of the spin of B^* must be opposite to that of the spin of the electron and the antineutrino. Since the spin and momentum of an electron emitted from an unpolarized nucleus are known to be correlated (owing to the polarization of $\beta^\pm$ particles from unpolarized nuclei), the spin of B^* is correlated with the direction of the β emission. After β decay, if the excited state immediately emits a γ ray before the orientation of the nuclear spin has been perturbed,

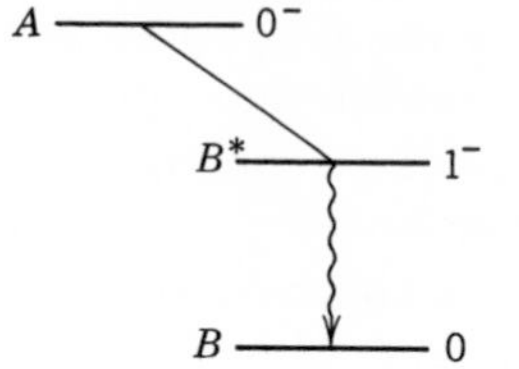

$$A(0) \longrightarrow B^*(1) + e^-(\tfrac{1}{2}) + \bar{\nu}(\tfrac{1}{2}) \longrightarrow$$
$$e^-(\tfrac{1}{2}) + \bar{\nu}(\tfrac{1}{2}) + B(0) + \gamma(1)$$

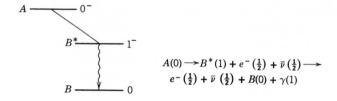

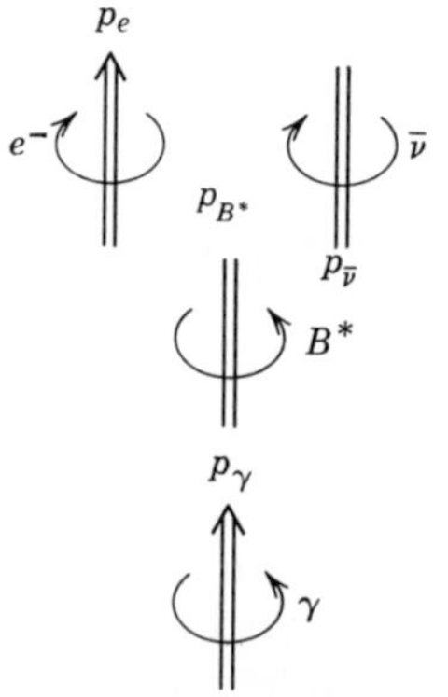

Fig. 4-27 Illustration of the helicity of a γ ray emitted along the direction of the previously emitted β particle. For an axial-vector interaction, the arrow for the neutrino should be pointed downward, but this is not relevant for the present experiment.

the γ ray emitted along the direction of the β emission will be right-handed circularly polarized, but left-handed if emitted in the opposite direction.

The angular correlation between the electron and γ ray can be written as

$$W(\theta_{\beta,\gamma}\tau) = 1 + \tau A \frac{v}{c} (\cos \theta_{\beta,\gamma}) \tag{4-49}$$

where $\tau = +1$ or -1 for right- or left-handed circularly polarized rays (a momentum parallel with or antiparallel to the direction of motion*); v and c are the velocities of the electrons and light, respectively; $\theta_{\beta,\gamma}$ is the angle between the electron and the γ ray. The asymmetry parameter A depends on the type of β interaction, the parity

* This definition, which has become customary in nuclear physics, is opposite to the definition of polarization used in classical optics. In the latter, the right-handed circularly polarized light is defined with the electromagnetic vectors rotating clockwise with respect to an observer facing the incoming wave.

and charge conjugation violation, and the spins and parities of the nuclear levels. The expressions for A were evaluated by Alder, Stech, and Winther (Ald-57), Morita and Morita (Mor-57), Jackson, Treiman, and Wyld (Ja-57), and others (Fe-57; Cur-57; Eb-57).

For the most frequent decay sequence, such as

$$I \xrightarrow[\beta]{\text{allowed}} I_1 \xrightarrow[\gamma]{2^L \text{ pole } \gamma \text{ radiation}} I_2 = I_1 - L$$

the expression for A, assuming a VA interaction, is

$$\frac{2}{\xi(L+1)}\Big[\mp \mu_{II_1} \operatorname{Re}(C_A{}^*C_A{}')\Big|\int \boldsymbol{\sigma}\Big|^2 - \delta_{II_1}\left(\frac{I+1}{I}\right)^{1/2} \operatorname{Re}(C_A{}^*C_V{}' + C_V{}^*C_A{}')\int 1 \cdot \int \boldsymbol{\sigma}\Big] \quad (4\text{-}50)$$

for $\beta^{\mp}$ decay, where

$$\begin{aligned} \delta_{II_1} &= 0 \quad \text{if} \quad I_1 \neq I \\ &\ 1 \qquad\quad\ \ I_1 = I \\ \mu_{II_1} &= 1 \quad \text{if} \quad I_1 = I - 1 \\ &\ -\frac{1}{I} \qquad I_1 = I \\ &\ -\frac{I+2}{I+1} \quad I_1 = I + 1 \end{aligned}$$

and $\quad \xi = [(C_V)^2 + (C_V{}')^2]\Big|\int 1\Big|^2 + [(C_A)^2 + (C_A{}')^2]\Big|\int \boldsymbol{\sigma}\Big|^2$

For a β transition with $I_1 = I - 1$, only the axial-vector term can contribute. If we use the conclusion deduced from the Co^{60} experiment, $C_A{}' = C_A$, we find

$$A = \mp \frac{1}{L+1} \quad (4\text{-}51)$$

Thus for the decay of Co^{60} $(5 \xrightarrow{\beta^-} 4 \xrightarrow{\gamma} 2 \xrightarrow{\gamma} 0)$ we find $A = -\frac{1}{3}$, and for $Na^{22}(3 \xrightarrow{\beta^+} 2 \xrightarrow{\gamma} 0)$, $A = \frac{1}{3}$.

For a β transition with $I \to I$ as in Na^{24}, Sc^{46} etc. (assuming $C_i{}' = C_i$), we obtain

$$A = \left\{\frac{1}{L+1}\left[\pm\frac{1}{I} - 2\left(\frac{I+1}{I}\right)^{1/2}\frac{C_V\int 1}{C_A\int\boldsymbol{\sigma}}\right]\right\}\frac{1}{1 + \left(\dfrac{C_V\int 1}{C_A\int\boldsymbol{\sigma}}\right)^2} \quad (4\text{-}52)$$

for $\beta^{\mp}$ decay. Of course, if $I_2 \neq I_1 - L$, or for mixed multipole transitions, different formulas apply.

Experimental Methods

The most successful method of detecting circular polarization of γ rays is to measure Compton scattering from polarized electrons available in magnetized iron (Gu-53). The scattering of circularly polarized γ rays is strongly dependent on the relative orientation of the spins of the electron and the γ ray. Reversal of the polarization of the electron results in a change in the scattered γ intensity. The differential Compton cross section $d\Phi/d\Omega$ is actually separable into spin-independent and spin-dependent parts.

$$\frac{d\Phi}{d\Omega} = \frac{r_0^{\,2}}{2}\left(\frac{k}{k_0}\right)^2\left(\Phi_0 + P_l\Phi_l + fP_c\Phi_c\right) \tag{4-53}$$

where $r_0 = e^2/mc^2$ = the classical electron radius

k_0 and k = the initial and final photon momentum

Φ_0 = the ordinary Compton cross section (Klein-Nishina formula)

P_l = the degree of linear polarization which is positive if the electric vector $\mathbf{E}$ is perpendicular to the k_0k plane and is negative if $\mathbf{E}$ lies in the plane of scattering.

P_c = the degree of circular polarization of the photons which is positive if the radiation is right circularly polarized.

f = the fraction of polarized electrons per atom.

Φ_l and Φ_c = the polarization dependent parts of the cross section.

If we define the relevant angles θ, ψ, and ϕ as shown in Fig. 4-28,

θ = the scattering angle between $\mathbf{k}_0\mathbf{k}$
ψ = the angle between $\mathbf{k}_0\boldsymbol{\sigma}$
ϕ = the angle between $\mathbf{k}$, $\boldsymbol{\sigma}$ plane and $\mathbf{k}_0$, $\mathbf{k}$ plane.

Then the cross sections can be expressed in terms of these angles:

$$\begin{aligned}\Phi_0 &= 1 + \cos^2\theta + (k_0 - k)(1 - \cos\theta)\\ \Phi_l &= \sin^2\theta\\ \Phi_c &= -(1 - \cos\theta)[(k_0 + k)\cos\theta\cos\psi + k\sin\theta\sin\psi\cos\phi]\end{aligned} \tag{4-54}$$

It can be seen that by reversing the electron spin direction the angle ψ changes to $\psi + \pi$, and therefore the cross section Φ_c reverses its sign.

By using N_+ to denote the number of scattered photons if the electron spin σ is roughly parallel to the incident γ quantum ($0 \leqslant \psi < \pi/2$) and N_- to denote the corresponding number with the spin approximately antiparallel ($\pi \leqslant \psi \leqslant 3\pi/2$), the relative difference in counting rate on reversing the electron spin is

$$\delta = \frac{N_- - N_+}{(N_- + N_+)/2} = \frac{2fP_c(\Phi_c^-/\Phi_0)}{1 + P_l(\Phi_l/\Phi_0)} \tag{4-55}$$

where $$\Phi_c^- \equiv \Phi_c(\pi \leqslant \psi \leqslant 3\pi/2)$$

It can be seen that the forward Compton scattering cross section is largest when the spin of the electron and the photon are antiparallel;

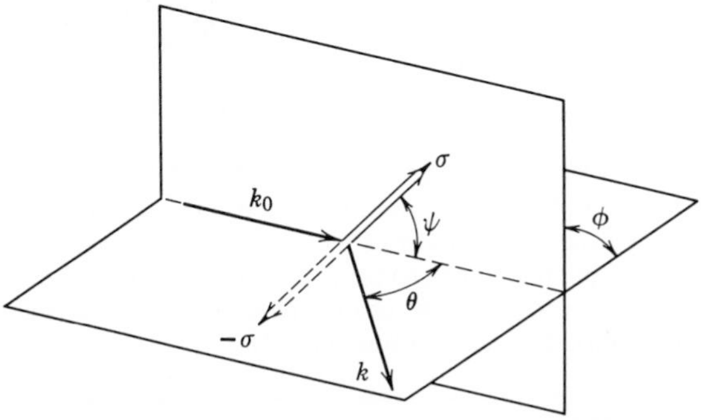

Fig. 4-28 Compton scattering. The incoming γ ray with momentary k_0 is scattered by an electron with spin σ; k is the scattered γ ray. A reversal of the spin of the electron, $\sigma \to -\sigma$, corresponds to a change $\psi \to \psi + \pi$. From (Fr-63).

and the backward scattering is largest when the two spins are in parallel (see Figs. 4-29, 4-30). In other words, right-handed photons are scattered more strongly in the forward direction if the magnetization in the scatterer points away from the γ-ray source.

Using the Compton scattering from polarized electrons as an analyzer, we can measure either the differential cross section by scattering or the total cross section by the absorption method. However, the measurement of differential scattering in a favorable ring geometry (as shown in Fig. 4-31) provides a large solid angle and, therefore, high counting efficiencies. On the other hand, when the energy discrimination is important, we may find the absorption method more favorable.

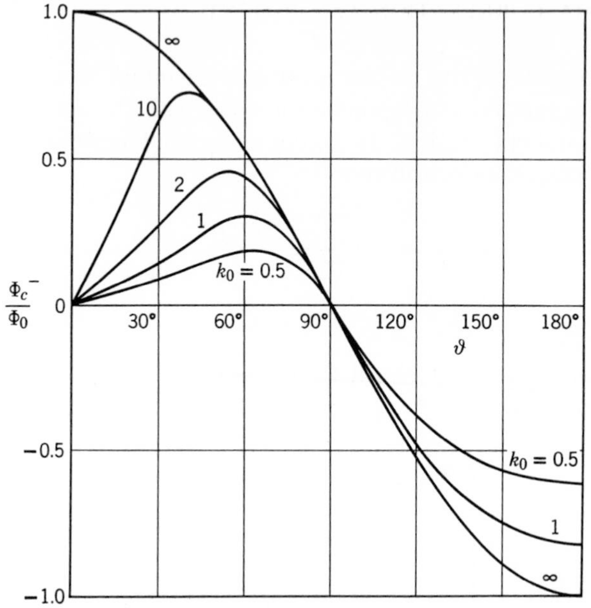

Fig. 4-29 The ratio of the differential Compton cross sections Φ_c^-/Φ_0 resulting from entirely polarized initial electrons with spin in the direction of the incident circularly polarized photon. The change is plotted as a function of the scattering angle θ of the photon to show the change of sign of the polarization effect for forward and backward directions. From (Gu-53).

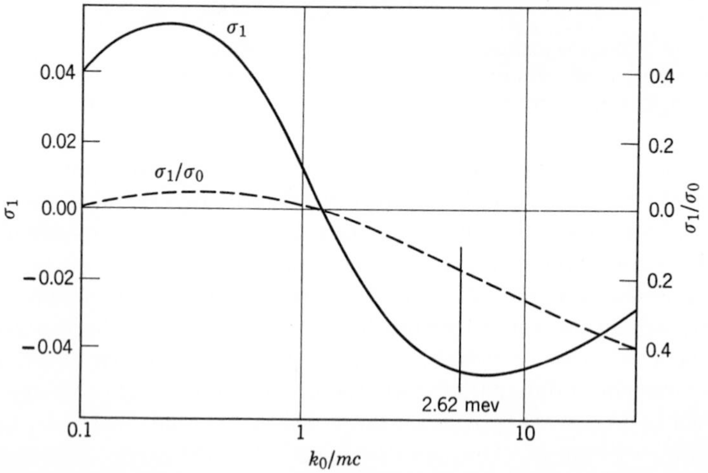

Fig. 4-30 The polarization sensitive part σ_1 of the total Compton cross section in units $2\pi r_0{}^2$ for the same polarization as in Fig. 4-29. The change in sign occurring in σ_1 for 1.25 mc^2 = 0.65 mev can be understood from the difference in sign for $d\sigma_1/d\Omega$ for forward and backward directions. From (Gu-53).

Experimental Results

Soon after the nonconservation of parity in β decay was known, Schopper (Scho-57) and Boehm and Wapstra (Bo-57a) applied this β-γ (circularly polarized) correlation method to Co^{60} and Na^{22}. The asymmetry parameters A that were observed were very close to $\frac{1}{3}$ in absolute magnitude—namely, $-\frac{1}{3}$ in the case of Co^{60} and $+\frac{1}{3}$ for Na^{22}, as predicted.

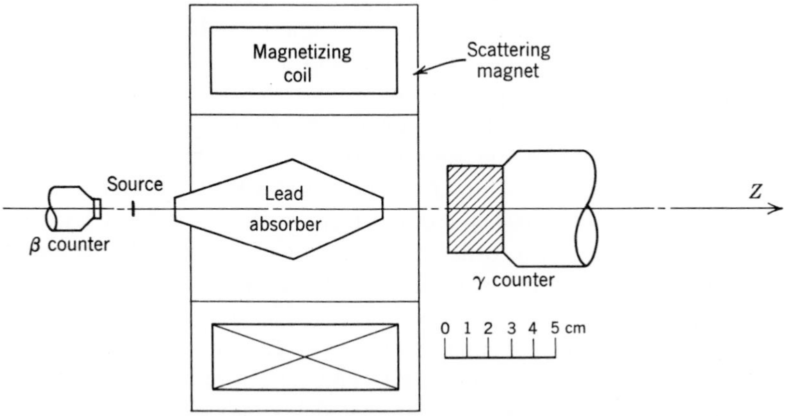

Fig. 4-31 Cylindrical polarimeter (ring geometry) with $\phi \simeq \theta/2$. From (Scho-57).

A more interesting aspect of this method is that it yields information on the interference between Fermi and Gamow-Teller interactions as represented by the mixing ratio $(C_V\int 1)/(C_A\int \boldsymbol{\sigma})$ for a VA interaction with $C_i' = C_i$.

This type of interference was looked for in $I \to I$ transitions such as Na^{24}, Ar^{41}, and Co^{58}, and by using Eq. 4-52 it was found that the experimental anisotropy coefficient is consistent with $|\int 1/\int \boldsymbol{\sigma}| \simeq 0$. This is rather understandable for, in transitions other than mirror and $0^+ \to 0^+$ transitions, the initial and final states have different isobaric spins. If the nuclear forces were strictly charge-independent, and if Coulomb effects could be ignored, then $\int 1$ should vanish for transitions between such nuclei, because the operator 1, acting on a state, does not change the isobaric spin. However, there were some puzzling cases, such as in Sc^{44}, Sc^{46}, and Mn^{52}. The early experimental results implied an appreciable mixture of Fermi and Gamow-Teller interactions. For instance, in Sc^{46} ($4 \xrightarrow{\beta^-} 4 \xrightarrow[L=2]{\gamma} 2$) the pure Gamow-Teller interaction would give

$$A = \frac{1}{L+1} \times \frac{1}{I} = \frac{1}{2+1} \times \frac{1}{4} = \frac{1}{12} \approx 0.08 \tag{4-56}$$

Experimentally, A was found to equal 0.33. The ratio $|\int 1|/|\int \boldsymbol{\sigma}|$ deduced from this measured value of A was 0.4 in order of magnitude, which immediately raised the important questions how valid are the isobaric spin selection rules in β decay and how big can the Coulomb correction be. Later experimental results (Blo-62; Ber-62, Mis-63; Da-63; Ha-62; Wei-64) have shown very small asymmetry for this nucleus, however, and the Fermi mixture is indeed very small, as theoretically expected. Thus a recent measurement by Mann et al. (Ma-64) gives $A = 0.094 \pm 0.007$ which implies a ratio $\int 1/\int \boldsymbol{\sigma} = 0.02 \pm 0.01$. Clearly, in order to deduce this ratio reliably, we must measure the asymmetry parameter with accuracy as well as with precision; that is, we must avoid systematic errors. Furthermore, during the β emission the nucleus may recoil from its original position into the surrounding atomic field, and therefore the interactions between the moments and the internal fields may cause appreciable amounts of attenuation of the nuclear polarization. However, the half-life of the second excited state in Ti^{46} is measured to be less than 5×10^{-12} sec (Le-63); attenuation by the internal fields is rather unlikely. It should also be pointed out that only 2 electrons out of the 26 electrons of the iron atom can be polarized even at magnetic saturation, and the optimum observable asymmetry effect in scattering, even for completely circularly polarized γ rays, is only of the order of 8%. In the pure Gamow-Teller interaction, it is therefore not more than 2–3%. The smallness of this observable asymmetry effect, which results from using iron, greatly limits the accuracy of the derived ratio.

Table 4-6 summarizes the β-γ (circularly polarized) correlation results on some of the more interesting isotopes. For all cases shown, the γ rays are quadrupole ($L = 2$). The complete lack of agreement on Sc^{44}, Sc^{46}, A^{41}, etc. between the two groups of results, each of which represents the investigation of several laboratories, points to the extreme difficulty of obtaining any accuracy in this type of experiment.

Table 4-6 Beta-Gamma (Circularly Polarized) Correlation Results

Nuclides	Asymmetry Coefficient A	$C_V \int 1 / C_A \int \sigma$	Reference
Pure G-T interaction			
$Co^{60}(\beta^-)$ $5^+ \rightarrow 4^+$	$A = -0.41 \pm 0.07$		(Scho-57)
	-0.41 ± 0.08		(Bo-57a)
	-0.32 ± 0.07		(Lun-57)
	-0.335 ± 0.018		(Ap-58)
	-0.344 ± 0.09		(Deb-57)
	-0.34 ± 0.02		(St-57)
$Na^{22}(\beta^+)$ $3^+ \rightarrow 2^+$	$A = +0.39 \pm 0.08$		(Scho-57)
	$+0.295 \pm 0.054$		(Ap-58)
Mixed interactions			
$Na^{24}(\beta^-)$ $4^+ \rightarrow 4^+$	$A = +0.085 \pm 0.028$	0.002 ± 0.04	(Blo-62)
	$+0.07 \pm 0.04$	$+0.02 \pm 0.05$	(Bo-58)
	$+0.06 \pm 0.03$	$+0.03 \pm 0.05$	(St-59)
	-0.063 ± 0.047	$+0.21 \pm 0.07$	(Ap-57)
	$+0.091 \pm 0.017$	-0.010 ± 0.02	(Man-63)
	$+0.104 \pm 0.026$	-0.040 ± 0.04	(Ha-63)
$Al^{24}(\beta^+)$ $4^+ \rightarrow 4^+$	$A = -0.086 \pm 0.054$	$+0.004 \pm 0.07$	(Man-63)
	-0.089 ± 0.057	$+0.008 \pm 0.07$	(Ha-63)
$Ar^{41}(\beta^-)$ $\frac{7}{2}^- \rightarrow \frac{7}{2}^-$	$A = +0.33 \pm 0.07$	-0.38 ± 0.15	(May-60)
	$+0.061 \pm 0.070$	0.04 ± 0.09	(Blo-62)
		0 ± 0.025	(Cham-62)
$V^{48}(\beta^+)$ $4^+ \rightarrow 4^+$	$A = +0.06 \pm 0.05$	-0.19 ± 0.07	(Bo-58)
	$+0.00 \pm 0.04$	-0.11 ± 0.05	(Da-61)
$Mn^{52}\beta^+$ $2^+ \rightarrow 2^+$	-0.023 ± 0.003	-0.048 ± 0.004	(Am-58)
	-0.062 ± 0.006	$+0.004 \pm 0.010$	(Pos-58)
	-0.089 ± 0.028	$+0.040 \pm 0.040$	(Blo-62)
	-0.10 ± 0.03	$+0.060 \pm 0.040$	(Bo-62a)
$Sc^{44}\beta^+$ $2^+ \rightarrow 2^+$	-0.02 ± 0.04	-0.18 ± 0.05	(Bo-58)
	-0.151 ± 0.030	-0.020 ± 0.035	(Blo-62)
	-0.156 ± 0.029	-0.013 ± 0.035	(Man-62)

Table 4-6 (Continued)

Nuclides	Asymmetry Coefficient A	$C_V \int 1 / C_A \int \sigma$	Reference
Mixed interactions			
$Sc^{46}\beta^-$	$+0.33 \pm 0.04$	-0.39 ± 0.07	(Bo-58)
$4^+ \rightarrow 4^+$	$+0.215 \pm 0.019$	-0.19 ± 0.03	(Bo-62b)
	$+0.29 \pm 0.11$	-0.32 ± 0.14	(Lun-57)
	$+0.24 \pm 0.04$	-0.22 ± 0.08	(Ju-58)
	$+0.19 \pm 0.03$	-0.15 ± 0.05	(St-63)
	$+0.075 \pm 0.018$	$+0.011 \pm 0.025$	(Blo-62)
	$+0.097 \pm 0.012$	-0.02 ± 0.02	(Mis-63)
	$+0.113 \pm 0.008$	-0.04 ± 0.01	(Da-63)
	$+0.11 \pm 0.02$	-0.04 ± 0.03	(Ber-62)
	$+0.079 \pm 0.012$	$+0.006 \pm 0.016$	(Ha-62)
	$+0.076 \pm 0.010$	$+0.010 \pm 0.013$	(Wei-64)

As can be seen from the table, most of the recent measurements give very small values for the Fermi matrix elements. This is in agreement with conservation of isobaric spin in β decay. These results have been summarized recently by Bloom (Blo-63) and Daniel (Da-65).

Beta-Gamma (Circularly Polarized) Correlation in the Mirror Transitions $Na^{24} \xrightarrow{\beta^-} Mg^{24} \xleftarrow{\beta^+} Al^{24}$

This ingenious experiment, suggested by Bouchiat (Bou-59), was stimulated by the observation of a large discrepancy between the experimentally determined Fermi matrix element $\int 1$ and the theoretically estimated isotopic spin impurities in Na^{24}. As we have already pointed out, the isotopic spin selection rule for the Fermi β interaction is given by $\Delta T = 0$, where T is the total isobaric spin. Therefore, in β transitions where $\Delta T = 1$ and $\Delta T_z = \pm 1$, only two possible sources other than $\Delta T = 0$ can contribute to the Fermi part of β interaction. One source is the previously mentioned isotopic spin impurity, which is introduced by the charge-dependent forces in nucleon-nucleon interaction, such as the Coulomb interaction between the protons. Such an asymmetrical potential clearly violates the charge-independent condition that the total isobaric spin T should be a good quantum number. Therefore, any charge-dependent potential perturbs and mixes states of different isobaric spins. The other source occurs only in the conventional theory of β decay where the pion current does not take part in the interaction, the virtual pions in the physical nucleon state thereby inducing a Fermi transition with $\Delta T \neq 0$. However, as was pointed out by Wigner (Wi-57) and Bernstein (Be-58), under the conserved vector current (C.V.C.) theory (see p. 260), the contribution of virtual pion states to the $\Delta T = 0$ Fermi transition is strictly zero, because the β-interaction Hamiltonian must commute with the total isotopic spin operator. Thus the observed deviations from the $\Delta T = 0$ selection rule in Fermi transitions have to be explained purely in terms of isobaric spin impurities.

Let us take the case of β decay from the $T = 1$, $I = 4^+$ state of Na^{24} to the $T = 0$, $I = 4^+$ state of Mg^{24*}. This is a case of $\Delta T = 1$. However, the contribution of $\int 1$, as determined by β-γ (circularly polarized) angular correlation, is found to be less than 10^{-3}, whereas a theoretical estimate using the j–j coupling shell model yields a value of $(1.3 - 1.7) \times 10^{-2}$ (Bo-60; Bli-63b), one order of magnitude larger.

There are two possible explanations of this discrepancy:

1. The Coulomb matrix element has possibly been overestimated by using j–j coupling model wave functions.
2. The C.V.C. theory may break down in the complex nuclei; then the virtual pion currents induce Fermi transitions. Furthermore, the mesonic term and the Coulomb term interfere and cancel each other in Na^{24}; therefore a much smaller value of $\int 1$ results.

In order to make a choice between these two possibilities without having to use *any* nuclear model, the following mirror experiment was suggested by Bouchiat.

Let us consider the $T = 1$ multiplet which consists of the ground state of Al^{24} and Na^{24} and of the 9.5-mev level of Mg^{24*}. The β^- decay of the ground state of Na^{24} has a 99.9% branch to the $T = 0$, $I = 4^+$ level of Mg^{24*}, and the β^+ decay of Al^{24} has a 10% branch to the same level:

$$Na^{24}(4+) \xrightarrow{\beta^-} Mg^{24*}(4+) \xrightarrow{\gamma} Mg^{24}(0+)$$

$$Al^{24}(4+) \xrightarrow{\beta^+} Mg^{24*}(4+) \xrightarrow{\gamma} Mg^{24}(0+)$$

As mentioned previously, the asymmetry coefficient $A^{\pm}$ (for $\beta^{\mp}$ decay), which is determined by the β-γ angular correlation, contains essentially the ratio of $\int 1$ to $\int \boldsymbol{\sigma}$. Under charge conjugation—that is, $\beta^+ \leftrightarrow \beta^-$—$\int \boldsymbol{\sigma}$ is odd and changes sign. If the C.V.C. theory is valid, $\int 1$ is even because the contribution comes solely from the Coulomb impurity. The contribution to $\int 1$ from the mesonic effect would be odd, but it only exists in conventional theory of β decay.

Thus the C.V.C. theory predicts that exactly

$$A^+ + A^- = 0 \tag{4-56}$$

This difficult experiment has now been performed independently by two different groups (Ha-63; Man-63). Their results are in substantial agreement:

$$A^+(\text{Na}^{24}) = +0.104 \pm 0.026 \text{ (Ha-63)}; = +0.091 \pm 0.017 \text{ (Ma-63)}$$
$$A^-(\text{Al}^{24}) = -0.089 \pm 0.057 \text{ (Ha-63)}; = -0.086 \pm 0.054 \text{ (Ma-63)}$$

Therefore, the experiment implies that β decay in complex nuclei is consistent with the C.V.C. theory well within experimental error. However, it is not necessarily in disagreement with the old Fermi theory, for the Fermi matrix element caused by the mesonic effect could be very small. The isobaric spin purity seems to be definitely better than the theoretical estimate using the *j-j* coupling shell model but is in agreement with calculations using Nilsson wave functions (Bl-65a).

CHAPTER 5

The Closely Related Processes

In this chapter we shall treat three processes closely related to nuclear β decay. As far as we know, these processes are all governed by essentially the same interaction as β decay itself. They are orbital electron capture, double β decay, and inverse β decay.

5-1 ORBITAL ELECTRON CAPTURE

An important process which always competes with positron emission is orbital electron capture (Yu-35a; Al-38). In this process no particle except the elusive neutrino is emitted. Schematically, it may be represented by

$$Z^A + e^- \rightarrow (Z - 1)^A + \nu \tag{5-1}$$

Orbital electron capture can, in fact, occur even when positron emission is energetically impossible, since the available energy required for the electron-capture process is

$$\Delta E = (M_Z - M_{Z-1})c^2 > E_K \text{ or } E_L \tag{5-2}$$

where M_Z and M_{Z-1} are the atomic masses and E_K and E_L are the binding energies of the K and L orbital electrons, respectively. The energy requirement in this case is different from that of positron emission where an energy difference of $2\,mc^2$ is required. The basic orbital electron-capture process is the capture of the electron by a proton

$$\mathrm{p} + e^- \rightarrow \mathrm{n} + \nu \tag{5-3}$$

However, this process cannot occur in free space because it is energetically forbidden. The most common kind of orbital electron capture is K capture, for the probability of electron capture depends on the probability of finding an orbital electron in the region of the nucleus. The latter is largest for the case of an $1s$ electron. Of course, K capture cannot occur if, in the decay, the change of nuclear spin is by several units. If the energy difference is less than the binding energy of a K electron, orbital electron capture can still occur from outer shells such as L, M, or N. However, in most of this section we shall consider K capture only.

Since the neutrino is difficult to detect directly, measurements are confined to determinations of the recoil energy of the final nucleus. Energy balance requires

$$E_\nu + E_R = \Delta E - |E_K| \tag{5-4}$$

where ΔE is the Q value for the reaction, $|E_K|$ is the binding energy of the electron in the K orbit, and E_R and E_ν are the recoil energy of the

Table 5-1 Nuclear Recoil in Orbital Electron Capture

Initial Nucleus	Disintegration Energy (mev)	(E_R) Cal.	(E_R) Exp.	Reference
Be^7	0.864 ± 0.003	(57.3 ± 0.5) ev	(56.6 ± 1.0) ev	(Sm-51)
	0.864 ± 0.003	(57.3 ± 0.5) ev	(55.9 ± 1.0) ev	(Da-52)
Ar^{37}	0.816 ± 0.004	(0.711 ± 0.004) cm/μsec	(0.71 ± 0.06) cm/μsec	(Rod-52)
	0.816 ± 0.004	(9.67 ± 0.08) ev	(9.6 ± 0.2) ev	(Ko-54b)
	0.815 ± 0.002	(9.65 ± 0.05) ev	(9.63 ± 0.06) ev	(Sn-55)

nucleus and the energy of the neutrino. From momentum considerations it is easy to show that

$$E_R \sim \frac{E_\nu^{\,2}}{2\,mc^2} \quad \text{or} \quad E_R = 140.2\,\frac{E^2 - m_\nu^{\,2}c^4}{M} \tag{5-5}$$

where E_R is in electron volts, E is the disintegration energy (in units of mc^2) released in the K-capture process, $m_\nu c^2$ is the neutrino rest energy in units of mc^2, and M is the atomic mass of the recoiling atom in atomic mass units. For example, for Be^7 K capture, $E \sim 860/511 = 1.68$, yielding a recoil energy of 57 ev. (The sharp recoil peak was strikingly demonstrated by a series of convincing and beautiful experiments. The results are summarized in Table 5-1.) For heavier nuclei the recoil energy becomes less, and we will neglect it in most of our considerations.

The transition probability for electron capture is calculated in the same way as for β decay. Of course, if we are dealing with a two-particle decay, the density of final states is different from that for β decay. Thus we have

$$\frac{dN_F}{dE} = \frac{p_\nu^{\,2}\,dp_\nu\,d\Omega}{(2\pi\hbar)^3\,dE} \tag{5-6}$$

This expression reduces to

$$\frac{dN_{\mathrm{F}}}{dE} = \frac{m^2c}{2\pi^2\hbar^3}\epsilon_\nu^{\ 2} \tag{5-7}$$

where

$$\epsilon_\nu = \frac{\Delta E - E_K - E_R}{m_0c^2} \tag{5-8}$$

We assume that the interaction is a mixture of V and A and that the two-component neutrino theory holds ($g_i = g_i'$). However, we write the interaction in the nonrelativistic form and assume, in addition, that the electron also moves nonrelativistically. (This assumption is justified, since the binding energy, even of a K electron, is small compared to its rest energy, except for the very heaviest nuclei.) Thus the Hamiltonian, expressed as an integral with respect to Pauli wave functions of the nucleons and leptons, becomes

$$H = g_V\left[-\int 1 \cdot \psi_\nu^{\ \dagger}\psi_e + \lambda\int \boldsymbol{\sigma} \cdot \psi_\nu^{\ \dagger}\boldsymbol{\sigma}\psi_e\right] \tag{5-9}$$

where $\lambda = -g_A/g_V$ (see Appendix VI for the derivation).

Let us, for simplicity, assume that the recoil nucleus is moving along the positive z axis. Then the neutrino must move along the negative z axis. Since the neutrino has negative helicity, its spin direction is along the positive z axis. The neutrino wave function ψ_ν can thus be written as $\begin{pmatrix}1\\0\end{pmatrix}$.

Since we are not treating the electron relativistically, it does not have to be polarized along its direction of motion. In fact, the absence of any net electron polarization is the reason why our Hamiltonian is actually the same as in a parity-conserving theory. For a K-orbital electron ψ_e is given by

$$\sqrt{Z^3/\pi a_0^{\ 3}}\, e^{-Zr/a_0} \tag{5-10}$$

times the spin wave function which is either $\begin{pmatrix}1\\0\end{pmatrix}$ or $\begin{pmatrix}0\\1\end{pmatrix}$, since the electron is in a definite spin state in the atom. We evaluate $\psi_e(r)$ at the origin where the reaction is assumed to take place and thus obtain

$$\psi_e(0) = \sqrt{Z^3/\pi a_0^{\ 3}}\begin{pmatrix}1\\0\end{pmatrix} \quad \text{or} \quad \begin{pmatrix}0\\1\end{pmatrix} \tag{5-11}$$

Two cases may arise in the evaluation of $|H|^2$; namely, the spin of the electron may be parallel to the neutrino (no spin flip), or it may be antiparallel (spin flip). In the absence of spin flip, we obtain

$$|H|_{\text{no flip}} = \sqrt{Z^3/\pi a_0^3}\, g \int \left(1 \cdot \psi_\nu^\dagger \psi_e - \lambda \int \sigma_z \cdot \psi_\nu^\dagger\, \sigma_z \psi_e \right) \tag{5-12}$$

where we note that only the matrix elements of σ_x and σ_y vanish because of the spin orthogonality condition. Thus

$$|H|^2_{\text{no flip}} = \frac{Z^3}{\pi a_0^3} g^2 \left[\left| \int 1 \right|^2 + \lambda^2 \left| \int \sigma_z \right|^2 \right] \tag{5-13}$$

for unpolarized nuclei since the cross terms vanish. For the spin-flip case the only surviving terms are those for $\int \sigma_x$ and $\int \sigma_y$. Thus we obtain

$$|H|^2_{\text{flip}} = \frac{Z^3}{\pi a_0^3} g^2 \lambda^2 \left[\left| \int \sigma_x \right|^2 + \left| \int \sigma_y \right|^2 \right] \tag{5-14}$$

If we are dealing with a filled K shell, either spin case is possible, so that the total decay probability is given by a sum over the spin-no-flip and spin-flip cases. If the K shell has only one electron, we must average over either spin flip or no spin flip. In either case we can write

$$\begin{aligned} |H|^2 &= [|H|^2_{\text{no flip}} + |H|^2_{\text{flip}}] \frac{N_K}{2} \\ &= \frac{Z^3}{2\pi a_0^3} g^2 \left[\left| \int 1 \right|^2 + \lambda \left| \int \boldsymbol{\sigma} \right|^2 \right] N_K \end{aligned} \tag{5-15}$$

where N_K is the number of K electrons. Letting

$$|M|^2 = \left[\left| \int 1 \right|^2 + \lambda^2 \left| \int \boldsymbol{\sigma} \right|^2 \right] \tag{5-16}$$

we obtain for the K-capture transition probability

$$w_K = \frac{m^2 c}{\hbar^4} \frac{N_K}{2\pi^2} g^2 \frac{Z^3}{a_0^3} \epsilon_\nu^2 |M|^2 \tag{5-17}$$

This can be written as

$$w_K = \frac{G^2}{2\pi^3} \frac{mc^2}{\hbar} 2\pi(\alpha Z)^3 \epsilon_\nu^2 |M|^2 \tag{5-18}$$

where $\hbar/mc = \alpha a_0$, α is the fine-structure constant, G is related to g by Eq. (2-24), and we have set $N_K = 2$ appropriate to a filled K shell. We define

$$f_K = 2\pi(\alpha Z)^3 \left(\frac{\Delta E - E_K}{m_0 c^2} \right)^2 \tag{5-19}$$

and write w_K as

$$w_K = \frac{G^2}{2\pi^3}\frac{mc^2}{\hbar} f_K |M|^2 \tag{5-20}$$

Now let us consider the ratio w_K/w_{β^+}, the relative probability of K capture to positron emission. The nuclear matrix element is the same for both K capture and positron decay; therefore it cancels out in the determination of this ratio. Thus we find that

$$\frac{w_K}{w_{\beta^+}} = \frac{f_K}{f_{\beta^+}} \tag{5-21}$$

Of course, f_K and f_{β^+} are independent of the details of nuclear structure. Putting in appropriate values for f_K and f_{β^+}, we obtain, for example,

$$\frac{w_K}{w_{\beta^+}} \rightarrow 60\pi\left(\frac{\alpha Z}{\epsilon_{0,K}}\right)^3 \qquad \text{for} \qquad \epsilon_0 \gg 1 \tag{5-22}$$

This limiting case illustrates the fact that a large ϵ_0 favors β^+ decay, whereas a large Z favors K capture. This result for the ratio w_K/w_{β^+} holds not only for the particular interactions $V - \lambda A$ chosen here, but also quite generally for any allowed β decay, with the provision that there are no Fierz interference terms. If a possible Fierz interference term is included, and if (let us suppose for simplicity) we have a pure Gamow-Teller interaction, the ratio w_K/w_{β^+} is modified from R_0 to

$$R_0\left[1 + \Phi(Z, \epsilon_0, \epsilon_K)\frac{g_T}{g_A}\right] \tag{5-23}$$

(The function of Φ can be found in the literature (Sh-54; Zw-57.)

Note that the foregoing ratio depends on the ratio of coupling constants itself, whereas the deviation of a β spectrum from the allowed shape depends on the square of this ratio. Thus the measurement of the ratio of K-capture decay rate to positron decay rate may provide a more sensitive test for the absence of Fierz interference terms than does the study of β-spectrum shapes itself. Such a measurement has been made in the decay of Na^{22} which is believed to be a $3^+ \rightarrow 2^+$ (pure Gamow-Teller) transition. The experimental value of the ratio R agrees within a few percent with R_0, and Φ is calculated to equal 3.4 in this case. Thus it is seen that g_T is no more than 2% of g_A, and quite possibly g_T is 0.

L Capture. Electron capture from the L shell is also possible and is related to K capture by the following ratio of transition probabilities

$$\frac{w_L}{w_K} = \frac{1}{8}\left(\frac{\Delta\epsilon - \epsilon_L}{\Delta\epsilon - \epsilon_K}\right)^2 \tag{5-24}$$

We need the factor $\frac{1}{8}$ because the ratio of electron wave functions at the nucleus is

$$\frac{|\psi_{2s}(0)|^2}{|\psi_{1s}(0)|^2} = \frac{1}{8} \quad \text{and also} \quad |\psi_{2p}(0)|^2 = 0 \tag{5-25}$$

provided that the electron screening effects are neglected.

For a more detailed calculation of orbital electron capture rates, it is, of course, necessary to take into account the screening by other electrons. Such screening will reduce the effective charge felt by each electron and will therefore tend to reduce the orbital capture rate.

5-2 DOUBLE BETA DECAY

Consider an isobaric triplet (N, Z), $(N \pm 1, Z \mp 1)$, $(N \pm 2, Z \mp 2)$ with the intervening isobar of higher mass than either of the pair. This situation occurs only between a pair of stable even-Z, even-N isobars and with an odd-Z, odd-N isobar as the intermediate state, for example, ${}_{20}\mathrm{Ca}^{48}_{28}$, ${}_{22}\mathrm{Ti}^{48}_{26}$, ${}_{60}\mathrm{Nd}^{150}_{90}$, ${}_{62}\mathrm{Sm}^{150}_{88}$, etc. The direct decay of one of these to the other via the intermediate isobar is energetically forbidden. The nucleus (N, Z) can decay to $(N \pm 2, Z \mp 2)$ by double β decay. The theory of the Dirac neutrino requires that four particles be emitted in the process; that is, two neutrinos (or antineutrinos) must accompany the emission of two positrons (or electrons). Consequently, the energy distribution of the sum of the two positrons (or electrons) will be continuous. If the neutrino and antineutrino were the same particle—a possibility considered by Majorana (Ma-37)—a neutrino might be emitted into a virtual state with the emission of the first electron and then reabsorbed in the subsequent emission of the second electron. The energy sum of the two positrons (electrons) would be unique and equal to the energy available in double β decay. This feature would greatly improve the sensitivity to and detection of double β decay. Since energy is only conserved between the initial (N, Z) and the final $(N \pm 2, Z \pm 2)$ states, and not in the intermediate state, the virtual neutrino may assume any energy up to approximately 30 mev, where its de Broglie wavelength becomes short compared to the nuclear radius. The volume of phase space accessible to the intermediate state is therefore very much larger than that for the Dirac neutrinos; hence the greatly increased transition probability for Majorana neutrinos.

The theory of double β decay was investigated in detail by Goeppert-Mayer (Go-35), Furry (Fu-39), Konopinski (Ko-49), Primakoff and Rosen (Pr-59a), and Greuling and Whitten (Gr-60).

A crude estimate for the transition rate of double β decay with Dirac neutrinos can be made as follows. If we have simple β decay, the transition rate can be given by

$$w_\beta \sim \frac{mc^2}{\hbar}\frac{G^2\,|M|^2}{2\pi^3}\frac{\epsilon_0{}^5}{30} \tag{5-26}$$

where we have neglected Coulomb effects and assumed that $\epsilon_0 \gg 1$. Thus it is plausible that the decay rate for double β decay in units of the characteristic rate $mc^2/\hbar$ is a simple square of the rate for single β decay. Consequently, for double β decay we may write approximately

$$w_{2\beta} \sim \frac{mc^2}{\hbar}\left(\frac{G^2\,|M|^2}{2\pi^3}\right)^2\left(\frac{\epsilon_0{}^5}{30}\right)^2 \tag{5-27}$$

Using $mc^2/\hbar \sim 10^{21}\ \text{sec}^{-1}$ and $G^2\,|M|^2/2\pi^3 \sim 3 \times 10^{-27}$, as deduced from β decay of light nuclei, we obtain $\tau_{2\beta} = w_{2\beta}^{-1} \sim 3 \times 10^{-27} \times \epsilon_0^{-10}$ yr. Thus if

$$\epsilon_0 \sim 5\,mc^2 \qquad \tau \sim 3 \times 10^{20}\ \text{yr}$$

A more accurate theory due to Primakoff gives

$$\tau_{2\beta}^{\text{F}} \cong 9(\tau_{2\beta})^{\text{GT}} \cong 6 \times 10^{19\pm2}\left(\frac{60}{Z}\right)^2(1 - e^{\mp 2\pi Z/137})^2\left[\frac{8}{\epsilon_0 - 2}\right]^{10}\ \text{yr} \tag{5-28}$$

where $\epsilon_0 - 2$ represents the maximum kinetic energy release in units of mc^2. Some correction for the Coulomb effect appears through the term containing Z.

The second main possibility for double β decay is that lepton conservation does not hold and that no neutrinos are emitted in the process. Thus we would have

$$i \rightarrow f + e + e \tag{5-29}$$

which could imply that a neutrino is emitted in the first step but reabsorbed in the second step. In such a case, since there are no neutrinos to carry off energy, the total energy of the emitted electrons is fixed and equal to the maximum possible energy release; moreover, distribution is not continuous, although it is continuous for double β decay accompanied by two neutrinos. If the ν and $\bar{\nu}$ were the same particle—the so-called Majorana neutrino—this might actually happen.

The lifetime for neutrinoless double β decay is expected to be about 10^5 shorter than for two-neutrino double β decay. This ratio is essentially equal to the fourth power of the energy ratio $(30 \text{ mev}/1 \text{ mev})^4 \sim 10^6$ between the virtual neutrino in the neutrinoless double β decay and that of the real neutrino in two-neutrino double β decay. In the neutrinoless case, a lifetime of the order 10^{15} to 10^{16} years would be expected for typical nuclei, as compared to 10^{20} to 10^{22} years for two-neutrino double β decay. Several experiments have been made in search of double β decay, but no conclusive evidence in its favor has been found to date. If the process occurs, its lifetime seems to be definitely longer than the expected value for the neutrinoless theory, but the experimental accuracy is not yet sufficient to enable us to detect double β decay accompanied by two neutrinos, even if it occurs. The experimental results and the theoretical predictions for several typical nuclei are given in Table 5-2. The existing evidence on the lower limit of the lifetime definitely points toward two-neutrino rather than neutrinoless double β decay. It has been shown (Lee-65) that if all neutrinoless double β decays can be definitely excluded, there must exist a way of assigning lepton numbers l to the neutrinos so that the algebraic sum of l is always conserved in all interactions. Therefore the apparent absence of the neutrinoless double β decay strongly supports the validity of the lepton conservation law.

On the other hand, it might be thought that these results do not necessarily imply lepton conservation (Pr-59a; Ko-59). According to the two-component neutrino theory, the neutrinos emitted in β^- decay are right-handed. In the second step of the double β^--decay process the neutrino might be absorbed, but according to the two-component theory it will have to be left-handed in order to be absorbed. Thus even if the neutrino and antineutrino are the same particle, neutrinoless double β^- decay still cannot occur.

Implicit in this argument, however, is the assumption of zero neutrino rest mass. Ryan and Okubo (Ry-63) have shown by a unitary

Table 5-2 Double Beta-Decay Experiments

Transition	Kinetic Energy Release (mev)	$t_{1/2}$ (in years) Experimental	Theoretical* Two-Neutrino	Neutrinoless	Reference
$_{20}Ca^{48} \rightarrow {}_{22}Ti^{48}$	4.3 ± 0.1	$> 4.3 \times 10^{18}(2\nu)$ $> 1.2 \times 10^{19}(\text{No } \nu)$	$4 \times 10^{20\pm2}$	$3 \times 10^{15\pm2}$	(Aw56; Do-58; de-64, Sh-65)
$_{60}Nd^{150} \rightarrow {}_{62}Sm^{150}$	3.7 ± 0.1	$> 4 \times 10^{18}$	$2 \times 10^{20\pm2}$	$2 \times 10^{15\pm2}$	(Cow-56)
$_{40}Zr^{96} \rightarrow {}_{42}Mo^{96}$	3.4 ± 0.3	$> 2 \times 10^{16}$	$1 \times 10^{21\pm2}$	$6 \times 10^{15\pm2}$	(Mc-53, Aw56)
$_{52}Te^{130} \rightarrow {}_{54}Xe^{130}$	3.2 ± 0.1	$= 1.4 \times 10^{21}$	$2 \times 10^{21\pm2}$	$8 \times 10^{15\pm2}$	(In-50,59; Hay-53; Koh-54; Se-54)
$_{48}Cs^{116} \rightarrow {}_{50}Sn^{116}$	2.6 ± 0.1	$> 10^{17}$	$6 \times 10^{21\pm2}$	$2 \times 10^{16\pm2}$	(Wi-55; De-55; Fr-52)
$_{42}Mo^{100} \rightarrow {}_{44}Ru^{100}$	2.3 ± 0.2	$> 10^{17}$	$4 \times 10^{22\pm2}$	$4 \times 10^{16\pm2}$	(Fr-52; Koh-54; Se-54)
$_{50}Sn^{124} \rightarrow {}_{52}Te^{124}$	2.0 ± 0.2	$> 10^{17}$	$4 \times 10^{22\pm2}$	$5 \times 10^{16\pm2}$	(Ka-52; Fi-52; Mc-53)
$_{92}U^{238} \rightarrow {}_{94}Pu^{238}$	1.1	$> 6 \times 10^{18}$	$3 \times 10^{25\pm2}$	$2 \times 10^{18\pm2}$	(Le-50)

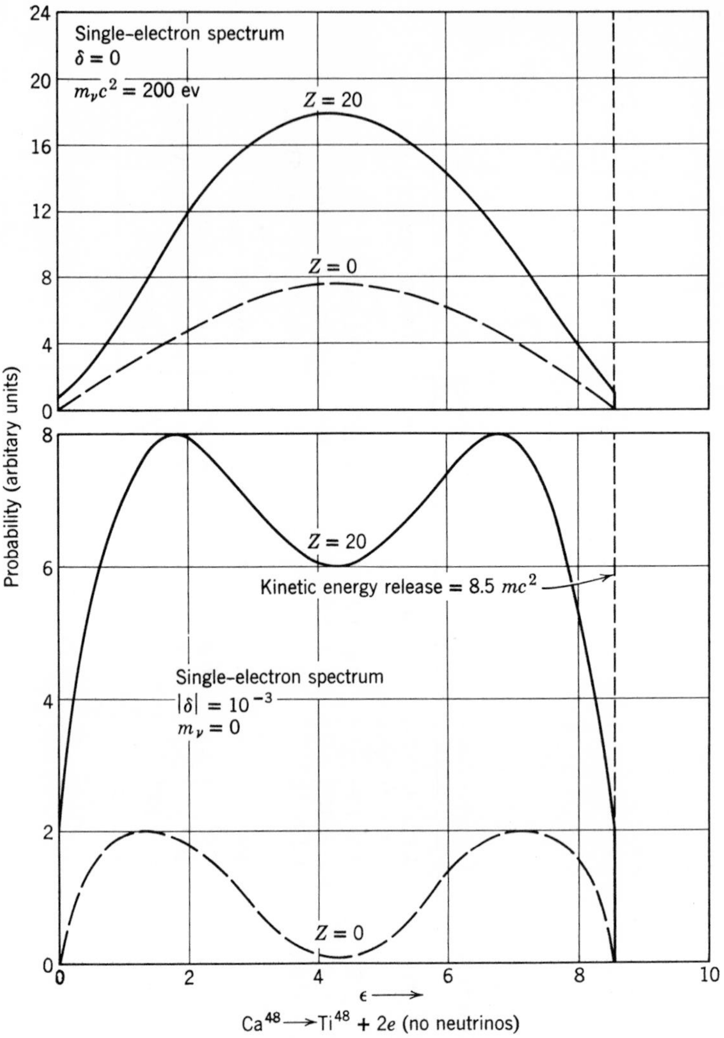

(a)

Fig. 5-1 (*a*) The single-electron energy spectrum of the neutrinoless double β decay of Ca^{48}. The upper curves are for $\delta = 0$, $m_\nu \neq 0$; the lower curves are for $m_\nu = 0$, $\delta \neq 0$. The $Z = 0$ spectra were obtained using plane wave electron wave functions. The $Z = 20$ spectra were obtained using point nucleus Coulomb electron wave functions appropriate for Ca^{48} (where δ represents the small violation of lepton conservation). (*b*) The coincidence and single-electron energy spectrum of the two-neutrino double β decay of Ca^{48}. The sum of the kinetic energies of the two electrons is $E = \epsilon_1 + \epsilon_2 \leqslant E_0$. See (Gr-60).

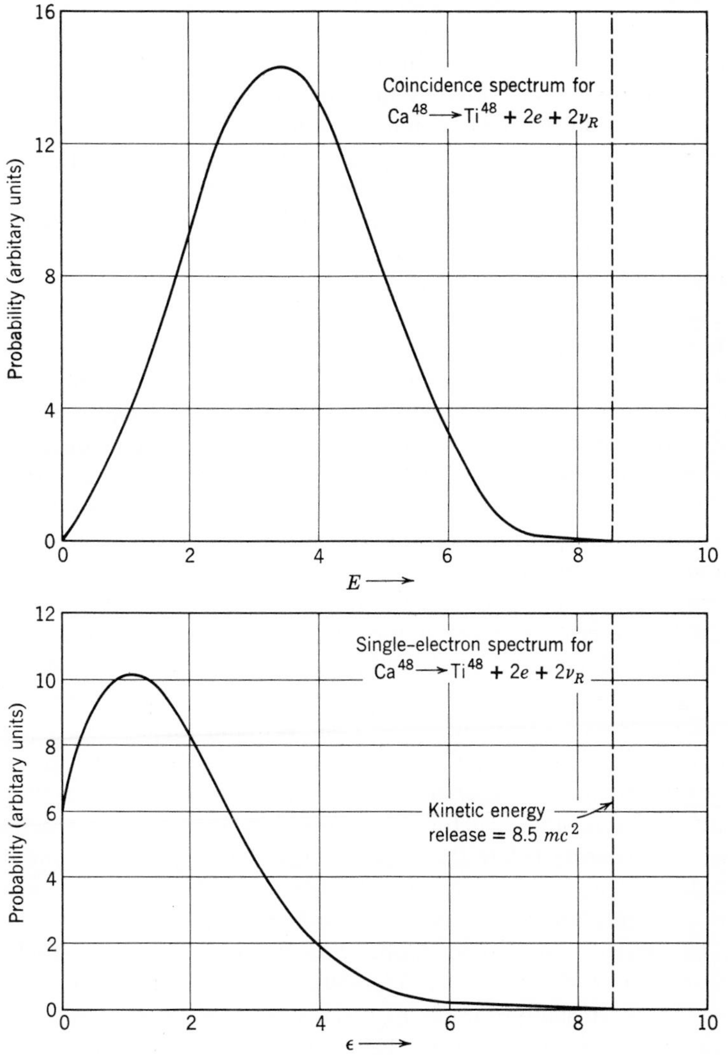
16
12
8
4
0
0
2
4
6
8
10
Probability (arbitary units)
Coincidence spectrum for
$Ca^{48} \longrightarrow Ti^{48} + 2e + 2\nu_R$
$E \longrightarrow$
12
10
8
6
4
2
0
Probability (arbitary units)
Single-electron spectrum for
$Ca^{48} \longrightarrow Ti^{48} + 2e + 2\nu_R$
Kinetic energy
release = 8.5 mc^2
$\epsilon \longrightarrow$

(b)

transformation that the Majorana and two-component theories of a massless neutrino are entirely equivalent as far as experimental results are concerned. Indeed, for zero rest mass we can *define* the two particles involved as the particle and antiparticle, which is equivalent to assuming the validity of lepton conservation. The finite neutrino rest would also imply an incomplete polarization of the neutrino.

If lepton conservation is violated, some neutrinoless double β processes must occur. Because the rate of decay for neutrinoless double β decay is 10^5 faster than two-neutrino double β decay, a search for neutrinoless double β decay is a very sensitive and effective method of revealing any small violation of lepton conservation in β decay.

It should be emphasized that the two-component theory alone does not require zero rest mass of the neutrino $m_\nu = 0$ (Ca-57). Only if *both* the two-component theory and the conservation law of lepton number are valid must the mass of neutrino be zero. Under that condition, the intermediate-state neutrino is completely polarized and may not be reabsorbed to produce a neutrinoless double β-decay final state. However, if the neutrino has a finite mass $m_\nu \neq 0$ and/or the effective V and A lepton currents are not exactly equal, that is, $|\delta| = |y - 1| \neq 0$, neutrinoless double β decay, in violation of lepton conservation, is possible. To give some idea of the different appearances of the spectra of the two different types of double β decays, Greuling and Whitten (Gr-60) computed the single-electron energy spectrum of the neutrinoless double β decay of Ca^{48} for $|\delta| = 0$, $m_\nu \neq 0$ and for $m_\nu = 0$, $|\delta| \neq 0$ (as shown in Fig. 5-1*a*) and the single-electron spectrum and the sum spectrum of the two-neutrino double β decay of Ca^{48} (Fig. 5-1*b*). It is interesting to note that for the neutrinoless final state the spectrum rises very sharply below the upper energy limit E_0, whereas the distribution of electrons in the two-neutrino double β decay increases very gradually below the kinetic energy release E_0.

The present situation in double β decay may be summarized by quoting Dubrokhotov et al. (Dub-59), "The search for double beta decay is an amazing example of a fantastic succession of periods of hope and of disillusionment. Two times in the course of a single decade, this phenomenon has been 'discovered,' and both times the discovery has been found to be erroneous. The history of the question is still not complete; the phenomenon has not been observed experimentally." Further studies of double β decay are needed.

5-3 INVERSE BETA PROCESSES

Shortly after the publication of the Fermi theory of β decay, Bethe and Peierls (Be-34) pointed out the possibility of inverse β decay. In inverse β decay, the nucleus captures a neutrino or antineutrino and simultaneously ejects an electron or positron. This process may be represented as

$$(Z^A) + \nu \rightarrow (Z+1)^A + e^-$$

or

$$(Z^A) + \bar{\nu} \rightarrow (Z-1)^A + e^+ \tag{5-30}$$

The cross sections for any inverse β reactions are expected to be extremely small—only about 10^{-44} cm^2—because of the characteristic weakness of the β interaction. It was only after the intense antineutrino flux from nuclear reactors became available that an intense and serious search for such rare occurrences was begun.

Antineutrino Capture by Protons

The first process that we will consider is neutrino capture or, more properly, antineutrino capture by protons:

$$\bar{\nu} + \mathrm{p} \rightarrow \mathrm{n} + e^+ \tag{5-31}$$

This process is, of course, the inverse of neutron decay, which may be seen by transposing the electron to the left and reversing the direction of the reaction. As written, this interaction satisfies the conservation of leptons. Another possible reaction, which, however, does not satisfy lepton conservation, is

$$\nu + \mathrm{p} \rightarrow \mathrm{n} + e^+ \tag{5-32}$$

It will be considered later. Let us now discuss the first type of reaction.

The transition probability for the reverse reaction is given by

$$w = \frac{2\pi}{\hbar} |H|^2 \frac{dN}{dE} \tag{5-33}$$

and the cross section will be given by the transition rate divided by the flux of incoming neutrinos. Thus we obtain

$$d\sigma = \frac{w}{c} = \frac{2\pi}{c\hbar} |H|^2 \frac{dN}{dE} \tag{5-34}$$

The essential difference between the direct and inverse β-decay processes occurs in the density of final-energy states. In ordinary β decay the available energy is shared by the antineutrino, the electron, and the recoiling nucleus, whereas for the inverse process the energy is shared only by the positron and the recoiling neutron. If we neglect the recoil energy of the neutron, the positrons emitted will be more energetic, and the density of the final states will be given by

$$\frac{dN}{dE} = \frac{p_e{}^2\, dp_e\, d\Omega_e}{(2\pi\hbar)^3\, dE_e} = \frac{m^2c}{(2\pi\hbar)^3}\,\epsilon\sqrt{\epsilon^2 - 1}\, d\Omega_e \tag{5-35}$$

where we define ϵ by E/mc^2, and $d\Omega$ refers to an element of solid angle. The cross section becomes

$$d\sigma = \frac{2\pi}{c\hbar}\,|H|^2\,\frac{m^2c}{(2\pi\hbar)^3}\,\epsilon\sqrt{\epsilon^2 - 1}\, d\Omega_e \tag{5-36}$$

and we assert that $|H|^2$ for the inverse process is the same as for ordinary β decay; that is,

$$|H_{\rm fi}|^2 = g^2\Big[\,|\textstyle\int 1\,|^2 + \lambda^2\,|\textstyle\int \boldsymbol{\sigma}\,|^2\Big] = g^2\,|M|^2 \tag{5-37}$$

giving

$$d\sigma = \frac{2\pi}{c\hbar}\,g^2\,\frac{|M|^2 m^2 c}{(2\pi\hbar)^3}\,\epsilon\sqrt{\epsilon^2 - 1}\, d\Omega_e \tag{5-38}$$

Since we are not interested in any angular distributions, we integrate over all angles between the positron and antineutrino and obtain for the total cross section

$$\sigma = \frac{g^2m^2}{\pi\hbar^4}\,|M|^2\,\epsilon\sqrt{\epsilon^2 - 1} = \left(\frac{\hbar}{mc}\right)^2 \frac{G^2\,|M|^2}{\pi}\,\epsilon\sqrt{\epsilon^2 - 1} \tag{5-39}$$

Table 5-3 shows the calculated cross sections for several values of the energy on the assumption that $G^2 \sim 9 \times 10^{-24}$, and $|M|^2 = |\int 1|^2 + \lambda\,|\int \boldsymbol{\sigma}|^2 \sim 5$.

Table 5-3 Calculated Neutrino-Capture Cross Sections

E_ν/mc^2	E_e/mc^2	$\sigma/10^{-44}\ \text{cm}^2$
4.5	2.0	8
5.5	3.3	20
10.8	8.3	180

It is interesting that the values of the calculated cross sections are actually twice as large as the values that would be obtained if we had not used the two-component theory of neutrinos and the conservation of leptons. The factor of 2 arises in the following way.

For two-component neutrinos, by applying the theory of the conservation of leptons, the outgoing neutrinos from the reactor have only one spin state instead of the usual two. By using the method of detailed balance, the absorption cross section for inverse β decay must be twice as great as the old one; that is,

$$\sigma_{2\text{component}} = 2\sigma_{\text{classical}}$$

In Cowan and Reines's experiments (Re-56) the principle of detection was as follows: The $\bar{\nu}$ entered the cadmium-loaded large liquid scintillators which served as proton targets as well as neutron capture material. A prompt pulse caused by the annihilation of the positron signaled the absorption of an antineutrino. The recoil neutron was slowed down and captured by cadmium in several microseconds. In this radiative neutron-capture process, several γ rays would be simultaneously emitted, and their detection results in a delayed pulse with respect to the annihilation pulse. To identify the observed signals as neutrino-induced, exhaustive supplementary checks were performed in order to justify the conclusion. Figure 5-2 illustrates the essential detection principle. The measured cross section per fission antineutrino for the inverse β decay of the proton is

$$\sigma_{\text{exp}} = (11 \pm 4) \times 10^{-44}\ \text{cm}^2$$

In order to compare this result with the theoretically expected cross section, we must know very accurately the positron energy or the antineutrino spectrum from the nuclear reactor; they are related by the equation $E_{\bar{\nu}} = 3.53 + E_{e^+}$ (mc^2 units). To obtain the $E_{\bar{\nu}}$ the β spectrum from the fission fragments of U^{238} was measured, and then the antineutrino spectrum was derived. The results are

σ_{theo}	
9.5×10^{-44} cm^2	Carter, Reines, Wagner, and Wyman (Ca-59)
12×10^{-44} cm^2	Muelhause and Oleksa (Mu-57)
15×10^{-44} cm^2	King and Perkins (Ki-58)

The agreement between σ_{exp} and σ_{theo} is very good.

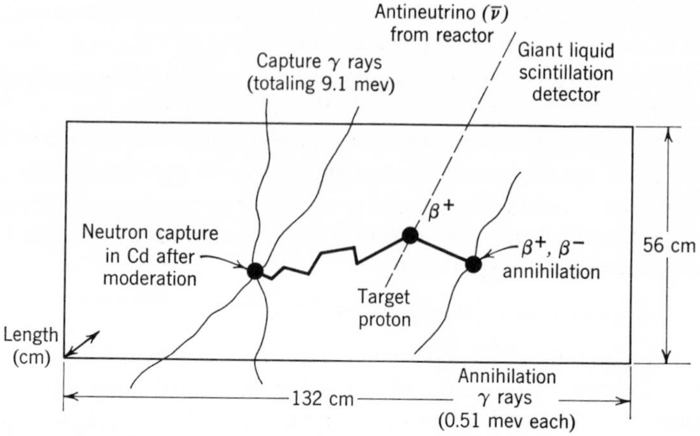

Fig. 5-2 Schematic antineutrino detector. An antineutrino is shown transmuting a proton to produce a neutron and positron. The positron slows down and annihilates, producing annihilation radiation. The neutron is moderated by the hydrogen of the scintillator and is captured by the cadmium, producing capture γ rays.

However, recent high-energy neutrino interactions, using neutrinos produced in pion decays in flight, yielded muons but failed to produce electrons. This provides strong evidence for the existence of two kinds of neutrinos (see Sec. 7-3).

Neutrino Capture

Ar^{37} decays by electron-capture process as

$$Ar^{37} + e^- \rightarrow Cl^{37} + \nu \tag{5-40}$$

Its inverse reaction would be

$$Cl^{37} + \nu \rightarrow Ar^{37} + e^- \tag{5-41}$$

Here a neutrino rather than an antineutrino is required for the absorption process according to lepton conservation. The intensive flux of antineutrinos pouring out of a reactor is actually from neutron-rich fission products which decay by β^- emission. Therefore the flux of antineutrinos does not provide the correct kind of neutrino for this process, and no Ar^{37} activity should be expected of the reactor neutrino.

Davis's experiment (Dav-55) involved irradiation of a large volume (1000 gallons) of carbon tetrachloride near a nuclear reactor for a long period of time. Afterward, Ar^{37} was removed and purified by physical methods. The amount of Ar^{37} was measured by counting the x rays from its electron capture decays in a low-background Geiger counter. The very small Ar^{37} counts (0.3 ± 3.4 counts per day) which Davis observed in his latest improved Geiger counter is equivalent to a cross section for neutrino capture of $(0.1 \pm 0.6) \times 10^{-45}$ cm²/atom. This is small in comparison with the theoretically expected inverse cross section $\sigma = 2 \times 10^{-45}$ cm²/atom by fission neutrinos if $\nu = \bar{\nu}$. Furthermore, the muon component in the cosmic background under the experimental condition was not known too clearly. The observed residue counts might be accounted for by the muon activation from the cosmic radiation. Therefore no evidence for a positive inverse effect on Cl^{37} from the reactor neutrinos exists at the present time.

The probability that a neutrino or antineutrino traveling through the earth will be captured is of the order of magnitude $\rho\sigma d$, with ρ the density of nucleons per cubic centimeter, say 10^{24}; and d the diameter of earth, say 10^4 km or 10^9 cm. A measured neutrino-capture cross section of 10^{-43} cm² implies that the probability of absorption is only 10^{-10}! Thus it is not surprising that tons of absorbing material are required to detect neutrinos experimentally.

On the other hand, the very weakness of neutrino interactions also means that neutrinos may come from otherwise inaccessible regions of the universe, for example, the center of the sun. Incidentally, these neutrinos are produced mostly in the reaction $\mathrm{p} + \mathrm{p} \to d + e^+ + \nu_e$. Thus they should be detected by capture in Ar^{37}, but not in hydrogen (unlike the antineutrinos produced in a nuclear reactor) (Bah-63).

CHAPTER 6

Other Weak Interactions with Leptonic Decays

Besides nuclear β decay, there are other weak decay processes involving leptons. These are π decay, μ decay, μ capture, and leptonic decays of strange particles. In this chapter we shall discuss the essential characteristics, formalism, and implications of the various decay processes and their relations to nuclear β decay.

6-1 DECAY OF THE MU MESON (MUON)

The experimental evidence from the helicity determination and the asymmetry distribution of leptons in the various lepton decay modes indicates that the helicity properties of neutrinos involved in nuclear β decay are the same types as those that occur in other lepton decays. For a long time it had been taken for granted that the neutrinos involved in pion decay, muon decay, and all weak interactions were the same as those resulting from nuclear β decay. But very recently it was brilliantly demonstrated (Da-62) that at least two kinds of neutrinos exist; that is, we now have evidence of neutrinos which produce μ mesons but do not produce electrons (see Sec. 7-4).

The free muon almost certainly decays into an electron and two neutrinos:

$$\mu^{\pm} \rightarrow e + \nu + \nu$$

The Q value of this decay is practically the entire muon rest energy, 105 mev, of which the electron can carry at most half. The lifetime of the μ is $(2.20 \pm 0.01) \times 10^{-6}$ sec. Actually, it is now believed that the two neutrinos emitted are different, one being properly a neutrino, the other an antineutrino. In addition, one of the neutrinos is associated with the electron and the other with the muon. Thus the decay of the

μ^- can be represented as

$$\mu^- \rightarrow e + \nu_\mu + \bar{\nu}_e$$

Here we shall first briefly review the types of phenomena in π-μ-e decays that are direct consequences of the two-component neutrino and lepton conservation. The existence of two neutrinos will be discussed in Sec. 7-4.

In analogy to β decay, the Hamiltonian density for μ decay is proportional to

$$g_i(\tilde{\psi}_e \hat{O}_i \psi_\mu)(\tilde{\psi}_{\nu_\mu} \hat{O}_i \psi_{\nu_e}) \tag{6-1}$$

Let us substitute two-component wave functions for neutrinos into the second covariant. We have

$$\tfrac{1}{4} g_i[\tilde{\psi}_{\nu_\mu}(1 \mp \gamma_5)\hat{O}_i(1 \pm \gamma_5)\psi_{\nu_e}] \tag{6-2}$$

For an arbitrary combination of S, T, and P, $\hat{O}_i$ is a sum of products involving an even number of $\gamma_\mu (\mu = 1, 2, 3, 4)$. Thus $\hat{O}_i$ commutes with γ_5 and the covariant vanishes identically. For a combination of V and A, $\hat{O}_i$ contains an odd number of γ matrices and thus anticommutes with γ_5; we therefore have for the neutrino covariant

$$\tfrac{1}{2} g_i[\tilde{\psi}_{\nu_\mu} \hat{O}_i(1 + \gamma_5)\psi_{\nu_e}] \tag{6-3}$$

Thus the μ^- decays into electron, neutrino, and antineutrino (where the latter two obey the two-component theory) can proceed only via a VA combination of interactions.

We have grouped the two-neutrino wave functions into one covariant for mathematical convenience. It might be argued that since electron and neutrino wave functions are grouped together in one covariant in β decay, we should probably do the same here for μ decay. This is done in Appendix VII. Nevertheless, according to the Fierz rearrangement theorem (Fi-37) relating to the permutation of fields, such a change of roles will result in a change of the coefficients in the linear combination of the interactions. However, if the linear combination is $V - A$, the linear combination is the same in both groupings:

$$(\tilde{\psi}_e \psi_\mu)(\tilde{\psi}_{\nu_\mu} \psi_{\nu_e}) \quad \text{and} \quad (\tilde{\psi}_{\nu_\mu} \psi_\mu)(\tilde{\psi}_e \psi_{\nu_e}) \tag{6-4}$$

The three measurements in μ decay which are of special interest here are (1) the Michel parameter ρ, (2) the energy dependence of the asymmetry parameter, and (3) the polarization of muons and electrons.

The Michel Parameter ρ

In the μ-decay process, the law of lepton conservation demands that the two neutrinos involved must be a particle and an antiparticle, such as

$$\mu^{\pm} \rightarrow e^{\pm} + \nu + \bar{\nu} \tag{6-5}$$

From the evidence for the two different types of neutrinos in β and μ decays, we must modify Eq. (6-5) to

$$\begin{aligned} \mu^{+} + \nu_{\mu} &\rightarrow e^{+} + \nu_{e} \\ \mu^{-} + \bar{\nu}_{\mu} &\rightarrow e^{-} + \bar{\nu}_{e} \end{aligned} \tag{6-5$'$}$$

If there were no lepton conservation, the emission of two neutrinos or two antineutrinos would also be permissible; that is,

$$\mu^{\pm} \rightarrow e^{\pm} + \nu_{e} + \nu_{\mu} \tag{6-6}$$

or

$$\mu^{\pm} \rightarrow e^{\pm} + \bar{\nu}_{e} + \bar{\nu}_{\mu} \tag{6-7}$$

From the two-component theory of the neutrino, the shape of the electron energy spectrum depends on whether these two neutrinos have identical or different helicities. The electron distribution is

$$N(x)\,dx = 4x^2[3(1 - x) + \tfrac{2}{3}\rho(4x - 3)]\,dx \tag{6-8}$$

where x is the electron energy in units of the maximum energy (the spectrum is normalized so that $\int_0^1 N(x)\,dx = 1$) and the electron rest mass has been neglected. The shape of the spectrum depends solely on the single parameter ρ which was introduced by Michel (Mi-50) and represents a combination of all the coupling constants occurring in the interaction. Figure 6-1 shows a plot of the electron spectrum for various ρ values. This parameter must be equal to zero if the electron is accompanied by two neutrinos or two antineutrinos (thus if the μ^- is an antiparticle, the μ decay would be: $\mu^- \rightarrow e^- + \bar{\nu}_{\mu} + \bar{\nu}_{e}$). This can be understood physically by the following reasoning. If the electron has maximum energy $E_{\text{max}} = \frac{1}{2}m_{\mu}c^2 \simeq 51.7$ mev, the two neutrinos must both be emitted in the opposite direction to it. If the neutrinos are of the same helicity, their relativisitic wave functions

$$\begin{pmatrix} 1 \\ 0 \\ 1 \\ 0 \end{pmatrix} e^{i\mathbf{p}\cdot\mathbf{r}}$$

are the same at the origin, even though their energies may be different or one is a ν_e and the other a ν_μ. The antisymmetrized wave function for the pair (taken at the origin) must therefore vanish. Consequently, $N(E_{\text{max}}) = 0$ in this case, which corresponds to a Michel parameter $\rho = 0$. If a neutrino and an antineutrino are emitted, we find $\rho = \frac{3}{4}$. For this case, $N(E_{\text{max}}) \neq 0$, but $dN/dE\,(E_{\text{max}}) = 0$ and $N(x)\,dx = (6x^2 - 4x^3)\,dx$, which is the result obtained in Appendix VII. (The value of ρ is slightly modified if an intermediate boson exists; see Sec. 7-4.)

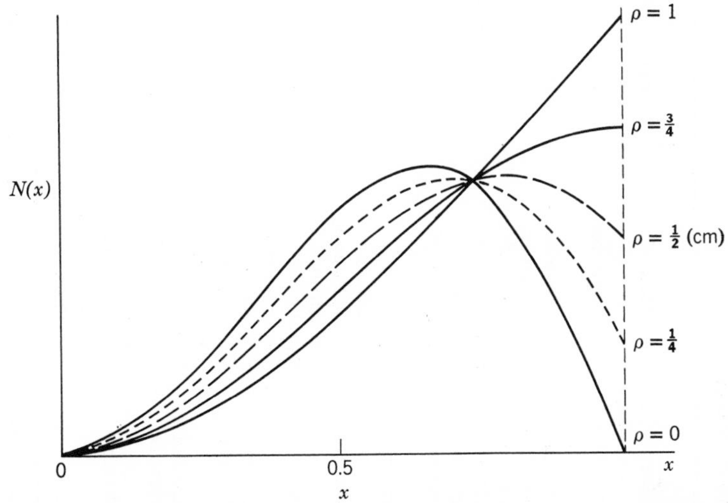

Fig. 6-1 Spectrum of the electrons from μ–e decay for various values of the Michel parameter ρ. The abscissa is the energy x and the ordinate is the decay probability.

Radiative Corrections. It must be mentioned that in μ decay a γ quantum may be emitted in addition to the electron and the neutrino pair. A quantum may also be emitted by the muon and then reabsorbed by the electron before it escapes. Experimentally, these two processes cannot be separately identified so as to differentiate them from ordinary decays (Be-56; Ki-59). Calculations show that these radiative processes modify the electron spectrum slightly and give a value of ρ slightly different from $\frac{3}{4}$.

The determination of ρ is made by using unpolarized muons. The instruments used include Wilson chambers, diffusion chambers, spectrometers, bubble chambers, and spark chambers. The present experimental values of ρ vary from 0.74 to 0.79 (see Table 6-1), which is certainly close to 0.75 for the emission of one neutrino and one

Table 6-1 A Summary of ρ Determinations from Muon Decay

Author	Year	Source	Method	Charge	Number of Events	Quoted Value of ρ*'
Leighton, Anderson, and Seriff	1949	Cosmic rays	Cloud chamber	$\mu^{\pm}$	75	0.075 ± 0.20
Sagane, Gardner, and Hubbard	1951	Accelerator	Cloud chamber	μ^{+}	150	<0.06
Lagarrigue and Peyrou	1951	Cosmic rays	Cloud chamber	$\mu^{\pm}$	150	0.19 ± 0.12
Bramson, Seifert, and Havens	1952	Accelerator	Nuclear emulsions	μ^{+}	301	0.41 ± 0.13
Hubbard	1952	Accelerator	Cloud chamber	μ^{+}	400	0.26 ± 0.26
Villain and Williams	1954	Accelerator	Cloud chamber	μ^{+}	280	0.50 ± 0.13
Sargent, Rinehart, Lederman, and Rogers	1955	Accelerator	Cloud chamber	μ^{-}	415	0.68 ± 0.11
Bonetti, Levi-Setti, Panetti, Rossi, and Tomassini	1956	Cosmic rays	Nuclear emulsions	$\mu^{\pm}$	506	0.57 ± 0.14
Crowe, Helm, and Tautfest	1956	Accelerator	Double-focusing spectrometer	μ^{+}		$(0.62 \pm 5)\%$
Sagane, Dudziak, and Vedder	1956	Accelerator	Spiral orbit spectrometer	μ^{+}		$(0.72 \pm 8)\%$
Rosenson	1958	Accelerator	Diffusion chamber	μ^{+}	1300	0.67 ± 0.05
Dudziak et al.	1959	Accelerator	Spiral orbit spectrometer	μ^{+}		0.741 ± 0.027
Block et al.	1962	Accelerator	Bubble chamber	μ^{-}	2276	0.751 ± 0.034
Plano et al.	1960	Accelerator	Hydrogen bubble chamber	μ^{+}	9213	0.785 ± 0.020
Bardon et al.	1965	Accelerator	Magnetic spectrometer with sonic spark chambers	μ^{+}	10^7	0.747 ± 0.005
Sherwood et al.	1965					

* Up to 1952 the quoted results for ρ were based on substantially higher values of muon mass than the presently accepted value of $m_\mu = 206.77\ m_\mu$. With the new muon mass, these experimental spectra would imply somewhat larger ρ values—$\sim$0.4 for the results of Leighton et al., Lagarrigue and Peyrou, and Hubbard, $<$0.1 for Sagane et al. and 0.48 ± 0.13 for Bramson et al.

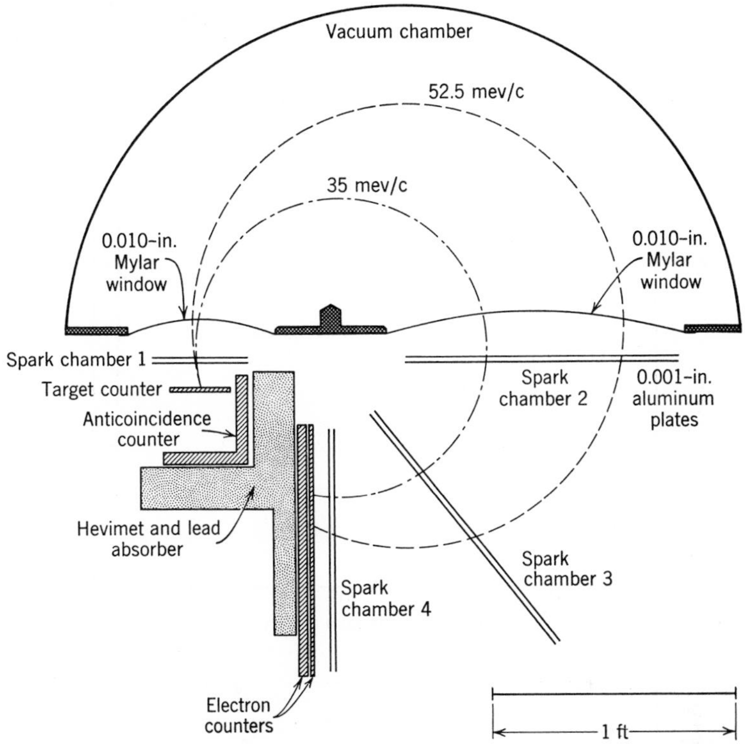

Fig. 6-2 Experimental arrangement. The entire setup is in a homogeneous magnetic field. The two circular trajectories have been drawn for the minimum and maximum positron momenta accepted at a field of 6.62 kgauss. The two 0.003-in. Mylar windows for each chamber, which are not shown, are the only other objects in the path of the positrons. From (Bar-65).

antineutrino. We may therefore confidently reject the assumption of two neutrinos or two antineutrinos in muon decay, which also justifies the assignment of particle and antiparticle roles in lepton conservation.

From 1959 to 1964, the value $\rho \approx 0.75 \pm 0.03$ as determined from the bubble chamber experiments (Pl-60; Bloc-62) and the magnetic spectrometer method (Du-59) was considered the most precise one. But in 1965 two greatly improved determinations were reported (Bar-65; She-65). These determinations were carried out by using a magnetic spectrometer with sonic spark chambers or wire spark chambers on line to a computer. The experimental arrangement of the Columbia's measurements (Bar-65) is shown in Fig. 6-2. Because

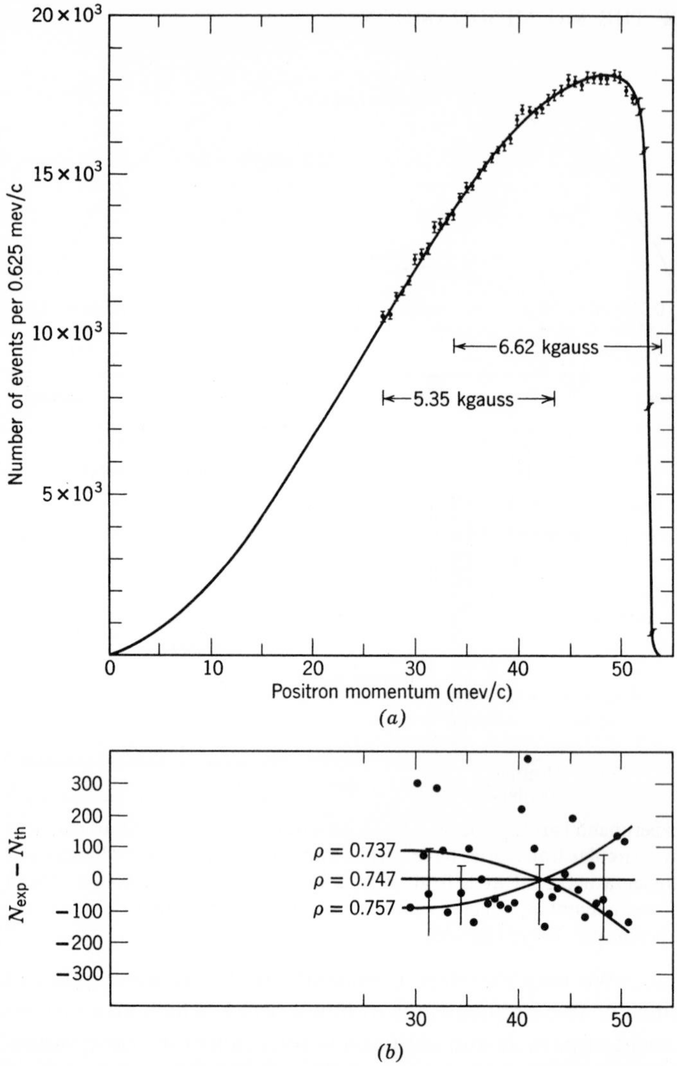

Fig. 6-3 (*a*) Experimental points for magnetic-field settings, normalized to the overlap region. The solid line is the theoretical spectrum for $\rho = 0.75$. The Michel spectrum,

$$\rho(x)\,dx = \tfrac{1}{2}[12x^2 - 12x^3 + \rho(\tfrac{32}{3}x^3 - 8x^2)]\,dx,$$

where x is the positron momentum divided by its maximum value, has been corrected for internal radiation, bremsstrahlung, and ionization loss. (*b*) The deviation of experimental points from the best-fit theoretical curve for $\rho = 0.747$, showing typical experimental errors for four points. Curves for $\rho = 0.737$ and 0.757 are shown for comparison. From (Bar-65).

of the much higher momentum resolution and the large apertures which reduce the bremsstrahlung as well as increase the number of observed events, the accuracy of the determined ρ value is greatly improved, as shown in Fig. 6-3. A square fit to the data gives a best value of $\rho = 0.747 \pm 0.005$.

Energy Dependence of the Asymmetry Parameter

Shortly after the first observation of nonconservation of parity and charge conjugation in the β decay of Co^{60}, the spatial asymmetrical distribution of the decay electrons from $\pi \rightarrow \mu \rightarrow e$ decays was observed by Garwin, Lederman, and Weinrich (Ga-57) in counter experiments, and also independently by Friedman and Telegdi (Fri-57) in nuclear emulsions. A schematic diagram of the experimental setup in the counter experiments is shown in Fig. 6-4. A beam of monochromatic π^+ mesons of 85 mev with about 10% μ^+ mesons was brought out from the synchrocyclotron. The separation of the pions and muons was made by the usual method of absorption in a graphite block, which stopped the π^+ meons but let through μ^+ mesons with reduced momentum. The muons were finally stopped in a graphite target. The incidence of a muon on the target was registered by a coincidence pulse from the scintillation counters 1 and 2. The subsequent $\mu \rightarrow e$ decay in the graphite target was detected by an electron telescope of two scintillation counters (3 and 4). The delayed coincidence gate of a duration of 1.25 μsec was triggered 0.75 μsec after the incident muon entered the carbon target.

Let us assume that the muons are polarized in the direction of their motion. The object of this experiment is to measure the spatial distribution of the electrons relative to this direction, characterized by the angle between the directions of motion of the muon and emergence of the decay electron.

As Fig. 6-4 shows, when no magnetic field is applied to the carbon target, the electron telescope registers electrons for which θ is close to 100°. If a current flows through the coil shown in the figure, a constant magnetic field (which is perpendicular to the plane of the drawing) will be produced in the target area, and the spin of the stopped muon inside of the target will precess at the frequency $\omega = geH/2m_\mu c$ rad/sec, where g is the gyromagnetic ratio for the muon and m_μ is the mass of muon. The pattern of the electron angular distribution will naturally follow the spin of the muon and precess (with respect to the magnetic field)

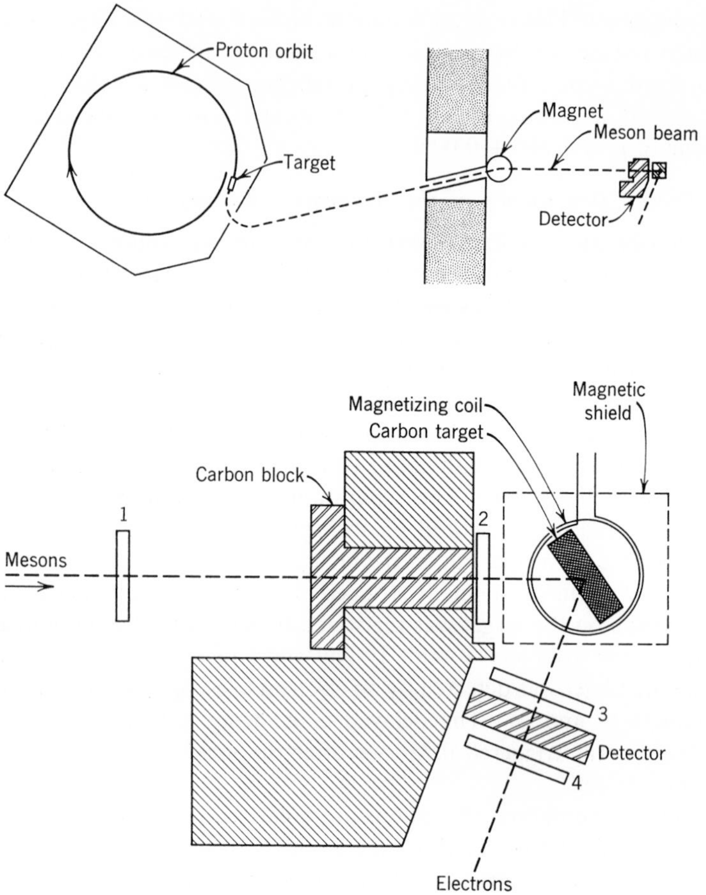

Fig. 6-4 Experimental arrangement for $\pi \to \mu \to e$ asymmetry observations. The magnetizing coil wound closely on carbon target to provide uniform vertical field. From (Ga-57).

with the same frequency as that of the muon spin. In this first experiment the experimental arrangement was fixed, but the current in the magnetizing coil was varied. Thus to each value of the current there corresponds a certain mean angle of rotation of the muon spin. The experimental results were plotted in Fig. 6-5 where an oscillatory variation with respect to the applied field is clearly shown. It was found that (1) parity is not conserved in both $\pi \to \mu$ and $\mu \to e$ decays;

(2) a maximum asymmetry as predicted by the two-component theory of the neutrino was observed; and (3) the gyromagnetic ratio g for the muon is very close to 2, as is expected for a simple Dirac particle.

Theoretically, the angular distribution of the decay electrons from a polarized μ meson at rest is

$$dN = \tfrac{1}{2}\pi x^2[(3 - 2x) \pm \xi(1 - 2x)\cos\theta]\, dx\, d\Omega \qquad (6\text{-}9)$$

for $\mu^\pm$ decay, where p = electron momentum, $x = p/p_{\max}$, and θ is the angle between the electron momentum and the spin direction of the

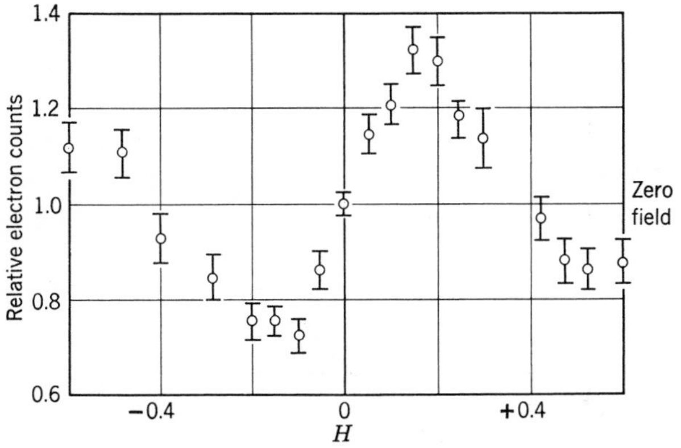

Fig. 6-5 Results of the electron counting rate as the precession magnetic field is varied. From (Ga-57).

decaying muon. For the derivation of Eq. 6-9 see Appendix VII. For the two-component neutrino,

$$\xi = \frac{g_V g_A^* + g_A g_V^*}{g_V^2 + g_A^2} \qquad (6\text{-}10)$$

and for a $V - A$ interaction, $\xi = -1$.

The angular asymmetry

$$I(\theta)\, d\theta = (1 + A\cos\theta)\sin\theta\, d\theta \simeq \left(1 \pm \xi\frac{1 - 2x}{3 - 2x}\cos\theta\right)\sin\theta\, d\theta \qquad (6\text{-}11)$$

for $\mu^\pm$ decay, where A is the asymmetry parameter and is equal to $\pm\xi(1 - 2x)/(3 - 2x)$, which depends on the energy of the electron x and is prominent for a larger value of $|\xi| \approx 1$. The variation of the asymmetry parameter A for $\mu^{\pm}$ decay is $A = \mp\xi$ for $x = 1$ (maximum energy), $A = 0$ for $x = \frac{1}{2}$ (sign reversed at this point), and $A = \pm\frac{1}{3}\xi$ for $x = 0$ (zero energy). For the integrated spectrum, $A = \mp\frac{1}{3}\xi$. Figure 6-6 shows a plot of the experimental A versus energy, compared with the predictions of the two-component neutrino theory.

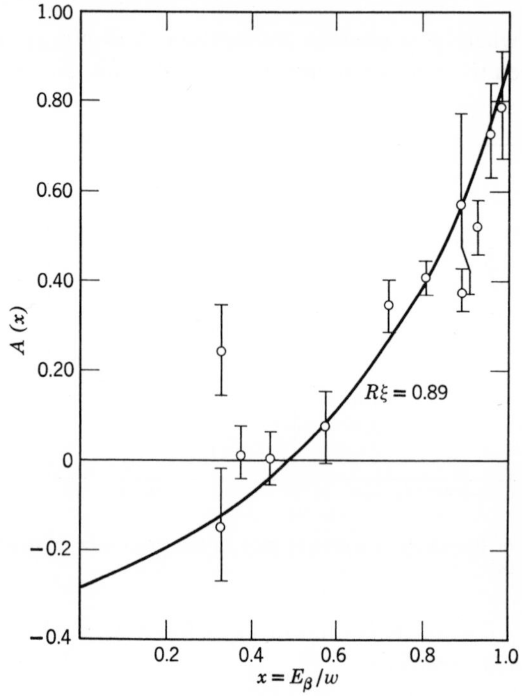

Fig. 6-6 Dependence $A(x)$ of the asymmetry coefficient on the energy for μ^+ decay, according to the data of Kruger and Crowe. The solid line is $A(x)$ according to the theory of the two-component neutrino. See (Kr-59).

It can be seen that of the electrons emitted in μ^- decay, the slow electrons tend to be peaked forward (parallel to the μ spin) and the fast electrons are emitted predominantly in the backward direction. This can be understood by the following simple argument.

First of all, in the preceding decay $\pi^- \to \mu^- + \bar{\nu}_\mu$, conservation of angular momentum and the known helicity of the emitted antineutrino require that the μ^- be right-handed (cf. Sec. 6-3), that is spin parallel to momentum, opposite to the usual left-handed polarization for lepton particles.

If the emitted electrons have the maximum energy, conservation of energy and momentum require that the ν_μ and $\bar{\nu}_e$ be emitted in the same direction (opposite to the electron momentum). These two particles have opposite helicity, and in the present case their spins cancel. Thus the electron spin is parallel to the muon spin and also to the muon momentum. Since electrons are polarized opposite to their direction of motion, they must tend to be emitted in the backward direction.

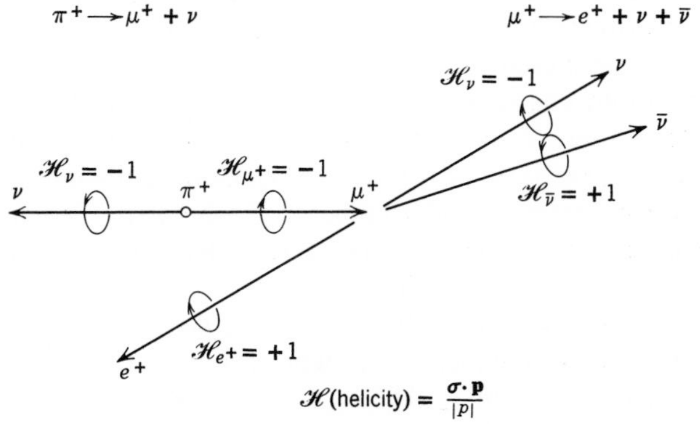

Fig. 6-7 Helicities in $\pi \rightarrow \mu \rightarrow e$ decay.

On the other hand, for slow electrons conservation of momentum requires that the two neutrino be preferentially emitted in opposite directions. Their spins thus tend to add. Conservation of angular momentum then favors an electron spin opposite to the muon spin, that is, emission in the forward direction.

For μ^+ decay, the momentum and angular-momentum considerations are the same as for μ^- decay, but since the positrons tend to be polarized parallel to their directions of motion, the asymmetry of the angular distribution is opposite to that for μ^- decay (see Fig. 6-7).

Experimentally, it was not known at first whether the sign of $\cos\theta$ was positive or negative, for we had no direct method by which to determine the average polarization ($\langle\boldsymbol{\sigma}\rangle$) of the muons; we knew only that it was along the direction of its motion. However, direct determination (Al-60; Bac-61; Pl-60) of the polarization of muons has been made and confirms the assignments of the helicities of muons by the method of indirect deduction, given in Sec. 4-6.

From Garwin, Lederman, and Weinrich's first experiment on parity nonconservation in muon decay, and also from Friedman and Telegdi's independent results, the large electron asymmetry shows a preponderant fraction of electrons coming out in the backward direction with respect to the muon-flight direction. The latest absolute value of $|\xi| = 3|A|$ is $\geq 0.975 \pm 0.054$. This was measured by the following method (Ba-59). A beam of μ mesons whose polarization was accurately known as a function of the kinetic energy was obtained by selecting the μ mesons emitted near the cutoff angle in the decay in flight of π^+ mesons of measured energy and stopped in a bromoform target. The bromoform target is known as a nondepolarizing target. A pulsed magnetic field was used to cause a precession of $\pm 90°$, first with the spin pointed into one set of detectors, then away from it, in one-hour cycles. This alternation of the precession direction permitted the measurement of the ratio of forward to backward emission in a single set of positron detectors and eliminated the necessity of considering the systematic asymmetries in the two sets of detectors. The measured value of $|\xi|$, which compares favorably with the predicted value from $V - A$ theory, is $\xi = -1[-1.003$ with radiative corrections (Ki-59)]. A hydrogen bubble chamber experiment carried out by Plano (Pl-60) gives a value of $|\xi| \geq 0.96 \pm 0.05$.

In the high-energy end of the spectrum, the data on asymmetry are in good agreement with the theory. In the low-energy region, measurements are difficult, and the statistical accuracy is still poor. However, as a whole, the energy dependence of the asymmetry distribution in μ decay agrees with the prediction of the two-component neutrino and $V - A$ thoery.

However, extensive work (Al-61) on asymmetry in the angular distribution of electrons from μ-e decay in nuclear emulsions placed in magnetic fields up to 35,000 oersteds revealed that the measured asymmetry parameter $A^* = PA$, where P is the polarization of the muon after stopping in the absorber, approaches 0.3 but always remains less than the maximum value $A^* = \frac{1}{3}$. It could be argued that the deviation from the maximum value is due to the depolarization effect from the formation of muonium in the nuclear emulsions (Or-57); however, according to the investigators, extensive checks of the value of A^* with emulsions of various gelatin content, and also investigations of the dependence of A^* on the magnetic field H, lead to the conclusion that the depolarization cannot be due to the formation of muonion.

If it is due to depolarization at all, it must be due to some yet unknown depolarization mechanisms.

Recently observed, positive evidence of the two kinds of neutrinos in neutrino-capture processes (see Sec. 7-4) has raised the question of the rest mass of the muon neutrino. Although the upper limit of the rest mass of the electron neutrino is 250 ev, which is not inconsistent with zero rest mass, we know much less about the mass of the muon neutrino. Its upper limit cannot be set at less than 3.5 mev at the present time (Ba-56)*. If the muon neutrino has a finite rest mass or if lepton conservation is not complete, the polarization of muon P will not be 1. Therefore, although the observation of A^* at less than the maximum value of $\frac{1}{3}$ may not have been caused by depolarization, it surely has profound significance in connection with the nature of the muon neutrino. Our discussion must remain speculative, however, until further experimentation.

Polarization of Muons and Electrons

Although the sign of cos θ in the asymmetry distribution was not known at first because of the lack of knowledge of the muon-spin direction, the helicity of the decay electrons could be deduced by the same argument used to deduce the longitudinal polarization of β particles in nuclear decays; that is,

$$\mathscr{P}_e = \pm\, \xi \frac{v}{c} \simeq \pm\, \xi \qquad \begin{array}{l} +\ \mu^- \text{ decay} \\ -\ \mu^+ \text{ decay} \end{array} \tag{6-12}$$

If the negative electron is left-handed polarized and the positron right-handed polarized, then $\xi = -1$. The backward asymmetry observed implies that the negative muon has positive helicity, and the positive muon has negative helicity. This can be visualized by considering an extreme case, as shown in Fig. 6-7.

When the neutrino and the antineutrino go in the same direction, the electron, which goes in the opposite direction, has to carry away the angular momentum of the muon. If μ^+ has a negative helicity, the decay e^+ must possess positive helicity. The experimental results on the polarization of the negative and positive electrons from muon

---

* In this experiment the error is due both to the measurement of the muon momentum and to the uncertainty in the pion mass ($m_{\pi^+} = (139.39 \pm 0.05)$ mev). If the best recently measured value of m_π is used, the result of Barkas et al. gives $m_{\nu\mu} < 3$ mev.

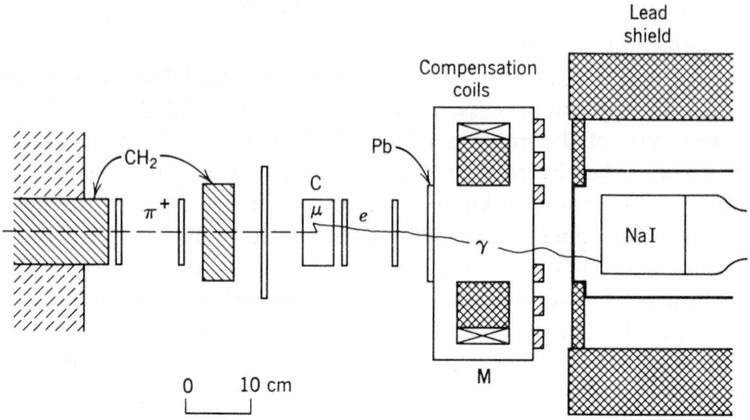

(a)

Fig. 6-8 (*a*) Measurement of the helicity of the electrons from $\mu \rightarrow e$ decay. (*b*) Experimental data for measurement of helicities of electrons—the abscissa is the pulse amplitude in the γ-ray counter (mev), and the ordinate is the difference of the numbers of counts with opposite directions of the magnetic field (in percent). From (Cu-59).

decays observed by measuring the circular polarization of the bremsstrahlung (Cul-57, 59; Macq-58) and the annihilation radiation, or by the Bhabha scattering method (An-58), all indicate positive helicity for e^+ and negative helicity for e^- (see Fig. 6-8).

In the summer of 1963 the results of $\mathscr{P}_{e^+} = (+28 \pm 16)\%$ on the helicity of the positron from μ^+ decay by positronium formation in a magnetic field (Di-63) called for further clarification of this problem by different methods.

The e^+ Annihilation Method (Buhl-63). The positron annihilates with a negative electron in a magnetized iron target, and the following reaction takes place:

$$e^+ + e^- \rightarrow \gamma + \gamma$$

According to Page (Pa-62) and McMaster (Mc-60), the cross sections for parallel and antiparallel electron-positron spins in the annihilation processes $(d\sigma/d\Omega)_{\uparrow\uparrow}$ and $(d\sigma/d\Omega)_{\uparrow\downarrow}$ are different. By comparing the experimental and theoretical values of $f(\theta_{\text{lab}}) = \dfrac{(d\sigma)_{\uparrow\uparrow} - (d\sigma)_{\uparrow\downarrow}}{(d\sigma)_{\uparrow\uparrow} + (d\sigma)_{\uparrow\downarrow}}$, they obtained the polarization of positron

$$\mathscr{P}_{e^+} = (105 \pm 30)\%$$

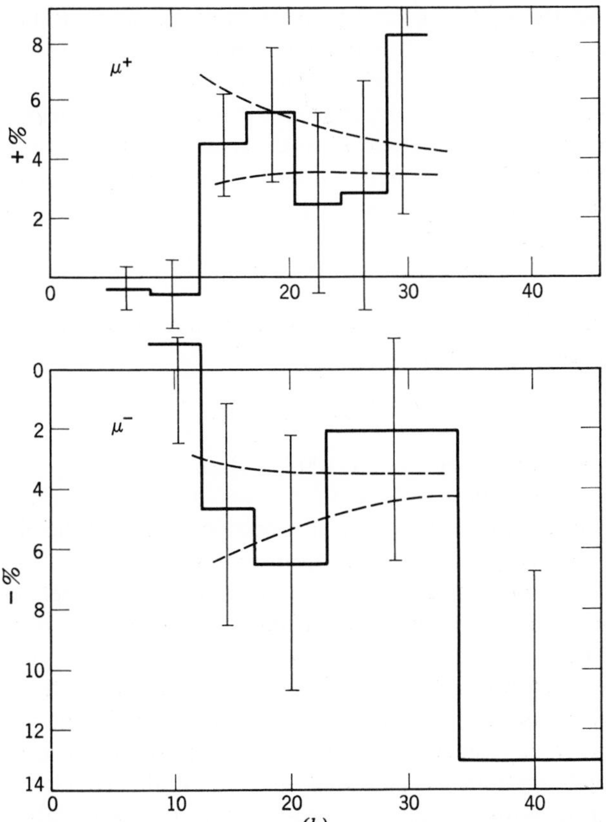

(b)

By Circular Polarization of the Bremsstrahlung (Blo-63). The polarization measurements reported by Bloom make use of the technique of transmission through magnetized iron of circularly polarized bremsstrahlung from the positrons of μ^+ decays. Thus the basic technique is the same as that used in earlier e^+ polarization measurements by Macq et al. (Macq-58) and Culligan et al. (Cul-57; Cu-59). Using the asymmetry results of the two highest energy points ($E_\gamma \geqslant 10$ mev) and taking the calculation of the effect to be accurate to $\pm 1\%$ in the asymmetry, they find the positrons to be right-handed with a polarization of

$$\mathscr{P}_{e^+} = (94 \pm 38)\%$$

Bhabha Scattering (Du-64). The Bhabha scattering method allows an absolute measurement of the polarization without slowing down the positrons. The cross section for positron-electron scattering $e^+ + e^- \rightarrow e^+ + e^-$ (Bhabha scattering) depends on the relative spin orientation of the two particles; for antiparallel spins the cross sections are larger than for parallel spins. The measured asymmetries are consistent with 100% polarization, the sign being the one expected for right-handed positrons. The final result is

$$\mathscr{P}_e{}^+ = 1.04 \pm 0.18$$

The Combined Result. The combined result of all three recent measurements just given is

$$\mathscr{P}_{e^+} = 1.03 \pm 0.14$$

The positrons from μ^+ decays are 100% polarized.

Although it is still desirable to narrow down substantially the uncertainty of the foregoing result, it is quite certain that the alarming results $\mathscr{P}_{e^+} = (28 \pm 12)\%$ from positronium experiments of Dick et al. (Di-63) are probably due to some unforeseen depolarizing mechanism in the degrading of electrons from 50 mev to 10 mev in Be (Dick-64).

Recently, the direct determination of the helicity of the muon, particularly of its sign, was carried out by several different methods. One group of experiments was based on the Møller scattering of high-energy longitudinally polarized muons by aligned electrons in magnetic iron, with cosmic rays (Al-60) and also with laboratory-produced muons at the CERN proton synchroton (Bac-61). The other method used the Mott scattering principle (Bar-61) in which the left-right asymmetry in backward scattering of transversely polarized muons from lead was measured. In the Mott scattering method (Bar-61), a beam of muons with known polarization (described on p. 224) was used. The measured number of scattering events agrees well with that calculated by assuming the muon to be a Dirac particle scattering in the static Coulomb field of an extended nuclear-charge distribution of the Fermi shape. With parameters determined from electron-scattering data, the measured left-right asymmetry of -0.090 ± 0.031 leads to the conclusion of positive helicity for the μ^- in π-μ decay. This same conclusion has been reached in Møller scattering experiments.

In $\pi^+ \rightarrow \mu^+ + \nu_\mu$ decay, the two particles μ^+ and ν_μ must come out in opposite directions and carry no total angular momentum. Theory predicts negative helicity for the neutrino. Here the results on the helicities of the neutrinos in nuclear β decays and those from π-μ-e decays are in excellent agreement.

6-2 MUON CAPTURE

As discussed in the preceding section, all muons can decay into an electron and two neutrinos. However, for the negative muon there is an alternative mode of transition. The μ^- may be captured by a nucleus in a manner analogous to orbital electron capture. The basic muon-capture process is

$$\mu^- + \mathrm{p} \rightarrow \mathrm{n} + \nu_\mu \tag{6-13}$$

Unlike orbital electron capture, this process is energetically possible in free space. If the μ and p are initially at rest, conservation of energy gives

$$E_0 = m_\mu c^2 = E_\nu + E_\mathrm{n}$$

where
$$E_\mathrm{n} = \frac{\mathrm{p_n}^2}{2m_\mathrm{n}} = \frac{\mathrm{p}_\nu^{\ 2}}{2m_\mathrm{n}} = \frac{E_\nu^{\ 2}}{2m_\mathrm{n}c^2}$$

(It is a good approximation to treat the recoiling neutron nonrelativistically and to neglect the n-p mass difference.)

Then
$$E_\nu + \frac{E_\nu^{\ 2}}{2m_\mathrm{n}c^2} = m_\mu c^2 = 105 \text{ mev}$$

Solving for E_ν and E_n, we find

$$E_\nu \sim 100 \text{ mev}$$

$$E_\mathrm{n} = 5 \text{ mev}$$

that is, most of the energy is carried off by the neutrino. In a heavy nucleus the other nucleons can carry off some of the momentum, and in addition the protons are not at rest, but form a Fermi gas; thus more energy may be given to the nucleus. The average excitation energy now turns out to be ~15 to 20 mev.

Next, let us calculate the transition rate for μ capture. Assuming that this process can be described in the same way as K capture* (see Eq. 5-18), we find for the capture rate per atom per second

$$w_{\mu^-+Z} = \frac{G^2}{2\pi^3}\frac{m_e c^2}{\hbar}\pi\left(\frac{\alpha m_\mu Z}{m_e}\right)^3\left(\frac{E_\nu}{m_e c^2}\right)^2 |M|^2 \tag{6-14}$$

Using the same value of the coupling constant as deduced from neutron decay and $|\boldsymbol{\sigma}|^2 = 3$,

$$|M|^2 = 1 + \left(\frac{g_A}{g_V}\right)^2 \left|\int \boldsymbol{\sigma}\right|^2 \sim 5.2 \tag{6-15}$$

we obtain $w = 270Z^3\ \text{sec}^{-1}$.

In making this estimate we have neglected the rest mass of the μ as compared to that of the nucleon. Correction for nucleon recoil reduces the capture rate by about 40%. In any case, we see that the capture rate of muons in hydrogen is less than 0.1% of the spontaneous decay rate, so that this fundamental capture process which is theoretically so important is nevertheless rather difficult to study experimentally (see later discussion). However, the experimental possibility is much more favorable for μ capture by heavier nuclei. Let us consider a nucleus of charge Z. The capture rate will be increased by a factor Z relative to the hydrogen case, simply because there are Z protons in each nucleus. In addition, there is a factor Z^3 arising from the large probability of muon wave function at the nucleus (for hydrogenic wave functions, $|\psi(0)|^2 \sim Z^3$). With heavy nuclei, recoil effects are still important, for the neutron produced in the capture reaction can recoil, leaving the residual nucleus in an excited state. In addition, of course, the nucleus can recoil as a unit, but this has only a small effect on the capture rate. Besides the effects just mentioned, we must also take into account two other corrections in calculating the capture rate.

First, in heavy nuclei, the muon will spend an appreciable part of the time inside the nucleus itself. Here the electrostatic potential no longer has the Coulomb form. Physically, by Gauss's theorem, the electric field felt by the μ depends only on the charge inside the μ orbit. Therefore, the effective charge felt is less than the actual nuclear charge. This effect can be accounted for if we replace Z by an effective charge Z_{eff}. For light nuclei we have $Z_{\text{eff}} \to Z$. However, even for as light a

* This assumption by itself implies that the β interaction is invariant under the simultaneous interchange $e \leftrightarrow \mu$ and $\nu_e \leftrightarrow \nu_\mu$. The assumption of $e \leftrightarrow \mu$ symmetry is consistent with a universal Fermi interaction (cf. Chap. 7-1) but does not necessarily require the UFI.

nucleus as Zn ($Z = 30$), Z_{eff} is reduced to 22, and for nuclei with Z of about 80 to 90, Z_{eff} is close to 35.

The muon capture rate is further reduced by the effect produced by Pauli's exclusion principle. The process cannot occur if, when the muon is captured by one of the protons, the resulting neutron finds itself in a state already occupied by another neutron. Altogether, we can write for the expected muon capture rate*

$$w_\mu = 270 \times Z_{eff}^4 \times C_{Pauli} \times C_{recoil} \tag{6-16}$$

For the heaviest nuclei, the experimental capture rate is about 10^7/sec, about twenty times the spontaneous decay rate.

Primakoff (Pr-59b) has studied this problem extensively, and his well-known closure calculation formula for the spin-average capture rate $w(Z, A)$ of a nuclide of charge Z, mass number A, is given by

$$w(Z, A) = Z_{eff}^4 w(1, 1)\gamma\left[1 - \frac{(A - Z)\delta}{2A}\right] \tag{6-17}$$

where Z_{eff}^4 can be calculated from known atomic properties. Here $w(1, 1)$ is the spin-averaged "proton" capture rate and is determined by the coupling constants of the capture process:

$$\begin{gathered} w(1, 1) \sim (g_V^2 + 3\Gamma_A^2) \\ \Gamma_A^2 = g_A^2 + \tfrac{1}{3}g_P^2 - 2g_P g_A \end{gathered} \tag{6-18}$$

It is interesting to note that an effective pseudoscalar coupling, g_P, occurs in the equation of muon capture rate. It is shown by Goldberger and Treiman (Goldb-58) and Wolfenstein (Wo-59) that even though it is in a Lagrangian containing only A and V terms, the presence of strong interactions such as in the four-step processes $\mu^- + p \rightarrow \mu^- + \pi^+ + n \rightarrow \mu^- + p + \bar{n} + n \rightarrow \nu + n$ generates additional terms in the S matrix. One of the terms behaves as a pseudoscalar coupling. This term is quite small in β decay but large in muon capture because of the large amount of energy released—large muon rest mass—and the consequent recoil of the residual nucleus. This induced pseudoscalar term was estimated to be eight times larger than the axial-vector coupling which generates it.†

* In the literature, the decay rate is also denoted by Λ.

† The rate for μ capture with simultaneous emission of γ radiation (Pr-59b) depends fairly sensitively on the ratio g_P/g_A. A recent study of this process in Ca^{40} (Co-63) gives $g_P/g_A \sim 12$.

In Eq. 6-17 γ is a parameter of nuclear properties. It accounts for the reduction in available neutrino phase space caused by the binding of the neutrons in complex nuclei, as well as for nuclear recoil effects. The exclusion principle manifests itself through the last bracket, where the fractional neutron number $(A - Z)/2A$ appears, multiplied by a nuclear correlation parameter δ.

Muon capture in complex nuclei has been systematically investigated by the Chicago group (Te-62) from Be to U. When the measured capture rate w normalized by $(Z_{\text{eff}})^4$ was plotted vs. the corresponding $(A - Z)/2A$, a linear plot was obtained, as shown in Fig. 6-9. The values of δ and γw thus determined from experiments are $\delta = 3.13$ and $\gamma w(1.1) = 183\ \text{sec}^{-1}$, which are in good agreement with the theoretically predicted value (Pr-59b) of $\delta = 3$ and $w(1,1) = 169\ \text{sec}^{-1}$ based on the theory of universal Fermi interaction. Therefore, in spite of the complicated nature of the capture data on complex nuclei, they are compatible with the theory of the universal Fermi interaction.

Muon Capture in Hydrogen and Helium[3]

To avoid complications from nuclear structure, we can study the fundamental muon-proton capture process. The capture rate is given by

$$w_{\mu^- + \text{p}} = \frac{G^2}{2\pi^3}\frac{m_e c^2}{\hbar}\pi\alpha^3\left(\frac{m_\mu}{m_e}\right)^5 C_{\text{recoil}}(1 + 3\lambda^2) \tag{6-19}$$

To a good approximation, we have for the correction factor C_{recoil}

$$C_{\text{recoil}} = \left(1 + \frac{m_\mu}{m_\text{p}}\right)^{-5} = 0.59 \tag{6-19a}$$

that is, in Eq. 6-19 we should replace the muon mass by the reduced mass of the muon-proton system. A more accurate evaluation of C_{recoil} (Pr-59) gives 0.58. By using the latter value, the calculated muon capture rate equals

$$w_{\mu^- + \text{p}} = 30(1 + 3\lambda^2)/\text{sec} \tag{6-20}$$

and setting $\lambda = |g_A/g_V| = 1.2$, we obtain 160/sec.

When we measure muon capture in hydrogen, there are some complications because of hyperfine structure and also molecular formation. Let us discuss both of these effects in turn.

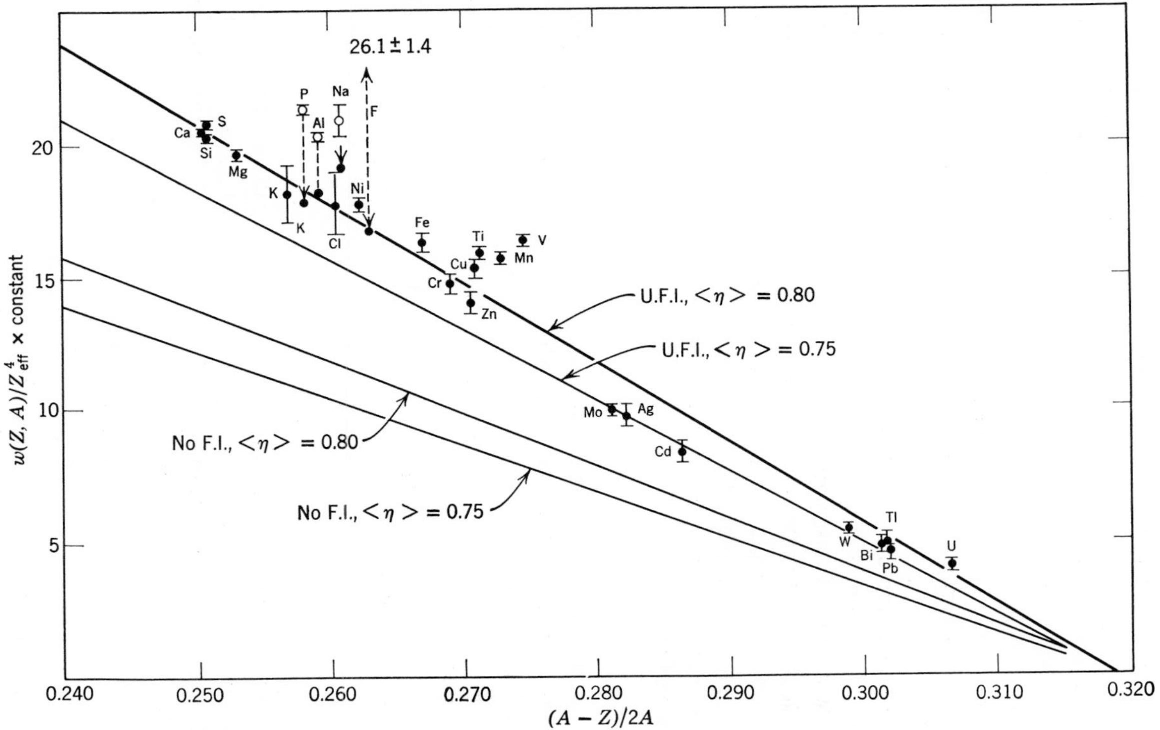

Fig. 6-9 Experimental values of $w(Z, A)/Z_{\text{eff}}^4$ versus $(A - Z)/2A$. The ordinate is actually $\pi a_0{}^3 w(Z, A)/Z_{\text{eff}}^4$ in units of 10^{-31} cm^3/sec. The heavy line through experimental points is best fit with $\delta = 3.13$, $\gamma w(1,1) = 183$/sec, that is, it corresponds to U.F.I. with $\langle \eta \rangle = 0.80$. From (Te-62).

Hyperfine Structure. The muonic atom μ^-p can be in either a singlet or triplet state. The hyperfine interaction (between magnetic moments of muon and proton) lowers the singlet state below the triplet state. The splitting is a few tenths of an electron volt; thus at thermal equilibrium only the singlet state is populated appreciably. (In atomic hydrogen there is a similar hyperfine splitting which is, however, less than 10^{-5} ev. Thus at equilibrium the singlet and triplet states are populated according to their statistical weights, namely in the ratio 1:3.)

The muon capture rate depends on the spin of the muonic atom. Suppose the atom is in the triplet state, with $S_z = 1$, that is, both μ and p have spin up. Conservation of angular momentum requires that the final neutron and neutrino also have spin up; thus there can be no spin flip during the capture. This case was already considered in the discussion of K capture (cf. Eq. 5-12). Of course, by rotational invariance the capture rate for unoriented nuclei is independent of S_z. Thus we find

$$w_{S=1} = 30(1 - \lambda)^2 \tag{6-21}$$

The capture rate in the singlet state may then be readily calculated since the spin-averaged capture rate w_{av} (which is just the rate calculated in Eq. 6-20) must satisfy

$$w_{\text{av}} = \tfrac{1}{4}w_{S=0} + \tfrac{3}{4}w_{S=1} \tag{6-22}$$

Consequently,

$$w_{S=0} = 30(1 + 3\lambda)^2 \tag{6-23}$$

For $\lambda = 1.2$, we find

$$w_{S=0} = 635/\text{sec}$$
$$w_{S=1} = 1.2/\text{sec}$$

Thus if the coupling is essentially $V - 1.2A$, practically all the capture occurs in the singlet state and very little in the triplet states. If, on the other hand, the β interaction were of the form $V + 1.2A$, the capture rate would be nearly spin-independent:

$$w_{S=0} \equiv 200/\text{sec}$$
$$w_{S=1} = 145/\text{sec}$$

(Of course, w_{av} is the same for the two cases.)

There is independent evidence for the $V - A$ interactions from the muon capture in the nucleus F^{19} (Lu-62). The hyperfine structure in the muonic atom was found, and it was established that the capture in the singlet state is much larger than that in the triplet state.

Molecular Formation. An additional complication in muon capture by hydrogen is that the muonic μp atom tends to combine with another proton to form the mu-molecule pμp. Muon capture occurs in this "molecule" rather than in the mesic atom itself. At equilibrium the total spin of pμp must be $\frac{1}{2}$ (since the hyperfine interaction lowers this state below the spin $\frac{3}{2}$ state). However, the spin can be shared among the three particles and thus the μp will be in the triplet state some of the time. And, although the muon can be captured by either proton (which would double the capture rate relative to that in the atom), the muon wave function at the position of each proton is less in the molecule pμp than in the muonic atom pμ. Detailed calculations (We-64) show that these two corrections happen to practically cancel; thus

$$w(\mathrm{p}\mu\mathrm{p})_{\mathrm{av}} \simeq w(\mu\mathrm{p})_{\mathrm{av}} \qquad (6\text{-}24)$$

where the average is taken over spins.* Now if the molecule has $S = \frac{3}{2}$, the atom *must* be in the $S = 1$ state, and there is essentially no capture (for a $V - A$ interaction). Thus, since

$$w(\mathrm{p}\mu\mathrm{p})_{\mathrm{av}} = \tfrac{1}{3}w(\mathrm{p}\mu\mathrm{p})_{1/2} + \tfrac{2}{3}w(\mathrm{p}\mu\mathrm{p})_{3/2} \qquad (6\text{-}25)$$

we find

$$w(\mathrm{p}\mu\mathrm{p})_{1/2} = 3w(\mu\mathrm{p})_0 = 480/\mathrm{sec} \qquad (6\text{-}26)$$

A more accurate calculation, taking into account the induced pseudoscalar terms in the interaction $g_P/g_A \sim 7$, gives (495 ± 22)/sec for $V - 1.2A$ (Ha-64). On the other hand, for a $V + 1.2A$ interaction, the capture is nearly spin-independent, just as in the atoms, and our argument gives $w \sim 190$/sec.

R. H. Hildebrand of Chicago (Hi-62) was the first one to observe this fundamental process in a liquid hydrogen bubble chamber. The capture of a muon by a proton is identified by the appearance of a recoil proton created by the neutron but without the presence of a decay electron. The expected energy of the neutron is 5.22 mev, and it is determined from the proton range and the angle of scattering (see Fig. 6-10). A similar experiment has since been carried out at CERN (Ce-62) and a counter experiment at Columbia (Ble-62).

---

* Earlier calculations had given a 20% higher capture rate for pμp (cf. Ro-63).

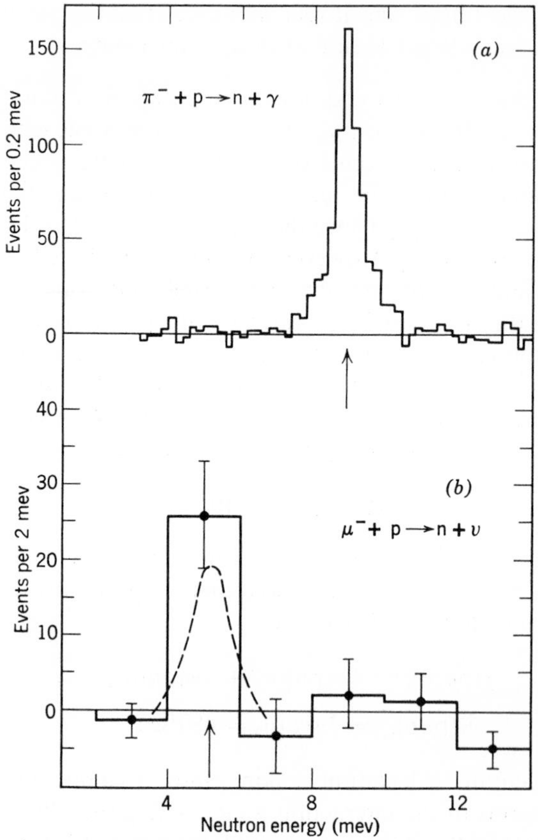

Fig. 6-10 Neutron spectra obtained from π^- captures (part *a*) and μ^- captures (part *b*). The arrows indicate the predicted energies of the neutrons for the two reactions (8.88 mev and 5.22 mev). The dashed curve shows the expected resolution for the μ-capture experiment. From (Hi-62).

The capture rates which have been observed recently are

$w = (450 \pm 50)\ \text{sec}^{-1}$ (CERN) C. Rubbia (Report to Weak Interaction Conference at Brookhaven 1963)

$w = (410 \pm 85)\ \text{sec}^{-1}$ (Chicago) Hildebrand (Hi-62)

$w = (464 \pm 62)\ \text{sec}^{-1}$ (Columbia) Lederman (Ro-63).

These values are in excellent agreement with the theoretically predicted values for a $V - A$ interaction.

Muon Capture in He^3. The μ capture in He^3 ($\mu^- + He^3 \to H^3 + \nu$) has been observed by Falomkin and his co-workers (Fa-63); and more recently by Auerbach et al. (Au-65) and Clay et al. (Cl-65). The experimental results are $w = (1410 \pm 140)$/sec for the first group and $w = (1505 \pm 46)$/sec and (1465 ± 67)/sec for the Auerbach and Clay groups respectively. This is in good agreement with a recent theoretical calculation based on a universal Fermi interaction which gives (1510 ± 10)/sec assuming $g_P/g_A = 7$.

In addition the μ capture by He^3 can lead to the final states n + d + ν and n + n + p + ν. The measured *total* capture rate is (2140 ± 180)/sec (Za-63), in excellent agreement with Yang's theoretical estimate of 2130/sec.

Partial Muon Capture in C^{12} and O^{16}

Because of the large energy release, the μ-capture process most frequently results in nuclear excitation and is finally followed by breakup. Under these conditions, the fundamental weak interactions become obscured by the involved many-body effects. However, in a fraction of the cases, transitions may occur to bound states.

A partial muon capture is one leading to a specific state of the residual nucleus, and its interpretation is therefore much more favorable. One such case—namely, the μ^- capture by C^{12} leading to the ground state of B^{12}— has been investigated in great detail. The reaction is shown in Fig. 6-11. The figure shows $0^+ \to 1^+$ transition; therefore in the simple "allowed" limit it would be a pure Gamow-Teller transition. Again, because of the large energy release, "forbidden" matrix elements begin to play an important role, even in "allowed" transitions.

The nuclear wave functions of both B^{12} and C^{12} can be calculated by using certain nuclear models. However, there are corrections to be made in the capture rate which depend on the nuclear model used. The most recent results for the μ capture rate in C^{12} are

$$w_{\text{exp}} = \left(6750 \pm \frac{300}{750}\right) \text{sec}^{-1} \quad \text{(Ma-64)}$$

$$w_{\text{theo}} = (6600 \pm 1000)\ \text{sec}^{-1}\ \text{(Ki-65).}$$

In conclusion, the agreement between the theoretical predictions from the universal Fermi interaction and experimental results on muon capture seems to be satisfactory, in both hydrogen and He^3.

Another important example of muon capture occurs in the nucleus O^{16} (Coh-64; As-64). Most of the capture leads to the ground state of N^{16}. According to Cohen et al., partial capture rate is (6300 ± 700)/sec. However, the capture leading to the low-lying states in N^{16} (0^- at 120 kev and 1^- at 392 kev) have also been observed, with rates (1100 ± 200) and (1730 ± 100)/sec, respectively. Within the accuracy of the measurements and uncertainties of the theoretical interpretation,

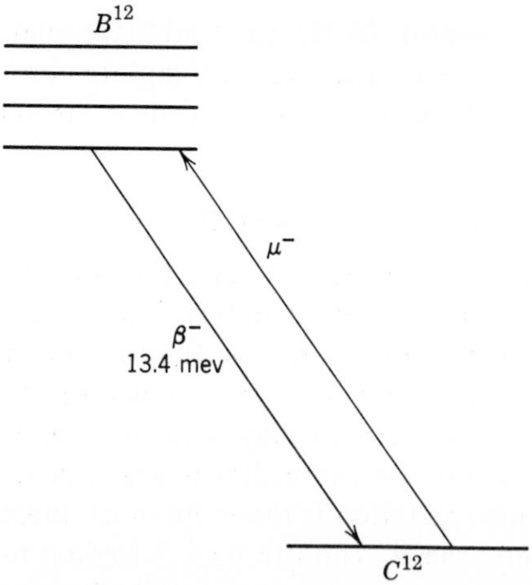

Fig. 6-11 Showing a partial muon capture in C^{12}.

for example, the nuclear wave function, these values are consistent with the assumption of a universal Fermi interaction and an induced pseudoscalar interaction with $g_P/g_A \sim 5$ to 10. On the other hand, it has not yet been possible to unravel finer details of the weak interactions, for example, whether the coupling constants are the same in complex nuclei as for free nucleons.

In conclusion, the agreement between universal Fermi interaction and experimental results on muon capture seems to be satisfactory in all cases investigated (H, He^3, C^{12} and O^{16}).

6-3 DECAY OF THE Pi MESON (PION)

A weak-interaction process of great interest is the decay of the charged π meson. A free π^+ or π^- has a lifetime of 2.5×10^{-8} sec;

it almost always decays into a μ and a neutral particle, presumably the neutrino. Since the emitted μ meson always has a unique energy equal to (4.17 ± 0.006) mev, we conclude that the π meson decays into two particles only. The neutrino must, of course, go in the direction opposite to the μ.

Another process—one which occurs infrequently—is the decay of a π into an electron and a neutrino. Until the early part of 1958, no π-e decays had been detected experimentally, and it was, in fact, widely believed that this process did not occur at all. However, by September

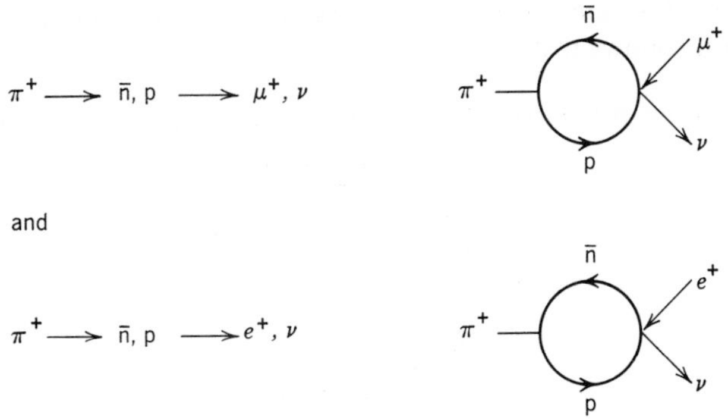

Fig. 6-12 Feynman diagram of $\pi^+ \to e^+ + \nu$ and $\pi^+ \to \mu^+ + \nu$ decays.

1958 it was found that π-e decay occurs, even though the branching ratio for π-e decays to π-μ decays is only about 1.2×10^{-4}. Physically, π-μ and π-e decays differ only in that the electron and the μ meson have different rest masses; there is no other well-understood difference between the electron and μ meson. It is very difficult to calculate the decay rate of π into either μ or electrons, but the branching ratio may be calculated quite easily.

A simple way of describing either process is

$$\pi^+ \to \bar{\text{n}} + \text{p} \to \begin{array}{l} \mu^+ + \nu_\mu \\ e^+ + \nu_e \end{array}$$

In other words, the π becomes a pair of nucleon and an antinucleon for a short time, and this pair then undergoes a process similar to ordinary β decay (see Fig. 6-12). Now, since the first step of this process depends on the pion-nucleon interaction, which is not known in exact detail (the natures of the intermediate nucleon and antinucleon states are not completely understood, either), it is quite difficult to calculate the lifetimes. However, since the first step is the same for both π-μ decay and π-e decay, this difficulty does not appear in a calculation of the branching ratio, for the latter depends only on the second step of this process, which is better understood.

Let us now calculate the branching ratio and compare it with the experimental value. First of all, the transition probability is proportional to the volume in phase space available to the particles. For the two-particle decay considered here, the transition rate is proportional to $p_\mu^2 dp_\mu/dE$ where E is the total energy available equal to $m_\pi c^2$.

Then it follows that

$$m_\pi c^2 = p_\mu c + [(m_\mu c^2)^2 + (p_\mu c)^2]^{1/2} \quad \text{and} \quad p_\nu c = p_\mu c = E_\nu$$

so that

$$\frac{p_\mu}{c} = \frac{m_\pi^2 - m_\mu^2}{2m_\pi}$$

$$E_\mu = m_\pi c^2 - E_\nu = \frac{m_\pi^2 + m_\mu^2}{2m_\pi} c^2 \tag{6-27}$$

$$\frac{dE}{dp_\mu} = \frac{2m_\pi c}{m_\pi^2 + m_\mu^2} \tag{6-28}$$

also

$$\frac{v_\mu}{c} = \frac{cp_\nu}{E_\nu} = \frac{m_\pi^2 - m_\nu^2}{m_\pi^2 + m_\nu^2}$$

Thus our phase space factor turns out to be a constant times

$$\frac{(m_\pi^2 - m_\mu^2)^2(m_\pi^2 + m_\mu^2)}{m_\pi^4} \tag{6-29}$$

If the transition probabilities were determined entirely by the available volume in phase space for the final particle, then π-e decay would occur more frequently than π-μ decay, since greater kinetic energy is available for electrons. The branching ratio would then be given by

$$\frac{(m_\pi^2 - m_e^2)^2(m_\pi^2 + m_e^2)}{(m_\pi^2 - m_\mu^2)^2(m_\pi^2 + m_\mu^2)} = 3.5 \qquad \begin{aligned} m_\pi &= 273\, m_e \\ m_\mu &= 207\, m_e \end{aligned} \tag{6-30}$$

The fact that π-μ decay predominates by a large factor shows that the transition rate must depend on details of the interaction itself; that is, the matrix element of the interaction for π-e decay is smaller than that for π-μ decay. This kind of effect follows readily from the two-component theory. The π is known to have zero angular momentum, and therefore in its rest system the two emitted particles go in opposite directions and must carry angular momentum in opposite directions. Consequently, the emitted particles must have the same handedness. If, as we assume, lepton conservation holds, one particle and one antiparticle must be emitted; therefore, if we regard the μ^+ or e^+ as an antiparticle, it is accompanied by a normal particle neutrino, not an antineutrino. Now consider π-e decay, and neglect electron rest mass. According to the $V - A$ theory, the neutrino is left-handed, and the e^+ is right-handed. This, however, is contrary to the kinematics of the process, as we pointed out previously. We must then conclude that if the electron has no rest mass *and* if $V - A$ theory and lepton conservation hold, π-e decay cannot occur at all.

In fact, the process occurs by virtue of the finite rest mass of the electron. The neutrino is indeed always left-handed, but on the other hand the positron is not always right-handed and, in fact, has a small probability [given by $\frac{1}{2}(1 - v_e/c)$] of being left-handed. Since π^+-e^+ decay can occur only when the positron is left-handed, the probability of this process is greatly reduced by such a restriction. The same considerations also apply for π-μ decay. However, because of the larger rest mass of the μ meson, there is a much greater probability that it is left-handed when emitted. Thus the branching ratio must be multiplied by the factor

$$\frac{\frac{1}{2}(1 - v_e/c)}{\frac{1}{2}(1 - v_\mu/c)} = \frac{m_e^2}{m_\pi^2 + m_e^2} \times \frac{m_\pi^2 + m_\mu^2}{m_\mu^2} \tag{6-31}$$

We finally obtain

$$\frac{w_{\pi\to e}}{w_{\pi\to\mu}} = \frac{m_e^2}{m_\mu^2}\left(\frac{m_\pi^2 - m_e^2}{m_\pi^2 - m_\mu^2}\right)^2 \sim 1.23 \times 10^{-4} \tag{6-32}$$

This ratio is exact to all orders in the strong pion-nucleon coupling (Ru-49). In comparison to π-μ decay, π-e decay is indeed a very rare event. For a long time, π-e decay was the object of an extensive search, but no such decay was observed. The experimental ratio of π-e/π-μ seemed to be much less than 10^{-5}. In the days when S and T were favored in the nuclear β interaction, the absence of π-e decay did not

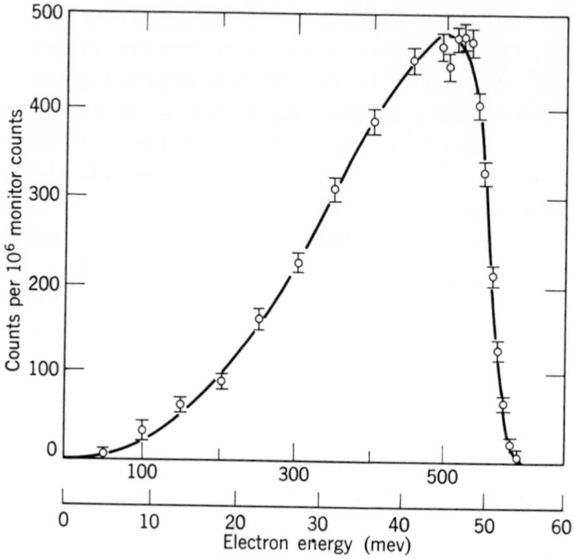

(a)

Fig. 6-13 (*a*) Spectrum of electrons from $\mu \to e$ decays in the experiment of Anderson et al. The abscissa is the electron energy and the ordinate is the number of $\mu \to e$ decays. (*b*) Energy distribution of electrons from $\pi \to e$ decays in the experiment of Anderson et al. From (An-59).

concern physicists too much,* because only two of the five β interactions—namely, A and P—can be formed out of the pseudoscalar pion field, and one four-vector, representing the nonlocal nature of the intermediate state. Therefore they are the only ones that can induce

---

* However, a number of theoreticians believed that if the interaction contained S and T, it would very likely be of the form $S - T + P$ (cf. Section 7-1), which would actually imply a predominance of π–e decay. The ratio for these two decay modes, calculated for the pseudoscalar interaction, is

$$R_P = \frac{w_{\pi \to e}}{w_{\pi \to \mu}} = \frac{m_\pi^2 - m_e^2}{m_\pi^2 - m_\mu^2} = 5.4 \tag{6-33}$$

which is precisely the ratio of the energy densities in phase space. (From the present observed ratio R of the two modes of pion decay the results of Treiman and Wyld (Tr-56) imply that

$$|g_P| \leqslant \frac{m_e}{m_p} |g_A| \approx 5 \times 10^{-4} |g_A| \tag{6-34}$$

The pseudoscalar coupling is indeed negligible.)

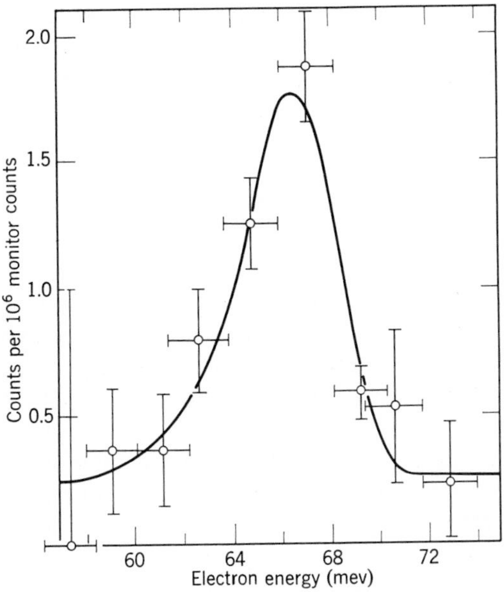

(b)

the decay of the pseudoscalar pion; the other three (S, V, T) are forbidden. If both A and P are lacking in β decay, then π-e is naturally forbidden. Had π-e decay been successfully observed in the early attempts, and observed in correct proportion to π-μ decay, the correctness of the ST combination in nuclear β decay probably would have been seriously questioned at an earlier date.

It had, in fact, been pointed out by Ruderman and Finkelstein in 1949 (Ru-49) that if failure to observe the π-e decay were due to its suppression by the factor 10^4, the hypothesis of a universal Fermi interaction would imply that the β interaction is at least partially axial-vector (and also that the pion is pseudoscalar.)

The inability to observe π-e decay demanded serious attention as soon as experimental evidence gave strong support to a universal $V - A$ interaction in all β decays. The conclusive finding of π-e events was reported soon afterward and was a great triumph for the universal $V - A$ interaction. Since that time, the ratio of π-e to π-μ has been determined with moderate precision in several laboratories. The most accurate determination has been made by H. Anderson et al. (An-59) (cf. Fig. 6-13a and b) and gives $(1.21 \pm 0.07) \times 10^{-4}$. A more recent determination (Dica-64) gives a ratio $(1.247 \pm 0.028) \times 10^{-4}$. (It is a matter of interest that the decay of the pion also constitutes one of the best methods of comparing the interaction strength of β decay and μ capture.) For a discussion of $\pi^+ \rightarrow \pi^0 + e^+ + \nu_e$ decays, see p. 273

6-4 STRANGE-PARTICLE DECAYS

Let us now briefly consider some of the decay modes of K mesons and of hyperons, the so-called strange particles. No attempt will be made to be complete, however, and we shall mention only those particular decays which have direct relevance to problems in nuclear β decay. [For excellent reviews of this subject, see (Dal-59; St-64).]

One mode of interest is that of the K^+ meson. It was, in fact, the study of K-meson decay which gave the first definite indication that something was wrong with the implicit assumption of parity conservation. The problem was the following: the K^+ meson can disintegrate in various ways. One way is the decay mode

$$K^+ \rightarrow \pi^+ + \pi^0 \tag{6-35}$$

However, there is an alternative decay mode typified by

$$K^+ \rightarrow \pi^+ + \pi^+ + \pi^- \tag{6-36}$$

A more detailed analysis of the decay product in the two cases suggested very strongly that the two-π system must have even parity, whereas the three-π system produced in K decay would have odd parity. What was the way out of this difficulty? One possibility, of course, was that the particles giving rise to these two decay modes were perhaps not the same. However, it was found that the masses of these two parent particles (the so-called θ and τ) were equal within one electron mass, and the lifetime also seemed to be equal within experimental error. Thus to say that they were two different particles seemed to be rather awkward, although the possibility could by no means be excluded.*

* As a matter of fact, we now know that there are two neutral K mesons, the K_1^0 and the K_2^0. The K_1^0 decays primarily into two pions with a lifetime of approximately 10^{-10} sec. If CP invariance holds exactly, the K_2^0 cannot decay in this way. The K_2^0 can, however, decay via other modes, for example 3π, $\pi + e + \nu$ with a lifetime of about 10^{-7} sec. It appears (Ch-64, Ab-64), however, that the K_2^0 can also decay into 2π (though only 0.3% as strongly as the K_1^0). This implies a slight breakdown of CP symmetry.

The other way out of the difficulty was the now-famous conjecture that parity is not conserved in weak interactions—of which both decays are examples—from which we could say that even if the K has definite parity, the system of its decay products does not have to have the same parity; indeed, products might have even parity in some cases and odd parity in other cases. Of course, this was merely a conjecture at the time, but it turned out to be correct, as shown by the parity experiments in weak interactions.

Another decay mode of the K's is given by

$$K \to \mu + \nu_\mu \tag{6-37}$$

This mode, which is analogous to pion decay, has been observed. On the other hand, the other possible mode

$$K \to e + \nu_e \tag{6-38}$$

has not been observed. The rarity of the $K \to e + \nu_e$ decay mode has, in fact, been anticipated on the basis of $V - A$ theory for the same reasons as in π-e decay. The branching ratio of the $e + \nu_e$ to the $\mu + \nu_\mu$ mode is expected to be even less for the K than for the π (the K has a larger rest mass and therefore the electron velocity is closer to c)—specifically, 1 per 40,000. Experimentally, it is found to be no larger than this (Bo-65).

A further similarity between $K \to \mu$ and $\pi \to \mu$ decay has been observed. If lepton conservation holds, we would expect the same kind of neutrino to be emitted in both cases, and in both cases we expect the μ to disintegrate as $\mu \to e + \nu_\mu + \bar{\nu}_e$. This should result in the same backward, asymmetric distribution of electrons with respect to muon motion (see Fig. 6-14). The predicted asymmetry in $K \to$

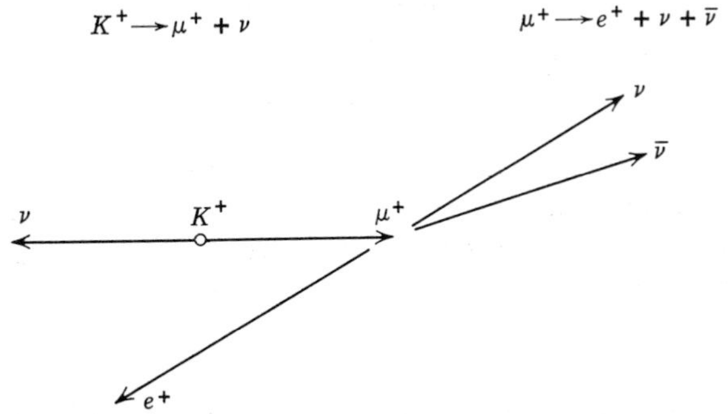

Fig. 6-14 Angular distribution in $K \to \mu \to e$ decay.

$\mu \rightarrow e$ decay has been observed, (Co-57) and it further strengthens the idea of lepton conservation, although it does not, of course, prove it.

A comparison of the $K \rightarrow \mu + \nu_\mu$ and $\pi \rightarrow \mu + \nu_\mu$ transition rates is also of interest. If the interaction strengths for the two decays were the same, the $K \rightarrow \mu + \nu$ rate would be considerably larger owing to the greater available kinetic energy of the emitted muons.

By the same arguments as in the problem of $\pi \rightarrow \mu$ and $\pi \rightarrow e$ decay (cf. see Sec. 6-3), we can show that if the interaction is the same, then

$$\frac{w_{K\rightarrow\mu}}{w_{\pi\rightarrow\mu}} = \left(\frac{m_\pi}{m_K}\right)^3 \left(\frac{m_K{}^2 - m_\mu{}^2}{m_\pi{}^2 - m_\mu{}^2}\right)^2 = 18 \tag{6-39}$$

In fact, however, the experimental ratio of decay rates is only slightly larger than unity ($\sim$1.2). Evidently, the interaction strength is only about one-fourth as large for K decay as for π decay.

Now let us consider some decay modes of the Λ hyperon. One mode of disintegration is

$$\Lambda^0 \rightarrow \pi^- + \mathrm{p}$$

This decay is believed to be governed by the weak interaction mainly because the lifetime, being about 10^{-10} sec, is much longer than would be expected if it were governed by nuclear or mesonic effects. However, this particular decay, unlike most of the others considered before (except the $K \rightarrow$ two-π or three-π modes), does not involve neutrinos. It is, therefore, of interest to see whether this weak interaction also exhibits properties that are due to the lack of parity conservation. Lack of parity conservation has, in fact, been observed in the Λ^0 decay. The Λ^0's were produced in the reaction

$$\pi^- + \mathrm{p} \rightarrow \Lambda^0 + K^0$$

Then Λ^0 in turn decays to

$$\Lambda^0 \rightarrow \pi^- + \mathrm{p}$$

The direction of the incident π^- and the outgoing Λ^0 defines a plane. It was found that the π^-'s emitted in Λ^0 decay have a definite asymmetric distribution with respect to this plane (see Fig. 6-15). In other words, the expectation value of the pseudoscalar

$$\langle \mathbf{p}_{\text{out}} \cdot \mathbf{p}_{\text{in}} \times \mathbf{p}_{\Lambda^0} \rangle$$

does not vanish. Thus parity cannot be conserved in Λ^0 decay.

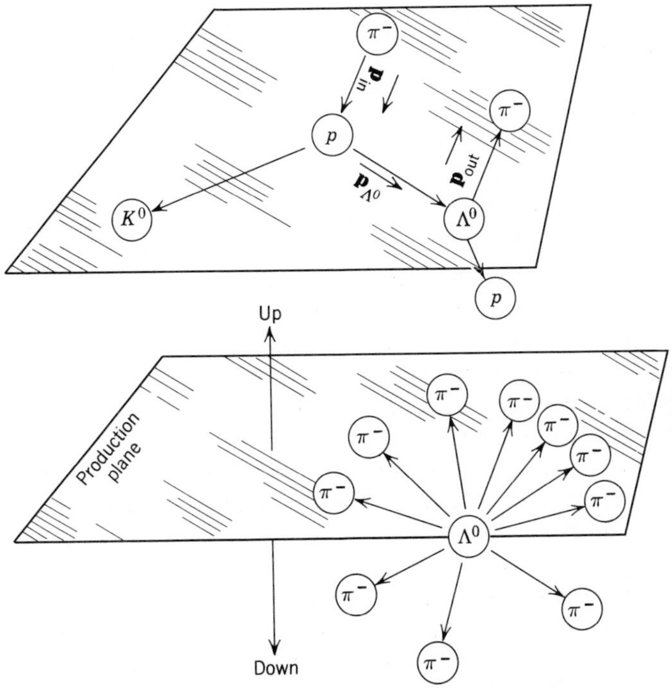

Fig. 6-15 Up and down asymmetry in Λ^0 decay; Λ^0 is produced by the reaction $\pi^- + p \rightarrow \Lambda^0 + K^0$ and in turn decays by $\Lambda^0 \rightarrow \pi^- + p$. The observation of the up-down asymmetry distribution of the decay pion $\mathbf{p}_{out}$ with respect to the production plane containing the two momentum vectors of $\mathbf{p}_{in}$ and $\mathbf{p}_{\Lambda^0}$ demonstrated non-vanishing of the expectation value of the pseudoscalar $(\mathbf{p}_{out} \cdot \mathbf{p}_{in} \times \mathbf{p}_{\Lambda^0})$ and therefore the nonconservation of parity in Λ^0 decay.

Finally, the Λ^0 can also decay as follows:

$$\Lambda^0 \rightarrow p + e^- + \bar{\nu}$$

This decay mode is analogous to the decay of the neutron, and, assuming the same interaction in the two cases, its decay rate may be predicted to be 1.4% of the total Λ^0 decay rate. The leptonic decay of the Λ^0 has, in fact, been observed. The fraction of Λ decays proceeding leptonically is, however, found to be only $(0.1 \pm 0.01)\%$ (El-63; Wi-64), about 5% of the expected value. Similarly, the Σ^- hyperons would also be expected to have a 6% probability of leptonic decay, namely, $\Sigma^- \rightarrow n + e^- + \bar{\nu}_e$, but the experimental branching ratio is $(0.14 \pm 0.02)\%$.

(The main decay mode is, of course, into $\pi^- + n$.) It appears that the effective coupling constants for these decays are an order of magnitude smaller than for nuclear β decay. A similar reduction is found for the decay modes:

$$\Lambda^0 \to \text{p} + \mu^- + \bar{\nu}_\mu \qquad \text{and} \qquad \Sigma^- \to \text{n} + \mu^- + \bar{\nu}_\mu$$

The muonic mode of decay is less favored than the electronic mode because of the smaller volume in phase space available to the particles; moreover, fewer events have been observed.

Recently, the decay mode $\Sigma^- \to \Lambda^0 + e^- + \bar{\nu}_e$ has been observed also, with 8 events out of 120,000. In this case, the decay energy is much smaller than for the other modes, and even according to the universal Fermi interaction we would have expected about 12 such events.

Why should the latter decay follow the universal Fermi interaction within the experimental uncertainty and the other decays remain greatly retarded? The answer seems to lie in the "strangeness" of the hyperons involved in the decay; the n and p have $S = 0$, and the Λ and Σ particles have $S = -1$. In ordinary β decay and in $\Sigma \to \Lambda$ decay, the strangeness does not change—that is, $\Delta S = 0$—whereas in the other decays—say, $\Lambda \to \text{p}$—we have $\Delta S = +1$. Evidently, the decay rates for transitions with $\Delta S = +1$ are retarded relative to those for which $\Delta S = 0$ by a factor 10 to 50 (after correction for the dependence of decay rate on energy).

There is another group of leptonic decay modes which appears to be retarded even more—the decays

$$\Sigma^+ \to n + (e^+ \text{ or } \mu^+) + \nu$$

Only one such event has been identified (Bar-62). The feature which distinguishes these decays from the ones discussed previously is that the charge on the baryon involved changes by -1 rather than by $+1$. Thus for the Λ and Σ^- decay we have $\Delta S = 1 = \Delta Q$, but for the Σ^+ decay, $\Delta S = 1 = -\Delta Q$. We have evidence for the operation of an additional selection rule. This $\Delta S = \Delta Q$ rule seems also to hold at least approximately for other decays, such as that of the K meson. (For more on strange-particle decays see the discussion of the Cabibbo hypothesis in Chap. 7, p. 284.)

CHAPTER 7

Recent Developments

As early as 1948 the great similarity in the strength of the coupling constants in β decay, μ decay, and μ capture had tempted several authors (Kl-48; Le-48; Ti-49; Pu-49) to postulate a universal Fermi interaction. This view was later reviewed extensively in a series of lectures (Fe-51) by Fermi. However, any universality should imply not only the equality of the coupling constants but also the similarity of the structure of the interactions. For a long time there was no conclusive evidence to substantiate the latter. Then, in 1957, came the discovery of the nonconservation of parity in β decay and also in μ decay. Following the tremendous activity of that period, overwhelming evidence showed that the interaction form of four fermions, such as in nuclear β decay and μ decay, can be represented by a $V - A$ interaction (Wu-59; De-59; Ko-59; Sc-60). Recent evidence indicates strongly that this also holds for μ capture (Wo-63). Furthermore, from experiments on the $0^+ \to 0^+$ transition in O^{14}, the vector coupling constant g_V in β decay was found to be very nearly (within 1 or 2%) equal to that of the Fermi constant g_μ of μ decay.

To explain this unexpectedly good agreement, Feynman and Gell-Mann (Fey-58) and earlier Gershtein and Zeldovich (Ge-55) proposed the conserved vector current theory (C.V.C. theory) based on its analogy in electromagnetism, where the observed coupling strength e with electromagnetic field is the same for all particles coupled. This universality of electric charge follows because the electromagnetic current is conserved. If the weak vector current is similarly conserved, the vector coupling constant will be a universal constant.

Because of the fundamental importance of the C.V.C. theory, several types of experiments have been proposed, designed, and executed to verify the validity of the C.V.C. hypothesis. So far, all the results are strongly in favor of the C.V.C. theory.

In this chapter we shall discuss mainly experimental results concerning β decay. In Sec. 7-1 we shall show the theoretical formulation of the $V - A$ Fermi interaction. The requirements of the continuity equation of the electromagnetic current will be discussed in Sec. 7-2 in order to lead to the formulation of the C.V.C. theory and the unique properties arising from it. Then we shall examine the present status of the question of equality between g_V and g_μ. Finally, we shall present and discuss the four different types of experiments and their results.

7-1 THEORETICAL FORMULATION OF THE UNIVERSAL ($V - A$) FERMI INTERACTION

If the interaction were pure $V - A$,* it would be interesting to explore some possible theoretical arguments which would lead to such a linear combination. In fact, the $V - A$ form has been reached independently by three different theoretical approaches, all based on the principal idea of representing the four-component spinor ψ in terms of two two-component spinors ϕ_+ and ϕ_-. In order to allow only one of the two two-component spinors to appear in the interaction, different hypothetical principles were proposed to justify its restriction.

These theoretical approaches are (a) the chirality invariance conjectured by Sudarshan and Marshak (Mar-58); (b) the two-component formulation of Dirac spinors by Feynman and Gell-Mann (Fey-58); and (c) the mass-reversal invariance proposed by Sakurai (Sa-58a).

Chirality Invariance

The word "chirality" (pronounced *kirality*) was derived from the Greek word "chir" (hand); thus it can be used to imply handedness.

The chirality transformation is defined as $\psi \rightarrow \gamma_5\psi$. For a particle of a given momentum, the Dirac equation has four solutions, each of them a four-component spinor. For a mass-zero particle, for example, a neutrino, of these four solutions, two have positive chirality, $\gamma_5\psi = \psi$, and two have negative chirality, $\gamma_5\psi = -\psi$.

Next let us consider the case $m \neq 0$. Here, of course, the general Dirac spinor is not an eigenstate of the operator γ_5. However, it can be expanded in terms of such eigenstates.

---

* This is not exactly correct in nuclear β decay where the axial-vector coupling is slightly stronger ($V - 1.2A$), probably owing to mesonic effects on the axial-vector interaction.

We can write

$$\psi = \psi_+ + \psi_- \tag{7-1}$$

where $\psi_\pm = \frac{1}{2}(1 \pm \gamma_5)\psi$. In terms of two-component spinors I, ϕ, ξ, we have

$$\gamma_5 = \begin{pmatrix} 0 & -I \\ -I & 0 \end{pmatrix}$$

and

$$\psi = \begin{pmatrix} \phi \\ \xi \end{pmatrix} = \frac{1}{2}\begin{pmatrix} \phi - \xi \\ -(\phi - \xi) \end{pmatrix} + \frac{1}{2}\begin{pmatrix} \phi + \xi \\ \phi + \xi \end{pmatrix} \tag{7-2}$$

Thus

$$\psi_+ = \begin{pmatrix} \phi_- \\ -\phi_- \end{pmatrix}$$

and

$$\psi_- = \begin{pmatrix} \phi_+ \\ \phi_+ \end{pmatrix}$$

where

$$\phi_\pm = \tfrac{1}{2}(\phi \pm \xi)$$

This can be verbally expressed as follows: If we project with the positive chirality operator, we obtain the two-component spinor ϕ_-; using the negative chirality operator yields the two-component spinor ϕ_+.

At this point, Sudarshan and Marshak (Mar-58) made a bold conjecture that *the total four-fermion interaction should be invariant under a γ_5 transformation on any of the ψ's, $\psi_i \to \gamma_5\psi_i$.*

The interesting consequence of this assumption of chirality invariance is that the interaction is now uniquely determined to be VA.

Consider the four-fermion interaction:

$$\frac{1}{\sqrt{2}}\, g(\tilde{\psi}_2 \hat{O} \psi_1)(\tilde{\psi}_4 \hat{O} \psi_3)$$

The factor $1/\sqrt{2}$ is introduced for convenience in order that the results for scalar quantities are the same in the parity-nonconserving theory with $g_i' = g_i$ as in the parity-conserving theory. Make the transformations $\psi_i \to \gamma_5\psi_i$ and

$$\tilde{\psi}_f = \psi_f^{\dagger}\gamma_4 \to \psi_f^{\dagger}\gamma_5\gamma_4 = -\psi_f^{\dagger}\gamma_4\gamma_5 = -\tilde{\psi}_f\gamma_5$$

Chirality invariance implies

$$\tilde{\psi}_f \hat{O} \psi_i = \tilde{\psi}_f \hat{O} \gamma_5 \psi_i = -\tilde{\psi}_f \gamma_5 \hat{O} \gamma_5 \psi_i \tag{7-3}$$

where $\hat{O}$ is any operator. We have

$$\hat{O}\gamma_5 = \hat{O} \quad \text{and} \quad -\gamma_5\hat{O} = \hat{O} \quad \text{or} \quad [\hat{O}, \gamma_5]_+ = 0$$

In other words, $\hat{O}$ and γ_5 anticommute.

Of the operators which transform as S, V, T, A, P, only V and A which contain an odd number of $\gamma_\mu (\mu = 1, 2, 3, 4)$ anticommute with γ_5 those corresponding to S, T, and P commute with γ_5. Therefore the operator $\hat{O}$ must be a linear combination of V and A:

$$\hat{O} = a\gamma_\mu + b\gamma_\mu\gamma_5$$

Next from the condition

$$\hat{O}\gamma_5 = \hat{O}, \qquad \hat{O} = a\gamma_\mu\gamma_5 + b\gamma_\mu = a\gamma_\mu + b\gamma_\mu\gamma_5$$

it follows that $a = b$ or $O = a\gamma_\mu(1 + \gamma_5)$. The interaction is thus

$$\frac{1}{\sqrt{2}} g[\tilde{\psi}_2\gamma_\mu(1 + \gamma_5)\psi_1][\tilde{\psi}_4\gamma_\mu(1 + \gamma_5)\psi_3] \tag{7-4}$$

Of course, we could have retained $(1 - \gamma_5)\psi$ instead of $(1 + \gamma_5)\psi$; then we would still have VA but with $g_i' = -g_i$. Theoretically, these two possibilities are equally good. It is the experimental evidence which has the final say.

The Two-Component Formulation of the Dirac Spinors

As we have shown, $m \neq 0$; therefore, the ψ_+ and ψ_- cannot be decoupled in the Dirac equation. It is rather mystical to write down an interaction involving only ψ_+ and not ψ_- for every particle. The great contribution by Feynman and Gell-Mann (Fey-58) in this respect is to explain the situation by showing that the Dirac equation can also be expressed in terms of the two-component wave function. However, the two-component wave function must satisfy a second-order Klein-Gordon equation. Once we accept this viewpoint, the hypothetical principles which were proposed to restrict the interaction term to VA seem to be more reasonable.

Let us write down the first-order Dirac equation for the four-component field ψ in terms of Dirac matrices:

$$H\psi = \boldsymbol{\alpha} \cdot \mathbf{p}\psi + \beta m\psi \tag{7-5}$$

We can express the four-component wave function ψ in terms of the two-component spinors ϕ and ξ. Then

$$H\phi = \boldsymbol{\sigma} \cdot \mathbf{p}\xi + m\phi \tag{7-6}$$
$$H\xi = \boldsymbol{\sigma} \cdot \mathbf{p}\phi - m\xi$$

Adding and subtracting these equations, we obtain

$$H\phi_+ = \boldsymbol{\sigma} \cdot \mathbf{p}\phi_+ + m\phi_- \tag{7-7}$$

$$H\phi_- = -\boldsymbol{\sigma} \cdot \mathbf{p}\phi_- + m\phi_+$$

The ϕ_+ and ϕ_- were already defined.

If $m = 0$, these equations are decoupled, and the functions ψ_+, ψ_-, which are eigenstates of the chirality operator γ_5 are also eigenfunctions of the Dirac equation. For $m \neq 0$, the two equations are coupled. However, the ϕ_+ and ϕ_- satisfy the Klein-Gordon equation since

$$\phi_+ = \frac{1}{m}(H + \boldsymbol{\sigma} \cdot \mathbf{p})\phi_- \tag{7-8}$$

and we have

$$m^2\phi_- = m(H - \boldsymbol{\sigma} \cdot \mathbf{p})\phi_+ = (H - \boldsymbol{\sigma} \cdot \mathbf{p})(H + \boldsymbol{\sigma} \cdot \mathbf{p})\phi_-$$

$$= [H^2 - (\boldsymbol{\sigma} \cdot \mathbf{p})^2]\phi_- = (H^2 - \mathbf{p}^2)\phi_- \tag{7-9}$$

or

$$\left(\frac{\partial^2}{\partial t^2} - \nabla^2 + m^2\right)\phi_- = 0 \tag{7-10}$$

This is the well-known Klein-Gordon equation. In other words, although ϕ_+ does not appear in the theory explicitly, it nevertheless appears implicitly via Eq. 7-8, expressed in terms of ϕ_- and its derivatives. This implies that the whole theory can be expressed in terms of a two-component wave function, either ϕ_- or ϕ_+, which, however, must satisfy the Klein-Gordon equation.

On experimental grounds, we know that the four-fermion interaction formulated in terms of ψ's is *linear in the fields and does not contain derivatives*. (This was the reason why the Konopinski-Uhlenbeck modification was rejected.) An arbitrary interaction form, even if it is linear in the ψ, will, in general, involve both ψ_+ and ψ_- or, in terms of two-component wave functions, both ϕ_- and ϕ_+. If expressed in terms of ϕ_- alone, the interaction must contain terms proportional to ϕ_- and also to $p\phi_- \sim \partial\phi_-/\partial x$. If, however, we *insist* that no such derivative terms should appear, the interaction, formulated in terms of the ψ, must contain only ψ_+ and not ψ_-, that is, only ϕ_-, not ϕ_+ (or vice versa). This requirement is identical with that which results from chirality invariance.

Mass-Reversal Invariance

Consider the behavior of the Dirac equation

$$\gamma_\mu p_\mu \psi = i\, m\psi \tag{7-11}$$

under the transformation $\psi \to \gamma_5\psi$. Since γ_5 anticommutes with each γ_μ, we have

$$\gamma_\mu p_\mu(\gamma_5\psi) = -i\, m(\gamma_5\psi) \tag{7-12}$$

Thus $\gamma_5\psi$ is not an eigenfunction of the Dirac equation, unless we also make the transformation $m \to -m$. The Dirac equation is then invariant under the combined mass-reversal transformation

$$\psi \to \gamma_5\psi,\ m \to -m \tag{7-13}$$

When we apply this transformation to each of the four fermions simultaneously and demand that the interaction be invariant, it is equivalent to γ_5 invariance.

Connection with the $V - A$ Interaction

All three hypotheses just discussed are equivalent to the assumption that the β interaction occurs only in states of positive chirality, that is, negative helicity. The requirement of negative helicity, that is, left-handed polarization for both neutrinos and electrons (in positive-energy states), implies the existence of a VA combination in β decay, even though the coefficients are arbitrary. An S, T, P combination implies opposite handedness for electrons and neutrinos—cf. App. IV). If we also require that the nucleons involved be left-handedly polarized (if their rest mass could be neglected), the interaction is uniquely fixed as $V - A$. Of course, the nucleons are only weakly polarized, $\mathscr{P}_\mu \sim v/c \sim 0.1$, because of their large rest mass.

By using the relations $\gamma_5(1 + \gamma_5) = (1 + \gamma_5)\gamma_5 = (1 + \gamma_5)$ the interaction can be rewritten as follows:

$$\begin{aligned} &\frac{1}{\sqrt{2}}\, g[\tilde{\psi}_2\gamma_\mu(1 + \gamma_5)\psi_1][\tilde{\psi}_4\gamma_\mu(1 + \gamma_5)\psi_3] \\ &\quad = \frac{1}{\sqrt{2}}\, g[\tilde{\psi}_2\gamma_\mu\psi_1][\psi_4\gamma_\mu(1 + \gamma_5)\psi_3] \\ &- \frac{1}{\sqrt{2}}\, g[\tilde{\psi}_2 i\gamma_\mu\gamma_5\psi_1][\psi_4 i\gamma_\mu\gamma_5(1 + \gamma_5)\psi_3] \end{aligned} \tag{7-14}$$

Since γ_μ and $i\gamma_\mu\gamma_5$ are the usual vector and axial-vector operators, respectively, we then obtain the $V - A$ interaction. (It is readily shown that a $V + A$ interaction would result if the nucleons are right-handed, that is, if nucleons have opposite helicity as leptons.) This universal $V - A$ four-fermion interaction gives the unique combination $V - A$, yields two-component neutrinos of negative helicity, leads to the conservation of leptons, and is invariant under the combined inversion of *CP*.

The universal $V - A$ interaction differs from the vector interaction originally proposed by Fermi,

$$\tilde{\psi}_2\gamma_\mu\psi_1\tilde{\psi}_4\gamma_\mu\psi_3 \tag{7-15}$$

only by the presence of the extra factor $1 + \gamma_5$. It is remarkable how close Fermi came to the correct β-decay interaction long before the understanding of β decay was as far advanced as it is today.

It should be mentioned here that, even before the discovery of parity nonconservation, numerous attempts had been made to justify a simple form for the β interaction on the basis of a simple symmetry principle.

The first such interaction, $S - A - P$, was proposed by Critchfield and Wigner (Cr-41) on the hypothesis that the β-interaction Hamiltonian is antisymmetric with respect to interchange of any two of the four wave functions. This particular combination, however, implies the presence of Fierz interference terms for quasi-allowed first forbidden spectra, that is, those for which the ξ approximation (cf. p. 78) holds (Ma-52). Such spectra are, however, known to have allowed shapes ruling out the $S - A - P$ interaction.

A slightly less restrictive condition, antisymmetry with respect to interchange of the created (or annihilated) particles,

$$\mathrm{H}_{\mathrm{n}+\nu\rightarrow\mathrm{p}+e} = -\mathrm{H}_{\mathrm{n}+\nu\rightarrow e+\mathrm{p}}$$

gives $$a(S - T + P) + b(V - A) + c(S - A - P)$$

See (Ca-53; Fi-53; Pe-53; Pu-52), where $c = 0$ in the foregoing argument,

Stech and Jensen (St-55) showed that either of the first two forms can also be derived on the assumption of isotropy of the β-decay process in the center of the mass system of the particles involved, that is, (nν) or (pe).

It is interesting to realize that if the π-e decay (suppressed by a factor $\sim 10^4$) had been found before 1957, then the assumption of a universal

Fermi interaction would have implied the presence of A, but not of P, in the β interaction. This, together with the symmetry principles just given, would have uniquely implied a $V - A$ interaction. Even without the π–e-decay results, the correct $V - A$ interaction (of course, without the parity-violating terms) would still have been deduced from foregoing arguments if the results of the He^6 e–ν angular correlation had been correct (giving axial vector).

Finally, in the meson decay both the $S - T + P$ and the $V - A$ interactions give a Michel parameter $\rho = 0.75$, which is close to the currently accepted value 0.74–0.79. However, from 1953 to 1957, ρ was generally believed to be between 0.5 and 0.7 (Mi-54; Ro-58) (see Table 6-1, p. 216), in disagreement with both of the combinations just given.

Although the attempts described came close to the now accepted form of the β interaction, none of the previous symmetry principles, taken together with parity conservation, could give a form as simple and beautiful for the interaction as the one now accepted.

7-2 THE THEORY OF CONSERVED VECTOR CURRENT

We have seen in the study of muon decay that there are small electromagnetic corrections (see Sec. 6-1), which result because the muons and the emitted electrons are charged particles and, therefore, interact with the surrounding electromagnetic field. This radiative correction in μ decay affects both the shape of the electron spectrum and the lifetime of μ decay. Similarly, there should be mesonic corrections in nuclear β decay owing to the strong coupling between the nucleons involved and π mesons. As supposed, nucleons can emit and absorb virtual pions such as $n \leftrightarrow n + \pi^0 \leftrightarrow p + \pi^- \leftrightarrow n + \pi^+ + \pi^- \leftrightarrow \cdots$ a neutron exists for a substantial fraction of its life as a neutron with a neutral pion or as a proton surrounded by a negatively charged pion cloud, etc. It had been assumed that the β-interaction strength of a bare nucleon should be considerably different from that of a dressed nucleon (a mixture of pion and nucleon). For example, in the case of the decay of the neutron, if we attribute the β-interaction strength only to the nucleon and not to the virtual pions, we cannot expect to have the electron emitted from the neutron during the time interval when the neutron existed as a proton surrounded by a negative pion cloud.

Using Feynman diagrams, we can illustrate the fundamental process (see Fig. 7-1) together with processes involving the emission of virtual mesons as shown in Fig. 7-2. Based on such suppositions, we must renormalize the β-interaction strength in nuclear β decay to take into account these mesonic effects.

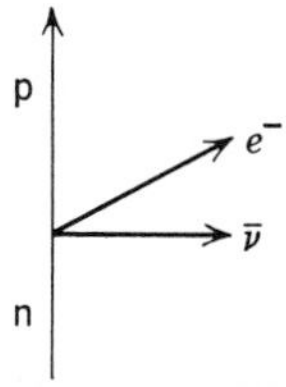

Fig. 7-1 Feynman diagram of nuclear β decay from bare nucleon.

The first attempts to calculate these effects in β decay were made by Finkelstein and Moszkowski (Fi-54), who showed that the Gamow-Teller part of the interaction would indeed be enhanced relative to the Fermi part, in agreement with experiment.

Later attempts were made to estimate the renormalization effects on the β-interaction strength by assigning the appropriate time fractions to the bare nucleon and different mixtures of the dressed nucleon. The appropriate time functions were derived from our knowledge of the pion-nucleon interaction and the anomalous magnetic moments of the nucleon. The ratio of the renormalized coupling constants turned out to be $|g_A|/|g_V| = \frac{7}{3}$, whereas the observed ratio of $|g_A|/|g_V|$ is actually ≈ 1.2. However, we should not expect any quantitative accuracy in such crude estimations. Recently, Adler (Ad-65) and Weisberger (We-65) have been able to relate the renormalization effect to pion-nucleon-scattering cross sections. Substituting in the experimentally known values of the latter, they find $g_A/g_V = -1.2$ in surprisingly good agreement with the experimental value.

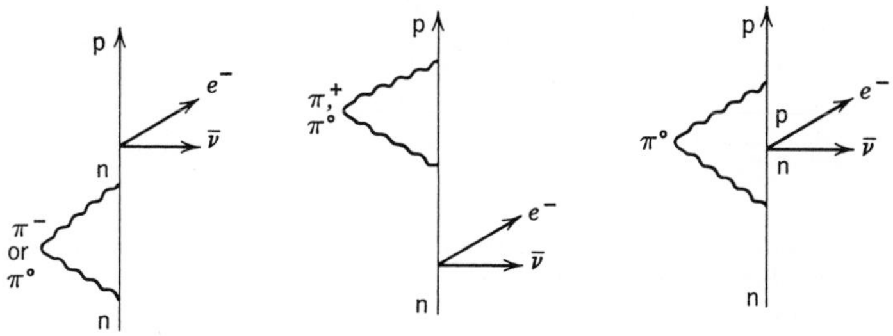

Fig. 7-2 Feynman diagram of nuclear β decay involving virtual mesons.

On the other hand, a muon does not have strong interactions. Its Fermi interaction strength needs no renormalization. Therefore, the effective coupling constant in muon decay should equal the intrinsic one. What mystified everyone was that the effective interaction strength of the vector couplings in both β decay and muon decay were found to be equal within $\sim 2\%$ (see the section on $g_V = g_\mu$, p. 263). Therefore the question arose: Why is no renormalization required between the effective and the bare interaction strength in β decay? To explain the unexpected good agreement, Feynman and Gell-Mann's interpretation of the equality of the vector interaction strength in nuclear β decay and μ decay is to assume that the pions carry with them the β-interaction strength when they are virtually emitted from the nucleons (Fig. 7-3) and that the vector part of the nuclear β interaction is arranged to have no renormalization effects.

Analogy with Electromagnetism

The fact that the vector interaction in β decay appears to be unaffected by pionic corrections has its analogy in electromagnetism. The electron

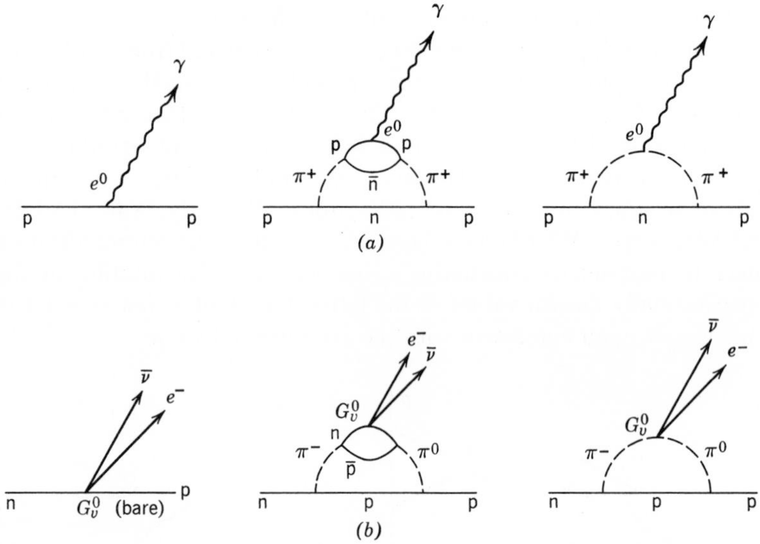

Fig. 7-3 Feynman diagram showing that the pions carry with them the β-interaction strength. (*a*) Electromagnetic interaction of the physical proton, (*b*) β decay of the physical neutron.

is believed to be a simple Dirac particle with no charge distribution—that is, essentially a point charge (except for small radiative corrections of order $\alpha/2\pi \sim 10^{-3}$)—whereas the proton is a very complicated object containing a meson cloud surrounding a bare nucleon core. Yet the total charge of the proton, which we measure in electron-proton scattering at very low energies, is the same as the proton charge we would measure if there were no pion interaction. As a matter of fact, *all* interactions are arranged in such a way that the equality between the physical electric charge and the bare charge is not disturbed, so that the electric charge of the proton is the same as the electric charge of the positron (of course, in the presence of pion interactions the charge of the nucleon core *alone* is not the same). How is this equality achieved in electromagnetism?

First, electric-charge conservation holds in the process

$$\mathrm{p} \leftrightarrows \mathrm{n} + \pi^+$$

that is, the π^+ has the same charge as the proton.

Secondly, even while the proton is in the "dissociated" state, the interaction of the π^+ with the electromagnetic field is the same as that of the proton (see Fig. 7-3*a*). Mathematically, the vector potential $\mathbf{A}_\mu$ couples to the *conserved charge current*, which consists of the sum of the p and π^+ currents.

Of course, if the pion interaction with the electromagnetic field were different from the proton interaction, which happens for the magnetic moment, this conservation law would not hold. Thus the magnetic moment of the physical proton differs from that of the bare proton.

The Conserved Electromagnetic Current

The charge current for a proton is a polar vector whose four components are given by

$$\begin{aligned} j_\mu &= \psi_{\mathrm{p}}^{\dagger}\alpha_\mu\psi_{\mathrm{p}} = \rho\frac{v_\mu}{c} \qquad \text{for } \mu = 1, 2, 3 \\ &= i\psi_{\mathrm{p}}^{\dagger}\psi_{\mathrm{p}} = i\rho \qquad\qquad \mu = 4 \end{aligned} \tag{7-16}$$

in units of the electric charge e.

In covariant notation we have, apart from a factor i,

$$j_\mu = \tilde{\psi}_{\mathrm{p}}\gamma_\mu\psi_{\mathrm{p}} \tag{7-17}$$

Of course for neutrons there is no charge current.

We can combine the results for proton and neutron in terms of isobaric spin operators (see p. 63). For proton and neutron, we have respectively $\tau_z = +1$ and -1. Thus

$$j_\mu = \tilde{\psi}_{\mathrm{N}}\gamma_\mu\tfrac{1}{2}(1 + \tau_z)\psi_{\mathrm{N}} \tag{7-18}$$

where ψ_N represents a general nucleon wave function. The nucleon current can be decomposed into an isobaric spin scalar and isobaric spin vector:

$$j_\mu = \underset{\text{isoscalar}}{\tfrac{1}{2}\tilde{\psi}_N\gamma_\mu\psi_N} + \underset{\text{isovector}}{\tfrac{1}{2}\tilde{\psi}_N\gamma_\mu\tau_z\psi_N} = j_\mu{}^S + j_\mu{}^V \tag{7-19}$$

The isoscalar term satisfies the continuity equation

$$\sum_\mu \frac{\partial j_\mu{}^S}{\partial x_\mu} = \nabla \cdot j_\mu{}^S + \frac{\partial \rho}{\partial t} = 0 \tag{7-20}$$

The conservation of isoscalar current implies the conservation of the number of nucleons. However, the second term of Eq. 7-19, which is the z component of an isobaric spin vector, is not conserved by itself but only if it is supplemented by the pion term; that is,

$$j_\mu{}^z = \tfrac{1}{2}\tilde{\psi}_N\gamma_\mu\tau_z\psi_N + \left(\pi \times \frac{\partial \pi}{\partial x_\mu}\right)_z + \cdots \tag{7-21}$$

The Formulation of the Conserved Vector Current Theory (C.V.C.)

For a conventional vector β interaction, the nucleon current is given by

$$j_\mu{}^+ = \frac{1}{\sqrt{2}}\,\tilde{\psi}_N\gamma_\mu\tau_+\psi_N \tag{7-22}$$

for β^- decay, where (cf. p. 64)

$$\tau_+\psi_n = \frac{\tau_x + i\tau_y}{\sqrt{2}}\,\psi_n = \sqrt{2}\psi_p, \quad \tau_+\psi_p = 0 \tag{7-23}$$

Similarly

$$j_\mu{}^- = \frac{1}{\sqrt{2}}\,\tilde{\psi}_N\gamma_\mu\tau_-\psi_N \tag{7-24}$$

for β^+ decay. These currents are very similar to the electromagnetic isovector current $j_\mu{}^z$. The $j_\mu{}^+, j_\mu{}^z, j_\mu{}^-$ are the three components of one and the same isobaric spin current j_μ.

It was suggested by Feynman and Gell-Mann (Fey-58) that, just as for electromagnetism, we must supplement the nucleonic current by a pionic term—in other words, not only $j_\mu{}^z$ but also $j_\mu{}^+$ and $j_\mu{}^-$ contain a pionic vector current:

$$j_\mu{}^+ = \frac{1}{\sqrt{2}}\,\tilde{\psi}_N\gamma_\mu\tau_+\psi_N + \left(\pi \times \frac{\partial \pi}{\partial x_\mu}\right)_+ + \cdots \tag{7-25}$$

Physically, this is equivalent to attributing the same β-interaction strength to the direct pion-lepton as to the baryon-lepton vertex, as shown in Fig. 7-3. Since the strong interactions are charge-independent, we have conservation of isobaric spin T, a generalization of conservation of charge—that is, of T_z. Thus the Feynman–Gell-Mann hypothesis amounts to the assumption that the total isobaric spin current, including both nucleonic and pionic terms, is conserved.*

Table 7-1 Correspondences between Beta Interaction and Electromagnetism

	Electrodynamics	Vector-Type Beta Interaction
Coupling Constant	e	$(1/\sqrt{2})g_V$
Current	j_μ^z	j_μ^+
Field Potential	A_μ	$\tilde{\psi}_e\gamma_\mu(1+\gamma_5)\psi_{\nu_e}$
Interaction Hamiltonian	$ej_\mu^z A_\mu$	$(1/\sqrt{2})g_V j_\mu^+\tilde{\psi}_e\gamma_\mu(1+\gamma_5)\psi_{\nu_e}$

It is interesting to recall here the comments which Gershtein and Zeldovich (Ge-55) made at a time when the Fermi part of the β interaction was believed to be scalar rather than vector. They wrote:

It is of no practical significance but only of theoretical interest if the interaction is vector type, then g_V(bare) $= g_V$(effective). No renormalization can be foreseen by analogy with Ward's identity for the interaction of a charged particle with the electromagnetic field: in this case, virtual processes involving particles do not lead to charge renormalization of the particle.

The analogy between the β interaction and electromagnetism is illustrated by the correspondences given in Table 7-1.

Connection between Weak and Electromagnetic Form Factors

The conserved isotriplet vector current theory relates the isovector weak-interaction form factors uniquely to the well-known isovector electromagnetic form factors which have been extensively measured by the electron-scattering experiments.

---

* A more appropriate name instead of C.V.C. might be conserved isotriplet vector current (Lee-65). This name does indeed imply conservation of charge (see Eq. 7-20), but the converse does not necessarily hold. Thus a current of the form $K_\mu \sim (\partial/\partial x_\mu)\psi_n^\dagger\gamma_4\sigma_{\mu\nu}\psi_p$ satisfies Eq. 7-20 but is not related to the $I = 1$ component of the electromagnetic current.

The matrix element of the isobaric vector part of the electromagnetic interaction between two nucleons can be written as

$$M_V^{\text{E-M}} = e\tilde{u}_2\left[F_Q^{\text{E-M}}(q^2)\gamma_\mu + \frac{\mu_{\text{p}}^a - \mu_{\text{n}}^a}{2m_{\text{N}}} F_M^{\text{E-M}}(q^2)\sigma_{\mu\nu}q_\nu\right]u_1 \quad (7\text{-}26)$$

where q is the momentum transfer and

$$\sigma_{\mu\nu} = \frac{\gamma_\mu\gamma_\nu - \gamma_\nu\gamma_\mu}{2}$$

that is, $\sigma_{12} = i\sigma_3$, etc.; μ_{p}^a and μ_{n}^a are the anomalous magnetic moments of the proton and neutron; and $\mu_{\text{p}}^a \cong 1.79$, and $\mu_{\text{n}}^a = -1.91$ nuclear Bohr magneton. $F_Q^{\text{E-M}}$ and $F_M^{\text{E-M}}$ are the well-known isovector parts of the charge and magnetic form factors for the nucleon (Fourier transform of the spatial distribution of these quantities). In the limit $q^2 \to 0$, $F_Q^{\text{E-M}}(0) = 1$, and $F_M^{\text{E-M}}(0) = 1$.

By analogy, the matrix element for the conserved vector current in weak interaction is given by

$$M_V{}^W = \frac{g_V}{\sqrt{2}}\tilde{u}_2[f_1{}^V(q^2)\gamma_\mu + f_2{}^V(q^2)\sigma_{\mu\nu}q_\nu]u_1 \quad (7\text{-}27)$$

where $f_1{}^V(q^2)$ and $f_2{}^V(q^2)$ are the form factors in the vector part of the weak interaction. The unique correspondences between these two sets of form factors bring out significant consequences.

Renormalizability of the Vector Current. $f_1{}^V(q^2)$ should behave like $F_Q^{\text{E-M}}(q^2)$. Since $F_Q^{\text{E-M}}(0) = 1$, which is the static limit of the charge, we should also have $f_1{}^V(0) = 1$. This implies that the vector coupling constant of the weak interaction in the C.V.C. theory should not be renormalized.

Weak Magnetism Term. $f_2{}^V(q^2)$ should behave like $[(\mu_{\text{p}}^a - \mu_{\text{n}}^a)/2m_{\text{N}}]F_M^{\text{E-M}}(q^2)$. This implies that the anomalous magnetic term resulting from the pion cloud must also appear in weak interactions. In fact, a relation between $f_2{}^V(0)$ and $f_1{}^V(0)$ in weak interactions can be obtained from the corresponding relation in electromagnetic interaction:

(Weak interaction) (E-M interaction)

$$\frac{f_2{}^V(0)}{f_1{}^V(0)} = \frac{(\mu_{\text{p}}^a - \mu_{\text{n}}^a)/2M}{1} \quad (7\text{-}28)$$

Since the relation of the term f_2^V to the term f_1^V in weak interactions is equivalent to the relation of the magnetism term to the charge term in the electromagnetic interaction, the f_2^V term is the corresponding magnetism term in weak interactions and has been called "weak magnetism" by Gell-Mann (Ge-58). This second relation enables us to interrelate β-decay transitions to electromagnetic transitions in nuclei. The investigation of the triad B^{12}, C^{12}, and N^{12} is interpreted mainly by this relation.

It can also be seen that in high-energy neutrino processes where high q values enter, we can actually determine the form factors by measuring the high-energy neutrino-capture cross section. Results from CERN (Bi-64) appear to be consistent with the form factors deduced from electron scattering:

$$f(q^2) \sim \frac{f(0)}{(1 + q^2/q_0^2)^2}, \qquad q_0 \sim 1 \text{ bev/c}$$

7-3 THE CONSEQUENCES OF THE C.V.C. THEORY AND THE SIGNIFICANT EXPERIMENTAL EVIDENCE

We will now review the observed evidence from four different types of experiments. These are

(a) The equality of the coupling constants g_V in β decay and g_μ in μ decay.

(b) The equivalence of the weak-vector form factors and the electromagnetic form factors. Possible evidence can come from a study of the β spectra of B^{12} and N^{12}.

(c) Determination of the absolute decay rate of $\pi^+ \rightarrow \pi^0 + e^+ + \nu_e$.

(d) β-α angular-correlation measurements in Li^8 and B^8.

A fifth method, β-γ (circularly polarized) correlation, in the mirror transition $Na^{24} \xrightarrow{\beta^-} Mg^{24} \xleftarrow{\beta^+} Al^{24}$, has already been discussed in Sec. 4-8. All these experiments are extremely difficult, but their results are all strongly in favor of the C.V.C. hypothesis.

Equality of g_V and g_μ

How good is the equality between g_V for β decay and g_μ for μ decay? At present it appears that the two coupling constants are indeed nearly equal with g_μ perhaps 1–2% larger. However, the accuracy of some of the small theoretical corrections is not beyond question. The situation can be briefly summarized as follows:

Fermi Coupling Constant in Beta Decay g_V. The constant g_V can be deduced from the *ft* values of a series of superallowed $0^+ \rightarrow 0^+$ transitions by the following relation:

$$g_V^2 \left|\int 1\right|^2 ft = 2\pi^3\hbar^7(\ln 2)/m_e^5c^4 \tag{7-29}$$

The $|\int 1|^2$ for $0^+ \rightarrow 0^+$ transitions is equal to 2 in the absence of charge-dependent effects. In order to calculate the *ft* values accurately, we must have the following information.

ACCURATE MEASUREMENTS OF MAXIMUM BETA ENERGY AND HALF-LIVES. OF $0 \rightarrow 0$ TRANSITIONS. Seven of these transitions (O^{14}, Al^{26*}, Cl^{34}, Sc^{42}, V^{46}, Mn^{50}, and Co^{54}) have been carefully determined by measuring nuclear Q values (Bar-62; Ja-63; Fr-62, 65). These results are summarized in Table 7-2.

Table 7-2 Seven Accurately Measured $0^+ \xrightarrow{\beta^+} 0^+$ Transitions and Their Calculated *ft* Values

$0^+ \xrightarrow{\beta^+} 0^+$ Transition	$t_{\frac{1}{2}}$ (sec)	$E_{\max}$ (kev)	$(ft)_{\rm I}$	$(ft)_{\rm II}$	Reference
${}_8O^{14} \rightarrow {}_7N^{14}$	71.36×0.09	1812.6 ± 1.4	3066	3127 ± 10	Ba-62; Du-63
${}_{13}Al^{26*} \rightarrow {}_{12}Mg^{26}$	6.374 ± 0.016	3208.0 ± 2.3	3015	3086 ± 12	Fre-62,63; Du-63
${}_{17}Cl^{34} \rightarrow {}_{16}S^{34}$	1.565 ± 0.007	4460 ± 4.5	3055	3140 ± 20	Fre-62,63; Du-63
${}_{21}Sc^{42} \rightarrow {}_{20}Ca^{42}$	0.6830 ± 0.0015	5409.0 ± 2.3		3122 ± 9	Fr-65
${}_{23}V^{46} \rightarrow {}_{22}Ti^{46}$	0.4259 ± 0.0008	6032.1 ± 2.2	3004 ± 8	3131 ± 8	Fr-65
${}_{25}Mn^{50} \rightarrow {}_{24}Cr^{50}$	0.2857 ± 0.0006	6609.0 ± 2.6		3125 ± 9	Fr-65
${}_{27}Co^{50} \rightarrow {}_{27}Fe^{54}$	0.1937 ± 0.0010	7229 ± 5	2966	3134 ± 18	Fre-62,63; Fre-64

$(ft)_{\rm I}$ a point-charge nucleus.
$(ft)_{\rm II}$ with nuclear-size effect, Rose's screening formula, and radiative correction from (Fr-63). The values for O^{14}, Al^{26*}, and Cl^{34} are from (Du-63)

F FUNCTIONS. To calculate the value *f*, we must integrate the β spectrum. To do this we have to rely on the computed tables of the Fermi function F. Unfortunately, the widely used Fermi function tables (NBS-52) by the National Bureau of Standards were computed, based on a point charge nucleus and retaining only the leading term in the expansion of the Fermi function. For precision results, several additional factors must be taken into account in evaluating the Fermi function, such as the finite-charge distribution of the nucleus, the orbital electron screening, the finite electron De Broglie wavelength, etc. The nuclear-size correction has been calculated recently by several authors (Dz-56; Du-63; Bh-61), and the results are all in good agreement. There is no such accord for the screening corrections given by the detailed calculations of Reitz (Re-50) and the approximate method of Rose (Ro-36). The discrepancy in ft values resulting from screening corrections varies from 2% in O^{14} to 1% in Co^{54}. This screening correction is now being reexamined by several authors. L. Durand (Dur-64) and W. Bühring (Bü-65a) reported that their results are in agreement with those obtained by Rose and by Longmire and Brown; however, they are in marked disagreement with Reitz's numerical calculation. The latter results therefore appear to be incorrect.

RADIATIVE CORRECTIONS. Because of various radiative processes—photon emission and absorption, both virtual and real, bremsstrahlung, etc.—we must also apply radiative corrections in the β decay This gives:

$$\frac{\Delta ft}{ft} = \frac{\alpha}{4\pi}\left(6 \ln \frac{\Lambda}{m_p} + 3 \ln \frac{m_p}{2E_{max}} - 2.85\right) \tag{7-30}$$

where Λ is a "cutoff parameter." Kinoshita and Sirlin (Ki-59) used $\Lambda = m_p$ and obtained

$$\frac{(\Delta ft)_{O^{14}}}{(ft)_{O^{14}}} \cong +1.7\%$$

which implies a reduction in the effective coupling constant by 0.8%. More detailed calculations by Berman and Sirlin (Be-62) give essentially the same result. However, this theoretical evaluation of $\Delta ft/ft$ may not be reliable. At least we know of no case in which such a divergent radiative correction formula, derived for a bare particle, is applicable to any properties of any strongly interacting particles. For example, such a calculation for the mass difference between p and n would lead to a completely wrong answer. Finally, relativistic corrections (Al-58), competition from K capture, and contributions from second forbidden matrix elements (Bli-60) were estimated and found to be too small to be relevant.

To compare the magnitude of these different corrections, Freeman et al. (Fr-63) calculated the *ft* values for (a) $(ft)_{\mathrm{I}}$ a point-charge nucleus; (b) $(ft)_{\mathrm{II}}$ with nuclear-size effect, Rose's screening formula, and radiative correction.

These two different calculations of *ft* values are listed in Table 7-2. It is interesting to note the extreme uniformity of the *ft* values, especially (b), of the seven transitions in spite of the large range of Z. Apparently, the atomic number has very little effect on the matrix element.

IMPURITY CORRECTIONS TO $|\int 1|^2$. We have mentioned that for $0^+ \rightarrow 0^+$ transitions, $|\int 1|^2 = 2$. This is true only for perfect isobaric-spin states. It is expected that the Coulomb interaction between protons, which violates isobaric-spin conservation, will distort the nuclear wave functions to some extent, so that the nuclear matrix element is decreased. Detailed calculations of this effect (Macd-58; We-62) indicate that the effect in O^{14} is likely to be very small. The upper limit of $\Delta\, |\int 1|^2/|\int 1|^2 < \frac{1}{4}\%$.

Weidenmüller (We-62) pointed out that should an appreciable configuration mixing of higher states be present at the 1*p*-shell states involved in the decay, then the Coulomb effects may be boosted up to 1–2%. However, there have been no experimental demonstrations of the presence of such mixing yet. Meantime, the introduction of a small percentage of charge-dependent nuclear potential—that is, different p-p and p-n potential of electromagnetic but non-Coulomb origin—was investigated by Blin-Stoyle and collaborators (Bli-62, 63a; Lo-63). It was shown that even a very small departure from charge symmetry could lead to corrections of the desired amount in the matrix element. However, MacDonald and Altman (Alt-62) calculated the possible magnitude of the charge-dependent nuclear potential from the existing experimental data and found it to be too small to give the required reduction of the nuclear matrix element. Therefore this question is not yet completely settled.

When $|\int 1|^2 = 2$ was assumed, and the unweighted average *ft* value from O^{14}, Al^{26*}, Cl^{34}, V^{46}, and Co^{54} was used in calculation, Freeman et al. (Fr-63) obtained the following:

With Rose's screening formula: $(ft)_{\mathrm{av}} = (3125 \pm 10)$ sec;* $g_V = (1.4029 \pm 0.0022) \times 10^{-49}$ erg cm^3; without radiative corrections the

* A more recent analysis by Bühring and Schopper (Bü-65b) gives $ft = (3111 \pm 15)$ sec.

coupling constant would equal $(1.4149 \pm 0.0022) \times 10^{-49}$ erg cm^3.

g_μ of Muon Decay. To obtain g_μ, we can use the muon lifetime equation (for its derivation, see Appendix VII):

$$\frac{1}{\tau_\mu} = \frac{g_\mu^{\,2} m_\mu^{\,5} c^4}{192\pi^3 \hbar^7} \tag{7-31}$$

where the latest measurements (Ch-62; Fa-62) gave

$$m_\mu = (206.768 \pm 0.003)m_0$$
$$\tau \to \tau_\mu \text{ (uncorrected)} = 2.198 \pm 0.001 \ \mu\text{sec}$$
$$g_\mu \text{ (uncorrected)} = (1.4320 \pm 0.0011) \times 10^{-49} \text{ erg cm}^3$$

The radiative correction was estimated (Ki-59; Be-62) to be

$$\frac{\Delta\tau_\mu}{\tau_\mu} \cong -0.42\% \quad \text{or} \quad \frac{\Delta g_\mu}{g_\mu} \cong +0.21\%$$

Therefore g_μ, including the radiative correction, is

$$g_\mu = (1.4350 \pm 0.0011) \times 10^{-49} \text{ erg cm}^3$$

Discussion. From the values of g_V and g_μ, we obtain

$$\frac{g_\mu - g_V}{g_\mu} = (2.2 \pm 0.15)\% \text{ using Rose's screening correction}$$

Indeed, if the equality of $g_V = g_\mu$ is required by the C.V.C. theory, the observed discrepancy of 2–3% may appear to be in contradiction to the C.V.C. theory. On the other hand, the *ft* values of the seven transitions shown in the table are so remarkably constant that we may very well wonder how reliable the radiative corrections to the β decay or the impurity corrections to the $|\int 1|^2$ are. After all, the radiative correction for β decay is calculated purely for a *bare* nucleon and not for nucleons inside of a complex nucleus. How justified this assumption may be is hard to say. In addition to these uncertainties, we now discover that we also need a more accurately computed Fermi function with proper electron screening corrections. It was also suggested that if the intermediate vector boson *W* exists, the lifetime of the muon will be modified depending on the mass of the intermediate vector boson (Le-60; On-59). The effect produced by the existence of the *W* particle can be expressed by a correction:

$$(\Delta\tau_{\text{p}})_W = -[\tau_\mu] \times \frac{3}{5}\left(\frac{m_\mu}{m_W}\right)^2$$

The recent high-energy neutrino experiments at CERN have shown that the mass of the intermediate boson is probably larger than 2 bev (Ce-63).

Therefore the correction to the muon-decay coupling from this term is less than 0.1%.

In view of these uncertain theoretical corrections involved in comparing g_V and g_μ, we should probably not be discouraged by the existing discrepancy of 2–3%. In fact, an intriguing hypothesis to explain this discrepancy has been suggested by Cabibbo (Ca-63) and is discussed later. See p. 284.

We should now turn to an examination of the evidence for the C.V.C. theory from other experimental investigations.

The B^{12}- C^{12}- N^{12} Experiment

As we have pointed out, the C.V.C. theory relates the nucleon current in the vector part of the β interaction to the charge current in electromagnetism. Although the effective coupling strength is not renormalized by pionic corrections, a nucleon also possesses a magnetic moment which is greatly altered by the pion cloud. Physically, for a given charge, the bare pion carries a larger magnetic moment because of its smaller mass; this larger magnetic moment is responsible for the anomalous nucleon magnetic moment. The C.V.C. theory implies that such anomalous magnetic-moment terms must also appear in β decay.

Theoretical Expectations. A very ingenious way to test the effect of the C.V.C. theory in β decay was suggested by Gell-Mann (Ge-58) and was successfully observed in various laboratories (May-62; Gl-63; Le-63). This test involves the β and γ transitions in the $A = 12$ nuclei, as indicated in Fig. 7-4. There are three transitions from the three levels of an isotopic triplet $T = 1$, $I = 1$ to the common ground state of C^{12}: the β^- transition from B^{12}, the corresponding β^+ transition from N^{12}, and the γ transition from C^{12}.

Let us consider the β^- transition from the $T_z = -1$ level. The dominant contribution should come from the axial-vector current, in allowed order. Its effective matrix element is

$$g_A \int \boldsymbol{\sigma} \left(e^+ \boldsymbol{\sigma} \frac{1 + \gamma_5}{\sqrt{2}} \nu \right)_z \tag{7-32}$$

Now we consider the forbidden corrections from both V and A interactions. However, the matrix element of the V interaction of j_μ^+ from the $T_z = -1$ state is now uniquely related to that of j_μ^z of the analogous electromagnetic transition from the $T_z = 0$ state. For the γ transition [$\Delta I = -1$ (no)], we expect magnetic-dipole effects to dominate, and since $\Delta I = -1$, only the isobaric vector part of electromagnetic current

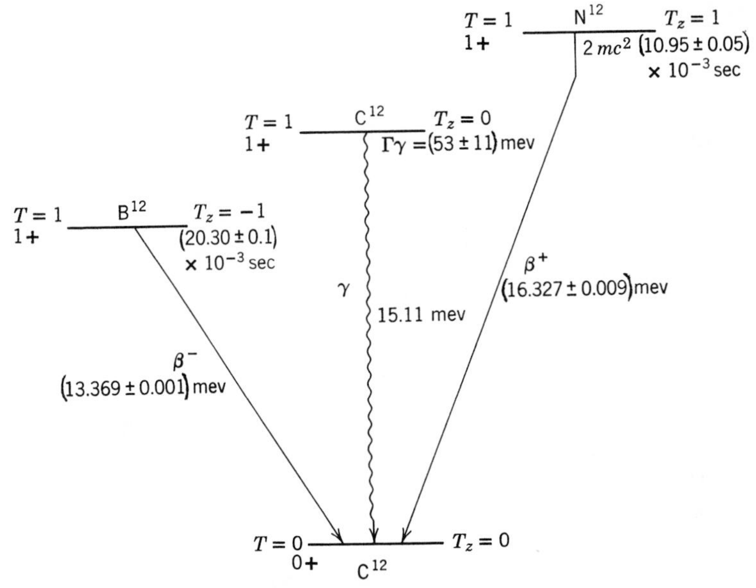

Fig. 7-4 The $A = 12$ triad.

will contribute. All orbital currents are negligible, as shown by the detailed calculations of Weidenmüller (We-60). Therefore,

$$M_{\text{el}} = -\frac{\mu e}{2M}(\boldsymbol{\nabla} \times \mathbf{A})_z \tag{7-33}$$

where μ is the transition magnetic moment in units of the proton Bohr magneton $(e/2M)$ and $\boldsymbol{\nabla} \times \mathbf{A}$ is evaluated at the nucleus.

The matrix element from the vector β interaction is

$$-\sqrt{2}\,\frac{\mu e}{2M}\,\frac{g_V}{e}\left[\nabla \times \left(e^\dagger \boldsymbol{\alpha}\,\frac{1+\gamma_5}{\sqrt{2}}\,\nu\right)\right]_z \tag{7-34}$$

It is important to point out here that the forbidden vector interaction is now determined by the transition magnetic moment μ in the analogous γ transition. The transition magnetic moment μ can be calculated from the observed radiation width Γ_γ of the $T = 1$ state in C^{12} by the relation $\Gamma_\gamma = [\mu^2/3(137)]/(W^3/m_p^2)$, where W is the γ-ray energy, and $\Gamma_\gamma = (53 \pm 11)$ ev (Hay-57). This gives $\mu = 2.2$. It is also important to demonstrate that the anomalous magnetism plays a dominant role in this $M1$ transition. This can be shown by using the relation

$$\mu = \frac{1}{\sqrt{2}}(\mu_p - \mu_n)\int \boldsymbol{\sigma}$$

The value of $\mu_p - \mu_n$ deduced from the empirical $\int \boldsymbol{\sigma} \simeq 0.8$ and $\mu \simeq 2.2$ is $\sim$4.0, which agrees fairly well with the difference $\mu_p - \mu_n = 4.7$. Since in the old theory of β decay the pions were not coupled to leptons and, therefore, possessed no β-emitting power, the large anomalous magnetic moments coming from the pion clouds had no claim to be in β decay.

For completeness, we must also consider the lowest forbidden corrections coming from the axial-vector current, for example, corrections resulting from the gradient of the lepton fields. In summary the $\beta^{\pm}$-transition matrix element in the foregoing cases is made up from the allowed A interaction plus forbidden corrections from the A interaction plus or minus a forbidden matrix element from the V interaction (cf. p. 78),

$$-g_A\int \boldsymbol{\sigma}\left[e^{\dagger}(\boldsymbol{\sigma} - ia(\mathbf{k}\times\boldsymbol{\alpha}) - b\mathbf{k}\gamma_5)_z \frac{1+\gamma_5}{\sqrt{2}}\nu\right] \tag{7-35}$$

allowed A term — interference term between A and V — correction in A term

where

$$a \equiv \frac{\mu}{\sqrt{2}m_p}\left|\frac{g_V}{g_A}\right|\frac{1}{\int \boldsymbol{\sigma}} \tag{7-35a}$$

The spectrum can be represented by the standard allowed shape, multiplied by a correction factor

$$1 + \tfrac{8}{3}a\left(E - \frac{E_0}{2} - \frac{m_e^2}{2E}\right) + \tfrac{2}{3}b\left(E_0 - \frac{m_e^2}{E}\right) \tag{7-36}$$

For fast β^- particles, the b term fortunately does not contribute to the spectrum shape. Therefore the correction factor is reduced to

$$1 + \tfrac{8}{3}aE$$

For the β^+ transition, we obtain the same result; however, the sign in front of the energy term changes to negative. The correction factor is $1 - \frac{8}{3}aE$ for β^+. The change of sign comes about because the coefficient a results from a $V - A$ interference, which changes sign in *going* from β^- to β^+ transitions (cf. Appendix IV, p. 342). Therefore the ratio of the B^{12} and N^{12} correction factors is

$$R(E) = 1 + AE$$

where $A = \frac{16}{3}a$.

More extensive calculations on the spectral deviation from the allowed Fermi shapes for B^{12} and N^{12} were also carried out by Morita (Mo-59), Gell-Mann and Berman (Ge-59), and Huffaker and Greuling (Hu-62). All the contributions due to weak magnetism, electromagnetic correction, finite de Broglie wavelength effect, and second forbidden matrix elements of various coordinate and momentum types were included. These calculations turned out to be in very good accord. The curves showing correction factor versus energy in Morita's and Huffaker's calculations exhibit very slight curvatures. The slopes $A^-(\beta^{12})$ and $A^+(N^{12})$ are about equal, and opposite in sign. According to a single-particle model, we obtain

$$A^{\mp} = \pm\frac{8}{3}\frac{\mu_p - \mu_n}{2m_p}\left|\frac{g_V}{g_A}\right| = \frac{\pm 0.0029}{mc^2}$$

$$= \pm 0.57\,\%/\text{mev}$$

If we use the old Fermi theory instead, $\mu_p - \mu_n$ must be taken as 1 rather than as 4.7, and

$$A^{\mp} \sim \pm 0.12\,\%/\text{mev}$$

More accurate calculations give

$$A^{\mp}(\text{C.V.C.}) = (\pm 0.55 \pm 0.09)\,\%/\text{mev}$$

$$A^{\mp}(\text{Fermi}) = \pm 0.05\,\%/\text{mev}$$

The expected difference between A (C.V.C.) and A (Fermi) is very striking. This experiment, therefore, is a very suitable test for the C.V.C. hypothesis.

Experimental Confirmation. The shape factors for the β spectra of B^{12} and N^{12} have been measured by several laboratories. The B^{12} and N^{12} nuclei are produced on electrostatic accelerators using the reactions B^{11}(d, p), B^{12}, and B^{10} (He^3, p) N^{12}, respectively.

The first measurements were made by Mayer-Kuckuk and Michel at California Institute of Technology (May-62) and by Glass and Peterson at Los Alamos (Gla-63). Both groups determined the ratio of the shape factors, that is, the difference $A^- - A^+$, and found $(1.30 \pm 0.31)\%$/mev and $(1.62 \pm 0.28)\%$/mev, respectively, in good agreement with the C.V.C. prediction of $(1.10 \pm 0.17)\%$/mev. However, the deviations

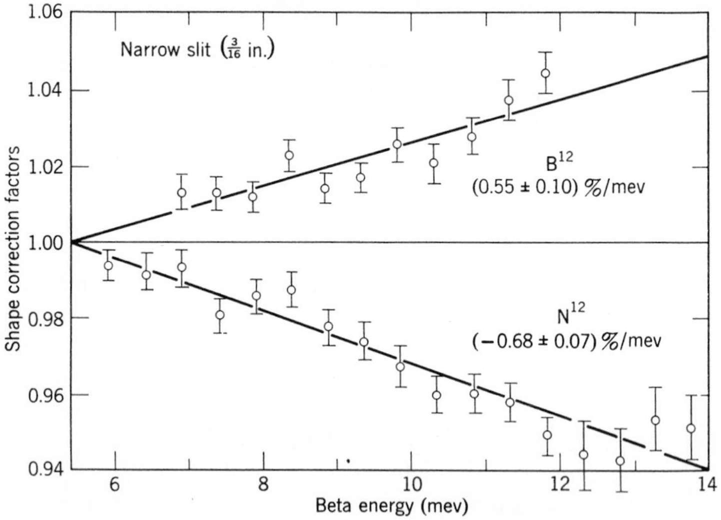

Fig. 7-5 The deviation of the experimental results of the B^{12} and N^{12} spectra from the calculated shape factor versus energy.

of the shape factors of the *individual* spectra were not accurately determined in the early measurements.

Later, Lee, Mo, and Wu (Le-63) at Columbia University measured the two spectra with their iron-free intermediate-focusing magnetic spectrometer and found that the deviation of the shape factor for the B^{12} spectrum is $A^- = (+0.55 \pm 0.10)\%$/mev, and for the N^{12} spectrum, $A^+ = (-0.52 \pm 0.06)\%$/mev, as shown in Fig. 7-5. As predicted, the deviations are in opposite directions to each other. The difference of the two shape factors is $(1.07 \pm 0.24)\%$/mev, in excellent agreement with the C.V.C. prediction. Furthermore, these curves have also been run with different slit systems, and the same conclusions were obtained. The evidence, therefore, strongly supports the theory of conserved vector current. The results are summarized in Table 7-3.

ft VALUES OF B^{12} AND N^{12}. Careful study of the β decays of B^{12} and N^{12} has led to the possible discovery of some new unexpected effects. From these very accurate measurements of decay energies and lifetimes for these β transitions (Fi-63; Pe-63; Wh-63), it is possible to calculate the *ft* values quite accurately. On this basis it is found that $ft = 11{,}700$ for B^{12} and 12,900 for N^{12} (the uncertainties are 0.5 to 1%). Thus the *ft* value for N^{12} is 10% larger than that for B^{12}. Assuming equality of the mirror matrix elements and no other effects, these two *ft* values should be equal.

Table 7-3 The Experimentally Determined Shape Correction Factors for B^{12} and N^{12} and Their Differences

	Lee, Mo, and Wu (Le-63)	Mayer-Kuckuk and Michel (May-62)	Glass and Peterson (Gla-63)	Theoretical Prediction (Mo-59; Ge-59; Hu-62)
$A^-(B^{12})$	$(+0.55 \pm 0.10)\%$	$(+1.82 \pm 0.08)\%$		$(+0.55 \pm 0.12)\%$
$A^+(N^{12})$	$(-0.52 \pm 0.06)\%$	$(+0.52 \pm 0.20)\%$		$(-0.55 \pm 0.12)\%$
$A = A^- - A^+$	$(1.07 \pm 0.24)\%$	$(1.30 \pm 0.31)\%$	$(1.62 \pm 0.28)\%$	$(1.10 \pm 0.17)\%$

It might appear that the weak-magnetism term which changes the spectrum shape for β^- and β^+ decay in opposite directions could also change the *ft* values, but such is not the case. The average of E (integrated over the allowed spectrum) is, in fact, precisely $\frac{1}{2}E_0$; thus the correction in the shape factor (Eq. 7-36) averages zero. Consequently, in the approximation just considered there is no difference between *ft* values. However, other correction terms exist besides the weak magnetism term; they are the "induced couplings" (for example, the induced pseudoscalar coupling and possibly also an induced tensor coupling). These terms might conceivably account for the difference of *ft* values (We-58; Hu-63), although they have negligible effect on allowed spectrum shapes. However, in a recent paper (Ei-64) it was shown that Coulomb effects alone, as manifested in single-particle binding energies, are large enough to account for the observed 10% difference in *ft* values. A similar calculation for the O^{14} decay gave single-particle radial matrix elements which differ from unit by less than 0.1%.

The $\pi^+ \rightarrow \pi^0 + e^+ + \nu$ *Decay*

An important consequence of the C.V.C. theory is the predicted occurrence of decay of π^+ into π^0.

It was pointed out previously that, according to the C.V.C. theory, pions are endowed with β-interaction strength. Therefore charged π^+ should be able to decay into π^0. For example, we can have

$$\pi^+ \rightarrow \pi^0 + e^+ + \nu$$

This decay is very similar, in principle, to a nuclear $0^+ \rightarrow 0^+$ transition such as, for example, the $O^{14} \rightarrow N^{14}$ decay. In both cases the decaying particle has spin 0 and isobaric spin $T = 1$, and T_z changes from $+1$ to 0. As in nuclear β decay, we find

$$w = \frac{mc^2}{\hbar}\frac{G^2}{2\pi^3}|M|^2 f \tag{7-37}$$

Expressing the dimensionless coupling constant in terms of the g_V and using

$$|M|^2 = \left|\int 1\right|^2 = 2$$

and

$$f \sim \frac{E_0{}^5}{30} \quad \text{for} \quad E_0 \gg 1 \tag{7-38}$$

where E_0 is the maximum energy in units mc^2, the electron rest energy, we obtain

$$w = g_V{}^2 \frac{m^5c^4}{\hbar^7}\frac{E_0{}^5}{30\pi^3} \tag{7-39}$$

The decay energy $= (m_{\pi^+} - m_{\pi^0})c^2 = 4.6$ mev. We find that

$$w = 0.43 \text{ sec}^{-1} \tag{7-40}$$

and a branching ratio

$$R = \frac{\pi^+ \rightarrow \pi^0 + e^+ + \nu}{\pi^+ \rightarrow \mu^+ + \nu} = (1.07 \pm 0.02) \times 10^{-8} \tag{7-41}$$

Actually, this process could have also occurred in the old form of the theory, by

$$\pi^+ \rightarrow \mathrm{p} + \bar{\mathrm{n}} \rightarrow \begin{pmatrix}\mathrm{p} + \bar{\mathrm{p}} \\ \mathrm{n} + \bar{\mathrm{n}}\end{pmatrix} + e^+ + \nu \rightarrow \pi^0 + e^+ + \nu \tag{7-42}$$

In this theory the calculation of the decay rate is beset with mathematical difficulties owing to both the strong coupling of pions to nucleons and divergent integrals. The calculated R is between 5×10^{-9} and 10^{-8}, depending on the assumptions made (Fe-58). It should be pointed out that the processes (Eq. 7-42 as well as direct decay) are included in the C.V.C. calculation, since the β-decay current is the same for a bare pion or a nucleon-antinucleon pair, as in the case of the vector part of nuclear β decay.

The $\pi^+ \rightarrow \pi^0 + e^+ + \nu$ decay can be detected by observing the following series of events. A slow neutral π^0 is created after a positive pion π^+ is stopped and decays. The π^0 immediately decays into two 70-mev γ rays. Meanwhile, the e^+ produced in the π^+ decay annihilates into two $\frac{1}{2}$-mev γ rays. This sequence of events—two 70-mev γ rays and two $\frac{1}{2}$-mev γ rays, created practically simultaneously—is so typical that it is possible to distinguish it by multiple-coincidence experiments

Table 7-4 Summary of Experimental Results on the Ratio of $\dfrac{\pi^+ \rightarrow \pi^0 + e^+ + \nu}{\pi^+ \rightarrow \mu^+ + \nu}$

	Reference	R	Events Observed
CERN	(Dep-63)	$(1.15 \pm 0.22) \times 10^{-8}$	52 ± 3
		$(1.08 \pm 0.22) \times R_{\text{C.V.C.}}$	
Lawrence Lab	(Bac-65)	$(1.12 \pm 0.08) \times 10^{-8}$	38
Dubna	(Dun-63)	$(1.30 \pm 0.35) \times 10^{-8}$	40 ± 8
Columbia	(Ba-64)	$(1.0 \pm 0.3) \times 10^{-8}$	33

(by factor 10^8) from the tremendous background of normal $\pi \rightarrow \mu \rightarrow e$ decays. Even the rare $\pi \rightarrow e + \nu$ decays occur 10^4 times as frequently! Several laboratories have carried out experiments to measure this ratio. The reported results are summarized in Table 7-4. It can be seen that the measured ratio is in good agreement with the ratio predicted by the C.V.C. theory.

The Beta-Alpha Angular Correlations in the Li^8 and B^8 Beta Decays

Another test of the C.V.C. theory, similar in principle to that for the $A = 12$ nuclei, can be made by studying the β-α angular correlation in the decays of Li^8 and B^8.

Although the radiations following allowed β decay of unoriented nuclei are uncorrelated in direction with β rays, forbidden effects may produce correlations of the form

$$W(\theta_{\beta\alpha}) = 1 + B \cos^2 \theta_{\beta\alpha} \tag{7-43}$$

where the small coefficient B depends on the details of the matrix elements involved. Bernstein and Lewis (Be-58) and Morita (Mo-59) suggested that second forbidden vector interference terms should lead to deviations from isotropy in the β-α angular correlations of the Li^8 and B^8 decays [Li^8 $(\beta^-, \bar{\nu})Be^{8*}$ $(\alpha)He^4$ and $B^8(\beta^+, \nu)Be^{8*}$ $(\alpha)He^4$].

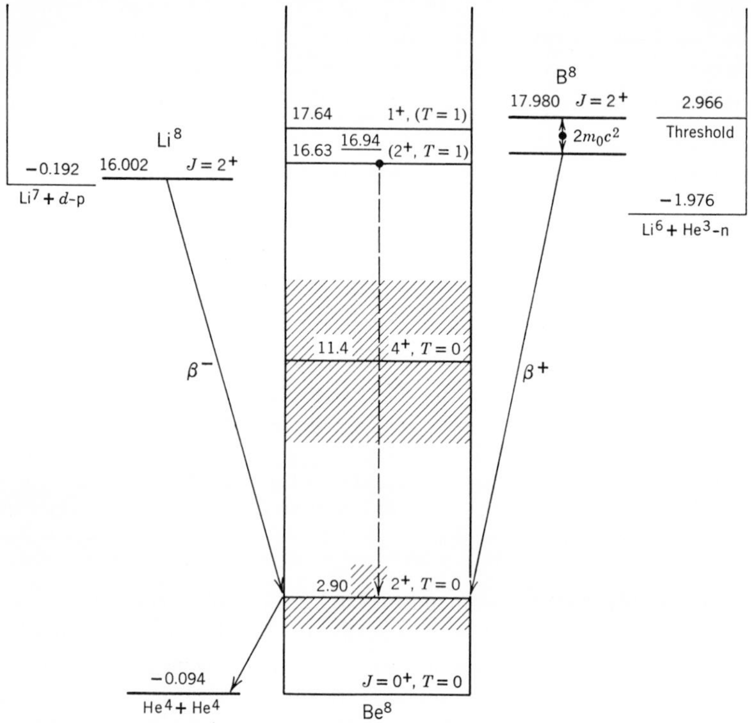

Fig. 7-6 Energy-level diagram and the mass-8 triplet. The Li^8 electron decay and the B^8 positron decay are followed by the α-particle breakup of the 2.90-mev Be^{8*} level.

These mirror nuclei decay primarily by an allowed Gamow-Teller transition to the 2.90-mev level of Be^8, which promptly decays into two α particles. The mass-8 triplet is illustrated in Fig. 7-6, where the dashed line represents the $M1$ γ transition to the 2.90-mev level of Be^8 from the $I = 2^+$, $T = 1$ level,* analogous to the Li^8 and B^8 ground states.

* Actually both the 16.63-mev and 16.96-mev states are 2^+ and appear to be mixtures of $T = 1$ and $T = 0$ components, with nearly equal amplitudes. This is one of the very few known cases of strong isospin mixing in light nuclei.

Because of the recoil of Be^{8*} from the β decay, the β-α angular correlation transformed from the Be^{8*} rest system to the laboratory system is of the form

$$W(\theta_{\beta\alpha}) = 1 + A \cos \theta_{\beta\alpha} + B \cos^2 \theta_{\beta\alpha} \tag{7-44}$$

where A is equal to $-E_\beta/p_\alpha c$ to the first order. E_β and p_α are the electron total energy and the α-particle momentum, respectively. The coefficient B may be represented by $B = aE_\beta$, where a is defined by Eq. 7-35a, p. 270. The situation here is similar to that for the $A = 12$ sequence, but it is not possible to draw definite conclusions.

First of all, the radiation width of the $M1$ γ ray is not known experimentally. It has been calculated theoretically by Weidenmüller (We-60) and Kurath (Ku-60), using the intermediate-coupling shell model. Weidenmüller's estimate gives Γ_γ between 1 and 4 ev, whereas Kurath estimates it to be between 3 and 5 ev.

Proceeding as in the case of the $A = 12$ sequence and using Weidenmüller's result, we can show that the anisotropy parameter B is given by

$$0.0025E < B < 0.0045E \quad \text{(for C.V.C.)} \quad \text{(E in mev)}$$

and

$$0.0005E < B < 0.002E \quad \text{(for conventional Fermi theory)}$$

for Li^8, with the same magnitude but opposite sign for B^8.

The coefficient B is extremely small. This difficult comparison has been carried out by Nordburg, Morinigo, and Barnes (No-62) with high precision. Their measurements were made by counting coincidences between α particles detected in a gold-silicon surface-barrier detector and electrons or positrons detected in a plastic scintillator, which could be rotated about the target to positions of 0°, 90°, or 180°, relative to the alpha detector. The α-particle pulse-height spectra in coincidence with electrons from the Li^8 β decay and B^8 β decay at various angles are shown in Figs. 7-7 and 7-8, respectively. The total areas of the curves are used to determine the coefficients A and B in Eq. 7-43. Their final results were

$$B_{Li^8} = (0.00316 \pm 0.00060)E_\beta$$

and

$$B_{B^8} = (-0.00386 \pm 0.00100)E_\beta$$

A recent independent determination of the Li^8 β-α correlation (Gr-63) gives $B_{Li^8} = (0.0037 \pm 0.0010)E_\beta$, in good agreement with the results of Nordburg et al. Thus we may conclude that the measured value lies within the range of the theoretical values of B for the C.V.C. theory and disagrees with the prediction of the old Fermi theory.

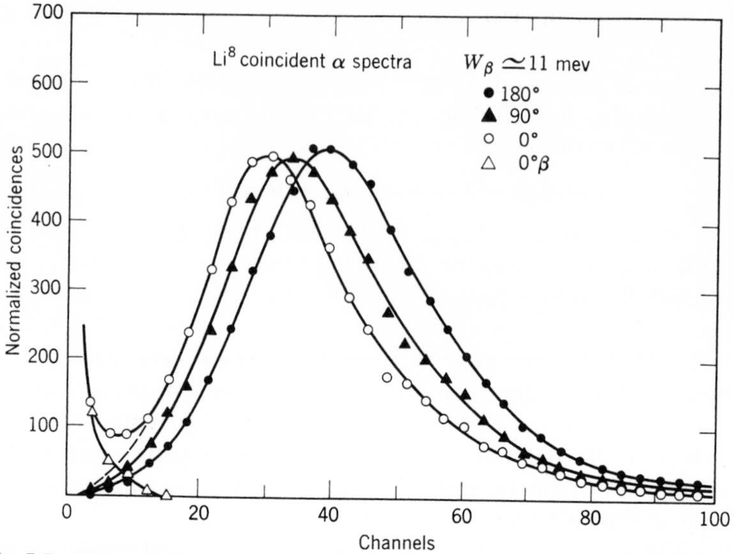

Fig. 7-7 The α-particle pulse weight spectra in coincidence with electrons from the Li^8 β decay at various angles. A prominent feature of the curves is the energy shift with angle which is the result of the Be^{8*} recoil from the β decay. This experiment measured the total areas of the curves to determine the coefficients of the angular distribution, $W(\theta_{\beta\alpha}) = 1 + A \cos \theta_{\beta\alpha} + B \cos^2 \theta_{\beta\alpha}$. The points marked "0°$\beta$" were the response of the gold-silicon detector to the electrons.

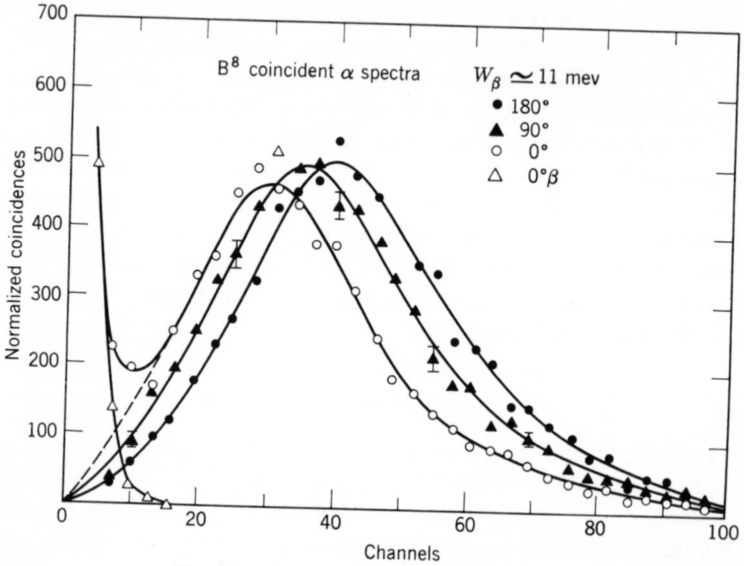

Fig. 7-8 Same as Fig. 7-7 for B^8 β decay.

Other Weak Processes

In general, the Hamiltonian density of weak interaction can be expressed by

$$\mathscr{H} = \frac{1}{\sqrt{2}} gJJ^{\dagger} + \text{h.c.} \tag{7-45}$$

This is known as the current-current hypothesis (Fe-58), where J is a general weak current containing several terms. The part of J involving *nucleons and leptons only* is

$$J = J_{\text{np}} + j_{e\mu_e} + j_{\mu\nu_\mu} \tag{7-46}$$

where $$J_{\text{np}} = \text{nucleon current} = \tilde{\psi}_{\text{p}}\gamma_\mu(1 + \lambda\gamma_5)Q^+\psi_{\text{n}} \tag{7-47}$$

We include here an axial-vector term as well as the vector term and $\lambda = -g_A/g_V$. The vector current is conserved according to the C.V.C. theory. The $j_{e\nu_e}$ and $j_{\mu\nu_\mu}$ represent leptonic currents:

$$j_{e\nu_e} = \tilde{\psi}_{\nu_e}\gamma_\mu(1 + \gamma_5)\psi_e \tag{7-48a}$$
$$j_{\mu\nu_\mu} = \tilde{\psi}_{\nu_\mu}\gamma_\mu(1 + \gamma_5)\psi_\mu \tag{7-48b}$$

In addition, of course, J contains terms involving pions, for example, $J_{\pi^-\pi^0}$ and strangeness-violating terms, for example, $J_{\Lambda\text{p}}$ (cf. p. 284; also see the discussion of Cabibbo's hypothesis).

The cross term $J_{\text{np}}j^+_{e\nu_e}$ gives rise to conventional β decay with a $V - A$ interaction:

$$\mathscr{H} = \frac{1}{\sqrt{2}} g\{[\tilde{\psi}_{\text{p}}\gamma_\mu(1 + \lambda\gamma_5)Q^+\psi_{\text{n}})[\tilde{\psi}_e\gamma_\mu(1 + \gamma_5)\psi_{\nu_e}]\} + \text{h.c.} \tag{7-49}$$

while the other cross term $j_{e\nu_e}J^+_{\text{np}}$ gives β^+ decay and orbital electron capture.

The Hamiltonian (7-28) with the currents given by (7-29) implies that there are also other weak processes, besides β decay, μ decay, and μ capture. These are illustrated in Table 7-5. (Related processes which involve only reordering of one or more of the particles, for example inverse β decay, $\nu_e + \text{n} \rightarrow e + \text{p}$, are not shown in the table.)

Neutrino Electron Scattering. First of all we can have the scattering of neutrinos by electrons

$$\nu_e + e \rightleftarrows \nu_e + e \tag{7-50}$$

The predicted cross section for this process is

$$\sigma = 8 \times 10^{-45} E_\nu \text{ cm}^2$$

where E_ν = neutrino energy (in units of mc^2) $\gg 1$. In addition, processes such as

$$e^+ + e^- \rightleftarrows \bar{\nu}_e + \nu_e \tag{7-51}$$

which are essentially equivalent to ν_e scattering, are expected to occur, as are similar processes involving muon and muon neutrettos. In fact, if it can be measured, the angular distribution of the scattered

Table 7-5 Possible Weak-Interaction Processes Involving Nucleon and Lepton Currents

	n, p	e, ν_e	μ, ν_μ
n, p	n + p → n + p	$n \to p + e^- + \bar{\nu}_e$	$\mu^- + p \to n + \nu_\mu$
e, ν_e		$\nu_e + e \to \nu_e + e$	$\mu \to e + \bar{\nu}_e + \nu_\mu$
μ, ν_μ			$\nu_\mu + \mu \to \nu_\mu + \mu$

electrons in reaction 7-50 may give interesting information concerning the charge distribution of the ν_e. Although ν_e is of course neutral, according to the intermediate-boson hypothesis (Sec. 7-4), it can dissociate into a virtual e^- and a W^+. Lee and Sirlin (Le-64) estimate this to happen a fraction 10^{-5} of the time. Thus the ν_e can have a charge distribution.

Parity Violating Nucleon-Nucleon Interaction. Finally, we can expect to have the process

$$n + p \to n + p. \tag{7-52}$$

coming from the interaction of the nucleon current with itself. This process, unlike the basic nucleon-nucleon interaction, violates parity conservation. The n-p interaction induced by the weak coupling would of course be very weak compared to the normal nucleon-nucleon interaction.

We know that the interaction energies from strong interactions are of the order of magnitude

$$U_{\text{strong}} \sim m_\pi c^2 \tag{7-53}$$

On the other hand, the interaction energies from weak interactions in nuclei are of the order

$$U_{\text{weak}} \sim g_\beta \rho \tag{7-54}$$

where ρ is the density of nucleons, approximately $(\hbar/m_\pi c)^{-3}$. In terms of the dimensionless coupling constant G_β (cf. Eq. 2-24) we obtain

$$U_{\text{weak}} \sim G_\beta \left(\frac{m_\pi}{m_e}\right)^2 m_\pi c^2 \quad (7\text{-}55)$$

and thus

$$\frac{U_{\text{weak}}}{U_{\text{strong}}} \sim G_\beta \left(\frac{m_\pi}{m_e}\right)^2 \sim 10^{-7} \quad (7\text{-}56)$$

The presence of such a weak nucleon-nucleon interaction would show up as a slight violation of parity conservation in nuclear reactions of order 10^{-7}.

According to the notation of Lee and Yang, F will be used to denote the relative strength of the parity–nonconserving coupling. All wave functions can be written as

$$\psi = \psi(\text{parity-conserving}) + F\psi(\text{parity-nonconserving}) \quad (7\text{-}57)$$

Naturally our aim is first to determine the order of magnitude of the relative strength F in order to confirm the current-current hypothesis. Then, from the value of F, we may obtain some added information on the structure of weak interactions.

Wilkinson had proposed and discussed various methods of determining F or F^2 (Wil-57), and Blin-Stoyle has made several theoretical calculations (Bl-61) on this subject. Michel and Blin-Stoyle have written very detailed theoretical papers (Mi-64; Bl-65b) on the nuclear parity impurity from the point of view of current-current hypothesis and have suggested several feasible investigations. In general, if we look for violations of absolute selection rules based on strict parity conservation (as for example, α emission from a state of even I but odd parity leading to a final state 0^+), the sensitivity is proportional to the *intensity* of the parity-nonconserving wave function or F^2. However, if we measure longitudinal polarization of product heavy particles or circular polarization of γ rays from initially unpolarized systems, the sensitivy is proportional to F and not to F^2. In this case the longitudinal polarization or circular polarization represents directly the interference term between the parity-conserving and parity-nonconserving parts of the interactions. This is in contrast to the measurement of the odd powers of $\cos\theta$ in the angular distribution (or correlations) of radiation, for which the sensitivity is proportional to F^2. The reason for this difference is that the intensity of emission of radiation is symmetrical backward and forward relative to the spin direction of the emitting nucleus so that the polarization by itself does not give an asymmetry (unlike the case of β decay).

In the type of experiment where we measure F, the parity-nonconserving effect will be relatively enhanced if the parity-conserving part is greatly hindered because of some approximate selection rules. For instance, there are several M1 transitions in the deformed nuclei region whose rates of decay are greatly hindered by the selection rules on so-called "asymptotic quantum numbers." If now an E1 transition is admixed because of the presence of parity-nonconserving nucleon-nucleon interaction, the emitted radiation will be partially circularly polarized and by an amount much larger than F itself. Therefore the circular polarization is given by $2RF$ where R is the ratio of $E1$ and $M1$ matrix elements. A search for the parity-nonconserving effect postulated by current-current hypothesis has been initiated in several laboratories as reported at the Paris Conference on Nuclear Structure, July 1964. An indication $P \sim 10^{-4}$ and $F \sim 10^{-7}$ has been reported, but further refined investigations should be made to substantiate the results.

Forbidden Processes. Although the current-current hypothesis predicts the occurrence of some new weak processes, there are others which are forbidden. Thus both

$$\mu^- + \text{p} \rightarrow e^- + \text{p}$$

and

$$\mu^\pm \rightarrow e^\pm + e^- + e^- \tag{7-58}$$

have been looked for but not found (Co-62; Al-62). This can be readily understood if we assume the conservation of the "muonic number" ($m = 1$) for $\mu^-\nu_\mu$ (as discussed in Sec. 4-4).

Absence of Neutral Lepton Currents. Note that the weak current (Eq. 7-29) is charged, that is, the process involves exchange of a charge. Thus nuclear β decay can be represented as $J_{\text{np}} j^\dagger_{e\nu_e}$. Even the other reactions such as νe scattering can be really written as $j_{\nu_e e} j^\dagger_{\nu_e e}$.

The question now arises: Are there any *neutral* leptonic currents? No evidence for such neutral currents has been found so far. However, such processes as $\mu + \text{p} \rightarrow e + \text{p}$ which would have to go via neutral currents $j_{\mu e} J^\dagger_{\text{pp}}$ are in any case forbidden by conservation of electronic and muonic number.

On the other hand, other processes such as $K^+ \rightarrow \pi^+ + e^+ + e^-$ which are consistent with conservation of lepton number but require neutral lepton currents $J_{K^+\pi^+} j^\dagger_{ee}$ are also not found experimentally (Cam-64). Yet $K^+ \to \pi^0 + e^+ + \nu_e$, which involves charge exchange $J_{K^+\pi^0} j^\dagger_{\nu_e e}$, does occur.

Nonrenormalizability of the Axial-Vector Interaction

Although the coupling constant for the vector part of the β interaction seems to be unaffected by pionic corrections, this is not the case for the axial-vector part. It can also be shown theoretically that the axial-vector current is not conserved. Perhaps the simplest argument is that given by Taylor (Ta-58).* Consider $\pi \to \mu + \nu$ decay. We write the matrix element for the decay as follows,

$$\langle J_i \rangle \tilde{\psi}_\mu \gamma_i (1 + \gamma_5) \psi_\nu \tag{7-59a}$$

where

$$\langle J_i \rangle = \langle 0 | J_i | \psi_\pi \rangle \tag{7-59b}$$

and ψ_π and 0 represent respectively the pion wave function and the vacuum.

For a *VA* interaction, J_i is a combination of a vector and axial vector. Now, because the π has zero spin, its momentum vector is the only vector (or axial vector) which can occur in the process, that is, $\langle J_i \rangle$ must be a vector and can be written

$$\langle J_i \rangle = C(p^2) p_i \tag{7-60}$$

On the other hand, because the π has odd parity, ψ_π is a pseudoscalar; thus only the axial-vector part of J_i can contribute to the $\pi \to \mu\nu$ (and also the $\pi \to e\nu$ decay).

Now if the axial-vector current is conserved, we will have

$$\sum_i \left\langle \frac{\partial J_i}{\partial x_i} \right\rangle = C(p^2) \sum_i p_i p_i = 0 \tag{7-61}$$

but since

$$\sum_i p_i p_i = -m_\pi^2 \tag{7-62}$$

this would require $C(p^2)$ to vanish.

Thus if the axial-vector current were conserved, the $\pi \to \mu + \nu$ and $\pi \to e + \nu$ decay would not occur, contrary to experiment. In this case,

---

* A more detailed treatment given by Goldberger and Treiman (Goldb-58) leads to a relation between the axial-vector coupling constant and the pion-nucleon and pion-lepton coupling constants. See also the footnote on page 257.

then, the only decay mode of the π^+ would be into $\pi^0 + e^+ + \bar{\nu}_e$. Thus the π^+ would have a lifetime of about 1 sec (in vacuum). Of course, the π^0 would still decay into 2γ with $t \sim 10^{-16}$ sec, and the predominant annihilation mode of π^- would be reactions with nuclei. It is an amusing exercise to speculate on further implications of a hypothetical universe in which there is conservation of axial-vector current.

The Cabibbo Hypothesis (*Ca*-63)

As we have pointed out, the effective coupling constants for nuclear β decay and muon decay are slightly different. The situation is much worse when we compare the rates of strangeness-conserving and strangeness-violating leptonic decays. Under the assumption of universality of weak interactions, the rates of decay for $|\Delta S| = 1$ processes such as in

$$K^+ \rightarrow \mu^+ + \nu_\mu \quad \text{and} \quad K^+ \rightarrow \pi^0 + e^+ + \nu_e. \tag{7-63a}$$

are 20 to 40 times slower than expected from the rates of corresponding processes with $\Delta S = 0$ (cf. Sec. 6-4):

$$\pi^+ \rightarrow \mu^+ + \nu_\mu \quad \text{and} \quad \pi^+ \rightarrow \pi^0 + e^+ + \nu_e. \tag{7-63b}$$

It is also known that the $|\Delta S| = 1$ processes such as

$$\Lambda \rightarrow \text{p} + e^- + \bar{\nu}_e \quad \text{and} \quad \Sigma^- \rightarrow \text{n} + e^- + \bar{\nu}_e \tag{7-63c}$$

are 20 to 40 times slower than that of neutron decay where $\Delta S = 0$:

$$\text{n} \rightarrow \text{p} + e^- + \bar{\nu}_e$$

Why are the $|\Delta S| = 1$ processes so greatly retarded? Could it perhaps be blamed on strong interaction effects? It can indeed be shown that the C.V.C. theory cannot be applied to $|\Delta S| = 1$ processes; therefore not only the axial-vector interaction but the vector interaction as well is not conserved and subject to renormalization in $|\Delta S| = 1$ processes. Nevertheless, the recent success of SU_3 symmetry strongly suggests the near equality of the strong interactions for hyperons and nucleons and also for kaons and pions. It is thus difficult to see how renormalization alone can account for the observed large difference between the decay rates of $|\Delta S| = 1$ and $\Delta S = 0$ processes. Probably a modification of the principle of universal Fermi interaction is in order.

Cabibbo proposed a very attractive hypothesis in connection with his analysis of leptonic decays using unitary symmetry. He postulated that the apparent failure of universality as we have described it may be due to our naivity in taking the observed particles (as they appear under the SU_3 breaking interactions) as the basic particles. To illustrate this point, consider, for simplicity, the pair of mesons π^+, K^+ (of course, it is now well known that these particles are the plus-charged members of an octet which contains, altogether, the π^+, π^0, π^-, η, K^+, K^0, $\bar{K}^0$, and K^-).

Let us now return to a consideration of the $K \to \mu\nu$ and $\pi \to \mu\nu$ decays mentioned earlier. The discussion closely follows that given by Cabibbo (Ca-63). The interaction Hamiltonian for both of these modes can be written as

$$H = \frac{1}{\sqrt{2}} \sum_i [g_\pi \langle 0 | J_i | \psi_{\pi^+} \rangle + g_K \langle 0 | J_i | \psi_{K^+} \rangle] \tilde{\psi}_\mu \gamma_i (1 + \gamma_5) \psi_\nu \quad (7\text{-}64)$$

where g_π and g_K define the coupling constants and represent the current discussed earlier. Until 1963 it was generally believed that a universal Fermi interaction should imply $g_\pi = g_K$. However, we now know that if the interactions *strictly* obeyed SU_3 invariance, the two charged mesons (and indeed all eight members of this meson octet) would have the same mass. The mass difference between the K^+ and π^+ is believed to be due to an SU_3 breaking interaction. In the SU_3 approximation there is really no reason to choose the π^+ and K^+ as basic particles. Indeed, under this artificial assumption it is more natural to choose as basic particles the two orthogonal combinations:

$$\psi_{\pi'} = \frac{g_\pi \psi_\pi + g_K \psi_K}{\sqrt{g_\pi^2 + g_K^2}}, \qquad \psi_{K'} = \frac{g_K \psi_\pi - g_\pi \psi_K}{\sqrt{g_\pi^2 + g_K^2}} \quad (7\text{-}65)$$

The decay Hamiltonian can be rewritten as

$$H = \frac{1}{\sqrt{2}} \sum_i \sqrt{g_\pi^2 + g_K^2} \langle 0 | J_i | \psi_{\pi'} \rangle \tilde{\psi}_\mu \gamma_i (1 + \gamma_5) \psi_\nu \quad (7\text{-}66)$$

Thus the K' would be stable with respect to decay into $\mu\nu$ while the π' would have maximum decay amplitude (Fig. 7-9).

Clearly we cannot expect $g_K = g_\pi$ to be the only solution as defined by the universal Fermi interaction theory. Instead, we may for convenience define

$$g_0 = \sqrt{g_\pi^2 + g_K^2} \quad (7\text{-}67a)$$

and

$$g_\pi = g_0 \cos\theta \quad (7\text{-}67b)$$

$$g_K = g_0 \sin\theta \quad (7\text{-}67c)$$

The angular parameter θ specifies the relative coupling strengths for $K \to \mu\nu$ and $\pi \to \mu\nu$ decay and, more generally, for $|\Delta S| = 1$ and $|\Delta S| = 0$ processes. Thus

$$\frac{g_{|\Delta S|=1}}{g_{|\Delta S|=0}} = \tan \theta \tag{7-68}$$

If $\theta = 0°$, there will be no $|\Delta S| = 1$ processes.

If $\theta = 45°$, there will be equal coupling constants for $|\Delta S| = 0$ and $|\Delta S| = 1$ processes.

If $\theta = 90°$, there will be no $|\Delta S| = 0$ processes.

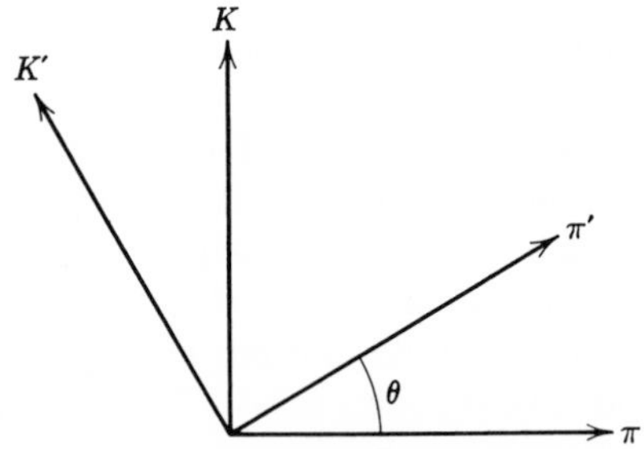

Fig. 7-9 The $(\pi' K')$ system is obtained by rotating the (πK) system through an angle θ.

The angular parameter θ which represents the relative strength of these two currents can be determined by the known rates of leptonic decays. From a comparison of the rates $K^+ \to \mu + \nu_\mu$ and $\pi^+ \to \mu + \nu_\mu$ (which are governed by the axial-vector coupling, since K^+ and π^+ are 0-), we can deduce θ_A. We have

$$\frac{P_{K^+ \to \mu^+ + \nu_\mu}}{P_{\pi^+ \to \mu^+ + \nu_\mu}} = \tan^2 \theta \, \frac{m_K(1 - m_\mu{}^2/m_K{}^2)^2}{m_\pi(1 - m_\mu{}^2/m_\pi{}^2)^2} \tag{7-69}$$

The phase space factor involving m_K and m_π has been discussed in Sec. 6-4. Substituting in numerical values, we obtain

$$1.2 = 18 \tan^2 \theta_A \tag{7-70}$$

from which it follows that $\theta_A \sim 0.26$ rad. The corresponding angle θ_V for the vector interaction can be deduced from a comparison of the rates $K^+ \to \pi^0 + e^+ + \nu_e$ and $\pi^+ \to \pi^0 + e^+ + \nu_e$; it is found that $\theta_V = 0.26$ rad, which happens to equal θ_A.

Now let us compare μ decay and nuclear β decay. Since there is no strange μ, the μ carries with it the full share of weak current. Thus for μ decay we must have $g_\mu = g_0$. On the other hand, for β decay of a neutral baryon the weak current must be divided among

$$\mathrm{n} \rightarrow \mathrm{p} + e^- + \bar{\nu}_e \quad (\Delta S = 0), \qquad \Lambda \rightarrow \mathrm{p} + e^- + \bar{\nu}_e \quad (\Delta S = 1),$$

and

$$\Sigma^0 \rightarrow \mathrm{p} + e^- + \bar{\nu}_e \quad (\Delta S = 1). \tag{7-71}$$

(The last reaction is actually overshadowed by $\Sigma^0 \rightarrow \Lambda^0 + \gamma$ and thus is difficult to observe, whereas the decay $\Xi^0 \rightarrow \mathrm{p} + e^- + \bar{\nu}_e$ probably cannot occur since it involves $|\Delta S| = 2$.) Thus the vector coupling constant g_V for nuclear β decay in the strangeness-conserving current J is now no longer g but

$$g_V = g_0 \cos\theta = 0.966 g_\mu. \tag{7-72}$$

We can express this result by saying that the weak-interaction current in μ decay carries one unit of "weak charge" g_0. On the other hand, in meson and baryon decay, the weak charge is divided among the $\Delta S = 0$ and $\Delta S = 1$ currents; that is,

$$\begin{aligned} g_{\Delta S=0} &= g_0 \cos\theta \\ g_{\Delta S=1} &= g_0 \sin\theta \end{aligned} \tag{7-73}$$

The percentage difference between g_μ and g_V is now

$$\frac{g_\mu - g_V}{g_\mu} = \frac{g_0 - g_{\Delta S=0}}{g_0} = 3.4\% \tag{7-74}$$

which is larger than the observed discrepancy of 2.2% as described in the section on the equality of g_V and g_μ. However, it has been suggested (Sa-64) that the angular parameter θ_V (and also θ_A) should be reduced slightly (by about 20%) because of the slight breakdown of SU_3 symmetry. This would give

$$g_V \sim 0.98 g_\mu \tag{7-75}$$

in very good accord with the discrepancy observed between the nuclear β decay and μ decay. Therefore the Cabibbo hypothesis does seem to account for (a) the weak component of $|\Delta S| = 1$ and (b) the discrepancy between g_V and g_μ after applying the radiative corrections.

7-4 THE QUESTION OF AN INTERMEDIATE BOSON IN WEAK INTERACTIONS AND THE OBSERVATION OF TWO NEUTRINOS IN HIGH-ENERGY NEUTRINO REACTIONS

The Possible Existence of an Intermediate Boson

One distinguishing feature of weak interactions is that four particles participate in the "elementary" process in contrast to the basic electromagnetic process where only a single quantum is emitted (that is, three particles are involved). In the low-energy region, the treatment of the effective Lagrangian as a strict point interaction has been found to be adequate. However, the breakdown of the local four-fermion interaction in the high-energy region must occur because of its violation of the so-called "unitarity condition." How does this happen? First, according to the local theory of weak interactions, the cross section increases as the available phase space volume, that is, with the square of momentum p in the C-M system.

Consider now the process of $\bar{\nu}$ capture by protons

$$\bar{\nu} + \mathrm{p} \rightarrow e^{+} + \mathrm{n} \tag{7-76}$$

According to Eq. 5-39, the cross section for this process is given by

$$\sigma \sim \frac{4G^2}{\pi}\left(\frac{\hbar}{mc}\right)^2 \frac{E_e^{\,2}}{(mc^2)^2} \tag{7-77}$$

where E_e = energy of emitted e^{+} (assuming $E_e \gg mc^2$) and we have set

$$|M|^2 = \left|\int 1\right|^2 + \left|\int \boldsymbol{\sigma}\right|^2 = 4. \tag{7-78}$$

Equation 7-77 holds only if nucleon recoil can be neglected, that is, if the electron energy is much less than the nucleon rest energy. In this case the electron and neutrino energies are nearly equal. Thus we can write

$$\sigma \sim G^2\left(\frac{\hbar}{mc}\right)^2 \epsilon_\nu^{\,2} \tag{7-79}$$

where ϵ_ν = neutrino energy in units of mc^2, and we have omitted numerical factors.

Our assumption of a point interaction implies that only S waves contribute to the reaction. The maximum possible S-wave cross section at any energy ϵ is given by the unitarity limit,

$$\sigma \leqslant \lambda\!\!\!^{-2} \sim \left(\frac{\hbar}{mc}\right)^2 \frac{1}{\epsilon^2} \tag{7-80}$$

apart from numerical factors. It is obvious that sooner or later the ever-increasing cross section as given by the increase of the phase space will surpass the upper limit set by the unitarity limit. This unitarity limit is reached when

$$\epsilon \sim G^{-1/2} \sim 5 \times 10^5 \tag{7-81}$$

which corresponds to a neutrino energy of about 300 bev. (Actually, if the neutrino energy becomes large compared to the nucleon mass, relativisitic kinematic effects become important and σ is proportional only to ϵ_ν rather than ϵ_ν^2.) This is physically unreasonable since it would imply that more neutrinos are captured than are in the beam itself. Thus either the perturbation expansion for σ fails (that is, σ is no longer proportional to g^2) or the interaction cannot be a pure point interaction.

This difficulty may be avoided if an intermediate vector boson mediates the weak interactions, so that we are no longer dealing with a local interaction. The possible existence of a weakly coupled boson $W^\pm$ has already been discussed in Yukawa's original work (Yu-35) on the meson. For instance, the muon-decay process may be interpreted as a two-step process, rather than a real elementary process. In the first step, an intermediate boson W is created. In the second step, the intermediate boson decays into two particles. Thus the decay of the μ proceeds as follows:

$$\mu^- \rightarrow W^- + \nu, \qquad W^- \rightarrow e^- + \bar{\nu} \tag{7-82}$$

and the overall process would, of course, be

$$\mu^- + \bar{\nu} \rightleftarrows W \rightleftarrows e^- + \bar{\nu} \tag{7-83}$$

Nuclear β decay can be generated through the coupling

$$\mathrm{n} + \bar{\mathrm{p}} \rightleftarrows W \rightleftarrows e^- + \bar{\nu} \tag{7-84}$$

In terms of a Feynman diagram, μ decay can be represented as in Fig. 7-10.

The boson W moves a small but finite distance before its decay, and therefore the electron is created at a point slightly different from where the μ^- disappeared, which implies that the β interaction, as a whole, is slightly nonlocal. In this case, the unitarity condition is no longer necessarily violated at high energy. Note that since the W lives only a short time, energy does not have to be conserved in the intermediate state.* Thus the intermediate boson will be a virtual particle and will not actually appear. Of course, it is also possible that such a particle is simply nonexistent. Nevertheless, the general properties of the

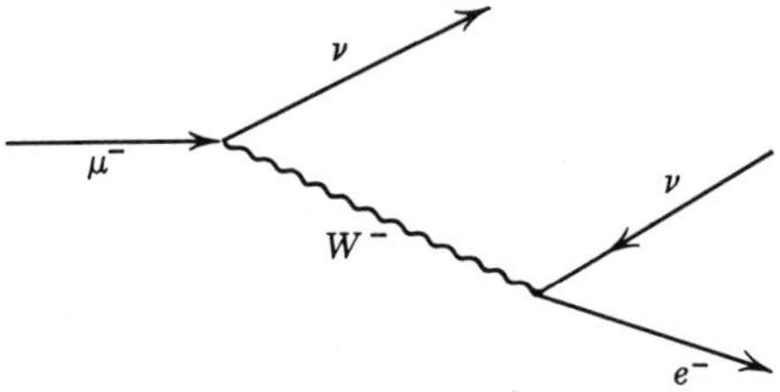

Fig. 7-10 Feynman diagram of μ decay through an intermediate boson.

hypothetical intermediate boson (if it exists) have been speculated on by Lee and Yang (Le-60b) and may be summarized as follows:

1. There must exist at least a W^+ and W^-.

2. The lifetime of the W must be very short. The upper limit of this lifetime is $\leqslant 10^{-18}$ sec, which is estimated by assuming that W's are coupled with a strength $g = m_W\sqrt{G}$ and $m_W \sim 1000 m_e$.

3. The W must be more massive than the K so as to avoid a fast $K^+ \to W^+ + \gamma$ decay.

4. The intermediate boson must have spin one (that is, it must be a vector particle) in order to lead to the V,A combination. A scalar ($S = 0$) boson will give an S,P combination of interactions.

5. The intermediate-boson hypothesis implies a small correction to the electron spectrum in μ decay (and also in other weak processes). Calculations show that the Michel parameter ρ is changed from $\frac{3}{4}$ to $\frac{3}{4} + \frac{1}{3}(m_\mu/m_W)^2$. If $m_W \sim 4000\ m_e$, the change in ρ amounts to about 0.1%, which is rather small for experimental tests.

* In the relativistically invariant Feynman technique, both energy and momentum are conserved in the intermediate state, but the energy-momentum relation is not appropriate to a particle of the W rest mass.

6. With W production, the cross section for neutrino reactions will be greatly increased owing to the pair creation of W^+ and e^- in the Coulomb field of a target nucleus; $\nu + Z \rightarrow W^+ + e^- + Z$. For instance, for neutrinos of $k_\nu \gg 2$ bev, the reaction cross section for $Z = 26$ is of the order of 10^{-35} cm^2 (Le-60a).

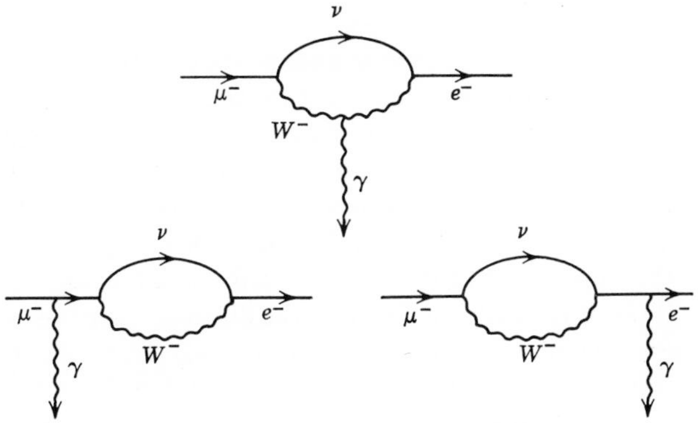

Fig. 7-11 Feynman diagram of the electromagnetic decay of muon ($\mu \rightarrow e + \gamma$) through an intermediate boson.

Although the existence of an intermediate boson may preclude the difficulty of violating unitarity, Feinberg (Fei-58) has pointed out that such a boson implies a branching ratio,

$$\frac{\mu \rightarrow e + \gamma}{\mu \rightarrow e + \nu + \bar{\nu}} \tag{7-85}$$

of the order of

$$\frac{1}{24\pi} \frac{e^2}{\hbar c} \sim 10^{-4} \tag{7-86}$$

unless the neutrinos associated with muons are different from those associated with electrons.

The Two-Neutrino Question

The process $\mu \rightarrow e + \gamma$ has never been seen. The upper limit of the branching ratio is set to be $\leqslant 10^{-8}$ (Bart-62; Fra-62; Co-62). If the $W^\pm$ exists, the W cloud around the μ (or the μ itself, or the electron) can shake off a photon, and lead to $e\gamma$. This process can be represented by the Feynman diagrams shown in Fig. 7-11.

Why then is the relative rate so low? It is important to point out here that although the difficulty of the low rate of electromagnetic decay of the muon ($\mu \rightarrow e + \gamma$) arose in connection with the postulate of the existence of $W^{\pm}$, it was noted by Lee and Yang (Le-61) that, in actuality, any effective nonlocality of the four-fermion interactions leads to the same predicament on the observed low relative rate of electromagnetic decay of the muon.

The way out of this difficulty is to assume the existence of at least two kinds of neutrinos of the same helicity (Le-60a); that is, in the two-decay mode of pions, the emitted neutrinos are different kinds of particles. Under this assumption, the π^+ can decay into $\mu^+ + \nu_\mu$ or $e^+ + \nu_e$. For the ν_e (β decay) we have evidence that its mass is small (if different from zero); that is, $m_{\nu_e} < 250$ ev (cf. p. 42). Of the ν_μ we know much less, and the upper limit of its mass can only be set as $m_{\nu_\mu} < 3.5$ mev (Ba-56). If this is the case, the fact that the direct $\mu^{\pm} \rightarrow e^{\pm} + \gamma$ process just discussed cannot occur will be seen easily from the Feynman diagram (Fig. 7-11), for the neutrinos destroyed and emitted in the process are not the same.

The Two-Neutrino Experiment. The two-neutrino hypothesis has recently been brilliantly demonstrated in a high-energy neutrino reaction experiment. The essence of this experiment is to generate a narrow neutrino beam from pion decays in flight. A natural source of high-energy neutrinos is high-energy pions. Such pions will produce neutrinos whose laboratory energy will range with equal probability from zero to 45% of the pion energy, and whose direction will tend very much toward the pion direction. For example, 1-bev pions will emit neutrinos with an average energy of approximately 220 mev in such a way that almost half of the neutrinos will fall within a cone of half angle 7°.

The feasibility of such neutrino experiments was independently proposed by Pontecorvo (Po-59) and Schwarz (Schw-60). If there is only one type of neutrino, then neutrino interactions should produce muons and electrons in equal abundance. In the event that there are two types of neutrinos, then the neutrino beam from π-μ decay will consist of the type ν_μ only, and therefore no electrons are to be expected.

In this first high-energy neutrino experiment (Da-62), the pions were produced by 15-bev protons striking a Be target. The resulting flux of particles, moving in its entirety in the general direction of the detector, strike a 13.5-meter-thick iron shield wall at a distance of 21 meters from the target. Neutrino interactions are observed in a spark chamber located behind this shield. Each of its ten 1-ton modules has nine aluminum plates, 44 in. × 44 in. × 1 in. thick, separated by $\frac{3}{4}$-in. Lucite spacers. The triggering counters were inserted between adjacent chambers. The general layout of the equipment is shown in Fig. 7-12.

First we must know the number and energy spectrum of neutrinos from π-μ decays and from $K^{\pm} \rightarrow \mu^{\pm} + \nu/\bar{\nu}$. The neutrinos from π-μ are calculated from the measured pion production rates (Bak-61) and the geometry. The neutrinos from K decay can only be estimated. Both of these spectra are shown in Fig. 7-13. It is also desirable to have some idea of the neutrino reaction cross sections involved. Calculations (Le-60a), based on the conserved vector current hypothesis (Fe-58) and information from the electron-scattering experiments, give two curves for the ν + n and $\bar{\nu}$ + p reactions, as shown in Fig. 7-14. The cross section is of the order of 10^{-38} cm^2.

It is important to set rather stringent geometric criteria for what may be accepted as a neutrino event in the spark chamber. The criteria require that the event originate within a fiducial volume whose boundaries lie 4 in. from the front and back walls of the chamber and 2 in. from the top and bottom walls. Therefore the first two gaps must not fire so as to exclude events which are initiated outside the chamber.

Out of an exposure of 3.48×10^{17} protons, 29 "single muons" of $p_\nu > 300$ mev/c^2 and 22 "vertex" events are attributed to the neutrino interaction. Strong arguments are convincingly presented to substantiate that these observed tracks are from muons and of neutrino origin, and not produced by cosmic rays or by neutrons. The appearance of the single-muon track of momentum above 300 mev/c^2 is distinctively different from that of showers produced by high-energy single electrons, which can be seen from Fig. 7-15.

If $\nu_\mu = \nu_e$, there should be of the order of 29 electron showers with a mean energy greater than 400 mev/c. Instead, there are only six showers observed. Furthermore, from the distribution of the number of their sparks, these six showers are totally different from those predicted for electrons with a mean energy greater than 400 mev/c. Therefore the most plausible explanation for the absence of the electron showers—and the only one which preserves universality of weak interactions—is *that* $\nu_\mu \neq \nu_e$, *that is, that there are at least two types of neutrinos.* With

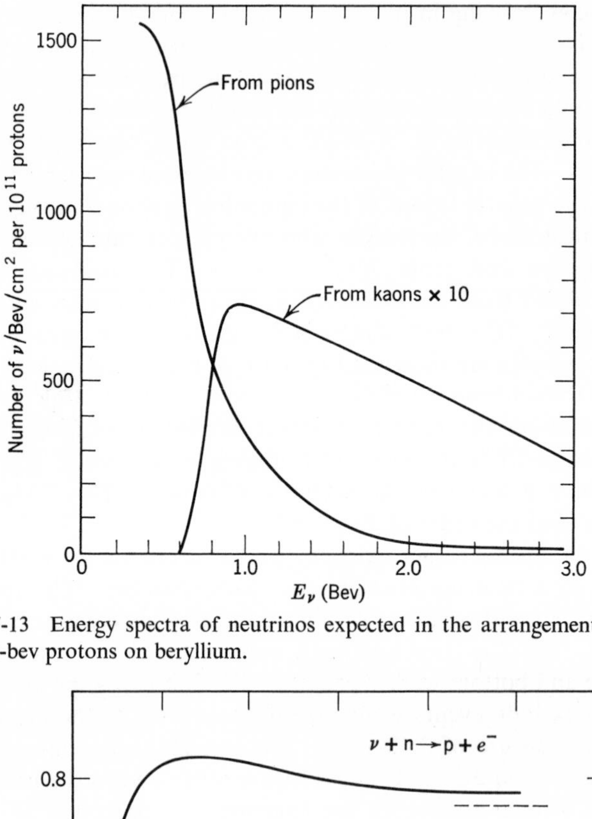

Fig. 7-13 Energy spectra of neutrinos expected in the arrangement of Fig. 7-12 for 15-bev protons on beryllium.

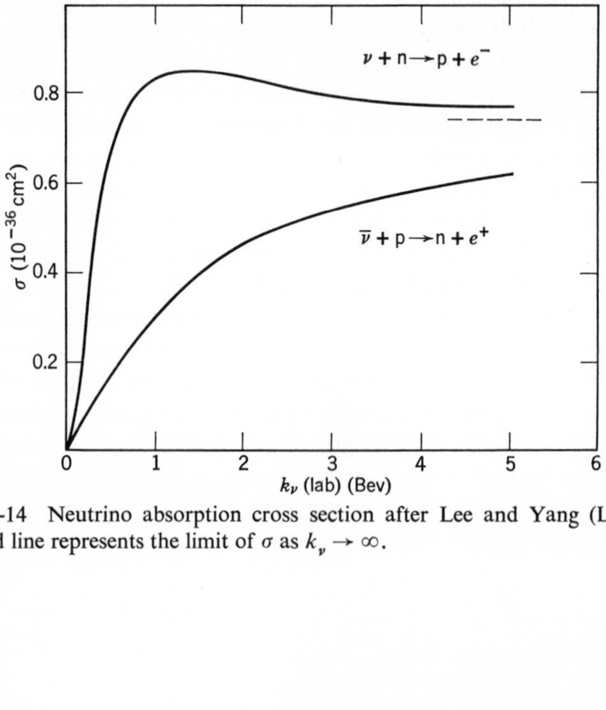

Fig. 7-14 Neutrino absorption cross section after Lee and Yang (Le-60). The dashed line represents the limit of σ as $k_\nu \to \infty$.

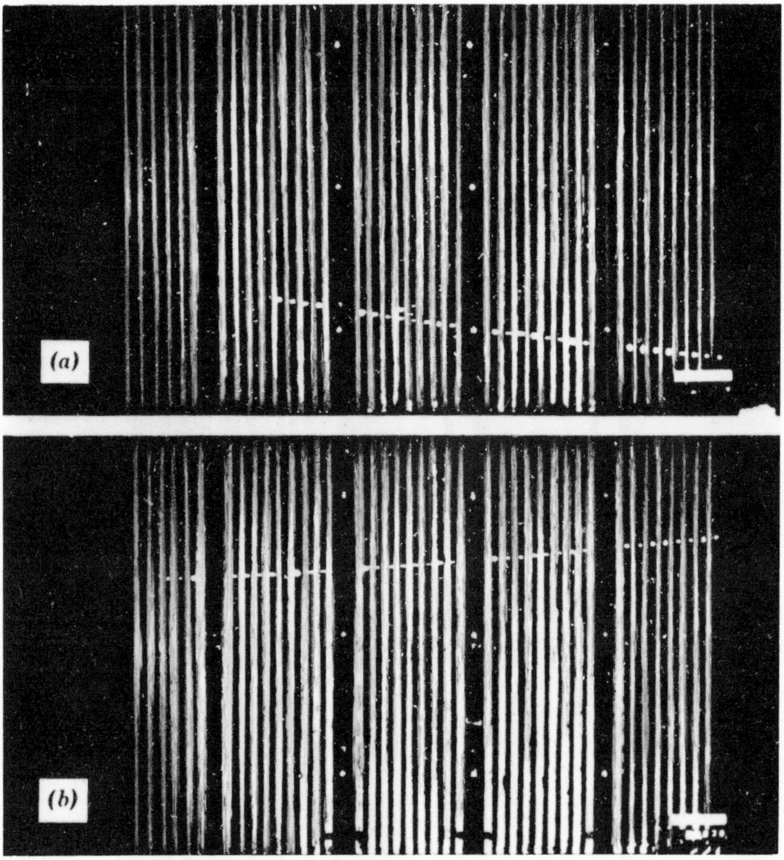

Fig. 7-15 (*a*) Single muon event, μ-meson track going downward, probably made by a neutrino from the left. (*b*) Single muon event, μ-meson track going upward, probably made by a neutrino from the left.

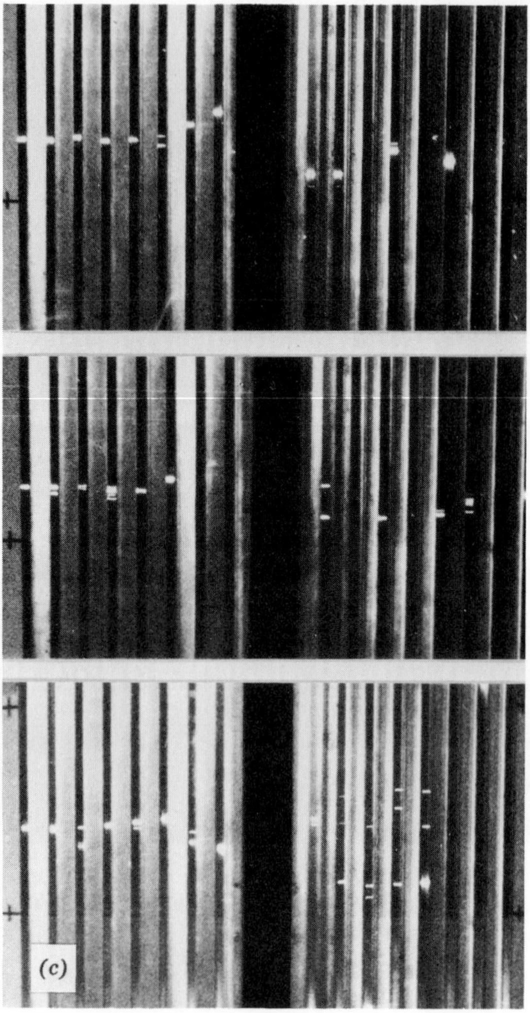

Fig. 7-15 (*c*) 400-mev electrons from the Cosmotron. From (Da-62).

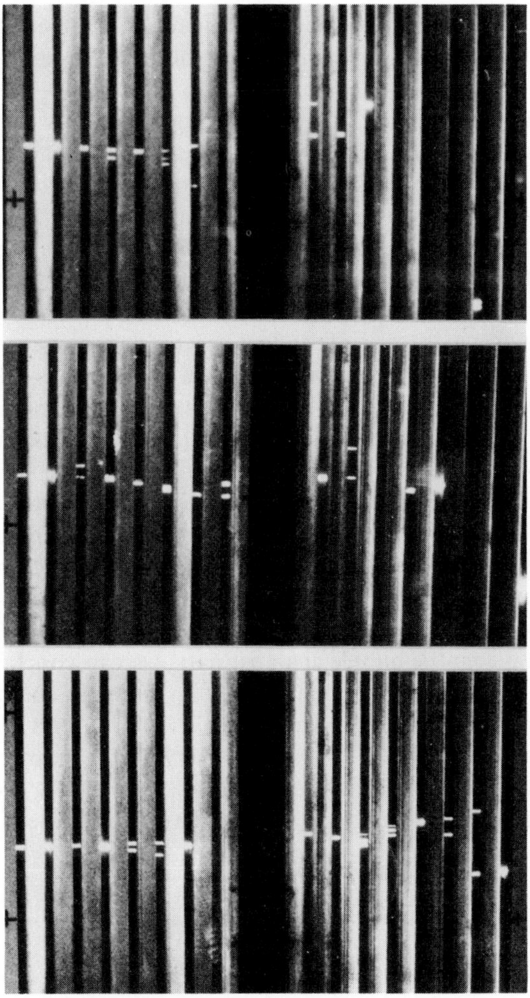

Fig. 7-15(*c*) Continued.

$\nu_\mu \neq \nu_e$, we might even assign different quantum numbers to ν_μ and ν_e and to μ and e. Then the forbiddenness of the $\mu^\pm \to e^- + \gamma$ is easily understood.

This pioneer experiment using high-energy neutrinos is very important in that it opens an entirely new avenue of exploration into the nature of weak interactions. Its success will undoubtedly elevate our understanding of weak interactions to a new plane.

In 1963, the CERN group succeeded in greatly increasing the high-energy neutrino flux by magnetically focusing the pion beam with an ingenious "neutrino horn" proposed by Van der Meer. The horn consists of two coaxial conical conductors, the inner having a semi-angle of 2.5 degrees and carrying a current which can rise to 300 kamp. The target is located in the neck of the horn. The secondary particles (pions and kaons in this case) emerging from the target with an inclination to the axis of greater than 2.5 degrees enter the azimuthal magnetic field between the inner and outer conductors and, according to sign, are either deviated toward the axis or further defocused. Those particles emerging from the target at less than 2.5 degrees are not influenced by the magnetic field. The investigation was carried out in a large spark chamber (45 tons) as well as in a freon bubble chamber (500 liters). From the bubble chamber data, we can conclude that the probability of $\nu_e = \nu_\mu$ is less than 2%. From the spark chamber results, $\nu_e \neq \nu_\mu$ can be concluded at a confidence level of at least 99% (Bi-64).

$\nu_\mu \neq \bar{\nu}_\mu$. A test on the μ-lepton conservation was carried out by examining the sign of the charge on the μ-like particles. If the muonic number is conserved, then from a π^+ beam one would expect to have

$$1.\ \pi^+ \to \underset{l=-1}{\underset{\uparrow}{\mu^+}} + \underset{l=+1}{\underset{\nwarrow}{\nu_\mu}} \qquad (7\text{-}87)$$

$$2.\ \underset{l=+1}{\underset{\uparrow}{\nu_\mu}} + \text{n} \to \underset{l=+1}{\underset{\uparrow}{\mu^-}} + \text{p} \qquad (7\text{-}88)$$

In the spark chamber (92 + 4)% of the μ-like particles were found to be negative. The expected contamination of the μ^+'s from the $\bar{\nu}_\mu$ may be as high as 5%; furthermore, some postively charged particles may be π^+ or protons. Thus μ-lepton conservation appears to be valid to a very high degree.

The Possible Existence of the Intermediate Boson W. The intermediate boson W can be produced by using currents of either J_λ or S_λ

or j_λ (p. 279). The method at both CERN and Brookhaven is to use the high-energy neutrinos,

$$\nu_\mu + Z \rightarrow W^+ + \mu^- + Z \quad (\text{or } Z^*) \tag{7-89}$$

where Z is the target nucleus and Z^* is one of its excited states (including the outgoing particles). The detection of W relies on its lepton-decay process

$$W^+ \rightarrow l^+ + \nu_e \tag{7-90}$$

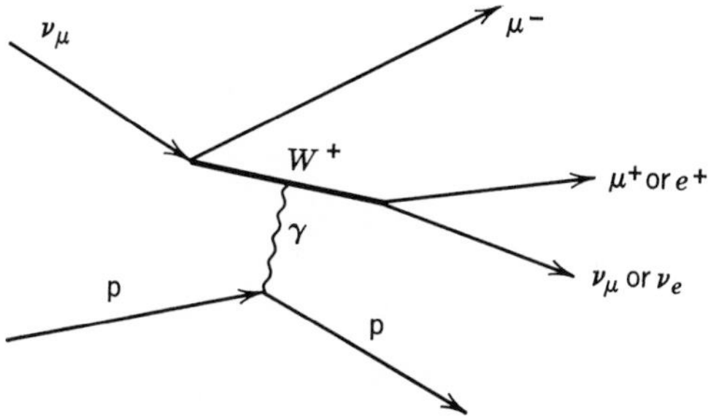

Fig. 7-16 Double lepton produced by pressure of intermediate boson.

Therefore the production process can be described as the *lepton pair process** as shown in Fig. 7-16. Since the lifetime of the W is so short, ($< 10^{-18}$ sec) the apparent processes are like

$$\nu_\mu + Z \rightarrow \mu^- + \mu^+ + \nu_\mu + Z \quad (\text{or } Z^*)$$

and

$$\nu_\mu + Z \rightarrow \mu^- + e^+ + \nu_e + Z \quad (\text{or } Z^*) \tag{7-91}$$

No conclusive evidence has been reported on the existence of *the lepton pairs*, and therefore we have no experimental evidence for the existence of the W boson. Since the rate of production of these lepton pairs is dependent on the mass of the boson W at the presently available neutrino energy, from the upper limit of its production cross section, we can put its lower mass limit at $M_W \geqslant 1.8$ bev (Bi-64; Be-64b). The question of the possible existence of the intermediate boson W has far-reaching consequences in our understanding of the weak interactions. Further clarifying information on this question will probably have to wait for availability of an intense beam of neutrinos of superhigh energy.

---

* There are possible neutrino reactions which lead to lepton pairs but involve no W production. However, the theoretically estimated cross section of these reactions is less than 0.05% of the dominant process $\nu_\mu + \text{n} \rightarrow \text{p} + \mu^-$ in the presently available neutrino energy region (Ya-63).

APPENDIX I

Nonrelativistic Transformations

I-1 PHYSICAL CONCEPTS

The transformation properties of various quantities (scalar, vector, etc.) under rotation, space inversion, or time reversal are important for understanding the theory of β decay. In this section we shall treat such transformations nonrelativistically and emphasize the physical concepts involved in each case. The generalized forms of relativistic transformations will be discussed in Appendix III.

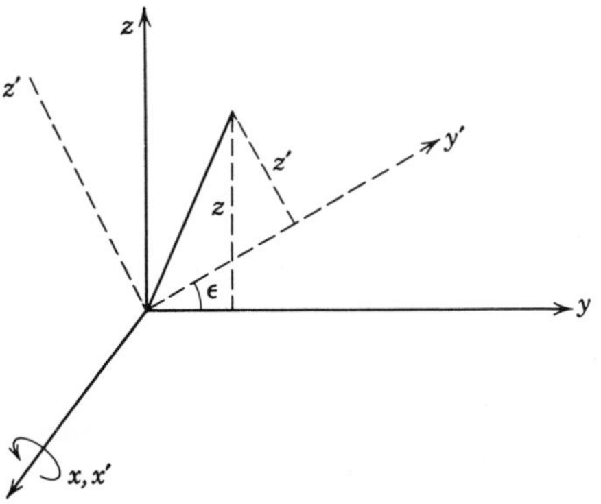

Fig. I-1 Infinitesimal rotations.

Rotation and Space Inversion

Consider the right-handed coordinate system x, y, z, undergoing a counterclockwise rotation about the x axis into a new system x', y', z', as shown in Fig. I-1. It is evident that any rotation can be built up out of the superposition of an infinite number of infinitesimal rotations, such as those indicated in Fig. I-1. Therefore all invariance properties derived for infinitesimal rotations also hold for finite rotations. In addition, space inversion in which the coordinate axes are simply inverted can also be performed. By properly combining these two operations, any nonrelativistic transformation which keeps the origin unchanged and also preserves all lengths can be realized. For example, *a mirror reflection* in the xz plane can be obtained by combining a space inversion with a 180° rotation about the y axis, as shown in Fig. I-2.

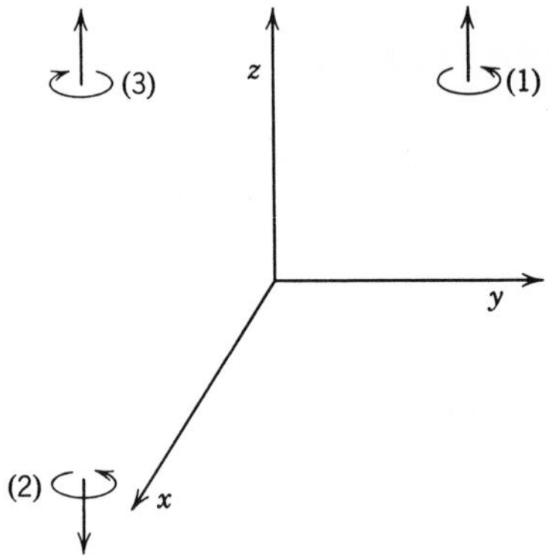

Fig. I-2 A mirror reflection is equivalent to a combination of a space inversion with a rotation:

(1) → (2) = inversion through origin,
(2) → (3) = 180° rotation about y axis,
(1) → (3) = mirror reflection through xz plane.

Now let us consider how various quantities transform under these operations.

AN INVARIANT. An invariant is a single mathematical quantity $f(\mathbf{r})$ which, under a rotation or space inversion of coordinates $\mathbf{r} \to \mathbf{r}'$, transforms as $f(\mathbf{r}) \to f'(\mathbf{r}')$ where $f'(\mathbf{r}') = f'(\mathbf{r}) = f(\mathbf{r})$. Any function $f(r)$ of the radial distance r is clearly an invariant.

A SCALAR. A scalar is a single mathematical quantity $f(\mathbf{r})$ which, under a rotation or space inversion of coordinates $\mathbf{r} \to \mathbf{r}'$, transforms as $f(\mathbf{r}) \to f'(\mathbf{r}')$. If it is also true that $f'(\mathbf{r}) = f(\mathbf{r})$, we are dealing with an "invariant." Any invariant is a scalar, but not all scalars are invariants. For example, the density $\rho(\mathbf{r}) = \rho(x, y, z)$ is a scalar, but is invariant only if ρ is a function of the distance r alone. Most of the scalars we consider in our discussion are also invariant, and we shall not make the distinction between these quantities.

A VECTOR. A vector is a quantity that has both magnitude and sense of direction. It can be resolved into three components along the three coordinate axes, and these three components transform under both rotations and space inversions in the same way as the coordinates x, y, z.

Under infinitesimal (and counterclockwise) rotation about the x axis,

$$x' = x, \quad y' = y + \epsilon z, \quad z' = z - \epsilon y \tag{I-1}$$

and thus

$$x = x', \quad y = y' - \epsilon z', \quad z = z' + \epsilon y \tag{I-2}$$

up to terms of order ϵ. We neglect higher-order terms, ϵ^2, etc., since for infinitesimal transformations they are infinitesimally small even relative to the ϵ terms.

Under space inversion

$$x' = -x, \quad y' = -y, \quad z' = -z \tag{I-3}$$

Linear displacements, velocities, and forces are all vectors. They are sometimes more specifically referred to as *polar* vectors, as distinguished from *axial* vectors.

AN AXIAL VECTOR. An axial vector or pseudovector is like a polar vector in that it has magnitude and direction and has three components which transform under rotation in the same way as the coordinates. However, these components do not change sign under space inversion. All cross products of two vectors $\mathbf{A} \times \mathbf{B}$, such as angular momenta, are axial vectors.

A PSEUDOSCALAR. A pseudoscalar is a quantity which is invariant under rotations but changes under space inversion. The triple product of any three vectors $\mathbf{A} \cdot \mathbf{B} \times \mathbf{C}$ is a pseudoscalar because each of the three vectors changes sign separately under space inversion. It is, in fact, the scalar product of an axial vector and a vector.

Parity Invariance

It has been believed that all physically observed quantities must be *scalars*, at least under rotations, since an isolated process, such as, for example, β decay, cannot really depend on the absolute orientation of the system in space. After all, space is known to be isotropic and homogeneous. However, isotropy of space alone is not sufficient to imply invariance under space inversion. On the other hand, invariance under space inversion is the direct consequence of the assumption (generally accepted until 1956) that all physical laws are the same in left-handed and right-handed systems. This left-right symmetry manifests itself, in the so-called law of conservation of parity (see Sec.1-4, p. 11), and all processes involving strong nuclear or electromagnetic interactions are found to be invariant under space inversion, thereby observing the law of parity.

As discussed earlier, a scalar is invariant under *both* rotation and space inversion, but a pseudoscalar is invariant only under rotation and changes sign under space inversion. The existence of a nonzero expectation value of a pseudoscalar quantity in an interaction violates the invariance under space inversion and therefore the law of parity. In β decay a quantity involving a scalar product of the spin of the nucleus (an axial vector) and the momentum (a polar vector) of the β particle—that is, $\mathbf{I} \cdot \mathbf{p}_\beta$—is a pseudoscalar quantity. If the expectation value of this quantity $\mathbf{I} \cdot \mathbf{p}_\beta$ is not zero, an asymmetrical distribution of β particles with respect to the nuclear spin will be observed, implying that the β interaction is not invariant under space inversion—in other words, that parity is not conserved in β decay.

Time Reversal

Another operation of interest is that of time reversal, in which we reverse the sense of the time. As can be seen classically, such a reversal has the effect of changing the sign of all velocities and also of angular momenta. It is still believed, however, that physical laws are invariant under time reversal.* Thus the presence of a nonvanishing expectation value of $\mathbf{I} \cdot \mathbf{p}_\beta$ in β decay is quite consistent with time-reversal invariance. On the other hand, a triple scalar product of spin and two momenta, such as $\mathbf{I}_i \cdot \mathbf{p}_j \times \mathbf{p}_k$, is invariant under space inversion but not under time reversal. Such a term has been looked for in the decay of polarized neutrons, but its absence seems to indicate that the β interaction is invariant under time reversal (see Sec. 4-7 and Appendix VI, p. 361).

I-2 MATHEMATICAL FORMALISM

Let us now study the transformation properties under rotations, and space and time inversions in more detail. First, consider the infinitesimal rotations just discussed.

* See, however, the footnote on p. 244.

Infinitesimal Rotations

It can be easily shown that the components of momentum transform among themselves in the same way as the coordinates. For example,

$$p_z' = \frac{\hbar}{i}\frac{\partial}{\partial z'} = \frac{\hbar}{i}\left(\frac{\partial y}{\partial z'}\frac{\partial}{\partial y} + \frac{\partial z}{\partial z'}\frac{\partial}{\partial z}\right) = \frac{\hbar}{i}\left(-\epsilon\frac{\partial}{\partial y} + \frac{\partial}{\partial z}\right) = p_z - \epsilon p_y \tag{I-4}$$

Similarly, for the components of angular momentum we have

$$L_z' = x'p_y' - y'p_x' = x(p_y + \epsilon p_z) - (y + \epsilon z)p_x = L_z - \epsilon L_y \tag{I-5}$$

Next consider the effect of rotation on the wave function $\psi(\mathbf{r})$. For simplicity suppose that ψ refers to a single spinless particle. We can then write

$$\psi(\mathbf{r}) = \psi(x, y, z) = \psi(r, \theta, \varphi) \tag{I-6}$$

where θ and φ are the usual polar angles. Now rotate the coordinate system by an angle ϵ (counterclockwise) about the z axis. Then we define the transformed wave function as follows:

$$\psi'(r, \theta, \varphi) = \psi(r, \theta, \varphi + \epsilon) \tag{I-7}$$

Clearly then

$$\psi'(\mathbf{r}) = \left(1 + \epsilon\frac{\partial}{\partial\varphi}\right)\psi(\mathbf{r}) = (1 + i\epsilon L_z)\psi(\mathbf{r}) \tag{I-8}$$

up to order ϵ. (We express the angular momentum in units of $\hbar$.) Similarly, for an infinitesimal rotation about the x axis, such as we considered at the beginning of this appendix,

$$\psi'(\mathbf{r}) = (1 + i\epsilon L_x)\psi(\mathbf{r}) \tag{I-9}$$

The adjoint or hermitian conjugate of the transformed wave function can be written as

$$\psi'^{\dagger} = [(1 + i\epsilon L_x)\psi]^{\dagger} = \psi^{\dagger}(1 - i\epsilon L_x) \tag{I-10}$$

(For a spinless particle, $\psi^{\dagger} = \psi^*$, where * denotes complex conjugate.) Thus it is seen that

$$\psi'^{\dagger}\psi' = \psi^{\dagger}\psi \tag{I-11}$$

that is, $\psi^{\dagger}\psi$ is a scalar under rotations. On the other hand, consider the more complicated bilinear combination of wave functions $\langle\hat{O}\rangle = \psi^{\dagger}\hat{O}\psi$, where $\hat{O}$ is some operator. Under rotations, this quantity transforms into

$$\psi'^{\dagger}\hat{O}\psi' = \psi^{\dagger}(1 - i\epsilon L_x)\hat{O}(1 + i\epsilon L_x)\psi = \psi^{\dagger}\hat{O}'\psi = \langle\hat{O}'\rangle \tag{I-12}$$

where

$$\hat{O}' = (1 - i\epsilon L_x)\,\hat{O}\,(1 + i\epsilon L_x) = \hat{O} + i\epsilon[\hat{O}, L_x]_- \tag{I-13}$$

to order ϵ and

$$[A, B]_- = AB - BA \tag{I-14}$$

(Note that we transform only the *wave function*, not the operator itself.) If $\hat{O}$ is a scalar, then

$$[\hat{O}, L_x]_- = -i\left(\hat{O}\frac{\partial}{\partial\varphi_x} - \frac{\partial}{\partial\varphi_x}\hat{O}\right) = i\frac{\partial\hat{O}}{\partial\varphi_x} = 0 \tag{I-15}$$

and $\hat{O}' = \hat{O}$. If $\hat{O}$ is a vector, then for example

$$\langle z'\rangle = \langle z\rangle + i\epsilon\langle[z, L_x]_-\rangle = \langle z\rangle - \epsilon\langle y\rangle \tag{I-16}$$

and

$$\langle L_z'\rangle = \langle L_z\rangle - \epsilon\langle L_y\rangle \tag{I-16a}$$

Thus, if $\hat{O}$ has the form of a scalar (or vector) under rotations, the quantities

$$\langle\hat{O}\rangle = \psi^\dagger\hat{O}\psi \tag{I-17}$$

transform under rotations in the expected way. It is easy to verify that these relations also hold for quantities of the form $\psi_2{}^\dagger\hat{O}\psi_1$ where ψ_1 and ψ_2 may be different wave functions, and for the matrix elements $\int \psi_2{}^\dagger\hat{O}\psi_1\, d^3\mathbf{r}$.

Suppose now that ψ happens to be an eigenfunction of L_z, that is,

$$L_z\psi = m\psi \tag{I-18}$$

In terms of the rotated wave function we have

$$L_z(1 - i\epsilon L_x)\psi' = m(1 - i\epsilon L_x)\psi' \tag{I-19}$$

Multiplying on the left by $1 + i\epsilon L_x$ and taking commutators, we obtain, in first order in ϵ,

$$(L_z + \epsilon L_y)\psi' = m\psi' \tag{I-20}$$

Note that this equation is *not* of the form given by a simple transformation of coordinate axes, which is

$$L_z'\psi' = (L_z - \epsilon L_y)\psi' = m\psi' \tag{I-21}$$

This difference in transformation properties originates because a transformation of *coordinate axes* has the opposite effect on wave functions from a rotation of the *system* itself with respect to fixed coordinate axes.

SPIN ONE-HALF PARTICLES. Up to now we have dealt only with spinless particles, that is, only wave functions depending on the coordinate were considered. If the particle has an intrinsic spin of $s = \frac{1}{2}$, it can be shown by a very natural generalization of the foregoing argument that we must replace the orbital angular-momentum operator **L** by the total angular momentum **J**, which is the vector sum of the orbital- and intrinsic-spin angular momentum

$$\mathbf{J} = \mathbf{L} + \tfrac{1}{2}\boldsymbol{\sigma} \tag{I-22}$$

where $\boldsymbol{\sigma}$ is the Pauli spin operator. The wave function for a particle with spin equal to $\frac{1}{2}$ has two components, which can be expressed in the form of a "spinor":

$$\psi = \begin{pmatrix} \psi^{(1)} \\ \psi^{(2)} \end{pmatrix} \tag{I-23}$$

Here $\psi^{(1)}$ and $\psi^{(2)}$ denote the relative probability amplitudes when we have the spin along or opposite to a certain axis of quantization, say the z axis.

Then the Pauli spin matrices are represented by

$$\sigma_x = \begin{pmatrix} 0 & 1 \\ 1 & 0 \end{pmatrix}, \quad \sigma_y = \begin{pmatrix} 0 & -i \\ i & 0 \end{pmatrix}, \quad \sigma_z = \begin{pmatrix} 1 & 0 \\ 0 & -1 \end{pmatrix} \tag{I-24}$$

Thus,

$$\sigma_z \begin{pmatrix} 1 \\ 0 \end{pmatrix} = \begin{pmatrix} 1 \\ 0 \end{pmatrix} \tag{I-25}$$

and

$$\sigma_z \begin{pmatrix} 0 \\ 1 \end{pmatrix} = -\begin{pmatrix} 0 \\ 1 \end{pmatrix} \tag{I-26}$$

In general, then, the transformation properties of wave functions under infinitesimal rotations about the x axis are described by

$$\psi' = (1 + i\epsilon J_x)\psi \tag{I-27}$$

It is also clear that for any operator $\hat{O}$ we have

$$\langle \hat{O}' \rangle = \langle \hat{O} \rangle + i\epsilon \langle [\hat{O}, J_x]_- \rangle \tag{I-28}$$

Thus the Hamiltonian is invariant under rotations only if it commutes with the total angular momentum. In particular, if we consider only the wave function at the *origin*, so that only the spin enters in, and not the coordinates, the transformation property is given by

$$\psi' = (1 + \tfrac{1}{2} i\epsilon\sigma_x)\psi \tag{I-29}$$

All the results just given still hold, with the substitution

$$L_i \rightarrow \tfrac{1}{2}\sigma_i \tag{I-30}$$

and, for example,

$$\langle \sigma_z' \rangle = \langle \sigma_z \rangle + \tfrac{1}{2} i\epsilon \langle [\sigma_z, \sigma_x]_- \rangle = \langle \sigma_z \rangle - \epsilon \langle \sigma_y \rangle \tag{I-31}$$

There are four independent bilinear products of two-component spinors, namely, $\psi^{*(i)}\psi^{(j)}$ with $i, j = 1$ or 2. We can construct the following independent linear combinations:

$$\langle 1 \rangle = \psi^\dagger \psi = \psi^{*(1)}\psi^{(1)} + \psi^{*(2)}\psi^{(2)} \tag{I-32a}$$

$$\langle \sigma_x \rangle = \psi^\dagger \sigma_x \psi = \psi^{*(1)}\psi^{(2)} + \psi^{*(2)}\psi^{(1)} \tag{I-32b}$$

$$\langle \sigma_y \rangle = \psi^\dagger \sigma_y \psi = -i\psi^{*(1)}\psi^{(2)} + i\psi^{*(2)}\psi^{(1)} \tag{I-32c}$$

$$\langle \sigma_z \rangle = \psi^\dagger \sigma_z \psi = \psi^{*(1)}\psi^{(1)} - \psi^{*(2)}\psi^{(2)} \tag{I-32d}$$

Under rotations the first combination is a scalar, and the last three transform among themselves as the components of an axial vector. For some purposes it is more convenient to use linear combinations of the Pauli matrices:

$$\sigma_1 = \frac{1}{\sqrt{2}}(\sigma_x + i\sigma_y) = \begin{pmatrix} 0 & \sqrt{2} \\ 0 & 0 \end{pmatrix}$$

$$\sigma_0 = \sigma_z$$

$$\sigma_{-1} = \frac{1}{\sqrt{2}}(\sigma_x - i\sigma_y) = \begin{pmatrix} 0 & 0 \\ \sqrt{2} & 0 \end{pmatrix}$$

Although σ_x and σ_y can *each* raise or lower s_z by one unit, σ_1 and σ_{-1} change s_z in a definite direction.

Thus

$$\langle \sigma_1 \rangle = \psi^\dagger \sigma_1 \psi = \sqrt{2}\psi^{*(1)}\psi^{(2)}$$

$$\langle \sigma_{-1} \rangle = \psi^\dagger \sigma_{-1} \psi = \sqrt{2}\psi^{*(2)}\psi^{(1)}$$

Note that in this representation the product $\boldsymbol{\sigma} \cdot \boldsymbol{\sigma}$ is $\sum_m \sigma_m \cdot \sigma_{-m}$.

Space Inversion

Next, let us treat the operation of space inversion, denoted by P. Space inversion acting on a wave function changes the sign of all coordinates. Thus

$$P\psi(\mathbf{r}, \boldsymbol{\sigma}) = \psi(-\mathbf{r}, \boldsymbol{\sigma}) \tag{I-33}$$

However, this operation, acting twice, restores the original wave function. Thus it is clear that (unlike for an infinitesimal rotation) space inversion of the coordinate *axes* is entirely equivalent to space inversion of the *system* relative to fixed coordinate axes. Under space inversion we have

$$x^P = -x \tag{I-34}$$

$$p_x{}^P = -p_x \tag{I-35}$$

but $L_x{}^P = L_x$ since

$$y' \frac{\partial}{\partial z'} = (-y)\left(-\frac{\partial}{\partial z}\right) = y \frac{\partial}{\partial z} \tag{I-36}$$

Transformation properties of matrix elements under space inversion are obtained very simply. The transformed matrix element $\langle \hat{O}^P(\mathbf{r}) \rangle$ is defined as

$$\langle \hat{O}^P(\mathbf{r}) \rangle = \int (P\psi^\dagger(\mathbf{r}))^\dagger \hat{O}(\mathbf{r})[P\psi(\mathbf{r})]\, d^3\mathbf{r} \tag{I-37}$$

which equals

$$\int \psi^\dagger(-\mathbf{r})\hat{O}(\mathbf{r})\psi(-\mathbf{r})\, d^3\mathbf{r} \tag{I-38}$$

Replacing $\mathbf{r}$ by $-\mathbf{r}$ everywhere, we then obtain

$$\int \psi^\dagger(\mathbf{r})\hat{O}(-\mathbf{r})\psi(\mathbf{r})\, d^3\mathbf{r} = \langle \hat{O}(-\mathbf{r}) \rangle \tag{I-39}$$

Therefore, since P does not involve spin components, we find

$$\langle \sigma_x{}^P \rangle = \langle \sigma_x \rangle \tag{I-40}$$

This is a very important conclusion; the components of angular momentum do not change sign under space inversion. In this way axial vectors, such as angular momenta, can be distinguished from polar vectors, such as momenta. In addition, it is evident that the Hamiltonian is invariant under space inversion if

$$\mathrm{H}(-\mathbf{r}) = \mathrm{H}(\mathbf{r}) \tag{I-41}$$

Time Reversal

The wave function of a system satisfies the time-dependent Schroedinger equation

$$\mathrm{H}(t)\psi(t) = i\hbar \frac{\partial \psi(t)}{\partial t} \tag{I-42}$$

(We do not explicitly indicate the dependence on **r**.) In constructing the time-reversed wave function, we cannot simply replace t by $-t$, for this would change the sign of the energy, a physically inadmissible result. However, Wigner suggested that we define the time-reversal operation as follows:

$$\psi'(t) = T\psi(t) = \psi^*(-t) \tag{I-43}$$

Since ψ^* satisfies

$$\mathrm{H}^*(t)\psi^*(t) = -i\hbar\,\frac{\partial\psi^*(t)}{\partial t} \tag{I-44}$$

it is clear that ψ' satisfies

$$\mathrm{H}^*(-t)\psi' = i\hbar\,\frac{\partial\psi'}{\partial t} \tag{I-45}$$

Thus the time-reversed wave function satisfies the same equation as the original wave function, provided

$$\mathrm{H}^*(-t) = \mathrm{H}(t) \tag{I-46}$$

If, as is usual, the Hamiltonian is not explicitly time-dependent, time-reversal invariance requires only that H be real.

SPIN ONE-HALF PARTICLES. The transformation properties under time reversal are slightly more complicated. Under time reversal all spins must change sign. Since the Pauli spin matrices σ_x and σ_z are real, whereas σ_y is imaginary, it is clear that taking the complex conjugate of ψ alone changes the sign of the expectation value of σ_y. In order to do the same for those of σ_x and σ_z, we must, in addition, make a rotation by 180° about the y axis; this can be accomplished by multiplying the wave function by σ_y or by any matrix differing from σ_y by a phase factor. In particular, it is convenient to use the real matrix

$$i\sigma_y = \begin{pmatrix} 0 & 1 \\ -1 & 0 \end{pmatrix}$$

Thus

$$T\psi(t) = i\sigma_y\psi^*(-t) \tag{I-47}$$

To consider a particular case, if

$$\psi = \begin{pmatrix} 0 \\ 1 \end{pmatrix} \exp\left[\frac{i}{\hbar}(\mathbf{p}\cdot\mathbf{r} - Et)\right] \tag{I-48}$$

then

$$\psi^* = \begin{pmatrix}0\\1\end{pmatrix} \exp\left[\frac{-i}{\hbar}(\mathbf{p}\cdot\mathbf{r} - Et)\right] \tag{I-49}$$

and

$$\psi' = T\psi = \begin{pmatrix}1\\0\end{pmatrix} \exp\left[\frac{-i}{\hbar}(\mathbf{p}\cdot\mathbf{r} + Et)\right] = \begin{pmatrix}1\\0\end{pmatrix} \exp\left[\frac{i}{\hbar}(-\mathbf{p}\cdot\mathbf{r} - Et)\right] \tag{I-50}$$

Thus ψ' has the same energy as ψ, but the directions of spin and momentum are reversed.

To calculate the transformation properties of matrix elements (which now form a 2×2 matrix) under time reversal, we begin with the definition

$$\langle \hat{O}^T(t)\rangle = \int [T\psi(t)]^\dagger \hat{O}(t) T\psi(t)\, d^3\mathbf{r} \tag{I-51}$$

(The index r (in ψ and $\hat{O}$) does not enter into this calculation and has been suppressed here.) Now we use Eq. I-47 and its conjugate

$$[T\psi(t)]^\dagger = [i\sigma_y\psi^*(-t)]^\dagger = -i\psi^T(-t)\sigma_y \tag{I-52}$$

Here ψ^T denotes the transpose of ψ,

$$\psi^\dagger = (\psi^T)^* \tag{I-53}$$

and we have used the fact that σ_y is Hermitean. Substituting this equation into Eq. I-51, we obtain

$$\langle \hat{O}^T(t)\rangle = \int \psi^T(-t)\sigma_y\hat{O}(t)\sigma_y\psi^*(-t)\, d^3\mathbf{r} \tag{I-54}$$

Since the matrix element, being an expectation value, is real, we can take the complex conjugate of every term on the right-hand side, obtaining

$$\int \psi^\dagger(-t)\sigma_y\hat{O}^*(t)\sigma_y\psi(-t)\, d^3\mathbf{r} \tag{I-55}$$

In addition, if the matrix element is independent of time (although $\hat{O}$ may not be), we can replace t by $-t$ to find

$$\langle \hat{O}^T(t)\rangle = \int \psi^\dagger(t)\sigma_y\hat{O}^*(-t)\sigma_y\psi(t)\, d^3\mathbf{r} = \langle \sigma_y\hat{O}^*(-t)\sigma_y\rangle \tag{I-56}$$

In particular, we have

$$\langle x_i{}^T \rangle = \langle x_i \rangle \tag{I-57}$$

$$\langle p_i{}^T \rangle = \left\langle \left(-i\hbar \frac{\partial}{\partial x_i} \right)^* \right\rangle = \left\langle i\hbar \frac{\partial}{\partial x_i} \right\rangle = \langle p_i \rangle \tag{I-58}$$

$$\langle L_i{}^T \rangle = \langle L_i \rangle \tag{I-59}$$

$$\langle \sigma_i{}^T \rangle = \langle \sigma_y \sigma_i{}^* \sigma_y \rangle = \pm\epsilon \langle \sigma_y \sigma_i \sigma_y \rangle = \langle \sigma_i \rangle \tag{I-60}$$

where plus applies for $i = x, z$ and minus applies for $i = y$. Therefore, as we expected, all components of angular momenta change sign under time reversal.*

---

* Strictly speaking, however, the foregoing remarks concerning time reversal hold only if the particles can be described by plane waves in the way that we have done, that is, if we neglect the effect of strong interactions, such as the nuclear Coulomb field on the electrons (cf. the discussion in Sec. 4-4, p. 142).

APPENDIX II

The Dirac Equation and Free-Particle Wave Functions

II-1 BACKGROUND

First consider a nonrelativistic particle moving in a field-free region, that is, one upon which no forces are acting. Such a particle is described by the classical expression

$$E = \frac{1}{2m} p^2 \tag{II-1}$$

Substituting the well-known quantum-mechanical operators for E and p,

$$E = i\hbar \frac{\partial}{\partial t}, \qquad p_i = -i\hbar \frac{\partial}{\partial x_i} \tag{II-2}$$

we obtain the Schroedinger equation

$$-\frac{\hbar^2}{2m} \nabla^2 \psi = i\hbar \frac{\partial \psi}{\partial t}$$

which is linear in time.

If we try the same approach to a field-free relativistic particle, the relativistic energy equation must be used:

$$E^2 = m_0{}^2 c^4 + p^2 c^2 \tag{II-3}$$

Substituting the same operators for E and p in Eq. II-3 as in the nonrelativistic case, we obtain

$$\left[\nabla^2 - \left(\frac{m_0 c}{\hbar}\right)^2\right] \psi = \frac{1}{c^2} \frac{\partial^2 \psi}{\partial t^2} \tag{II-4}$$

This is the well-known Klein-Gordon equation. Unlike the Schroedinger equation, it is not linear in time.

In 1928 Dirac formulated a theory to deal with relativistic spin $\frac{1}{2}$

particles. In keeping with the general formulation of quantum mechanics, he constructed a wave equation for ψ of first order in time. In the theory of relativity, there is complete symmetry between x, y, z, and t; therefore it is plausible that the space coordinates should also enter into the wave equation in first order.

Assume that ψ consists of N components of ψ_m. The most general first-order linear equation is then

$$\frac{1}{c}\frac{\partial \psi_m}{\partial t} + \sum_{k=1}^{3}\sum_{n=1}^{N} \alpha_{kmn}\frac{\partial \psi_n}{\partial x_k} + i\,\frac{m_0 c}{\hbar}\sum_{n=1}^{N}\beta_{mn}\psi_n = 0 \qquad \text{(II-5)}$$

This is equivalent to saying that the time derivative of one component can be expressed as a linear combination of *all* the components as well as their spatial derivatives, where $m, n = 1, 2, \ldots, N$; x_k denotes the spatial coordinates. Such a group of simultaneous differential equations can best be combined, by using matrix notation, into one matrix equation:

$$\frac{1}{c}\frac{\partial \psi}{\partial t} + \sum_{k=1}^{3}\alpha_k\frac{\partial \psi}{\partial x_k} + i\,\frac{m_0 c}{\hbar}\,\beta\psi = 0 \qquad \text{(II-6)}$$

This is one form of the Dirac equation. Here ψ is a one-column matrix of N rows, and α_1, α_2, α_3, and β are matrices. From the continuity conditions for the probability density, it can be shown that α and β must all be Hermitian matrices. Furthermore, any solution ψ of Eq. II-6 should also be a solution of the Klein-Gordon equation. After all, the Klein-Gordon equation was a logical deduction resulting from operational substitution into the relativistic relation between the energy and momentum for a free particle.

For this purpose we apply the operator

$$\frac{1}{c}\frac{\partial}{\partial t} - \sum_k \alpha_k\frac{\partial}{\partial x_k} - i\,\frac{m_0 c}{\hbar}\,\beta \qquad \text{(II-7)}$$

to the Dirac wave equation, thereby introducing second derivatives:

$$\frac{1}{c^2}\frac{\partial^2 \psi}{\partial t^2} = \frac{1}{2}\sum_k\sum_l(\alpha_k\alpha_l + \alpha_l\alpha_k)\frac{\partial^2 \psi}{\partial x_k\,\partial x_l} - \left(\frac{m_0 c}{\hbar}\right)^2\beta^2\psi$$
$$+\, i\,\frac{m_0 c}{\hbar}\sum_k(\alpha_k\beta + \beta\alpha_k)\frac{\partial \psi}{\partial x_k} \qquad \text{(II-8)}$$

II-2 SUMMARY OF THE DIRAC EQUATION AND DIRAC MATRICES

Equation II-8 reduces to the Klein-Gordon equation, if the following conditions are satisfied:

$$\begin{aligned} \tfrac{1}{2}(\alpha_k\alpha_l + \alpha_l\alpha_k) = \delta_{kl} &= 1 \quad \text{if } k = l \\ &= 0 \quad \text{if } k \neq l. \\ \alpha_k\beta + \beta\alpha_k &= 0 \\ \alpha_k^2 = \beta^2 &= I \end{aligned} \tag{II-9}$$

Thus we find that the α's as well as any α and β anticommute and that the square of all four matrices is unity.

Dirac Matrices

It is well known that the set of three Pauli 2×2 spin matrices (cf. Appendix I, p. 308) anticommute and that their square is unity. However, a fourth 2×2 matrix anticommuting with σ_x, σ_y, and σ_z cannot be found; therefore it is impossible to construct *four* mutually anticommuting 2×2 matrices. But if we go to 4×4 matrices, we can actually construct an anticommuting set of 4×4 matrices out of Pauli matrices and the 2×2 unit matrix

$$I = \begin{pmatrix} 1 & 0 \\ 0 & 1 \end{pmatrix}$$

These are

$$\alpha_k = \begin{pmatrix} 0 & \sigma_k \\ \sigma_k & 0 \end{pmatrix}, \quad k = 1, 2, 3, \qquad \beta = \begin{pmatrix} I & 0 \\ 0 & -I \end{pmatrix} \tag{II-10}$$

These matrices are Hermitian and anticommuting to each other. For example,

$$\alpha_k\beta = \begin{pmatrix} 0 & -\sigma_k \\ \sigma_k & 0 \end{pmatrix}, \qquad \beta\alpha_k = \begin{pmatrix} 0 & \sigma_k \\ -\sigma_k & 0 \end{pmatrix} \tag{II-11}$$

They are also unitary; that is,

$$\alpha_k^{\dagger}\alpha_k = \alpha_k^2 = I \tag{II-12}$$

If we write out the matrices completely,

$$\alpha_1 = \begin{pmatrix} 0 & 0 & 0 & 1 \\ 0 & 0 & 1 & 0 \\ 0 & 1 & 0 & 0 \\ 1 & 0 & 0 & 0 \end{pmatrix}, \quad \alpha_2 = \begin{pmatrix} 0 & 0 & 0 & -i \\ 0 & 0 & i & 0 \\ 0 & -i & 0 & 0 \\ i & 0 & 0 & 0 \end{pmatrix},$$

$$\alpha_3 = \begin{pmatrix} 0 & 0 & 1 & 0 \\ 0 & 0 & 0 & -1 \\ 1 & 0 & 0 & 0 \\ 0 & -1 & 0 & 0 \end{pmatrix} \qquad \text{(II-13)}$$

and

$$\beta = \begin{pmatrix} 1 & 0 & 0 & 0 \\ 0 & 1 & 0 & 0 \\ 0 & 0 & -1 & 0 \\ 0 & 0 & 0 & -1 \end{pmatrix} \qquad \text{(II-14)}$$

It is usually best *not to express the matrices explicitly when solving problems.* The pertinent properties to be remembered are their Hermitian character and their anticommuting and unitary properties.

Hamiltonian Form of the Dirac Equation

To express the Dirac equation in usual Hamiltonian form, we write

$$\left(-i\hbar\frac{\partial\psi}{\partial t} - i\hbar c\boldsymbol{\alpha}\cdot\boldsymbol{\nabla} + \beta m_0c^2\right)\psi = 0 \qquad \text{(II-15)}$$

or

$$(\boldsymbol{\alpha}\cdot\mathbf{p}c + \beta m_0c^2)\psi = i\hbar\frac{\partial\psi}{\partial t} = E\psi \qquad \text{(II-16)}$$

Since the Dirac matrices α_k and β are 4×4 matrices, the wave function ψ must have *four components* and no more. With the explicit form of α_k and β, the four components of ψ separate into two classes when v/c is small; ψ_1 and ψ_2 are large, and ψ_3 and ψ_4 are small.

Covariant Form of the Dirac Equation

To make the Dirac equation invariant under Lorentz transformations, it is more suitable to treat the space and time coordinates on an equal footing in the Dirac equation. Let us denote

$$x_4 = ict \tag{II-17}$$

Then

$$-i\hbar \frac{\partial}{\partial t} = \hbar c \frac{\partial}{\partial x_4} \tag{II-18}$$

Substituting Eq. II-18 into Eq. II-15, the Dirac equation, and multiplying it by $\beta/\hbar c$, we obtain

$$\left(\beta \frac{\partial}{\partial x_4} - i\beta\alpha \cdot \nabla + \frac{m_0 c}{\hbar}\right)\psi = 0 \tag{II-19}$$

To make this equation more symmetrical, *the gamma matrices* γ_k will be introduced:

$$\gamma_k = -i\beta\alpha_k, \qquad k = 1, 2, 3, \quad \gamma_4 = \beta. \tag{II-20}$$

Since β and α_k are Hermitian and anticommute with one another, γ_k is also hermitian:

$$\gamma_k^{\dagger} = (-i\beta\alpha_k)^{\dagger} = i\alpha_k^{\dagger}\beta^{\dagger} = -i\beta\alpha_k = \gamma_k \tag{II-21}$$

Finally, in covariant notation

$$\left(\sum_{\mu} \gamma_\mu \frac{\partial}{\partial x_\mu} + \frac{m_0 c}{\hbar}\right)\psi = 0 \tag{II-22}$$

and

$$\sum_{\mu} \gamma_\mu p_\mu \psi = i m_0 c \psi \tag{II-23}$$

It follows directly from the definition of the γ_k that

$$\gamma_\mu \gamma_\nu = -\gamma_\nu \gamma_\mu, \qquad \mu \neq \nu \tag{II-24}$$

and $\gamma_\mu^2 = I$, the unit matrix.

The product of the four γ_k matrices is defined as

$$\gamma_5 = \gamma_1 \gamma_2 \gamma_3 \gamma_4 \tag{II-25}$$

By using the definitions for γ_μ, β, and α_k we can see that γ_5 has the matrix form

$$\gamma_5 = \begin{pmatrix} 0 & -I \\ -I & 0 \end{pmatrix} = \begin{pmatrix} 0 & 0 & -1 & 0 \\ 0 & 0 & 0 & -1 \\ -1 & 0 & 0 & 0 \\ 0 & -1 & 0 & 0 \end{pmatrix} \tag{II-26}$$

Furthermore, we have the relations

$$\begin{aligned} \gamma_5\gamma_\mu &= -\gamma_\mu\gamma_5, \qquad \mu = 1, 2, 3, 4 \\ \gamma_5^{\,2} &= I \end{aligned} \tag{II-27}$$

Altogether, it follows that

$$\gamma_\mu\gamma_\nu + \gamma_\nu\gamma_\mu = 2\delta_{\mu\nu}, \quad \mu,\nu = 1, 2, 3, 4, 5 \tag{II-28}$$

If we express σ_k in four-component form, that is,

$$\sigma_k = \begin{pmatrix} \sigma_k & 0 \\ 0 & \sigma_k \end{pmatrix} \tag{II-29}$$

we can write

$$\alpha_k = -\gamma_5\sigma_k \quad \text{or} \quad \sigma_k = -\gamma_5\alpha_k \tag{II-30}$$

II-3 FREE-PARTICLE SOLUTIONS IN THE DIRAC EQUATION

Solutions in Terms of Two-Component Spinors

For a free particle with momentum p and energy E, the plane waveform can be represented by

$$\psi(\mathbf{r}, t) = \psi \exp\left[\frac{i}{\hbar}(\mathbf{p}\cdot\mathbf{r} - Et)\right] \tag{II-31}$$

where ψ, the wave function at the origin, is a four-component spinor. This spinor ψ satisfies the equation

$$E\psi = (c\boldsymbol{\alpha}\cdot\mathbf{p} + \beta m_0c^2)\psi \tag{II-32}$$

We can write ψ in the form

$$\psi = \begin{pmatrix} \Phi \\ \xi \end{pmatrix} \tag{II-33}$$

where both Φ and ξ are Pauli *two*-component spinors. Substituting Eq. II-33 into Eq. II-32, we obtain

$$E\begin{pmatrix} \Phi \\ \xi \end{pmatrix} = \left[\begin{pmatrix} 0 & I \\ I & 0 \end{pmatrix} c\boldsymbol{\sigma}\cdot\mathbf{p} + \begin{pmatrix} I & 0 \\ 0 & -I \end{pmatrix} m_0c^2\right]\begin{pmatrix} \Phi \\ \xi \end{pmatrix} \tag{II-34}$$

We can separate this equation into two equations, each containing the two-component functions Φ and ξ:

$$c(\boldsymbol{\sigma} \cdot \mathbf{p})\xi = (E - m_0c^2)\Phi \tag{II-35a}$$

and

$$(c\boldsymbol{\sigma} \cdot \mathbf{p})\Phi = (E + m_0c^2)\xi \tag{II-35b}$$

For a state of positive energy,

$$E_+ = +(c^2p^2 + m_0^2c^4)^{1/2} \tag{II-36}$$

we have

$$\xi = \frac{c\boldsymbol{\sigma} \cdot \mathbf{p}}{E_+ + m_0c^2}\Phi \tag{II-37}$$

Therefore, in the nonrelativistic limit $E_+ \to m_0c^2$,

$$\xi \to \frac{c\boldsymbol{\sigma} \cdot \mathbf{p}}{2m_0c^2}\Phi = \frac{\boldsymbol{\sigma} \cdot \mathbf{v}}{2c}\Phi \tag{II-38}$$

that is, the spinor ξ approaches zero as v goes to zero, which implies that Φ is associated with positive-energy states. Similarly, for negative-energy states it can be seen that $\Phi \to 0$ as $v \to 0$. This leaves ξ to be associated with negative-energy states; Φ and ξ are referred to as "large" and "small" components. Of course, even after the *sign* of E is fixed, there are still two solutions for the components of ψ, corresponding to the two spin states of the particle described by the Dirac equation.

Explicit Form

We have seen that the two-component functions Φ and ξ are associated with positive- and negative-energy states. It is obvious that for spin $\frac{1}{2}$ particles, which this theory describes, the other two degrees of freedom should be associated with the spin orientations "up" and "down." Therefore, for positive-energy solutions $E = +|E|$,

$$\psi_\sigma{}^+ = \psi^{E>0}_{\uparrow \text{ or } \downarrow} = \begin{pmatrix} \Phi \\ \xi \end{pmatrix} = \begin{pmatrix} \chi_\sigma \\ \dfrac{c\boldsymbol{\sigma} \cdot \mathbf{p}}{|E| + m_0c^2}\chi_\sigma \end{pmatrix} \tag{II-39}$$

where

$$\chi_\uparrow = \begin{pmatrix} 1 \\ 0 \end{pmatrix} \tag{II-40a}$$

and

$$\chi_\downarrow = \begin{pmatrix} 0 \\ 1 \end{pmatrix} \tag{II-40b}$$

Now we define

$$\eta = \frac{cp}{|E| + m_0c^2} \tag{II-41}$$

Then the normalized positive-energy wave function becomes

$$\psi_\sigma^+ = (1 + \eta^2)^{-1/2} \begin{pmatrix} \chi_\sigma \\ \eta \boldsymbol{\sigma} \cdot \hat{\mathbf{p}} \chi_\sigma \end{pmatrix} \tag{II-42}$$

The term $(1 + \eta^2)^{-1/2}$ is a normalization factor and $\hat{\mathbf{p}}$ is the unit vector in the direction of momentum. If the spin is in the positive z direction, we have

$$\chi_\sigma = \chi_\uparrow = \begin{pmatrix} 1 \\ 0 \end{pmatrix} \tag{II-43}$$

$$(\boldsymbol{\sigma} \cdot \hat{\mathbf{p}})\chi_\sigma = \begin{pmatrix} p_z/p \\ (p_x + ip_y)/p \end{pmatrix} \tag{II-44}$$

and thus

$$\psi_\uparrow^+ = \frac{1}{(1 + \eta^2)^{1/2}} \begin{pmatrix} 1 \\ 0 \\ \eta p_z/p \\ \eta(p_x + ip_y)/p \end{pmatrix} \tag{II-45}$$

Similarly, if the spin is in the negative z direction,

$$\psi_\downarrow^+ = \frac{1}{(1 + \eta^2)^{1/2}} \begin{pmatrix} 0 \\ 1 \\ \eta(p_x - ip_y)/p \\ -\eta p_z/p \end{pmatrix} \tag{II-46}$$

If the momentum is also along the z direction, $p_z = \pm p$, and then the expressions simplify to

$$\psi_\uparrow^+ = \frac{1}{(1 + \eta^2)^{1/2}} \begin{pmatrix} 1 \\ 0 \\ \pm\eta \\ 0 \end{pmatrix}, \qquad \psi_\downarrow^+ = \frac{1}{(1 + \eta^2)^{1/2}} \begin{pmatrix} 0 \\ 1 \\ 0 \\ \mp\eta \end{pmatrix} \tag{II-47}$$

For negative-energy solutions, $E = -|E|$, and we obtain

$$\psi_\sigma^- = (1 + \eta^2)^{-1/2}\begin{pmatrix} -\eta(\boldsymbol{\sigma}\cdot\hat{\mathbf{p}})\chi_\sigma \\ \chi_\sigma \end{pmatrix} \tag{II-48}$$

and more specifically

$$\psi_\uparrow^- = \frac{1}{(1+\eta^2)^{1/2}}\begin{pmatrix} -\eta p_z/p \\ -\eta(p_x + ip_y)/p \\ 1 \\ 0 \end{pmatrix},$$

$$\psi_\downarrow^- = \frac{1}{(1+\eta^2)^{1/2}}\begin{pmatrix} -\eta(p_x - ip_y)/p \\ \eta p_z/p \\ 0 \\ 1 \end{pmatrix} \tag{II-49}$$

We have listed the various components of the Dirac wave functions explicitly because a clear understanding of these functions has direct bearing on an understanding of the derivation of the theory of β decay.

II-4 THEORY OF POSITRONS

Negative-Energy States

According to the Dirac theory of electrons, for a fixed momentum p there are *four* independent solutions representing two different spin states for positive E and two for negative E. Yet, can solutions of both positive and negative energy be possible? If the electrons in the positive-energy states would make fast transitions to negative states, the positive states could not remain occupied. Furthermore, how would a particle in a negative-energy state behave? A particle with negative energy ($E \rightarrow -m_0c^2$) is equivalent to a particle with a negative mass. If we apply a force in one direction, it moves in the opposite direction, a behavior characterized by the name of "donkey electron." On the other hand, the Dirac equation was successful in accounting for the spin and the magnetic moment of the electron, the fine structure of the hydrogen levels, etc. It was therefore of the utmost importance to develop a physical interpretation which would give sense to the Dirac formalism.

Dirac Hole Theory

It was Dirac who postulated the interpretation in the form of the famous *hole theory*. He assumed that since electrons obey Fermi statistics, all the negative-energy states are normally completely occupied by electrons, making transitions to negative-energy states impossible. A vacuum is, then, a sea of electrons in the negative-energy states. The presence of this negative charge is not observed because it is uniformly distributed. When one electron is missing in the distribution of negative-energy states, the empty state manifests itself as a particle of positive energy and positive charge, for a particle of negative energy and negative charge is absent. Consequently, the empty place or "Dirac hole" behaves as a normal particle would. At first Dirac unsuccessfully attempted to interpret these positive particles as protons. However, with Anderson's discovery of positrons in cosmic radiation, the Dirac equation, and the hole theory were finally vindicated as correct physical theories.

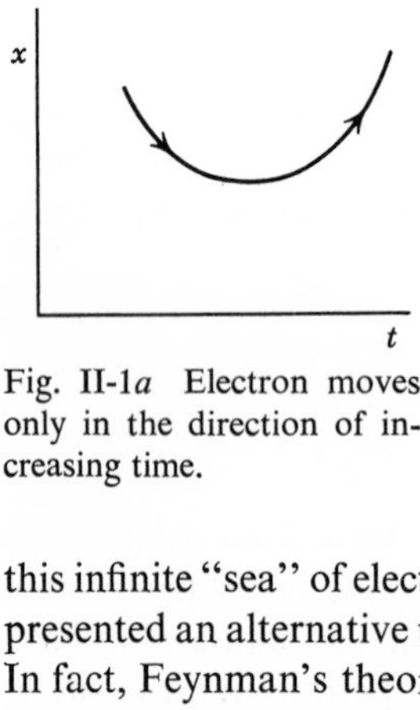

Fig. II-1*a* Electron moves only in the direction of increasing time.

Feynman's Theory

The Dirac hole theory is perfectly consistent and suitable for a description of positrons. It is, however, conceptually unsatisfactory in one respect: We must have an *infinite* number of electrons filling up all the negative-energy states. Then a hole in this infinite "sea" of electrons behaves like a positron. In 1949 Feynman presented an alternative theory of positrons which avoids this difficulty. In fact, Feynman's theory is easier to use than Dirac's for more complicated electrodynamic processes. However, since Dirac's theory is, after all, quite adequate for β decay, we wish merely to sketch the basic physical ideas underlying Feynman's description.

Consider an electron moving classically in one dimension. We can make a space-time diagram of the electron's path, which might look like that shown in Fig. II-1*a*.

As indicated, the electron can move in either direction along the x axis, but it moves only in the direction of increasing time. Feynman pointed out that this is an unnecessary restriction. Suppose we permit the electron to move backward in time also. Then its path might look like the one indicated in Fig. II-1b. Let us take a "snapshot" of the electron at some given time. In Fig. II-1a we see, of course, one electron. On the other hand, in Fig. II-1b, the electron appears twice for $t < t_0$, once moving forward and once backward: however, it does not appear at all for $t > t_0$.

The process in Fig. II-1b looks very much like *two* particles coming together and annihilating. In fact, the electron moving backward in

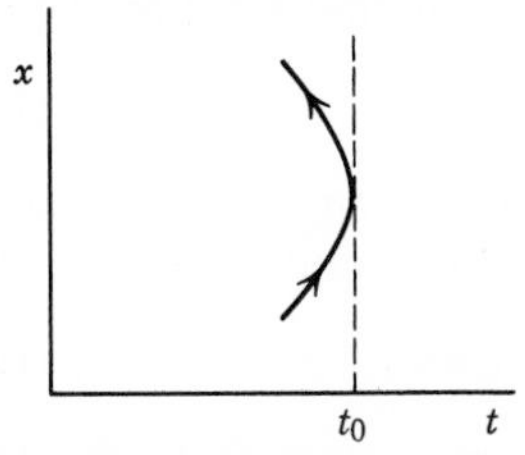

Fig. II-1b Electron can also move backward in time.

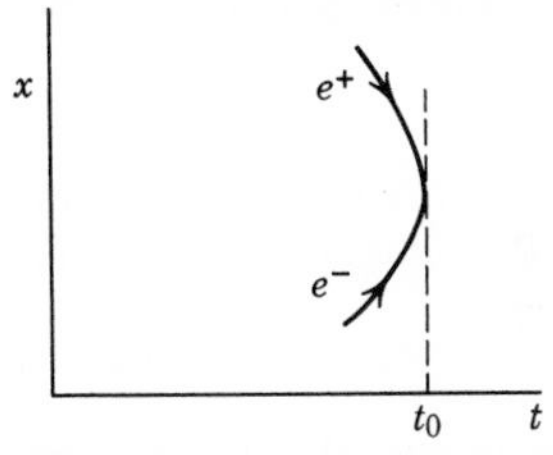

Fig. II-1c Electron-positron annihilation—an alternative descripton of part b.

time behaves exactly as a positron moving forward in time. Therefore in the Dirac language the process of Fig. II-1b can be described as shown in Fig. II-1c. In this way Feynman was able to derive a consistent theory of positrons without having to invoke an infinite filled sea of negative-energy states.

II-5 PARTICLES OF ZERO REST MASS

When $m_0 = 0$, the parameter η defined in Eq. II-41 equals unity, and the expressions for the Dirac spinors simplify considerably. Consider a $m_0 = 0$ particle in a positive-energy state with spin along the positive z axis and momentum in the xz plane. The spinors are given by

$$\psi_\uparrow{}^+ = \frac{1}{\sqrt{2}}\begin{pmatrix} 1 \\ 0 \\ \cos\theta \\ \sin\theta \end{pmatrix}, \qquad \psi_\downarrow{}^+ = \frac{1}{\sqrt{2}}\begin{pmatrix} 0 \\ 1 \\ \sin\theta \\ -\cos\theta \end{pmatrix} \tag{II-50}$$

If, in addition, we suppose that the momentum is also directed along the z axis, say the positive z direction, the wave functions simplify further. In particular, we find for the positive-energy states that

$$\psi_{\uparrow}{}^{+} = \frac{1}{\sqrt{2}}\begin{pmatrix}1\\0\\1\\0\end{pmatrix}, \qquad \psi_{\downarrow}{}^{+} = \frac{1}{\sqrt{2}}\begin{pmatrix}0\\1\\0\\-1\end{pmatrix} \tag{II-51}$$

These spinors satisfy the so-called chirality equation (cf. Sec. 7-1),

$$\gamma_5\psi = \mp\psi. \tag{II-52}$$

but the more general spinors in Eq. II-50 do not. In addition, since the spin is parallel (or antiparallel) to the momentum, and $m_0 = 0$, we have

$$c\boldsymbol{\sigma}\cdot\mathbf{p}\psi = \pm cp\psi = \pm E\psi \tag{II-53}$$

which is the Weyl equation. In fact, we may start from the Dirac equation for $m_0 = 0$ particles:

$$E\psi = c\boldsymbol{\alpha}\cdot\mathbf{p}\psi = -c\boldsymbol{\sigma}\cdot\mathbf{p}\gamma_5\psi \tag{II-54}$$

Then if Eq. II-52, the chirality equation, is satisfied (with sign $\mp$), so is the Weyl equation (with sign $\pm$).

We can proceed in a similar way for negative-energy states. For massless particles with momentum along the positive z axis, the Dirac spinors are

$$\psi_{\uparrow}{}^{-} = \frac{1}{\sqrt{2}}\begin{pmatrix}-1\\0\\1\\0\end{pmatrix}, \qquad \psi_{\downarrow}{}^{-} = \frac{1}{\sqrt{2}}\begin{pmatrix}0\\1\\0\\1\end{pmatrix} \tag{II-55}$$

Next, let us define the helicity $\mathfrak{H}$:

$$\mathfrak{H} = \frac{\boldsymbol{\sigma}\cdot\psi\mathbf{p}}{E\psi}, \qquad \hbar = c = 1 \tag{II-56}$$

Clearly $\psi_{\uparrow}{}^{+}$ has helicity $+1$, spin parallel to momentum (right-handed), whereas $\psi_{\downarrow}{}^{+}$ has helicity -1, spin antiparallel to momentum (left-handed). The negative-energy solutions also have helicity ± 1, that is, -1 for $\psi_{\uparrow}{}^{-}$ and $+1$ for $\psi_{\downarrow}{}^{-}$. We may also define the chirality $\gamma_5\psi/\psi$. By comparing Eqs. II-52 and II-53, it is clear that positive chirality is equivalent to negative helicity (and vice versa).

In the two-component neutrino theory it is assumed that *all* neutrinos must have the same helicity (which is known to be -1 from experiment); that is, *only* solutions $\psi_{\downarrow}{}^{+}$ and $\psi_{\uparrow}{}^{-}$ exist (for neutrinos moving along the positive z axis). The second solution corresponds to an *antineutrino* with sign of p, σ, and E reversed and thus of helicity $+1$. If only two solutions occur in nature, the wave functions are effectively characterized by only *two* components instead of the usual four—thus the name *two-component theory*. We can write

$$\psi_{\downarrow}{}^{+} = \begin{pmatrix} 0 \\ 1 \end{pmatrix}, \qquad \psi_{\uparrow}{}^{-} = \begin{pmatrix} 1 \\ 0 \end{pmatrix} \tag{II-57}$$

Since for these two wave functions,

$$\gamma_5 \psi = \psi.$$

the last two components are the same as the first two, except for a change of sign. Finally, any Dirac particle obeying the Weyl equation *must* have zero rest mass, which can be seen by taking the square of Eq. II-53.

Relativistic Transformations

III-1 PHYSICAL CONCEPTS

We now generalize the treatment in Appendix I to take into account all possible Lorentz transformations. In other words, we also consider transformations to other reference frames moving with uniform relative velocity in addition to rotation. For two frames moving with a relative velocity v in the x direction, we have the so-called "*pure Lorentz transformations*," which can be represented in the well-known form:

$$\begin{aligned} x' &= \left(1 - \frac{v^2}{c^2}\right)^{-1/2}(x - vt) \\ y' &= y \\ z' &= z \\ t' &= \left(1 - \frac{v^2}{c^2}\right)^{-1/2}\left(t - \frac{vx}{c^2}\right) \end{aligned} \tag{III-1}$$

However, the so-called *proper Lorentz transformations* include rotations and pure Lorentz transformations, that is, *all* Lorentz transformations except those containing a space inversion or time reversal (or both). For the purpose of representing all Lorentz transformations in a unified way, we introduce new coordinates, as follows:

$$x_1 = x, \quad x_2 = y, \quad x_3 = z, \quad x_4 = ict \tag{III-2}$$

Then all proper Lorentz transformations can be built up of infinitesimal rotations of the form

$$\begin{aligned} x_i' &= x_i + \epsilon x_j \\ x_j' &= x_j - \epsilon x_i \\ x_k' &= x_k \\ x_l' &= x_l \end{aligned} \tag{III-3}$$

where i, j, k, l are the indices 1, 2, 3, 4 (in some order). For example, take $i = 2$, $j = 3$, $k = 1$, $l = 4$; we are dealing with an ordinary rotation about one of the axes, that is, the case previously discussed. The rotation is generally ordinary if both i and j are either 1, 2, or 3. However, if one of these quantities is the fourth coordinate, we have a *pure Lorentz transformation.* For example, the transformation discussed at the beginning of this section can be characterized, to first order in ϵ, by $i = 1$, $j = 4$, $\epsilon = iv/c$. Quite generally ϵ is imaginary for pure Lorentz transformations but real for ordinary rotations.

There are also the so-called *general Lorentz transformations*, which include proper Lorentz transformations as well as space inversion and time reversal. Space inversion is a transformation characterized by

$$x_i' = -x_i, \quad i = 1, 2, 3, \qquad x_4' = x_4 \tag{III-4}$$

whereas for time reversal

$$x_i' = x_i, \quad i = 1, 2, 3, \qquad x_4' = -x_4 \tag{III-5}$$

We can again characterize quantities according to the way in which they transform under general Lorentz transformations. A scalar, as before, is invariant under general Lorentz transformations. However, a vector now has four components instead of three. Under proper Lorentz transformations the four components transform in the same way as the x_i; under space inversion the first three components change sign and the last one remains unchanged. Therefore the energy momentum vector has

$$\begin{aligned} p_1 &= p_x \\ p_2 &= p_y \\ p_3 &= p_z \\ p_4 &= \frac{iE}{c} \end{aligned} \tag{III-6}$$

We can see that for a single particle

$$\sum_i p_i^2 = p^2 - \frac{E^2}{c^2} = -m_0^2c^2 \tag{III-7}$$

The *cross product of two vectors* $\mathbf{U} \times \mathbf{V}$ is defined as

$$t_{ij} = U_iV_j - U_jV_i \tag{III-8}$$

This cross product is an antisymmetric tensor of rank 2 possessing *six* independent components. We have seen before that in the three-dimensional case the cross product $\mathbf{U} \times \mathbf{V}$ forms *both* an antisymmetric tensor of rank 2 and also an axial vector. However, in the four-dimensional case the cross product of two vectors does not form an axial vector.

Now let us consider an *antisymmetric product of three vectors*,

$$S_{ijk} = \sum (-1)^{\zeta} U_{\alpha} V_{\beta} W_{\gamma} \tag{III-9}$$

where α, β, and γ are various permutations of i, j, and k. The sum extends over all six such permutations. Thus if $(ijk) = (123)$, then

$$\begin{aligned} \zeta &= +1 \quad \text{for} \quad \alpha\beta\gamma = 123,\ 231,\ 312 \\ &= -1 \qquad\qquad\quad = 213,\ 132,\ 321 \end{aligned} \quad . \tag{III-10}$$

Now ijk can have four sets of values (123, 234, 341, 412). Thus the antisymmetric product has four components. Each of these transforms under Lorentz transformations as a component of an axial vector. However, under space inversion, only the component S_{123} changes sign, whereas the other three components, that is, S_{234}, S_{341}, S_{412}, remain unchanged.

Finally, we construct the *antisymmetric product of four vectors*

$$T_{1234} = \sum (-1)^{\zeta} U_{\alpha} V_{\beta} W_{\gamma} X_{\delta} \tag{III-11}$$

where $\zeta = +1(-1)$ if $(\alpha\beta\gamma\delta)$ is an even (odd) permutation of (1234). This quantity is analogous to the triple product of three vectors in three dimensions; as in the three-dimensional case it is a pseudoscalar.

III-2 TRANSFORMATION PROPERTIES OF WAVE FUNCTIONS AND BILINEAR COMBINATIONS UNDER PROPER LORENTZ TRANSFORMATIONS

Wave Functions

First consider an infinitesimal rotation about the x axis. This case was already treated in Appendix I for nonrelativistic transformations, but is is instructive to consider it also from the relativistic standpoint. As was seen previously from (I-29), we have

$$\psi' = (1 + \tfrac{1}{2} i \epsilon \sigma_x) \psi \tag{III-12}$$

This equation also holds in the relativistic case, provided we define σ_x as a 4 × 4 matrix (cf. Appendix II-2, p. 318). Now σ_x can be expressed in terms of the γ matrices. For example, it is easily verified that $\gamma_2\gamma_3 = i\sigma_x$. Thus our wave function transforms as follows:

$$\psi' = (1 + \tfrac{1}{2}\epsilon\gamma_2\gamma_3)\psi \tag{III-13}$$

This result suggests that for a general infinitesimal proper Lorentz transformation of the form of Eq. III-3 we have

$$\psi' = (1 + \tfrac{1}{2}\epsilon\gamma_i\gamma_j)\psi \tag{III-14}$$

We can see this, in general, as follows: ψ satisfies the Dirac equation

$$\sum_\mu \gamma_\mu p_\mu \psi = im_0 c\psi \tag{III-15}$$

In terms of ψ' we have

$$\sum_\mu \gamma_\mu p_\mu (1 - \tfrac{1}{2}\epsilon\gamma_i\gamma_j)\psi' = im_0 c(1 - \tfrac{1}{2}\epsilon\gamma_i\gamma_j)\psi' \tag{III-16}$$

Multiplying both sides by $1 + \frac{1}{2}\epsilon\gamma_i\gamma_j$ on the left and making use of the commutation relations between γ matrices, we obtain

$$\sum_\mu \gamma_\mu p_\mu \psi' - \epsilon(\gamma_j p_i - \gamma_i p_j)\psi' = \sum_\mu \gamma_\mu p_\mu' \psi' = im_0 c\psi' \tag{III-17}$$

where

$$\begin{aligned} p_i' &= p_i + \epsilon p_j \\ p_j' &= p_j - \epsilon p_i \\ p_k' &= p_k \\ p_l' &= p_l \end{aligned} \tag{III-18}$$

The foregoing are merely the transformation properties of the momentum and coordinate components under Lorentz transformations. Note that in moving from the unprimed to the primed system, we should *not* alter the matrices themselves. These can be regarded as merely a device for writing the four equations coupling the components of ψ as a single matrix equation.

Adjoint Wave Functions

The Hermitean conjugate of the wave function is given by

$$\psi'^\dagger = [(1 + \tfrac{1}{2}\epsilon\gamma_i\gamma_j)\psi]^\dagger = \psi^\dagger[1 + \tfrac{1}{2}\epsilon^*\gamma_j^\dagger\gamma_i^\dagger] = \psi^\dagger[1 - \tfrac{1}{2}\epsilon^*\gamma_i\gamma_j] \tag{III-19}$$

Thus

$$\psi'^\dagger\psi' = \psi^\dagger[1 + \tfrac{1}{2}(\epsilon - \epsilon^*)\gamma_i\gamma_j]\psi \tag{III-20}$$

That is, $\psi^\dagger\psi$ is invariant under those Lorentz transformations for which ϵ is real. This is the case for rotations but not for pure Lorentz transformations. For pure Lorentz transformations ϵ is pure imaginary and $\psi^\dagger\psi$ is not invariant. Indeed, $\psi^\dagger\psi$ is not a scalar; rather it forms the fourth component of a four-vector:

$$\psi^\dagger\gamma_4\gamma_\mu\psi = \begin{pmatrix} -i\psi^\dagger\alpha_\mu\psi \\ \psi^\dagger\psi \end{pmatrix}, \qquad \begin{matrix} \mu = 1, 2, 3 \\ \mu = 4 \end{matrix} \tag{III-21}$$

On the other hand, if we define an adjoint wave function by

$$\tilde{\psi} = \psi^\dagger\gamma_4 \tag{III-22}$$

we can prove that $\tilde{\psi}\psi$ is indeed a scalar under *all* proper Lorentz transformations. Thus

$$\tilde{\psi}' = \psi'^\dagger\gamma_4 = \psi^\dagger(1 - \tfrac{1}{2}\epsilon^*\gamma_i\gamma_j)\gamma_4 = \psi^\dagger\gamma_4(1 \pm \tfrac{1}{2}\epsilon^*\gamma_i\gamma_j) \tag{III-23}$$

If both i and j equal 1, 2, or 3, the minus sign applies and ϵ is real. On the other hand, if either i or j equals 4, the plus sign applies, and $\epsilon^* = -\epsilon$. In *either* case we have

$$\tilde{\psi}' = \tilde{\psi}(1 - \tfrac{1}{2}\epsilon\gamma_i\gamma_j) \tag{III-24}$$

and thus

$$\tilde{\psi}'\psi' = \tilde{\psi}\psi \tag{III-25}$$

Bilinear Combinations

Based on the invariance properties just mentioned, we can investigate the transformation properties of bilinear combinations of wave functions. Therefore, analogous to the nonrelativistic case (Appendix I, p. 306), these bilinear combinations are defined by

$$\langle\hat{\mathrm{O}}\rangle = \tilde{\psi}\hat{\mathrm{O}}\psi \tag{III-26}$$

Then

$$\langle\hat{\mathrm{O}}'\rangle = \tilde{\psi}'\hat{\mathrm{O}}\psi' = \langle\hat{\mathrm{O}}\rangle + \tfrac{1}{2}\epsilon\langle[\hat{\mathrm{O}}, \gamma_i\gamma_j]_-\rangle \tag{III-27}$$

Thus matrix elements of γ_j transform among themselves just as the components of a four-vector do. For example,

$$\langle\gamma_j'\rangle = \langle\gamma_j\rangle - \epsilon\langle\gamma_i\rangle \tag{III-28}$$

On the other hand, we have seen that

$$p_j' = p_j - \epsilon p_i \tag{III-29}$$

It can be readily verified that

$$\sum_{\mu} \langle \gamma_\mu{}' p_\mu{}' \rangle = \sum_{\mu} \langle \gamma_\mu p_\mu \rangle \tag{III-30}$$

This proves that the Dirac equation is invariant under proper Lorentz transformations. The chirality equation $\gamma_5\psi = \pm\psi$ is invariant under such transformations, since

$$\langle \gamma_5{}' \rangle = \langle \gamma_5 \rangle + \tfrac{1}{2}\epsilon \langle [\gamma_5, \gamma_i\gamma_j]_- \rangle \tag{III-31}$$

and the commutator vanishes.

III-3 INVERSION OPERATIONS P, T, AND C

Space Inversion P

The Dirac equation can be written as

$$\sum \left(\gamma_\mu \frac{\partial}{\partial x_\mu} \right) \psi(\mathbf{r}) = -k_0 \psi(\mathbf{r}) \tag{III-32}$$

where

$$k_0 = \frac{m_0 c}{\hbar} \tag{III-33}$$

Now we replace x, y, z by $-x$, $-y$, $-z$ everywhere and obtain

$$\left(-\gamma_1 \frac{\partial}{\partial x_1} - \gamma_2 \frac{\partial}{\partial x_2} - \gamma_3 \frac{\partial}{\partial x_3} + \gamma_4 \frac{\partial}{\partial x_4} \right) \psi(-\mathbf{r}) = -k_0 \psi(-\mathbf{r}) \tag{III-34}$$

Suppose that the space-inverted wave function is of the form

$$P\psi(\mathbf{r}) = \rho_P \psi(-\mathbf{r}) \tag{III-35}$$

where ρ_P is some matrix involving only γ matrices. Then we have

$$\psi(-\mathbf{r}) = \rho_P^{-1} P \psi(\mathbf{r}) \tag{III-36}$$

and

$$\rho_P \left(-\gamma_1 \frac{\partial}{\partial x_1} - \gamma_2 \frac{\partial}{\partial x_2} - \gamma_3 \frac{\partial}{\partial x_3} + \gamma_4 \frac{\partial}{\partial x_4} \right) \rho_P^{-1} P\psi = -k_0 P\psi \tag{III-37}$$

This equation is equivalent to Eq. III-32, provided

$$\begin{aligned} \rho_P \gamma_i \rho_P^{-1} &= -\gamma_i, \qquad i = 1, 2, 3 \\ \rho_P \gamma_4 \rho_P^{-1} &= \gamma_4 \end{aligned} \tag{III-38}$$

which is satisfied only if $\rho_P = \gamma_4$ (apart from a possible phase factor). Thus $P\psi(\mathbf{r}) = \gamma_4\psi(-\mathbf{r})$ satisfies the Dirac equation: in other words, the Dirac equation is invariant under space inversion.

Proceeding exactly as in the nonrelativistic case, we can then show that the matrix elements of operators transform under space inversion as follows:

$$\langle \hat{\mathrm{O}}^P(\mathbf{r})\rangle = \langle \gamma_4 \hat{\mathrm{O}}(-\mathbf{r})\gamma_4\rangle \qquad \text{(III-39)}$$

In particular, we can derive

$$\langle x_i{}^P\rangle = -\langle x_i\rangle, \qquad i = 1, 2, 3 \qquad \text{(III-40a)}$$

$$\langle x_4{}^P\rangle = \langle x_4\rangle \qquad \text{(III-40b)}$$

$$\langle p_i{}^P\rangle = -\langle p_i\rangle \qquad i = 1, 2, 3 \qquad \text{(III-40c)}$$

$$\langle p_4{}^P\rangle = \langle p_4\rangle \qquad \text{(III-40d)}$$

That is, under space inversion the first three components of a vector change sign, but the fourth component does not. Similarly for the γ matrices we have

$$\langle \gamma_i{}^P\rangle = -\langle \gamma_i\rangle, \qquad i = 1, 2, 3 \qquad \text{(III-41a)}$$

$$\langle \gamma_4{}^P\rangle = \langle \gamma_4\rangle \qquad \text{(III-41b)}$$

Evidently, the quantity $\Sigma\gamma_\mu p_\mu$ and therefore the Dirac equation itself are invariant under space inversion. However, since γ_5 anticommutes with γ_4, it is clear that we have $\langle \gamma_5{}^P\rangle = -\langle \gamma_5\rangle$. Therefore $\langle\gamma_5\rangle$ is a pseudoscalar, and the *two-component neutrino equation is not invariant under space inversion.* In addition, the quantities $\langle \gamma_5\gamma_\mu\rangle$ transform as axial vectors; that is,

$$\langle (\gamma_5\gamma_i)^P\rangle = \langle \gamma_5\gamma_i\rangle, \qquad i = 1, 2, 3 \qquad \text{(III-42a)}$$

$$\langle (\gamma_5\gamma_4)^P\rangle = -\langle \gamma_5\gamma_4\rangle \qquad \text{(III-42b)}$$

The quantities $\langle \gamma_\mu\gamma_\nu - \gamma_\nu\gamma_\mu\rangle$ have the same transformation properties as $x_\mu x_\nu - x_\nu x_\mu$, and thus they form the six components of an antisymmetric tensor. In particular, since $i\sigma_x = \gamma_2\gamma_3$, for example, the components of spin are invariant under space inversion.

Time Reversal T

The operation of time reversal is essentially the same in the nonrelativistic case (see Appendix I-2, p. 310), namely,

$$T\psi(\mathbf{r}, t) = i\sigma_y\psi^*(\mathbf{r}, -t) \qquad \text{(III-43)}$$

where, of course, $i\sigma_y$ is now a 4×4 matrix.

In order to verify this relation explicitly, we express the Hamiltonian operator H in the Hamiltonian form of the Dirac equation:*

$$H(t)\psi(t) = \left(-\hbar i \sum_i \alpha_i \frac{\partial}{\partial x_i} + \beta m_0 c^2\right)\psi(t) \qquad \text{(III-44)}$$

Taking the complex conjugate of every term and changing t to $-t$ everywhere, we obtain

$$H^*(-t)\psi^*(-t) = \left(\hbar i \sum_i \alpha_i^* \frac{\partial}{\partial x_i} + \beta m_0 c^2\right)\psi^*(-t) \qquad \text{(III-45)}$$

Now suppose that

$$T\psi(t) = \rho_T \psi^*(-t) \qquad \text{(III-46)}$$

where ρ_T is some matrix involving only the γ matrices, just as for space inversion. Then

$$(\rho_T H^*(-t)\rho_T^{-1})T\psi = \rho_T\left(\hbar i \sum_i \alpha_i^* \frac{\partial}{\partial x_i} + \beta m_0 c^2\right)\rho_T^{-1}T\psi \qquad \text{(III-47)}$$

This is precisely of the original form, provided

$$\rho_T \alpha_i^* \rho_T^{-1} = -\alpha_i \qquad \text{(III-48a)}$$

$$\rho_T \beta \rho_T^{-1} = \beta \qquad \text{(III-48b)}$$

$$\rho_T H^*(-t)\rho_T^{-1} = H(t) \qquad \text{(III-48c)}$$

The only matrix which satisfies the first two conditions is (apart from a possible phase factor)

$$\rho_T = i\sigma_y \qquad \text{(III-49)}$$

Therefore our nonrelativistic results also hold in this case. In addition, if (as is usual) H does not depend explicitly on the time, it is invariant under time reversal, provided (cf. Eq. I-56)

$$\sigma_y H \sigma_y = H^* \qquad \text{(III-50)}$$

If the interaction commutes with σ_y, a condition which is satisfied by the weak interactions (since they involve products of the form $\boldsymbol{\sigma}_\mu \cdot \boldsymbol{\sigma}_\mu$ etc.), the condition for time reversal invariance is that H is real. On the other hand, the Dirac Hamiltonian is not real, that is, α_x and α_z are real but α_y is imaginary. However, it satisfies Eq. III-50 and thus it is also invariant under time reversal.

---

* Of course, H and ψ also depend on the coordinate **r**.

The matrix elements of γ_μ transform as follows:

$$\langle \gamma_\mu{}^T \rangle = \langle \sigma_y \gamma_\mu{}^* \sigma_y \rangle \tag{III-51}$$

Now σ_y commutes with γ_2 and γ_4 and anticommutes with γ_1 and γ_3. On the other hand, γ_2 and γ_4 are real, whereas γ_1 and γ_3 are pure imaginary. Thus we find, for all four components,

$$\langle \gamma_\mu{}^T \rangle = \langle \gamma_\mu \rangle \tag{III-52}$$

We also have

$$\left\langle \frac{\partial}{\partial x_\mu}^T (t) \right\rangle = \left\langle \frac{\partial}{\partial x_\mu} (-t) \right\rangle^* = \left\langle \frac{\partial}{\partial x_\mu} (t) \right\rangle \tag{III-53}$$

It follows, for example, that $\langle p_i{}^T \rangle = -\langle p_i \rangle$ for $i = 1, 2, 3$, but $\langle E^T \rangle = \langle E \rangle$ for the four components of the energy momentum vector. In addition, $\Sigma \gamma_\mu (\partial / \partial x_\mu)$ and the Dirac equation itself are invariant under time reversal. Finally, the two-component equation is invariant, for

$$\langle \gamma_5{}^T \rangle = \langle \sigma_y \gamma_5{}^* \sigma_y \rangle = \langle \gamma_5 \rangle \tag{III-54}$$

Charge Conjugation C

Consider one of the positive-energy wave functions given previously—for example, the wave function of a particle with spin along the z direction. The wave function for the normal particle with momentum p, $E > 0$, and $\sigma \uparrow$ is (cf. Eq. II-45)

$$\psi_\uparrow{}^+ = \frac{1}{(1 + \eta^2)^{1/2}} \begin{pmatrix} 1 \\ 0 \\ \eta p_z / p \\ \eta (p_x + i p_y)/p \end{pmatrix} \exp \left[\frac{i(\mathbf{p} \cdot \mathbf{r} - Et)}{\hbar} \right] \tag{III-55}$$

How can we construct a wave function of the corresponding antiparticle? This antiparticle would correspond to a particle with momentum, energy, and spin all reversed. Its wave function with momentum $-p$, $E < 0$ will be given by Eq. II-49, p. 321, with the sign of p reversed, that is, by

$$\psi_\downarrow{}^- = \frac{1}{(1 + \eta^2)^{1/2}} \begin{pmatrix} \eta (p_x - i p_y)/p \\ -\eta p_z / p \\ 0 \\ 1 \end{pmatrix} \exp \left[\frac{-i(\mathbf{p} \cdot \mathbf{r} - Et)}{\hbar} \right] \tag{III-56}$$

It is readily noted that the wave function for the antiparticle may be obtained in terms of the wave function for the normal particle by taking the complex conjugate and, in addition, turning the spinor upside down with some changes in sign. More precisely, we may formulate the transformation from the particle wave function ψ to the antiparticle wave function $C\psi$ by the following relation,

$$C\psi = -\gamma_2\psi^* \qquad \text{(III-57)}$$

where γ_2 is one of the γ matrices defined previously:

$$\gamma_2 = -i\beta\alpha_2 = \begin{pmatrix} 0 & 0 & 0 & -1 \\ 0 & 0 & 1 & 0 \\ 0 & 1 & 0 & 0 \\ -1 & 0 & 0 & 0 \end{pmatrix} \qquad \text{(III-58)}$$

The physical meaning of particle-antiparticle conjugation may also be illustrated by considering Eq. III-32, the Dirac equation. For a charged particle this equation, in covariant form, is

$$\sum \gamma_\mu\left(\frac{\partial}{\partial x_\mu} - \frac{ie}{\hbar c}A_\mu\right)\psi = -k_0\psi \qquad \text{(III-59)}$$

where A_μ are the components of the vector potential. Let us take the complex conjugate of this equation. Now γ_1 and γ_3 are purely imaginary, whereas γ_2 and γ_4 are real. The fourth components of $\partial/\partial x_\mu$ and A_μ, namely

$$\frac{\partial}{\partial x_4} = -\frac{i}{c}\frac{\partial}{\partial t} \quad \text{and} \quad A_4 = i\phi$$

are imaginary, but the first three components are real, Thus we obtain

$$\sum \epsilon_i\gamma_i\left(\frac{\partial}{\partial x_i} + \frac{ie}{\hbar c}A_i\right)\psi^* = -k_0\psi^* \qquad \text{(III-60)}$$

where

$$\epsilon_i = 1 \quad \text{for} \quad i = 2$$
$$= -1 \quad\quad = 1,3,4$$

In terms of the charge-conjugated wave function we have

$$\psi^* = -\gamma_2 C\psi \qquad \text{(III-61)}$$

Substituting this result into Eq. III-60 and multiplying by $-\gamma_2$ on the left, we find

$$\gamma_2 \sum \epsilon_i \gamma_i \left(\frac{\partial}{\partial x_i} + \frac{ie}{\hbar c} A_i\right) \gamma_2 C\psi = -k_0 C\psi \qquad \text{(III-62)}$$

and since $\gamma_2 \gamma_i \gamma_2 = \epsilon_i \gamma_i$, we obtain

$$\sum \gamma_i \left(\frac{\partial}{\partial x_i} + \frac{ie}{\hbar c} A_i\right) C\psi = -k_0 C\psi \qquad \text{(III-63)}$$

Therefore the charge-conjugated equation obeys the Dirac equation, but the sign of the charge is reversed.

On the other hand, the two-component equation $\gamma_5 \psi = \pm\psi$ is not invariant under C, and, in fact, it transforms in exactly the same way as under space inversion:

$$\langle \gamma_s{}^C \rangle = \langle \gamma_2 \gamma_s{}^* \gamma_2 \rangle = -\langle \gamma_s \rangle \qquad \text{(III-64)}$$

However, this equation is invariant under the combined *CP* operation.

The CPT Operation

We have shown that the Dirac equation is invariant under Lorentz transformations, space inversion, time reversal, and charge conjugation. As far as we know, the classical laws of motion, classical electromagnetic theory, quantum electrodynamics, and very likely the strong nuclear interactions are all invariant under each of these operations. The invariance of these interactions under Lorentz transformations is the direct consequence of our fundamental conception that there should be no preferred direction in space. Nevertheless, there is no *a priori* reason for expecting that any arbitrary theory should be invariant under the other operations; and, in fact, it is now known that the β decay interaction is not invariant under space inversion. However, there is an important operation of interest, namely, that of the combined *CPT* operation. Since the Dirac equation is invariant under each of these operations separately, it must be invariant under the combined operation. Moreover, there is a general theorem which states that *any* reasonable field theory obeying a wide class of conditions —that is, Lorentz invariance and "locality"—must also be invariant under *CPT*.

Using our previous definitions of the effect of these operations, namely

$$P\psi(\mathbf{r}, t) = \gamma_4\psi(-\mathbf{r}, t) \qquad \text{(III-65)}$$

$$T\psi(\mathbf{r}, t) = i\sigma_y\psi^*(\mathbf{r}, -t) \qquad \text{(III-66)}$$

$$C\psi(\mathbf{r}, t) = -\gamma_2\psi^*(\mathbf{r}, t) \qquad \text{(III-67)}$$

we see that

$$CPT\psi(\mathbf{r}, t) = \gamma_5\psi(-\mathbf{r}, -t) \qquad \text{(III-68)}$$

The order of the operations is irrelevant. Under the *CPT* operation any operator transforms as follows:

$$\langle \hat{O}^{CPT}(\mathbf{r}, t)\rangle = \langle \gamma_5\hat{O}(-\mathbf{r}, -t)\gamma_5\rangle \qquad \text{(III-69)}$$

It is significant that both the Dirac and Weyl equations are invariant under *CPT*.

APPENDIX IV

Simple Derivations for Allowed Transitions

According to the discussion in Chaps. 2 and 3, the general expression for the energy distribution of an allowed β spectrum is

$$N(E) = (2\pi^3\hbar^7c^5)^{-1}F(\pm Z, E)H_{fi}^2 pE(E_0 - E)^2\, dE \qquad \text{(IV-1)}$$

where H_{fi} is the matrix element of the interaction and $F(\pm Z, E)$ is a Coulomb correction factor (for $\beta^{\mp}$ decay).

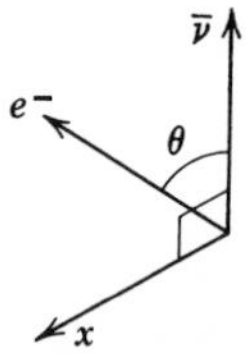

Fig. IV-1 Momentum diagram for e and $\bar{\nu}$ in β decay.

IV-1 VECTOR INTERACTION

e-$\bar{\nu}$ Angular Correlation for Vector Interaction

If we take the vector interaction as an example and consider only the even coupling—that is, the parity-conserving one—contributing, then the β-decay matrix element equals

$$H_{fi} = g_V \int 1\ \psi_e{}^{\dagger}\psi_{\nu} \qquad \text{(IV-2)}$$

where ψ refers to the lepton wave functions at the origin. We must sum the square of H_{fi} over all possible spin directions of the e and ν, that is,

$$|\mathrm{H}_{fi}|^2 = g_V{}^2 \left|\int 1\right|^2 \sum_{\substack{\sigma_e \\ E_e>0}} \sum_{\substack{\sigma_\nu \\ E_\nu<0}} |\psi_e{}^{\dagger}\psi_\nu|^2 \qquad \text{(IV-3)}$$

Suppose that the $\bar{\nu}$ is emitted along the z axis, and the electron moves in the xz plane with its momentum at an angle θ with the z axis. Then the absorbed ν comes from the opposite direction. This is illustrated in Fig. IV-1.

The Dirac wave function of the electron in the two possible spin states (cf. Eqs. II-45, II-46) are given as follows:

$$\psi_{e\uparrow} = \frac{1}{(1+\eta^2)^{1/2}}\begin{pmatrix} 1 \\ 0 \\ \eta\cos\theta \\ \eta\sin\theta \end{pmatrix}, \quad \psi_{e\downarrow} = \frac{1}{(1+\eta^2)^{1/2}}\begin{pmatrix} 0 \\ 1 \\ \eta\sin\theta \\ -\eta\cos\theta \end{pmatrix} \tag{IV-4}$$

where

$$\eta = \frac{cp_e}{E_e + m_e c^2} \tag{IV-5}$$

An antineutrino moving along the positive z axis corresponds to a negative-energy neutrino moving along the negative z axis (with direction of spin reversed). The appropriate neutrino wave functions can be obtained from Eq. II-55 by changing the sign of the first two components:

$$\psi_{\nu\uparrow(\bar\nu\downarrow)} = \frac{1}{\sqrt{2}}\begin{pmatrix} 1 \\ 0 \\ 1 \\ 0 \end{pmatrix}, \qquad \psi_{\nu\downarrow(\bar\nu\uparrow)} = \frac{1}{\sqrt{2}}\begin{pmatrix} 0 \\ -1 \\ 0 \\ 1 \end{pmatrix} \tag{IV-6}$$

Thus

$$(\psi_e^\dagger\psi_\nu)_{\uparrow\uparrow} = -(\psi_e^\dagger\psi_\nu)_{\downarrow\downarrow} = [2(1+\eta^2)]^{-1/2}(1+\eta\cos\theta) \tag{IV-7}$$

$$(\psi_e^\dagger\psi_\nu)_{\uparrow\downarrow} = (\psi_e^\dagger\psi_\nu)_{\downarrow\uparrow} = [2(1+\eta^2)]^{-1/2}\,\eta\sin\theta \tag{IV-8}$$

$$\sum_\sigma |\psi_e^\dagger\psi_\nu|^2 = \frac{(1+\eta\cos\theta)^2 + (\eta\sin\theta)^2}{1+\eta^2} \tag{IV-9}$$

$$= 1 + \frac{2\eta}{1+\eta^2}\cos\theta \tag{IV-10}$$

$$= 1 + \frac{cp_e}{E_e}\cos\theta \tag{IV-11}$$

$$= 1 + \frac{v_e}{c}\cos\theta \tag{IV-12}$$

Owing to rotational invariance, this result for the angular correlation between electron and antineutrino holds quite generally if the angle between the momenta of these particles is θ, even when the $\bar\nu$ is not emitted along the z axis.

Polarization of Neutrinos

Suppose that the neutrino is described by a two-component theory. Under these circumstances we no longer have parity conservation. The neutrino must be polarized in a definite direction. Therefore we must sum only over states with one given polarization of the neutrino, say right-handed helicity. It turns out that the angular correlation is not altered by adopting the two-component theory of neutrinos. This is to be expected, since the electron-neutrino correlation is a scalar.

It is of interest, however, to study this point in more detail. Let us express the interaction in terms of even and odd couplings. Thus we write

$$H_{fi} = \frac{1}{\sqrt{2}} \int 1\, \psi_e^{\dagger}(g_V + g_V'\gamma_5)\psi_\nu \tag{IV-13}$$

(The factor of $1/\sqrt{2}$ will guarantee that the results for scalar quantities will be the same for $g_V' = g_V$ as in the parity-conserving theory with g_V only.) We do *not*, however, require that the two-component neutrino theory holds, that is, g_V' may not be equal to $\pm g_V$.

If the $\bar{\nu}$ has its spin "up" ($\uparrow$), the ν must have spin down ($\downarrow$) and vice versa. Now, since the neutrino obeys the chirality equation $\gamma_5\psi_\nu = \mp\psi_\nu$ for spin up and down and $E_\nu < 0$ (see Appendix II-5), we find that

$$(g_V + g_V'\gamma_5)\psi_{\nu\downarrow} = (g_V + g_V')\psi_{\nu\downarrow} \tag{IV-14a}$$

$$(g_V + g_V'\gamma_5)\psi_{\nu\uparrow} = (g_V - g_V')\psi_{\nu\uparrow} \tag{IV-14b}$$

Thus

$$\sum_\sigma H_{fi}^2 = \tfrac{1}{2}[(g_V + g_V')^2 + (g_V - g_V')^2] \times \frac{(1 + \eta\cos\theta)^2 + (\eta\sin\theta)^2}{2(1+\eta^2)} \left|\int 1\right|^2 \tag{IV-15}$$

$$= \tfrac{1}{2}(g_V^2 + g_V'^2)\left(1 + \frac{v_e}{c}\cos\theta\right)\left|\int 1\right|^2 \tag{IV-16}$$

which is the same as in the parity-conserving theory, except for replacement of g_V^2 by $\frac{1}{2}(g_V^2 + g_V'^2)$. The ratio of the probabilities that the *antineutrino* has a spin directed up or down equals

$$\frac{|g_V + g_V'|^2}{|g_V - g_V'|^2} \tag{IV-17}$$

If $g_V' = g_V$, the $\bar{\nu}$ must always be polarized "upward", that is, along its direction of motion. In general, the polarization of the $\bar{\nu}$ is given by

$$\mathscr{P}_{\bar{\nu}} = \frac{N_\uparrow - N_\downarrow}{N_\uparrow + N_\downarrow} = \frac{2g_V g_V'}{g_V^2 + g_V'^2} \qquad \text{(IV-18)}$$

Of course, if $g_V = 0$ or $g_V' = 0$, equal numbers of antineutrinos are polarized up and down. Thus there is no net polarization for a β interaction of even or odd coupling *alone*. However, when parity is not conserved in the β interaction—that is, in the presence of *both* even and odd couplings—the antineutrino emitted is polarized.

The Polarization of the Emitted Electrons

If the electron moves along the z direction, its wave function is given by Eq. II-47:

$$\psi_{e\uparrow} = \frac{1}{(1+\eta^2)^{1/2}}\begin{pmatrix}1\\0\\\eta\\0\end{pmatrix}, \qquad \psi_{e\downarrow} = \frac{1}{(1+\eta^2)^{1/2}}\begin{pmatrix}0\\1\\0\\-\eta\end{pmatrix} \qquad \text{(IV-19)}$$

The lepton covariant is

$$\psi_e^\dagger(g_V + g_V'\gamma_5)\psi_\nu = [\psi_\nu^\dagger(g_V + g_V'\gamma_5)\psi_e]^\dagger \qquad \text{(IV-20)}$$

Since

$$(g_V + g_V'\gamma_5)\psi_{e\uparrow} = (1+\eta^2)^{-1/2}\begin{pmatrix}g_V - g_V'\eta\\0\\-g_V' + g_V\eta\\0\end{pmatrix} \qquad \text{(IV-21)}$$

and

$$(g_V + g_V'\gamma_5)\psi_{e\downarrow} = (1+\eta^2)^{-1/2}\begin{pmatrix}0\\g_V + g_V'\eta\\0\\-g_V' - g_V\eta\end{pmatrix} \qquad \text{(IV-22)}$$

the relative probability that the electron is spinning up or down is given by

$$(g_V \mp g_V'\eta)^2 + (g_V' \mp g_V\eta)^2 = (g_V^2 + g_V'^2)(1+\eta^2) \mp 4g_V g_V'\eta \qquad \text{(IV-23)}$$

Thus the electron polarization is

$$\mathscr{P}_{e^-} = -\frac{2g_V g_V'}{g_V^2 + g_V'^2}\frac{2\eta}{1+\eta^2} = -\frac{v_e}{c}\mathscr{P}_{\bar{\nu}} \qquad \text{(IV-24)}$$

For positrons, the sign of the polarization is reversed (see discussion below). As $v_e \to c$,

$$\mathscr{P}_{e^-} \to \mp 1 \qquad \text{for} \qquad g_V' = \pm g_V \qquad \text{(IV-25)}$$

For relativistic electrons, the polarization is nearly complete. However, because of its finite rest mass, the electrons can never be completely polarized. This may be seen by making a Lorentz transformation to a new reference frame in which the electron velocity is reversed. However, in this new frame the spin direction and the energy are unchanged; therefore the polarization $\boldsymbol{\sigma} \cdot \mathbf{p}/p$ will be reversed, which means that the electron polarization cannot be invariant under Lorentz transformations. On the other hand, since the neutrinos move with the velocity of light, they will do so with respect to *any* reference frame, and the neutrino polarization is invariant under Lorentz transformations.

Transformation of Coupling Constants under Charge Conjugation

The sign of the lepton polarizations is opposite for β^- and β^+ decay, which follows from the fact that the $g_V + g_V'\gamma_5$ interaction for β^- decay becomes $g_V - g_V'\gamma_5$ when expressed in terms of positron and antineutrino wave functions; this is usually done for β^+ decay.

The lepton covariant for β^- decay can be written as $\psi_e^\dagger \hat{O} \psi_\nu$, but conventionally for β^+ decay we must write it as $\psi_{e+}^\dagger \hat{O}' \psi_{\bar{\nu}}$, where $\hat{O}'$ may now differ from $\hat{O}$. To obtain the relation between $\hat{O}'$ and $\hat{O}$ we consider the behavior of the covariant under charge conjugation. In Appendix III it is shown that the wave function of a particle and its antiparticle are related by

$$\psi_\nu = -\gamma_2 \psi_{\bar{\nu}}^* \qquad \text{(IV-26)}$$

where * denotes complex conjugate. Thus we find that

$$\psi_e^\dagger \hat{O} \psi_\nu = [(\psi_{e+}^\dagger)^* \gamma_2 \hat{O} \gamma_2 \psi_{\bar{\nu}}^*] = \psi_{e+}^\dagger \gamma_2 \hat{O}^* \gamma_2 \psi_{\bar{\nu}} \qquad \text{(IV-27)}$$

where we have used the fact that both the covariant and γ_2 are real. Since this must be equal to $\psi_{e+}^\dagger \hat{O}' \psi_{\bar{\nu}}$, it follows that

$$\hat{O}' = \gamma_2 \hat{O}^* \gamma_2 \qquad \text{(IV-28)}$$

The covariants for g_V and $g_V'\gamma_5$ differ merely by the presence of a factor γ_5 in $\hat{O}$. It is clear, however, that

$$(\gamma_5\hat{O})' = \gamma_2(\gamma_5\hat{O})^*\gamma_2 = -\gamma_5\gamma_2\hat{O}^*\gamma_2 = -\gamma_5\hat{O}' \qquad \text{(IV-29)}$$

that is, the g_V and $g_V'\gamma_5$ lepton covariants transform *oppositely* under charge conjugation. Thus the $g_V + g_V'\gamma_5$ interaction for β^- decay becomes $g_V - g_V'\gamma_5$ when applied to β^+ decay with the e^+ and $\bar{\nu}$ treated as the basic leptons. The same argument can also be applied to the other interactions in β decay, e.g., $g_A + g_A'\gamma_5$, and also to an arbitrary combination of vector and axial-vector interactions. The lepton covariants for the V and A terms differ merely by the presence of a factor γ_5. Thus a $V - \lambda A$ combination for β^- decay is effectively $V + \lambda A$ for β^+ decay.

IV-2 APPLICATION OF TRACE METHOD AND PROJECTION OPERATORS

The Trace Method

The foregoing calculations involving summation over spins can be greatly simplified by using the so-called "trace method." First consider the matrix element of H which can be written as the bilinear combination

$$H = \psi_e^\dagger \hat{O} \psi_\nu \qquad \text{(IV-30)}$$

where $\hat{O}$ is some hermitian operator, $\hat{O}^\dagger = \hat{O}$. We wish to calculate

$$|H_{fi}|^2 = \sum_{\substack{\sigma_e \\ E_e>0}} \sum_{\substack{\sigma_\nu \\ E_\nu<0}} H_{fi}^2 \qquad \text{(IV-31)}$$

Since

$$H_{fi}^2 = \psi_e^\dagger \hat{O}\psi_\nu(\psi_e^\dagger \hat{O}\psi_\nu)^* = \psi_e^\dagger \hat{O}\psi_\nu\psi_\nu^\dagger \hat{O}\psi_e \qquad \text{(IV-32)}$$

this can be written in the form AB, where

$$\left.\begin{aligned} A &= \psi_e^\dagger && \text{(4 columns, 1 row)} \\ B &= \hat{O}\psi_\nu\psi_\nu^\dagger\hat{O}\psi_e && \text{(4 rows, 1 column)} \end{aligned}\right. \qquad \text{(IV-33)}$$

The matrices A and B do not commute; $AB \neq BA$. In fact, AB is merely a number, but BA is a 4×4 matrix.

Now let us define the trace

$$\mathrm{Tr}\,\phi = \sum_i \phi_{ii} \qquad \text{(IV-34)}$$

which has a very important property, namely,

$$\mathrm{Tr}\,(AB) = \sum_i \sum_k A_{ik}B_{ki} = \mathrm{Tr}\,(BA) \tag{IV-35}$$

Since AB is merely a number, it equals

$$AB = \mathrm{Tr}\,(AB) \tag{IV-36}$$

Consequently,

$$H_{fi}^2 = AB = \mathrm{Tr}\,(BA) = \mathrm{Tr}\,(\hat{O}\psi_\nu\psi_\nu^\dagger\hat{O}\psi_e\psi_e^\dagger) \tag{IV-37}$$

and

$$|H_{fi}|^2 = \mathrm{Tr}\left[\hat{O}\sum_{E_\nu<0}(\psi_\nu\psi_\nu^\dagger)\hat{O}\sum_{E_e>0}(\psi_e\psi_e^\dagger)\right] \tag{IV-38}$$

Suppose for the moment that the sum goes over *all* states including both positive- and negative-energy states. It can then be verified that for our Dirac wave functions (and, in fact, quite generally)

$$\sum_{\sigma,E}\psi\psi^\dagger = I = \begin{pmatrix} 1 & & & \\ & 1 & & \\ & & 1 & \\ & & & 1 \end{pmatrix} \tag{IV-39}$$

This is the well-known "closure" property of wave functions. Therefore in this case we would have

$$|H_{fi}|^2 = \mathrm{Tr}\,(\hat{O}I\hat{O}I) = \mathrm{Tr}\,(\hat{O}\hat{O}) \tag{IV-40}$$

Since operator BA is a 4×4 matrix, it is a linear combination of the Dirac matrices 1, α_μ, β, γ_5, and products thereof. There are altogether sixteen linearly independent Dirac matrices. In fact, any of these sixteen matrices can be written as

$$\alpha_x^\lambda\alpha_y^\mu\alpha_z^\nu\beta^\tau \tag{IV-41}$$

where λ, μ, ν, $\tau = 0$ or 1.

The sixteen matrices together with their transformation properties are listed in Table IV-1. If any matrix appears twice in the combination, this combination can always be reduced to one with order of two fewer in the index by using commutation relations of the Dirac matrices. Of course, there may then be a change of sign; for instance

$$\alpha_x\beta\alpha_x = -\beta \tag{IV-42}$$

Table IV-1 Sixteen Linearly Independent Dirac Matrices and Their Transformation Properties When Interposed between $\tilde{\psi}$ $(= \psi^\dagger \beta)$ and ψ

Type		Independent Number of Each Type	Transformation Properties
Dirac Matrices	Gamma Matrices		
I	I	1	Scalar
β $\beta\alpha_1, \beta\alpha_y, \beta\alpha_z$	γ_μ	4	Vector
$\alpha_x, \alpha_y, \alpha_z$ $\sigma_x = -i\alpha_y\alpha_z$ $\sigma_y = -i\alpha_z\alpha_x$ $\sigma_z = -i\alpha_x\alpha_y$	$\gamma_\mu\gamma_\nu$ $(\mu \neq \mu)$	6	Tensor of second rank
$\beta\sigma_x = -i\beta\alpha_y\alpha_z$ $\beta\sigma_y = -i\beta\alpha_z\alpha_x$ $\beta\sigma_z = -i\beta\alpha_x\alpha_y$ $\beta\gamma_5 = i\beta\alpha_x\alpha_y\alpha_z$	$\gamma_\mu\gamma_\nu\gamma_\lambda$ $\mu \neq \nu, \lambda \neq \mu$ $\nu \neq \lambda$	4	Axial vector
$\gamma_5 = i\alpha_x\alpha_y\alpha_z$	$\gamma_1\gamma_2\gamma_3\gamma_4$	1	Pseudoscalar

Furthermore, it turns out that the trace of any of these sixteen matrices except I vanishes, that is,

$$\operatorname{Tr} \alpha_\mu = \operatorname{Tr} \beta = \operatorname{Tr} \alpha_\mu \alpha_{\nu \neq \mu} = \cdots = 0 \tag{IV-43}$$

But

$$\operatorname{Tr} I = 4 \tag{IV-44}$$

Then it can be seen clearly that if *any* α or β occurs an odd number of times in the matrix, its trace equals zero. This feature simplifies calculations considerably. We may readily eliminate from the matrix element those terms for which the trace vanishes. Sometimes this may be accomplished merely by inspection without any further calculation.

Projection Operators

GENERAL FORM. We wish to sum only over states of the desired energy, that is, positive energy for electrons and negative energy for neutrinos. To accomplish this, we introduce projection operators Λ, which have the property that they project into the sum range only those parts that are needed. These operators can be symbolically represented by

$$\Lambda_e^+\psi_e = \psi_e \quad \text{for} \quad E_e > 0 \qquad\qquad 0 \quad E_e < 0 \tag{IV-45}$$

$$\Lambda_\nu^-\psi_\nu = 0 \quad \text{for} \quad E_\nu > 0 \qquad\qquad \psi_\nu \quad E_\nu < 0 \tag{IV-46}$$

Then

$$\sum_{\sigma,E_e>0} \psi_e\psi_e^\dagger = \sum_{\sigma,E_e} \Lambda_e^+\psi_e\psi_e^\dagger = \Lambda_e^+\sum_{\sigma,E_e}\psi_e\psi_e^\dagger = \Lambda_e^+ \tag{IV-47}$$

where we used the closure property of wave functions,

$$\sum_{\sigma,E_e} \psi_e\psi_e^\dagger = I \tag{IV-48}$$

Similarly,

$$\sum_{\sigma,E_\nu<0} \psi_\nu\psi_\nu^\dagger = \Lambda_\nu^- \tag{IV-49}$$

for the neutrino wave functions. Thus

$$|H_{fi}|^2 = \text{Tr}\,(\hat{O}\Lambda_\nu^-\hat{O}\Lambda_e^+) \tag{IV-50}$$

EXPLICIT EXPRESSIONS. The Dirac equation can be written as follows*:

$$(c\boldsymbol{\alpha}\cdot\mathbf{p}_e + \beta m_ec^2)\psi_e^+ = |E_e|\,\psi_e^+ \tag{IV-51}$$

$$(c\boldsymbol{\alpha}\cdot\mathbf{p}_e + \beta m_ec^2)\psi_e^- = -\,|E_e|\,\psi_e^-$$

Suppose now that we construct the operator:

$$\Lambda_e^+ = \frac{c\boldsymbol{\alpha}\cdot\mathbf{p}_e + \beta m_ec^2 + |E_e|}{2\,|E_e|} = \frac{1}{2}\left(1 + \frac{\beta m_ec^2}{|E_e|} + \frac{\boldsymbol{\alpha}\cdot\mathbf{v}_e}{c}\right) \tag{IV-52}$$

Let it act on ψ_e^+:

$$\Lambda_e^+\psi_e^+ = \frac{1}{2\,|E_e|}\,[(c\boldsymbol{\alpha}\cdot\mathbf{p}_e + \beta m_ec^2)\psi_e^+ + |E_e|\,\psi_e^+] \tag{IV-53}$$

$$= \frac{|E_e| + |E_e|}{2\,|E_e|}\,\psi_e^+ = \psi_e^+$$

When it operates on ψ_e^- it gives

$$\Lambda_e^+\psi_e^- = \frac{-|E_e| + |E_e|}{2\,|E_e|}\,\psi_e^- = 0 \tag{IV-54}$$

---

* ψ_e^+ specifies positive energy, whereas $\psi_e^\dagger$ means Hermitean conjugate.

Therefore this operator has the desired properties for Λ_e^+. Similarly,

$$\Lambda_\nu^- = \frac{c\boldsymbol{\alpha}\cdot\mathbf{p}_\nu - |E_\nu|}{-2\,|E_\nu|} = \frac{1}{2}\left(1 - \frac{\boldsymbol{\alpha}\cdot\mathbf{v}_\nu}{c}\right) = \frac{1}{2}\left(1 + \frac{\boldsymbol{\alpha}\cdot\mathbf{v}_{\bar\nu}}{c}\right) \qquad \text{(IV-55)}$$

e-$\bar\nu$ Angular Correlation for Vector Interaction

For the vector interaction, $\hat{O} = I$. Thus

$$|H_{fi}|^2 = \mathrm{Tr}\,(\Lambda_\nu^-\Lambda_e^+) = \tfrac{1}{4}\,\mathrm{Tr}\left[\left(1 + \frac{\boldsymbol{\alpha}\cdot\mathbf{v}_{\bar\nu}}{c}\right)\left(1 + \frac{\beta m_e c^2}{|E_e|} + \frac{\boldsymbol{\alpha}\cdot\mathbf{v}_e}{c}\right)\right] \qquad \text{(IV-56)}$$

By inspection, the only terms not containing an odd number of α or β are $I\cdot I$ and $(\boldsymbol{\alpha}\cdot\mathbf{v}_{\bar\nu})(\boldsymbol{\alpha}\cdot\mathbf{v}_e)$. Now we have

$$(\boldsymbol{\alpha}\cdot\mathbf{v}_{\bar\nu})(\boldsymbol{\alpha}\cdot\mathbf{v}_e) = (\boldsymbol{\sigma}\cdot\mathbf{v}_{\bar\nu})(\boldsymbol{\sigma}\cdot\mathbf{v}_e) \qquad \text{(IV-57)}$$

By using the commutation relations for σ matrices, it is readily verified that

$$(\boldsymbol{\sigma}\cdot\mathbf{v}_{\bar\nu})(\boldsymbol{\sigma}\cdot\mathbf{v}_e) = (\mathbf{v}_{\bar\nu}\cdot\mathbf{v}_e) + i(\boldsymbol{\sigma}\cdot\mathbf{v}_{\bar\nu}\times\mathbf{v}_e) \qquad \text{(IV-58)}$$

But

$$\mathrm{Tr}\,\sigma_i = 0 \qquad \text{(IV-59)}$$

Therefore we obtain

$$|H_{fi}|^2 = 1 + \frac{\mathbf{v}_{\bar\nu}\cdot\mathbf{v}_e}{c^2} = 1 + \frac{v_e}{c}\cos\theta_{e,\bar\nu} \qquad \text{(IV-60)}$$

which is exactly the same expression that we obtained previously.

Now we shall use the method of traces to show that the results are not changed by the existence of parity-nonconserving terms in the interaction. For example, for the vector interaction we obtain

$$|H_{fi}|^2 = \tfrac{1}{2}\,\mathrm{Tr}\,[(g_V + g_V'\gamma_5)\Lambda_\nu^-(g_V + g_V'\gamma_5)\Lambda_e^+] \qquad \text{(IV-61)}$$

Now γ_5 commutes with α_i, and thus with Λ_ν^-; consequently,

$$\begin{aligned}|H_{fi}|^2 &= \tfrac{1}{2}\,\mathrm{Tr}\,[(g_V + g_V'\gamma_5)^2\Lambda_\nu^-\Lambda_e^+] \\ &= \tfrac{1}{2}\,\mathrm{Tr}\,[(g_V^2 + g_V'^2 + 2g_Vg_V'\gamma_5)\Lambda_\nu^-\Lambda_e^+]\end{aligned} \qquad \text{(IV-62)}$$

The first two terms give the same result as before, but the third term gives 0 because

$$\mathrm{Tr}\,\gamma_5 = \mathrm{Tr}\,(i\alpha_x\alpha_y\alpha_z\beta) = 0 \qquad \text{(IV-63)}$$

and also

$$\mathrm{Tr}\,(\gamma_5\alpha_i) = \mathrm{Tr}\,(\gamma_5\sigma_i) = \mathrm{Tr}\,(\gamma_5\beta) = 0 \qquad \text{(IV-64)}$$

IV-3 SCALAR INTERACTIONS AND FIERZ INTERFERENCE

For a scalar interaction there is an extra factor β in the lepton covariant. The expressions for quantities of interest are similar to those for a vector interaction, except for some changes in sign.

Lepton Polarization

For a combination of even and odd couplings the matrix element is given by

$$H_{fi} = \frac{1}{\sqrt{2}} \int 1 \; \psi_e^{\dagger} \beta (g_S + g_S' \gamma_5) \psi_\nu \tag{IV-65}$$

The expression for the neutrino (and antineutrino) polarization is the same as that of Eq. IV-18 (p. 341) for a vector interaction, with $g_V \to g_S$, $g_V' \to g_S'$. However, for the electron we rewrite Eq. IV-65 as

$$H_{fi} = \frac{1}{\sqrt{2}} \int 1 \left[\int \psi_\nu^{\dagger} \beta (g_S - g_S' \gamma_5) \psi_e \right]^* \tag{IV-66}$$

Comparing this with Eq. IV-20, we see that the electron polarization will now have opposite sign; that is, for a scalar interaction,

$$\mathscr{P}_{e^-} = \frac{v_e}{c} \mathscr{P}_{\bar{\nu}} \tag{IV-67}$$

Historically, the electron polarization was measured first and found to be negative $\approx -v_e/c$. This requires

$$g_V' = g_V \qquad \text{for a vector interaction}$$

$$g_S' = -g_S \qquad \text{for a scalar interaction}$$

The neutrino polarizations for *these* two interactions are, of course, opposite in sign.

e-$\bar{\nu}$ Correlation

For a scalar interaction we have (assuming parity conservation)

$$|H_{fi}|^2 = \mathrm{Tr}\,(\beta \Lambda_\nu^- \beta \Lambda_e^+) \tag{IV-68}$$

Using the commutation rule for the Dirac matrices, we see that this is the same as $|H_{fi}|^2$ for the vector interaction (see Eq. IV-56), except that the direction of the neutrino momentum is reversed Thus

$$|H_{fi}|^2 = 1 - \frac{v_e}{c}\cos\theta_{e,\bar{\nu}} \tag{IV-69}$$

Mixed S and V Interaction

If both S and V appear in the β interaction, we obtain the extra term

$$2g_Sg_V \operatorname{Tr}(\beta\Lambda_\nu^{-}\Lambda_e^{+}) = 2g_Sg_V\frac{m_ec^2}{E_e} \tag{IV-70}$$

in the Hamiltonian. This is the Fierz interference term.

IV-4 GAMOW-TELLER INTERACTIONS

For Gamow-Teller interactions, the explicit summations over all possible spin states are extremely tedious. However, if the trace method is used, the calculations are only slightly more complicated than for a Fermi interaction.

Lepton Polarizations for Axial-Vector Interaction

For a combination of even and odd couplings, the matrix element is

$$H_{fi} = \frac{1}{\sqrt{2}}\sum_\mu \int \sigma_\mu \cdot \psi_e^{\dagger}\sigma_\mu(g_A + g_A'\gamma_5)\psi_\nu \tag{IV-71}$$

and, since the σ_μ commute with γ_5,

$$H_{fi} = \frac{1}{\sqrt{2}}\sum_\mu \int \sigma_\mu \cdot [\psi_\nu^{\dagger}\sigma_\mu(g_A + g_A'\gamma_5)\psi_e]^* \tag{IV-72}$$

Thus all lepton polarizations are given by the same expressions as for a vector interaction, provided we replace g_V by g_A and g_V' by g_A'.

e-$\bar{\nu}$ Correlation for Axial-Vector Interaction

If $g_A' = 0$ (for which we compensate by removing the factor $1/\sqrt{2}$), Eq. IV-72 reduces to

$$H_{fi} = g_A\sum_\mu \int \sigma_\mu \cdot \psi_e^{\dagger}\sigma_\mu\psi_\nu \tag{IV-73}$$

$$|H_{fi}|^2 = g_A^2\sum_\mu\sum_\eta \int \sigma_\mu\left(\int\sigma_\eta\right)^* \psi_e^{\dagger}\sigma_\mu\psi_\nu(\psi_e^{\dagger}\sigma_\eta\psi_\nu)^* \tag{IV-74}$$

Assume that the nuclei are not polarized. Then, averaging over the nuclear spin direction, we find by rotational invariance that

$$\int \sigma_\mu \int \sigma_\eta^* = 0 \qquad \text{if} \quad \mu \neq \eta \tag{IV-75}$$

that is, $\int \sigma_x \int \sigma_z = 0$. On the other hand,

$$\left|\int \boldsymbol{\sigma}\right|^2 = \left|\int \sigma_x\right|^2 + \left|\int \sigma_y\right|^2 + \left|\int \sigma_z\right|^2 \tag{IV-76}$$

$$\left|\int \sigma_\mu\right|^2 = \tfrac{1}{3}\left|\int \boldsymbol{\sigma}\right|^2 \tag{IV-77}$$

We then have

$$|H_{fi}|^2 = \tfrac{1}{3} g_A^2 \left|\int \boldsymbol{\sigma}\right|^2 \sum_\mu (\psi_e^\dagger \sigma_\mu \psi_\nu)^2 \tag{IV-78}$$

$$= \tfrac{1}{3} g_A^2 \left|\int \boldsymbol{\sigma}\right|^2 \operatorname{Tr}\left(\sum_\mu \sigma_\mu \Lambda_\nu^- \sigma_\mu \Lambda_e^+\right) \tag{IV-79}$$

Substituting in Λ_ν^- and Λ_e^+, we find

$$\sum_\mu \sigma_\mu \Lambda_\nu^- \sigma_\mu \Lambda_e^+ = \frac{1}{4} \sum_\mu \left[\sigma_\mu \left(1 + \frac{\boldsymbol{\alpha} \cdot \mathbf{v}_{\bar{\nu}}}{c}\right) \sigma_\mu \left(1 + \frac{\beta m_e c^2}{|E_e|} + \frac{\boldsymbol{\alpha} \cdot \mathbf{v}_e}{c}\right)\right] \tag{IV-80}$$

Now

$$\sum_\mu \sigma_\mu \sigma_\mu = 3 \tag{IV-81}$$

$$\begin{aligned} \sum_\mu \sigma_\mu \alpha_x \sigma_\mu &= \sigma_x \alpha_x \sigma_x + \sigma_y \alpha_x \sigma_y + \sigma_z \alpha_x \sigma_z \\ &= \alpha_x - \alpha_x - \alpha_x \\ &= -\alpha_x \end{aligned} \tag{IV-82}$$

Thus

$$\sum_\mu \sigma_\mu (\boldsymbol{\alpha} \cdot \mathbf{v}_{\bar{\nu}}) \sigma_\mu = -(\boldsymbol{\alpha} \cdot \mathbf{v}_{\bar{\nu}}) \tag{IV-83}$$

$$\sum_\mu \sigma_\mu \Lambda_\nu^- \sigma_\mu \Lambda_e^+ = \frac{1}{4}\left(3 - \frac{\boldsymbol{\alpha} \cdot \mathbf{v}_\nu}{c}\right)\left(1 + \frac{\beta m_e c^2}{E_e} + \frac{\boldsymbol{\alpha} \cdot \mathbf{v}_e}{c}\right) \tag{IV-84}$$

Taking the trace, we find

$$\operatorname{Tr}\left(\sum_\mu \sigma_\mu \Lambda_\nu^- \sigma_\mu \Lambda_e^+\right) = 3 - \frac{\mathbf{v}_{\bar{\nu}} \cdot \mathbf{v}_e}{c^2} \tag{IV-85}$$

and finally

$$|H_{fi}|^2 = g_A^2 \left|\int \boldsymbol{\sigma}\right|^2 \left(1 - \frac{1}{3} \frac{v_e}{c} \cos \theta_{e,\bar{\nu}}\right) \tag{IV-86}$$

General Combination of Interactions

For a tensor interaction the results are the same for the axial-vector interaction, except that the sign of the v/c term is reversed. Finally, consider a β interaction which is a linear combination of the forms S, V, T, and A. The only interference terms which occur are the Fierz terms between S and V and between T and A. By rotational invariance it may be readily shown that cross terms between Gamow-Teller and Fermi interactions vanish, at least for unpolarized nuclei. Averaging over all directions.we find for $\beta^{\mp}$ decay

$$|H_{fi}|^2 = (g_S^2 + g_V^2) \left(\left|\int 1\right|^2 + (g_T^2 + g_A^2) \right) \left|\int \boldsymbol{\sigma}\right|^2 \pm \frac{2m_e c^2}{E_e}\left(g_S g_V \left|\int 1\right|^2 + g_T g_A \left|\int \boldsymbol{\sigma}\right|^2\right) \quad \text{(IV-87)}$$

and the electron-neutrino angular correlation is given by

$$1 + a\frac{v_e}{c}\cos\theta_{e,\nu} \quad \text{(IV-88)}$$

where

$$a = \frac{(g_V^2 - g_S^2)\left|\int 1\right|^2 + \frac{1}{3}(g_T^2 - g_A^2)\left|\int \boldsymbol{\sigma}\right|^2}{(g_V^2 + g_S^2)\left|\int 1\right|^2 + (g_T^2 + g_A^2)\left|\int \boldsymbol{\sigma}\right|^2} \quad \text{(IV-89)}$$

Calculation of Gamow-Teller Matrix Element According to Single-Particle Model

The Gamow-Teller matrix element for a β^- transition is given by

$$\langle \psi_f^+ \left| \sum_i \sigma_\mu(i) Q^+(i) \right| \psi_i \rangle$$

where ψ_i and ψ_f denote, respectively, the initial and final state of the nucleus, and Q^+ changes a neutron n into a proton p.

According to the single-particle model, the two wave functions differ only with respect to the state of a single nucleon. We assume a $j \rightarrow j$ transition.

In order to calculate $|\int \boldsymbol{\sigma}|^2$, which is proportional to the β-decay transition probability, we must, of course, sum over the azimuthal quantum number m_f of the final state and over the Cartesian components μ of $\sigma_\mu (\mu = x, y, z)$.

For decay of unpolarized nuclei, rotational invariance requires that $|\int \boldsymbol{\sigma}|^2$ be independent of the azimuthal quantum number m_i of the initial state.

Thus we have

$$\left| \int \boldsymbol{\sigma} \right|^2 = \sum_\mu \sum_{m_f} \langle \psi_{\mathrm{p}}^{m_f} | \sigma_\mu Q^+ | \psi_{\mathrm{n}}^{m_i} \rangle^2 \tag{V-1}$$

where m_i is fixed and n and p specify the wave function of the nucleon in initial and final state. For β^+ decay we must of course interchange n and p and replace Q^+ by Q^-, but the rest of the argument and the conclusions remain unchanged.

Our assumption that j is a good quantum number implies that

$$\mathbf{j} = \mathbf{l} + \mathbf{s} \tag{V-2}$$

is a constant of the motion. Using the vector model, we can then write

$$\sigma_\mu = \frac{2(\mathbf{s} \cdot \mathbf{j})}{\mathbf{j} \cdot \mathbf{j}} j_\mu = \frac{\mathbf{j} \cdot \mathbf{j} + \mathbf{s} \cdot \mathbf{s} - \mathbf{l} \cdot \mathbf{l}}{\mathbf{j} \cdot \mathbf{j}} j_\mu = \frac{j(j+1) + \frac{3}{4} - l(l+1)}{j(j+1)} j_\mu \tag{V-3}$$

and

$$\sigma_\mu = Dj_\mu \tag{V-4}$$

where

$$D = j^{-1} \qquad \text{for} \quad j = l + \tfrac{1}{2} \tag{V-5a}$$

$$D = -(j+1)^{-1} \qquad \text{for} \quad j = l - \tfrac{1}{2} \tag{V-5b}$$

Substituting into Eq. V-1 we obtain

$$\left|\int \boldsymbol{\sigma}\right|^2 = D^2 \sum_\mu \sum_{m_f} \langle \psi_{\rm p}^{m_f} | j_\mu Q^+ | \psi_{\rm n}^{m_i} \rangle^2 \tag{V-6}$$

We can extend the sum m_f over *all* states of the proton (denoted by f) without changing the results. (All the final states with j or spatial wave function *different* from the initial state will contribute vanishing matrix elements since j_μ connects only states of the same j and spatial wave function.)

Thus

$$\left|\int \boldsymbol{\sigma}\right|^2 = D^2 \sum_\mu \langle \psi_{\rm n}^{m_i} | Q^- j_\mu | \sum_{\text{All } f} \psi_{\rm p}^{f} \rangle \langle \psi_{\rm p}^{f} | j_\mu Q^+ | \psi_{\rm n}^{m_i} \rangle \tag{V-7}$$

Next we use closure, which gives

$$\begin{aligned} \left|\int \boldsymbol{\sigma}\right|^2 &= D^2 \sum_\mu \langle \psi_{\rm n}^{m_i} | Q^- j_\mu j_\mu Q^+ | \psi_{\rm n}^{m_i} \rangle \\ &= D^2 \langle \psi_{\rm n}^{m_i} | \sum_\mu j_\mu{}^2 | \psi_{\rm n}^{m_i} \rangle \\ &= D^2 \langle \psi_{\rm n}^{m_i} | j^2 | \psi_{\rm n}^{m_i} \rangle \\ &= D^2 j(j+1) \end{aligned} \tag{V-8}$$

Substituting the value of D from Eq. V-5, we obtain the final result

$$\begin{aligned} \left|\int \boldsymbol{\sigma}\right|^2 &= \frac{j+1}{j} \qquad \text{for} \quad j = l + \tfrac{1}{2} \\ &= \frac{j}{j+1} \qquad \text{for} \quad j = l - \tfrac{1}{2} \end{aligned} \tag{V-9}$$

Beta Decay of Polarized Nuclei

Let us consider here β emission from polarized nuclei. We shall assume that the interaction is a mixture of V and A, that the two-component neutrino theory holds ($g_i' = g_i$), and also that the rest mass of the electron can be neglected in comparison with its energy, that is, that $v_e = c$. In this limit the electron is completely polarized opposite to its direction of motion while the antineutrino is polarized along its direction of motion.

VI-1 LEPTON WAVE FUNCTIONS

As is shown in Chap. 4, under the foregoing assumptions the leading (allowed) terms in the β-decay Hamiltonian density can be written as follows:

$$\mathscr{H} = \frac{g_V}{\sqrt{2}} \psi_f^\dagger \psi_i \psi_e^\dagger (1 + \gamma_5)\psi_\nu + \frac{g_A}{\sqrt{2}} \psi_f^\dagger \boldsymbol{\sigma} \psi_i \psi_e^\dagger \boldsymbol{\sigma}(1 + \gamma_5)\psi_\nu \qquad \text{(VI-1)}$$

The four-component wave functions ψ may be expressed in terms of two-component Pauli spinors χ (cf. Appendix II-3, p. 324). Thus

$$\chi = \begin{pmatrix} 1 \\ 0 \end{pmatrix} \quad \text{or} \quad \begin{pmatrix} 0 \\ 1 \end{pmatrix}$$

for $s_z = \frac{1}{2}$ and $-\frac{1}{2}$, respectively:

$$\psi_i = \begin{pmatrix} \chi_i \\ 0 \end{pmatrix}, \qquad \psi_f = \begin{pmatrix} \chi_f \\ 0 \end{pmatrix}$$
$$\psi_e = \frac{1}{\sqrt{2}}\begin{pmatrix} \chi_e \\ -\chi_e \end{pmatrix}, \qquad \psi_\nu = \frac{1}{\sqrt{2}}\begin{pmatrix} -\chi_\nu \\ \chi_\nu \end{pmatrix} \qquad \text{(VI-2)}$$

and

$$\begin{aligned} \mathscr{H} &= -\sqrt{2} g_V \chi_f^\dagger \chi_i \chi_e^\dagger \chi_\nu - \sqrt{2} g_A \chi_f^\dagger \boldsymbol{\sigma} \chi_i \chi_e^\dagger \boldsymbol{\sigma} \chi_\nu \\ &= \sqrt{2} g_V(-\chi_f^\dagger \chi_i \chi_e^\dagger \chi_\nu + \lambda \chi_f^\dagger \boldsymbol{\sigma} \chi_i \chi_e^\dagger \boldsymbol{\sigma} \chi_\nu) \end{aligned} \qquad \text{(VI-3)}$$

where

$$\lambda = -\frac{g_A}{g_V} \tag{VI-4}$$

(If, on the other hand, the electron energy is small compared to its rest mass, such as in low-energy β emission or in K capture, we have

$$\psi_e = \begin{pmatrix} \chi_e \\ 0 \end{pmatrix}$$

The result will be the same as Eq. VI-3 except that there is no factor $\sqrt{2}$.) For an electron traveling with its spin pointing along an axis characterized by the polar angles θ_σ, φ_σ, we have

$$\chi_\sigma = \begin{pmatrix} \cos \frac{1}{2}\theta_\sigma \\ \sin \frac{1}{2}\theta_\sigma e^{i\varphi_\sigma} \end{pmatrix} \tag{VI-5}$$

which may be verified by computing the expectation values of σ_x, σ_y, and σ_z. Thus, for example,

$$\chi_\sigma^\dagger \sigma_x \chi_\sigma = 2 \cos \tfrac{1}{2}\theta_\sigma \sin \tfrac{1}{2}\theta_\sigma \cos \varphi_\sigma = \sin \theta_\sigma \cos \varphi_\sigma \tag{VI-6}$$

The spin function corresponding to spin along the opposite direction is orthogonal to χ_σ. Thus

$$\chi_{-\sigma} = \begin{pmatrix} -\sin \frac{1}{2}\theta_\sigma e^{-i\varphi_\sigma} \\ \cos \frac{1}{2}\theta_\sigma \end{pmatrix} \tag{VI-7}$$

Hence the spinor for an electron moving in the direction θ_e, φ_e, with $\boldsymbol{\sigma} \cdot \hat{\mathbf{p}} = -1$, is

$$\chi_e = \begin{pmatrix} -\sin \frac{1}{2}\theta_e e^{-i\varphi_e} \\ \cos \frac{1}{2}\theta_e \end{pmatrix} \tag{VI-8}$$

The wave function χ_σ is the correct one for a negative-energy neutrino traveling in the direction θ_σ, φ_σ. We can, however, express this wave function in terms of the angles of the corresponding antineutrino, which are the angles of physical interest. Thus we have

$$\begin{aligned} \theta_{\bar{\nu}} &= \pi - \theta_\nu \\ \varphi_{\bar{\nu}} &= \pi + \varphi_\nu \end{aligned} \tag{VI-9}$$

Substituting these values into Eq. VI-5, we find

$$\chi_\nu = \begin{pmatrix} \sin \frac{1}{2}\theta_{\bar{\nu}} \\ -\cos \frac{1}{2}\theta_{\bar{\nu}} e^{i\varphi_{\bar{\nu}}} \end{pmatrix} \tag{VI-10}$$

VI-2 0 → 0 TRANSITION

If we have a $0 \to 0$ transition, then $\int \boldsymbol{\sigma} = 0$, so that we have

$$\mathscr{H} = -\sqrt{2} g_V \chi_f^{\dagger} \chi_i \chi_e^{\dagger} \chi_\nu \tag{VI-11}$$

$$H_{fi}^2 = 2 g_V^2 \left| \int 1 \right|^2 |\chi_e^{\dagger} \chi_\nu|^2 \tag{VI-12}$$

Note that we do not have to sum over spins. This is an example of a calculation which is *simpler* in the two-component neutrino theory than in the parity-conserving theory!

Substituting Eqs. VI-8 and VI-10 for the foregoing wave functions into Eq. VI-12, we find

$$H_{fi}^2 = 2 g_V^2 \left| \int 1 \right|^2 |-\sin \tfrac{1}{2}\theta_e \sin \tfrac{1}{2}\theta_{\bar{\nu}} e^{i\varphi_e} - \cos \tfrac{1}{2}\theta_e \cos \tfrac{1}{2}\theta_{\bar{\nu}} e^{i\varphi_{\bar{\nu}}}|^2 \tag{VI-13}$$

$$= 2 g_V^2 \left| \int 1 \right|^2 [\sin^2 \tfrac{1}{2}\theta_e \sin^2 \tfrac{1}{2}\theta_{\bar{\nu}} + \cos^2 \tfrac{1}{2}\theta_e \cos^2 \tfrac{1}{2}\theta_{\bar{\nu}} + 2 \sin \tfrac{1}{2}\theta_e \cos \tfrac{1}{2}\theta_e \sin \tfrac{1}{2}\theta_{\bar{\nu}} \cos \tfrac{1}{2}\theta_{\bar{\nu}} \cos (\varphi_e - \varphi_{\bar{\nu}})] \tag{VI-14}$$

By using elementary trigonometric relations, this can be put into the form

$$H_{fi}^2 = g_V^2 \left| \int 1 \right|^2 [1 + \cos \theta_e \cos \theta_{\bar{\nu}} + \sin \theta_e \sin \theta_{\bar{\nu}} \cos (\varphi_e - \varphi_{\bar{\nu}})] \tag{VI-15}$$

$$= g_V^2 \left| \int 1 \right|^2 (1 + \cos \theta_{e\bar{\nu}}) \tag{VI-16}$$

Equation VI-16 may be recognized as the special case of angular correlation $1 + a \cos \theta_{e\bar{\nu}}$ where $a = 1$ (the correct result for the vector interaction and $v = c$), as we have shown in Appendix IV. In addition, since there is no nuclear spin, the electron angular distribution is isotropic.

VI-3 $I \to I - 1$ TRANSITION

Let us now consider a transition in which the total angular momentum changes; specifically we treat an $I \to I - 1$ transition. The Co^{60} decay is of this type. Since such a transition involves an angular momentum change of 1, it is a Gamow-Teller transition, so that the Fermi matrix element $\int 1$ must vanish. We shall calculate the angular distribution of the emitted antineutrino and electron. For simplicity let us consider the case where $M_i = I_{zi} = I_i$. For this special case we must have $M_f = I_f = I_i - 1$. We may make use of the "raising" and "lowering" operators σ_+ and σ_- to simplify the calculations considerably. We can write

$$\int \boldsymbol{\sigma} \cdot \psi_e^\dagger \boldsymbol{\sigma} \psi_\nu = \int \sigma_z \cdot \psi_e^\dagger \sigma_z \psi_\nu + \int \sigma_+ \cdot \psi_e^\dagger \sigma_- \psi_\nu + \int \sigma_- \cdot \psi_e^\dagger \sigma_+ \psi_\nu \quad \text{(VI-17)}$$

where

$$\sigma_+ = \frac{1}{\sqrt{2}}(\sigma_x + i\sigma_y) = \begin{pmatrix} 0 & \sqrt{2} \\ 0 & 0 \end{pmatrix} \quad \text{(VI-18a)}$$

$$\sigma_- = \frac{1}{\sqrt{2}}(\sigma_x - i\sigma_y) = \begin{pmatrix} 0 & 0 \\ \sqrt{2} & 0 \end{pmatrix} \quad \text{(VI-18b)}$$

Since we know that χ_f has an M value lower by 1 than χ_i, we see that only the last term does not vanish. Thus $\mathscr{H}$ becomes

$$\mathscr{H} = \sqrt{2} g_V \lambda \chi_f^\dagger \sigma_- \chi_i \chi_e^\dagger \sigma_+ \chi_\nu \quad \text{(VI-19)}$$

If we write

$$\chi_e = \begin{pmatrix} \chi_e^{(1)} \\ \chi_e^{(2)} \end{pmatrix}, \qquad \chi_\nu = \begin{pmatrix} \chi_\nu^{(1)} \\ \chi_\nu^{(2)} \end{pmatrix} \quad \text{(VI-20)}$$

then

$$\mathscr{H} = 2 g_V \lambda \chi_f^\dagger \sigma_- \chi_i (\chi_e^{(1)})^* \chi_\nu^{(2)} \quad \text{(VI-21)}$$

But

$$(\chi_e^{(1)})^* \chi_\nu^{(2)} = \sin \tfrac{1}{2}\theta_e \cos \tfrac{1}{2}\theta_{\bar{\nu}} e^{i(\varphi_e + \varphi_{\bar{\nu}})} \quad \text{(VI-22)}$$

Thus for $M_i = I$ we obtain

$$H_{fi}^2 = 4 g_V{}^2 \lambda^2 \left| \int \sigma_- \right|^2 \sin^2 \tfrac{1}{2}\theta_e \cos^2 \tfrac{1}{2}\theta_{\bar{\nu}} \quad \text{(VI-23)}$$

or

$$H_{fi}^2 = g_V{}^2 \lambda^2 \left| \int \sigma_- \right|^2 (1 - \cos \theta_e)(1 + \cos \theta_{\bar{\nu}}) \quad \text{(VI-24)}$$

The angles are all measured with respect to the spin direction of the nucleus.

If we had begun with the nuclear magnetic quantum number $M_i = -I_i$, we would have found that the only nonzero term would be

$\int \sigma_+ \cdot \psi_e{}^\dagger \sigma_- \psi_\nu$ instead of $\int \sigma_- \cdot \psi_e{}^\dagger \sigma_+ \psi_\nu$. Carrying this through, we now find

$$H_{fi}^2 = g_V{}^2 \lambda^2 \left| \int \sigma_+ \right|^2 (1 + \cos \theta_e)(1 - \cos \theta_{\bar{\nu}}) \tag{VI-25}$$

In order to generalize these expressions to the more general case in which $M_i \neq \pm I_i$—that is, not all the nuclei are oriented parallel along the z-axis—we note that the two previous expressions can be combined to read

$$H_{fi}^2 = g_V{}^2 \lambda^2 \left| \int \sigma_\mp \right|^2 \left[1 - \cos \theta_e \cos \theta_{\bar{\nu}} - \frac{M_i}{I_i} (\cos \theta_e - \cos \theta_{\bar{\nu}}) \right] \tag{VI-26}$$

where $\pm$ corresponds to $M_i = \pm I_i$. A plausible generalization (which can be derived rigorously) would then be

$$H_{fi}^2 = g_V{}^2 \lambda^2 \left| \int \boldsymbol{\sigma} \right|^2 \left[1 - \cos \theta_e \cos \theta_{\bar{\nu}} - \frac{\langle I_z \rangle_i}{I_i} (\cos \theta_e - \cos \theta_{\bar{\nu}}) \right] \tag{VI-27}$$

The nuclear matrix element $|\int \boldsymbol{\sigma}|^2$ is given by

$$\left| \int \boldsymbol{\sigma} \right|^2 = \sum_{M_f} \left| \int \chi_f{}^\dagger \sigma_\mu \chi_i \right|^2 \tag{VI-28}$$

independent of the value of M_i (cf. Appendix V):

$$\left| \int \boldsymbol{\sigma} \right|^2 = \left| \int \chi_f{}^\dagger \sigma_z \chi_i \right|^2 + \left| \int \chi_f{}^\dagger \sigma_+ \chi_i \right|^2 + \left| \int \chi_f{}^\dagger \sigma_- \chi_i \right|^2 \tag{VI-29}$$

where for each term only one M_f value appears—M_i for σ_z and $M_i \pm 1$ for $\sigma_\pm$. If we choose $M_i = I_i$, the first two terms vanish, as M_f must $\leq I_f = I_i - 1$, and we obtain

$$\left| \int \boldsymbol{\sigma} \right|^2 = \left| \int \chi_f{}^\dagger \sigma_- \chi_i \right|^2 \tag{VI-30}$$

However, we are interested here only in the angular correlation which is independent of the value of $|\int \boldsymbol{\sigma}|^2$.

If we observe only the emitted electrons, we must average over the antineutrino direction. Thus, since $\langle \cos \theta_{\bar{\nu}} \rangle = 0$, we find that the angular distribution of the electrons is

$$1 - \frac{\langle I_z \rangle_i}{I_i} \cos \theta_e \tag{VI-31}$$

which corresponds to backward peaking for $\langle I_z \rangle_i > 0$. The antineutrino distribution is

$$1 + \frac{\langle I_z \rangle_i}{I_i} \cos \theta_{\bar{\nu}} \tag{VI-32}$$

which is forward-peaked. If we use the two-component theory of the neutrino as we have done, it is easy to see physically why this must be so. For an $I \to I - 1$ transition, the electron and antineutrino must each carry off $+\frac{1}{2}$ unit of angular momentum with the same direction. Now since $\boldsymbol{\sigma} \cdot \mathbf{p} = p$ for the antineutrino (spin parallel to its momentum) and $\boldsymbol{\sigma} \cdot \mathbf{p} = -p$ for the electron (spin antiparallel to its momentum), we see that the particles must be preferentially emitted in the foregoing manner, that is, antineutrinos parallel to I and electrons antiparallel, in order to conserve angular momentum.

If we have unpolarized nuclei, $\langle I_z \rangle_i = 0$, the angular distribution will be

$$1 - \cos \theta_e \cos \theta_{\bar{\nu}} \tag{VI-33}$$

If we use the vector addition theorem in the form

$$\cos \theta_{\bar{\nu}} = \cos \theta_{e\bar{\nu}} \cos \theta_e + \sin \theta_{e\bar{\nu}} \sin \theta_e \cos (\varphi_{e\bar{\nu}} - \varphi_e) \tag{VI-34}$$

and average over both θ_e and φ_e, we find, since

$$\langle \cos \theta_e \sin \theta_e \rangle = 0, \qquad \langle \cos^2 \theta_e \rangle = \tfrac{1}{3} \tag{VI-35}$$

that

$$H_{fi}^2 = g^2 \lambda^2 \left| \int \boldsymbol{\sigma} \right|^2 (1 - \tfrac{1}{3} \cos \theta_{e\bar{\nu}}) \tag{VI-36}$$

which is the result derived previously in Appendix IV, p. 350, for the axial-vector interaction.

IV-4 BETA DECAY OF THE NEUTRON ($\frac{1}{2} \to \frac{1}{2}$)

Now consider the β decay of the neutron. For this case the β-decay Hamiltonian density becomes

$$\mathscr{H} = \sqrt{2} g_V \left(-\chi_p{}^{\dagger} \chi_n \chi_e{}^{\dagger} \chi_\nu + \lambda \sum_{\mu} \chi_p{}^{\dagger} \sigma_\mu \chi_n \chi_e{}^{\dagger} \sigma_\mu \chi_\nu \right) \tag{VI-37}$$

Since both the neutron and proton have spin $\frac{1}{2}$, there are two possible final states which must be summed over. The proton spin may be parallel to the neutron (no spin flip) or it may be antiparallel (spin flip). Thus suppose that the neutron has its spin directed upward. Then

$$|H_{fi}|^2 = |H_{\uparrow\uparrow}|^2 + |H_{\downarrow\uparrow}|^2 \tag{VI-38}$$

For the special case of neutron decay the nuclear matrix elements can be evaluated exactly. Let us first compute the matrix element corresponding to no spin flip. In this case we must have

$$\int 1 = 1, \quad \int \sigma_+ = 0, \quad \int \sigma_- = 0, \quad \int \sigma_z = 1 \tag{VI-39}$$

so that

$$H_{\uparrow\uparrow} = \sqrt{2} g_V(-\chi_e^{\dagger}\chi_\nu + \lambda\chi_e^{\dagger}\sigma_z\chi_\nu) \tag{VI-40}$$

which becomes upon inserting the spinors and squaring

$$\begin{aligned} |H_{\uparrow\uparrow}|^2 = 2g_V^2\{&(1-\lambda)(1-\lambda^*)\sin^2\tfrac{1}{2}\theta_e \sin^2\tfrac{1}{2}\theta_{\bar\nu} \\ &+ (1+\lambda)(1+\lambda^*)\cos^2\tfrac{1}{2}\theta_e\cos^2\tfrac{1}{2}\theta_{\bar\nu} \\ &+ 2\,\mathrm{Re}\,[(1+\lambda^*)(1-\lambda)e^{i(\varphi_e-\varphi_{\bar\nu})}]\sin\tfrac{1}{2}\theta_e\cos\tfrac{1}{2}\theta_e\sin\tfrac{1}{2}\theta_{\bar\nu}\cos\tfrac{1}{2}\theta_{\bar\nu}\} \end{aligned} \tag{VI-41}$$

where

$$z = \mathrm{Re}\, z + i\,\mathrm{Im}\, z$$

Using elementary trigonometry and the relation

$$\mathrm{Re}\,[(1+\lambda^*)(1-\lambda)e^{i\varphi}] = (1-|\lambda|^2)\cos\varphi + 2\,\mathrm{Im}\,\lambda\sin\varphi \tag{VI-42}$$

we find

$$\begin{aligned} |H_{\uparrow\uparrow}|^2 = g_V^2\{&(1+|\lambda|^2)(1+\cos\theta_e\cos\theta_{\bar\nu}) \\ &+ (1-|\lambda|^2)[\sin\theta_e\sin\theta_{\bar\nu}\cos(\varphi_e-\varphi_{\bar\nu})] \\ &+ 2\,\mathrm{Re}\,\lambda(\cos\theta_e+\cos\theta_{\bar\nu}) \\ &+ 2\,\mathrm{Im}\,\lambda[\sin\theta_e\sin\theta_{\bar\nu}\sin(\varphi_e-\varphi_{\bar\nu})]\} \end{aligned} \tag{VI-43}$$

Since

$$\cos\theta_e\cos\theta_{\bar\nu} + \sin\theta_e\sin\theta_{\bar\nu}\cos(\varphi_e-\varphi_{\bar\nu}) = \cos\theta_{e\bar\nu} \tag{VI-44}$$

and

$$\sin\theta_e\sin\theta_{\bar\nu}\sin(\varphi_e-\varphi_{\bar\nu}) = -\cos\theta_{e\times\bar\nu} \tag{VI-45}$$

Eq. VI-43 can be rewritten as

$$\begin{aligned} H_{\uparrow\uparrow}|^2 = g_V^2[&1+|\lambda|^2+2|\lambda|^2\cos\theta_e\cos\theta_{\bar\nu}+(1-|\lambda|^2)\cos\theta_{e\bar\nu} \\ &+ 2\,\mathrm{Re}\,\lambda(\cos\theta_e+\cos\theta_{\bar\nu}) - 2\,\mathrm{Im}\,\lambda\cos\theta_{e\times\bar\nu}] \end{aligned} \tag{VI-46}$$

Next, we must evaluate $|H_{\downarrow\uparrow}|^2$. Since there is a spin flip, only the term $\int\sigma_-\int\sigma_+$ in Eq. VI-17 can contribute,

$$\int 1 = \int \sigma_+ = \int \sigma_z = 0, \qquad \int \sigma_- = \sqrt{2} \tag{VI-47}$$

and therefore

$$H_{\downarrow\uparrow} = 2g_V\lambda\chi_e^{\dagger}\sigma_+\chi_\nu \tag{VI-48}$$

Inserting the lepton spinors and squaring, we obtain, as in Eq. VI-24,

$$|H_{\downarrow\uparrow}|^2 = 2g_V^2\,|\lambda|^2(1 - \cos\theta_e + \cos\theta_{\bar{\nu}} - \cos\theta_e\cos\theta_{\bar{\nu}}) \tag{VI-49}$$

We may now add the two contributions, obtaining

$$\begin{aligned} |H_{fi}|^2 &= |H_{\uparrow\uparrow}|^2 + |H_{\downarrow\uparrow}| \\ &\quad g_V^2[1 + 3\,|\lambda|^2 + 2(\mathrm{Re}\,\lambda - |\lambda|^2)\cos\theta_e + 2(\mathrm{Re}\,\lambda + |\lambda|^2)\cos\theta_{\bar{\nu}} \\ &\qquad + (1 - |\lambda|^2)\cos\theta_{e\bar{\nu}} - 2\,\mathrm{Im}\,\lambda\cos\theta_{e\times\bar{\nu}}] \end{aligned} \tag{VI-50}$$

More detailed calculations (Ja-57) show that this form for $|H|^2$ is valid with slight modifications even when $v_e < c$ and $g_i' \neq g_i$. In this case we find that

$$|H_{fi}|^2 = \xi\left[1 + a\frac{\mathbf{v}_e\cdot\mathbf{v}_{\bar{\nu}}}{c^2} + A\frac{\mathbf{v}_e\cdot\mathbf{I}_i}{c} + B\frac{\mathbf{v}_\nu\cdot\mathbf{I}_i}{c} + D\frac{\mathbf{v}_e\times\mathbf{v}_{\bar{\nu}}\cdot\mathbf{I}_i}{c^2}\right] \tag{VI-51}$$

where

$$\xi = \tfrac{1}{2}[|g_V|^2 + |g_V'|^2 + 3|g_A|^2 + 3|g_A'|^2] \tag{VI-52a}$$

$$a\xi = \tfrac{1}{2}[|g_V|^2 + |g_V'|^2 - |g_A|^2 - |g_A'|^2] \tag{VI-52b}$$

$$A\xi = [-\mathrm{Re}\,(g_Vg_A'^* + g_V'g_A^*) \mp (g_Ag_A'^* + g_A'g_A^*)] \tag{VI-52c}$$

$$B\xi = [-\mathrm{Re}\,(g_Vg_A'^* + g_V'g_A^*) \pm (g_Ag_A'^* + g_A'g_A^*)[\tag{VI-52d}$$

$$D\xi = -\mathrm{Im}\,(g_Vg_A'^* + g_V'g_A^*) \tag{VI-52e}$$

for $\beta^{\mp}$decay. For β^- decay with maximum parity violation, $g_i' = g_i$, Eqs. VI-52a-e reduce to

$$\xi = g_V^2[1 + 3\,|\lambda|^2] \tag{VI-53a}$$

$$a\xi = g_V^2[1 - |\lambda|^2] \tag{VI-53b}$$

$$A\xi = 2g_V^2[\mathrm{Re}\,\lambda - |\lambda|^2] \tag{VI-53c}$$

$$B\xi = 2g_V^2[\mathrm{Re}\,\lambda + |\lambda|^2] \tag{VI-53d}$$

$$D\xi = -2g_V^2\,\mathrm{Im}\,\lambda \tag{VI-53e}$$

where λ is given by Eq. VI-4.

APPENDIX VII

Properties of Muon Decay

For convenience let us work with the decay

$$\mu^- \rightarrow e^- + \nu_\mu + \bar{\nu}_e \tag{VII-1}$$

and use the *CPT* theorem to convert those results into those for the μ^+ decay. From the *CPT* theorem we know that when all particles are replaced by their antiparticles, all quantities remain unchanged except the spins which are everywhere reversed.

VII-1 INTERACTION MATRIX ELEMENT

The process is written as

$$\mu^- + \nu_e \rightarrow \nu_\mu + e^- \tag{VII-2}$$

by analogy with the β-decay process

$$\mathrm{n} + \nu \rightarrow \mathrm{p} + e^- \tag{VII-3}$$

We assume that the β interaction is $V - A$ with maximum parity violation:

$$g_V' = g_V = -g_A' = -g_A = g_\mu \tag{VII-4}$$

Then, as shown in Sec. 7-1, p. 252, the Hamiltonian density is given by

$$\mathscr{H} = \frac{1}{\sqrt{2}} g_\mu \sum_\mu \tilde{\psi}_{\nu_\mu}\gamma_\mu(1 + \gamma_5)\psi_\mu\tilde{\psi}_e\gamma_\mu(1 + \gamma_5)\psi_{\nu_e} \tag{VII-5}$$

(No confusion should arise because of the double use of the subscript μ to represent both summation indices and the muon spinor.) Then

$$(1 + \gamma_5)\psi_{\nu_e} = 2\psi_{\nu_e} \tag{VII-6}$$

In addition,

$$\tilde{\psi}_{\nu_\mu}\gamma_\mu(1 + \gamma_5) = \psi_{\nu_\mu}^{\dagger}\gamma_4(1 - \gamma_5)\gamma_\mu = \psi_{\nu_\mu}^{\dagger}(1 + \gamma_5)\gamma_4\gamma_\mu = 2\tilde{\psi}_{\nu_\mu}\gamma_\mu \tag{VII-7}$$

Thus we obtain

$$\mathscr{H} = \sqrt{8}g_\mu \sum_\mu \tilde{\psi}_{\nu_\mu}\gamma_\mu\psi_\mu\tilde{\psi}_e\gamma_\mu\psi_{\nu_e} \tag{VII-8}$$

Expressing the γ_μ in terms of α_μ and β, and using $\tilde{\psi} = \psi^+\beta$, we find

$$\mathscr{H} = \sqrt{8}g_\mu(\psi_{\nu_\mu}^\dagger\psi_\mu\psi_{\nu_e}^\dagger\psi_{\nu_e} - \psi_{\nu_\mu}^\dagger\boldsymbol{\alpha}\psi_\mu\psi_e^\dagger\boldsymbol{\alpha}\psi_{\nu_e}) \tag{VII-9}$$

Neglecting the rest mass for the electron, we have the two-particle wave functions written in simple two-component form (see Appendix II, p. 318):

$$\psi_\mu = \begin{pmatrix}\chi_\mu \\ 0\end{pmatrix}, \qquad \psi_e = \frac{1}{\sqrt{2}}\begin{pmatrix}\chi_e \\ -\chi_e\end{pmatrix}$$

$$\psi_{\nu_\mu}^{E>0} = \frac{1}{\sqrt{2}}\begin{pmatrix}\chi_{\nu_\mu} \\ -\chi_{\nu_\mu}\end{pmatrix}, \qquad \psi_{\nu_e}^{E<0} = \frac{1}{\sqrt{2}}\begin{pmatrix}-\chi_{\nu_e} \\ \chi_{\nu_e}\end{pmatrix} \tag{VII-10}$$

It is then clear that

$$\psi_{\nu_\mu}^\dagger\psi_\mu = \frac{1}{\sqrt{2}}\chi_{\nu_\mu}^\dagger\chi_\mu \tag{VII-11}$$

$$\psi_{\nu_\mu}^\dagger\boldsymbol{\alpha}\psi_\mu = \frac{1}{\sqrt{2}}\chi_{\nu_\mu}^\dagger\boldsymbol{\sigma}\chi_\mu \tag{VII-12}$$

$$\psi_e^\dagger\psi_{\nu_e} = -\chi_e^\dagger\chi_{\nu_e} \tag{VII-13}$$

$$\psi_e^\dagger\boldsymbol{\alpha}\psi_{\nu_e} = -\chi_e^\dagger\boldsymbol{\sigma}\chi_{\nu_e} \tag{VII-14}$$

and $\mathscr{H}$ is given in terms of two-component wave functions by

$$\mathscr{H} = 2g_\mu(-\chi_{\nu_\mu}^\dagger\chi_\mu\chi_e^\dagger\chi_{\nu_e} + \chi_{\nu_\mu}^\dagger\boldsymbol{\sigma}\chi_\mu\chi_e^\dagger\boldsymbol{\sigma}\chi_{\nu_e}) \tag{VII-15}$$

For definiteness we quantize along the momentum direction of the emitted electron by calling i the z axis, and we consider the spin vector of the muon to lie in the xz plane.

These considerations are illustrated in the spin momentum diagram shown in Fig. VII-1.

As pointed out at the beginning of Appendix VI, the Pauli spinors are given by

$$\text{(a)}\quad \chi_{\nu_\mu} = \begin{pmatrix}\cos\frac{1}{2}\theta_{\nu_\mu} \\ \sin\frac{1}{2}\theta_{\nu_\mu}e^{i\varphi_{\nu_\mu}}\end{pmatrix}, \qquad \text{(b)}\quad \chi_\mu = \begin{pmatrix}\cos\frac{1}{2}\theta_\mu \\ \sin\frac{1}{2}\theta_\mu\end{pmatrix}$$

$$\text{(c)}\quad \chi_e = \begin{pmatrix}0 \\ 1\end{pmatrix}, \qquad \text{(d)}\quad \chi_{\nu_e} = \begin{pmatrix}\cos\frac{1}{2}\theta_{\nu_e} \\ \sin\frac{1}{2}\theta_{\nu_e}e^{i\varphi_{\nu_e}}\end{pmatrix} \tag{VII-16}$$

where the angles are the polar coordinate directions of the spin vector of the particles referred to the z axis. Now $\mathscr{H}$ is of the form

$$\mathscr{H} = -4g_\mu \sum_i (a\hat{O}_i b)(c\hat{O}_i d) \tag{VII-17}$$

where $\hat{O}_i = 1, i\sigma_x, i\sigma_y, i\sigma_z$, and the σ's are the usual Pauli matrices.

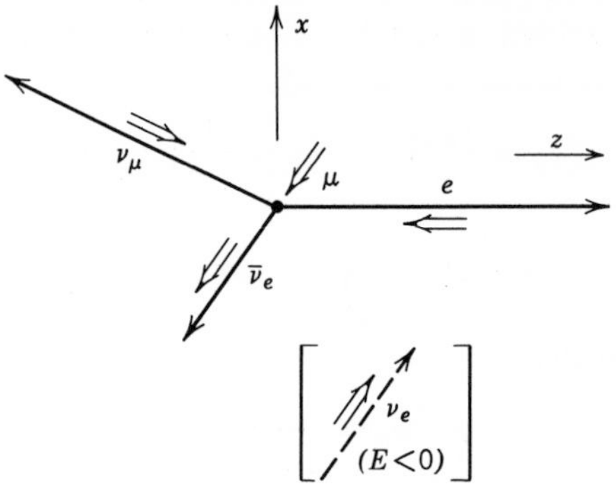

Fig. VII-1 Spin momentum diagram for muon decay. Long and short arrows indicate directions of momentum and spin. Momenta are indicated by long arrows and spins by short arrows. The vectors are not necessarily coplanar.

Writing $a = \begin{pmatrix} a_1 \\ a_2 \end{pmatrix}$ and similar notation for b, c, and d, we have

$$\begin{aligned} a^\dagger b &= a_1{}^*b_1 + a_2{}^*b_2 \\ a^\dagger \sigma_x b &= a_1{}^*b_2 + a_2{}^*b_1 \\ a^\dagger \sigma_y b &= -ia_1{}^*b_2 + ia_2{}^*b_1 \\ a^\dagger \sigma_z b &= a_1{}^*b_1 - a_2{}^*b_2 \end{aligned} \tag{VII-18}$$

Expanding the sum for $\mathscr{H}$ and collecting terms, we obtain for the matrix element

$$\begin{aligned} H_{fi} &= -4g_\mu(a_1{}^*b_1c_2{}^*\,d_2 + a_2{}^*b_2c_1{}^*\,d_1 - a_1{}^*b_2c_2{}^*\,d_1 - a_2{}^*b_1c_1{}^*\,d_2) \\ &= -4g_\mu(a_1{}^*c_2{}^* - a_2{}^*c_1{}^*)(b_1\,d_2 - b_2\,d_1) \end{aligned} \tag{VII-19}$$

Substituting the appropriate expressions for a, b, c, and d, we find

$$H_{fi} = -4g_\mu(\cos \tfrac{1}{2}\theta_{\nu_\mu})(\cos \tfrac{1}{2}\theta_\mu \sin \tfrac{1}{2}\theta_{\nu_e} e^{i\varphi_{\nu_e}} - \sin \tfrac{1}{2}\theta_\mu \cos \tfrac{1}{2}\theta_{\nu_e}) \tag{VII-20}$$

The square is given by

$$|H_{fi}|^2 = 16g_\mu^{\,2}(\cos^2 \tfrac{1}{2}\theta_{\nu_\mu}) \times (\cos^2 \tfrac{1}{2}\theta_\mu \sin^2 \tfrac{1}{2}\theta_{\nu_e} + \sin^2 \tfrac{1}{2}\theta_\mu \cos^2 \tfrac{1}{2}\theta_{\nu_e} - 2 \cos \tfrac{1}{2}\theta_\mu \sin \tfrac{1}{2}\theta_\mu \cos \tfrac{1}{2}\theta_{\nu_e} \sin \tfrac{1}{2}\theta_{\nu_e} \cos \varphi_{\nu_e}) \quad \text{(VII-21)}$$

By averaging over the azimuthal angle φ_{ν_e}, the last term, which contains $\cos \varphi_{\nu_e}$ as a factor, vanishes.

Using elementary trigonometry, we obtain

$$|H_{fi}|^2 = 4g_\mu^{\,2}(1 + \cos \theta_{\nu_\mu})(1 - \cos \theta_\mu \cos \theta_{\nu_e}) \quad \text{(VII-22)}$$

VII-2 TRANSITION PROBABILITY

We now use VII-22 to calculate the transition probability, which, in turn, leads us to the determination of the electron energy spectrum of the muon decay. Using Fermi's "golden rule" for transition probabilities, we have

$$P = \frac{2\pi}{\hbar} |H_{fi}|^2 \frac{dN_f}{dE} = \frac{2\pi}{\hbar} \int |H_{fi}|^2 \, dN_f \, \delta(E_f - E_i) \quad \text{(VII-23)}$$

where the integration represents averaging over final-energy states and the δ function guarantees conservation of energy in the whole process. Here dN is the phase space corresponding to the three particles e, $\bar{\nu}_e$, and ν_μ subject to the condition of the conservation of momentum. Therefore, any *two* particles can be chosen as independent; then the remaining one has a momentum uniquely fixed by the conservation condition. For definiteness let us choose the electron and the muon neutrino as the two independent particles. The number of final states available to these two particles is then given by

$$dN_f = \frac{E_e^{\,2} \, dE_e \, d\Omega_e}{(2\pi\hbar c)^3} \frac{E_{\nu_\mu}^2 \, dE_{\nu_\mu} \, d\Omega_{\nu_\mu}}{(2\pi\hbar c)^3} \quad \text{(VII-24)}$$

where $d\Omega = \sin \theta \, d\theta \, d\varphi \rightarrow 2\pi \, d(\cos \theta)$. Substituting into the expression for P, we obtain

$$P = \frac{2\pi}{\hbar} \frac{E_e^{\,2}}{(2\pi\hbar c)^6} \, dE_e \, d\Omega_e \, I \quad \text{(VII-25)}$$

where

$$I = \int 2\pi E_{\nu_\mu}^2 \, dE_{\nu_\mu} \, d\cos\theta_{\nu_\mu} \, |H_{fi}|^2 \, \delta(E_e + E_{\nu_\mu} + E_{\bar{\nu}_e} - 2E_m) \quad \text{(VII-26)}$$

and E_m is the maximum energy $\frac{1}{2}m_\mu c^2$. Conservation of momentum implies that

$$p_{\nu_\mu} = -p_{\bar{\nu}_e} - p_e \quad \text{(VII-27)}$$

Thus

$$p_{\nu_\mu}^2 = p_{\bar{\nu}_e}^2 + p_e^{\,2} + 2\mathbf{p}_{\bar{\nu}_e} \cdot \mathbf{p}_e = p_{\bar{\nu}_e}^2 + p_e^{\,2} - 2p_{\bar{\nu}_e} p_e \cos\theta_{\nu_e} \quad \text{(VII-28)}$$

Since, under our approximation $E_i = cp_i$ for electron as well as neutrinos, we obtain

$$\cos\theta_{\nu_e} = \frac{E_e^{\,2} + E_{\bar{\nu}_e}^2 - E_{\nu_\mu}^2}{2E_{\bar{\nu}_e} E_e} \quad \text{(VII-29)}$$

and similarly

$$p_{\bar{\nu}_e}^2 = p_{\nu_\mu}^2 + p_e^{\,2} + 2\mathbf{p}_{\nu_\mu} \cdot \mathbf{p}_e = p_{\nu_\mu}^2 + p_e^{\,2} - 2p_{\nu_\mu} p_e \cos\theta_{\nu_\mu} \quad \text{(VII-30)}$$

$$\cos\theta_{\nu_\mu} = \frac{E_e^{\,2} + E_{\nu_\mu}^2 - E_{\bar{\nu}_e}^2}{2E_{\nu_\mu} E_e} \quad \text{(VII-31)}$$

$$d\cos\theta_{\nu_\mu} = -\frac{E_{\bar{\nu}_e} \, dE_{\bar{\nu}_e}}{E_{\nu_\mu} E_e} \quad \text{(VII-32)}$$

We can then express I as a double integral over energies:

$$I = \frac{8\pi g_\mu^{\,2}}{E_e} \int\!\!\int E_{\bar{\nu}_e} E_{\nu_\mu} \left(1 + \frac{E_e^{\,2} + E_{\nu_\mu}^2 - E_{\bar{\nu}_e}^2}{2E_{\nu_\mu} E_e}\right)$$
$$\times \left(1 - \cos\theta_\mu \frac{E_e^{\,2} + E_{\bar{\nu}_e}^2 - E_{\nu_\mu}^2}{2E_{\bar{\nu}_e} E_e}\right) dE_{\bar{\nu}_e} \, dE_{\nu_\mu} \, \delta(E_e + E_{\bar{\nu}_e} + E_{\nu_\mu} - 2E_m) \quad \text{(VII-33)}$$

$$= \frac{2\pi g_\mu^{\,2}}{E_e^{\,3}} \int\!\!\int (2E_e E_{\nu_\mu} + E_e^{\,2} + E_{\nu_\mu}^2 - E_{\bar{\nu}_e}^2)$$
$$\times [2E_e E_{\bar{\nu}_e} - \cos\theta_\mu (E_e^{\,2} + E_{\bar{\nu}_e}^2 - E_{\nu_\mu}^2)]$$
$$\times dE_{\bar{\nu}_e} \, dE_{\nu_\mu} \, \delta(E_e + E_{\bar{\nu}_e} + E_{\nu_\mu} - 2E_m) \quad \text{(VII-34)}$$

The appearance of the δ function requires that

$$E_{\nu_\mu} = 2E_m - E_e - E_{\bar{\nu}_e} \quad \text{(VII-35)}$$

(here E_m equals the maximum electron energy $\frac{1}{2}m_\mu c^2$) and thus reduces I to a single integral:

$$I = \frac{16\pi g_\mu{}^2 E_m}{E_e{}^3} \int_{E_m-E_e}^{E_m} (E_m - E_{\bar{\nu}_e}) \times \{E_e E_{\bar{\nu}_e} + \cos\theta_\mu[2E_m(E_m - E_e) - E_{\bar{\nu}_e}(2E_m - E_e)]\}\, dE_{\bar{\nu}_e} \tag{VII-36}$$

The evaluation of this integral gives

$$I = \frac{8\pi g_\mu{}^2}{3} E_m[(3E_m - 2E_e) + \cos\theta_\mu(E_m - 2E_e)] \tag{VII-37}$$

Thus the number of emitted electrons in the energy range E_e to $E_e + dE_e$ and in a solid angle $d\Omega_e$ is

$$N(E_e, \Omega_e)\, dE_e\, d\Omega_e = P = \frac{g_\mu{}^2}{12\pi^4\hbar^7c^6} E_m E_e{}^2[(3E_m - 2E_e) + \cos\theta_\mu(E_m - 2E_e)]\, dE_e\, d\Omega_e \tag{VII-38}$$

VII-3 ELECTRON ENERGY SPECTRUM

The energy spectrum integrated over angles is given by

$$N(E_e)\, dE_e = \frac{g_\mu{}^2}{3\pi^3\hbar^7c^6} E_m E_e{}^2(3E_m - 2E_e)\, dE_e \tag{VII-39}$$

The distribution is shown schematically in Fig. 6-1, p. 215, and corresponds to a Michel parameter of $\rho = 0.75$. This distribution agrees well with experimental results apart from radiative corrections. It is clear that this same spectrum also holds for the μ^+ mode of decay, since there is no dependence on spin.

VII-4 ELECTRON ANGULAR DISTRIBUTION

The angular asymmetry of the electron distribution with respect to the spin orientation of the muon is given directly by

$$(3E_m - 2E_e) + \cos\theta_\mu(E_m - 2E_e) \tag{VII-40}$$

It should be recalled that we are dealing here with completely polarized muons—that is, muons whose spin vectors are all mutually parallel. Thus for μ^- decay the $\cos\theta$ coefficient is opposite in sign to that for μ^+ decay. For $\mu^\pm$ decay the anisotropy of the electron energy distribution is

$$1 \mp \tfrac{1}{3}\cos\theta \qquad \text{for} \quad E_e = 0$$

and

$$1 \pm \cos\theta \qquad \text{for} \quad E_e = E_m \tag{VII-41}$$

whereas the average over electron energy is

$$1 \pm \tfrac{1}{3}\cos\theta \tag{VII-42}$$

VII-5 TOTAL DECAY RATE

The total decay probability per second w (related to the mean life by $w/\lambda = \tau^{-1}$) may be obtained by integrating $P(E)$ over energy. This gives

$$w = \int_0^{E_m} N\,dE = \frac{g_\mu^{\,2}}{6\pi^3\hbar^7c^6}E_m^{\,5} = \frac{g_\mu^{\,2}}{192\pi^3\hbar^7}m_\mu^{\,5}c^4$$

$$= \frac{G^2}{192\pi^3}\left(\frac{m_ec^2}{\hbar}\right)^2\left(\frac{m_\mu}{m_e}\right)^5 \tag{VII-43}$$

where G is the dimensionless coupling constant defined on p. 27.

The experimental lifetime $\tau = 2.198 \times 10^{-6}$ sec is consistent with a coupling constant $g_\mu = 1.435 \times 10^{-49}$ erg cm^3, which is about 2% larger than the vector coupling constant in the 0^{14} β decay (see Sec. 7-3, p. 263 for a discussion of this point).

References

Ab-64 A. Abashian, R. J. Abrams, D. W. Carpenter, G. P. Fisher, B. M. K. Nefkens, and J. H. Smith, *Phys. Rev. Letters* **13,** 243 (1964), Chaps. 1, 4, 6.

Ad-62 J. B. Adams, *Phys. Rev.* **126,** 1567 (1962), Chap. 6.

Ad-65 S. L. Adler, *Phys. Rev. Letters* **14,** 105 (1965), Chap. 7.

Ah-52 T. Ahrens, E. Feenberg, and H. Primakoff, *Phys. Rev.* **87,** 663 (1952), Chap. 3.

Aj-59 F. Ajzenberg-Selove and T. Lauritsen, *Nucl. Phys.* **11,** 1 (1959), Chap. 3.

Al-37 L. W. Alvarez, *Phys. Rev.* **52,** 134(L) (1937), Chaps. 1, 5.

Al-50a D. E. Alburger, D. J. Hughes, and C. Eggler, *Phys. Rev.* **78,** 318 (1950), Chap. 1.

Al-50b D. E. Alburger, *Phys. Rev.* **79,** 236 (1950), Chap. 1.

Al-55 G. Alaga, K. Alder, A. Bohr, and B. R. Mottelson, *Kgl. Danske Videnskab. Selskab, Mat. Fys. Medd.* **29,** 9 (1955), Chap. 3.

Al-56 K. Alder, A. Bohr, T. Huus, B. Mottelson, and A. Winther, *Rev. Mod. Phys.* **28,** 432 (1956), Chap. 3.

Ald-57 K. Alder, B. Stech, and A. Winther, *Phys. Rev.* **107,** 728 (1957), Chaps. 3, 4.

All-57 J. S. Allen, *The Neutrino*, Princeton University Press, Princeton, N.J., 1957, Chap. 1.

Al-58 A. Altman and W. M. MacDonald, *Phys. Rev. Letters* **1,** 456 (1958), Chap. 7.

Al-59 Allen, Burman, Hermannsfeldt, Stähelin and Braid, *Phys. Rev.* **116,** 134 (1959), Chap. 3.

Al-60 Alikhanov, Galaktionov, Gorodkov, Eliseyev, and Lyubimov, *Proc. Intern. Conf. on High-Energy Physics*, Rochester, 1960, p. 539, Chap. 6.

Al-61 S. A. Ali-Zade, I. I. Gurevich, and B. A. Nikol'skii, *Soviet Phys. JETP* **13,** 313 (1961): translation of *JETP (USSR)* **40,** 452 (1961), Chap. 6.

Ali-62 Alikhanov, Babaev, Balats, Kaftanov, Landsberg, and Lyubimov, *Proc. Intern. Conf. of High-Energy Physics*, CERN, Geneva, 1962, p. 423, Chap. 6.

Alt-62 A. Altman and W. M. MacDonald, *Nucl. Phys.* **35,** 593 (1962), Chap. 7.

Am-58 E. Ambler, R. W. Hayward, D. D. Hoppes, and R. P. Hudson, *Phys. Rev.* **110,** 787 (1958), Chap. 4.

An-58 H. L. Anderson et al,. *Proc. Intern. Conf. on High-Energy Physics*, CERN, Geneva, 1958, p. 219, Chap. 6.

An-59 H. L. Anderson, T. Fujii, R. H. Miller, and L. Tau, *Phys. Rev. Letters* **2,** 53 (1959); *Phys. Rev.* **119,** 2050 (1960), Chap. 6.

Ap-57 H. Appel and H. Schopper, *Z. Physik* **149,** 103 (1957), Chap. 4.

Ap-58 H. Appel, H. Schopper, and S. D. Bloom, *Phys. Rev.* **109,** 221 (1958), Chap. 4.

Ar-53 W. Arber and P. Stähelin, *Helv. Phys. Acta* **26,** 433 (1953), Chap. 1.

As-64 Astbury, Auerbach, Cutts, Esterling, Jenkins, Lipman, and Shafer, *Bull. Am. Phys. Soc.* **9,** 81 (1964), Chap. 6.

Au-65 L. B. Auerbach, Esterling, Hill, Jenkins, Lach, and Lipman, *Phys. Rev.* **138,** B127 (1965), Chap. 6.

Aw-56 M. Awschalom, *Phys. Rev.* **101,** 1041 (1956), Chap. 5.

Ba-40 J. H. Bartlett and R. E. Watson, *Proc. Am. Acad. Arts Sci.* **74,** 53 (1940), Chap. 4.

Ba-56 W. H. Barkas, W. Birnbaum, and F. M. Smith, *Phys. Rev.* **101,** 778 (1956), Chaps. 2, 6, 7. In this experiment the error is due both to the measurement of the muon momentum and to the uncertainty in the pion mass ($m_\pi = 139.59 \pm 0.05$ mev).

Ba-59 M. Bardon, D. Berley, and L. M. Lederman, *Phys. Rev. Letters* **2,** 56 (1959), Chap. 6.

Ba-60 P. Banerjee and H. D. Zeh, *Z. Physik* **159,** 170 (1960), Chap. 3.

Bac-61 G. Backenstoss, B. D. Hyams, G. Knop, P. C. Marin, and U. Stierlin, *Phys. Rev. Letters* **6,** 415 (1961), Chap. 6.

Bak-61 Baker, Cool, Jenkins, Kycia, Lindenbaum, Love, Lüers, Niederer, Ozaki, Read, Russell, and Yuan, *Phys. Rev. Letters* **7,** 101 (1961), Chap. 7.

Bar-61 M. Bardon, P. Franzini, and J. Lee, *Phys. Rev. Letters* **7,** 23 (1961), Chap. 6.

Bac-62 R. B. Bacastow, T. Elioff, R. R. Larsen, C. E. Wiegand, and T. Ypsilantis, *Phys. Rev. Letters* **9,** 400 (1962), Chap. 7.

Bar-62 A. Barbaro-Galtieri, W. H. Barkas, H. H. Heckman, J. W. Patrick, and F. M. Smith, *Phys. Rev. Letters* **9,** 26 (1962), Chap. 6.

Bardi-62 R. K. Bardin, C. A. Barnes, W. A. Fowler, and P. A. Seeger, *Phys. Rev.* **127,** 583 (1962), Chaps. 2, 7.

Bardo-62 M. Bardon, P. Franzini, and J. Lee, *Phys. Rev.* **126,** 1826 (1962), Chap. 6.

Bart-62 D. Bartlett, S. Devons, and A. M. Sachs, *Phys. Rev. Letters* **8,** 120 (1962), Chap. 7.

Ba-63 B. F. Bayman, J. D. McCullen, and L. Zamick, *Phys. Rev. Letters* **11,** 215 (1963), Chap. 3.

Bah-63a J. N. Bahcall, W. A. Fowler, I. Iben, and R. L. Sears, *Astrophys. J.* **137,** 244 (1963), Chap. 5.

Bah-63b J. N. Bahcall, R. Davis, and R. L. Sears, *Proc. Steller Evolution Conf.*, NASA, New York, 1963, Chap 5.

Bar-63 M. Bardon, J. Lee, J. Peoples, A. Sachs, and G. Sutter, *Bull. Am. Phys. Soc.* **8,** 389 (1963), Chap. 6.

Ba-63 B. F. Bayman, J. D. McCullen, and L. Zamick, *Phys. Rev. Letters* **11,** 215 (1963), Chap. 3.

Ba-64 D. Bartlett, S. Devons, S. Meyer, and J. Rosen, *Bull. Am. Phys. Soc.* **9,** 71 (1964), Chap 7.

Bac-65 R. B. Bacastow, C. Ghesquiere, C. E. Wiegand, and R. R. Larsen, *Phys. Rev.* **139,** B407 (1965), Chap. 7.

Bar-65 M. Bardon, P. Norton, J. Peoples, A. Sachs, and J. Lee-Franzini, *Phys. Rev. Letters* **14,** 449 (1965), Chap. 6.

Be-34 H. A. Bethe and R. Peierls, *Nature*, **133,** 532 (1934), Chap. 5.

Be-49 P. R. Bell and J. M. Cassidy, *Phys. Rev.* **76,** 183 (1949), Chap. 1.

Be-50a P. R. Bell and J. M. Cassidy, *Phys. Rev.* **77,** 301 (1950), Chap. 1.

Be-50b P. R. Bell, B. Weaver, and J. M. Cassidy, *Phys. Rev.* **77,** 399 (1950), Chap. 1.

Be-56 R. E. Behrends, R. J. Finkelstein, and A. Sirlin, *Phys. Rev.* **101,** 866 (1956), Chap. 6.

Be-58 J. Bernstein and R. R. Lewis, *Phys. Rev.* **112,** 232 (1958), Chaps. 4, 7.

Be-62 S. M. Berman and A. Sirlin, *Ann. Phys.* (*N.Y.*) **20,** 20 (1962), Chap. 7.

Ber-62 J. Berthier, P. Debrienner, M. Lambert, and R. Lombard, *Compt. Rend.* **251,** 1065 (1962), Chap. 4.

Be-63 J. S. Bell, J. Lovseth, and M. Veltmann, *Proc. Intern. Conf. on Elementary Particles*, Sienna, Italy, 1963, Chaps. 1, 7.

Be-64a G. Bernardini, *Lecture Notes of Intern. School of Physics, Enrico Fermi*," Varenna (Como), Italy, 1964, Academic Press, New York, Chap. 7.

Be-64b G. Bernardini et al., *Phys. Letters* **13,** 86 (1964), Chap. 7.

Bh-36 H. J. Bhabha, *Proc. Roy. Soc.* (*London*) **A154,** 195 (1936), Chap. 4.

Bh-61 C. P. Bhalla and M. E. Rose, Table of Electronic Radial Functions at the Nuclear Surface and Tangents of Phase Shifts, ORNL, 3207 (1961), Chaps. 2, 3, 7.

Bh-62 C. P. Bhalla and M. E. Rose, *Phys. Rev.* **128,** 1774 (1962); and ORNL 3207 (1962), Chap. 2.

Bh-64 C. P. Bhalla, Nat. Bur. Std. (U.S.), Monograph 81 (August 1964), Chaps. 2, 3, 7.

Bi-57 A. M. Bincer, *Phys. Rev.* **107,** 1467 (1957), Chap. 4.

Bi-58 A. M. Bincer, *Phys. Rev.* **112,** 244 (1958), Chap. 4.

Bi-59 H. Bienlein, K. Güthner, H. von Issendorf, and H. Wegener, *Nucl. Instr.* **4,** 79 (1959), Chap. 4.

Bi-64 H. Bienlein et al., *Phys. Letters* **13,** 80 (1964), Chap. 7.

Bl-42 E. Bleuler, P. Scherrer, and W. Zunti, *Phys. Rev.* **61,** 95 (1942), Chap. 1.

Bl-60 R. J. Blin-Stoyle, V. Gupta, and J. S. Thomson, *Nucl. Phys.* **14,** 685 (1960), Chap. 7.

Bl-61 R. Blin-Stoyle and R. M. Spector, *Phys. Rev.* **124,** 1199 (1961); R. Blin-Stoyle, *Phys. Rev.* **118,** 1605 (1960); **120,** 181 (1960), Chap. 7.

Ble-62 E. Bleser, L. Lederman, J. Rosen, J. Rothberg, and E. Zavattini, *Phys. Rev. Letters* **8,** 288 (1962), Chap. 6.

Bli-62 R. J. Blin-Stoyle and J. Le Tourneux, *Ann. Phys.* (*N.Y.*) **18,** 12 (1962), Chap. 7.

Blo-62 S. D. Bloom, L. G. Mann, and J. A. Miskel, *Phys. Rev.* **125,** 2021 (1962); *Phys. Rev. Letters* **5,** 326 (1960), Chap. 4.

Bloc-62 M. Block, E. Fiorini, E. Kikuchi, G. Giacomelli, and S. Ratti, *Nuovo Cim.* **23,** 1114 (1962), Chap. 6.

Bli-63a R. J. Blin-Stoyle and S. C. K. Nair, *Phys. Letters* **7,** 161 (1963), Chap. 7.

Bli-63b R. J. Blin-Stoyle and L. Novakovic, *Nucl. Phys.* **51,** 133 (1964), Chap. 7.

Blo-63 S. Bloom, L. A. Dick, L. Feuvrais, G. R. Henry, P. C. Macq, and M. Spighel, *Phys. Letters* **8,** 87 (1963), Chap. 6.

Bl-64 M. M. Block et al., *Phys. Letters* **12,** 281 (1964), Chap. 7.

Bl-65a R. J. Blin-Stoyle and C. J. Yap, to be published, Chap. 4.

Bl-65b R. J. Blin-Stoyle, Proceedings of the Ninth Summer Meeting of Physicists, Herzegnova, Yugoslavia, 1965, Chap. 7.

Boe-53 F. Boehm and C. S. Wu, *Phys. Rev.* **90,** 369 (1953), Chap. 3.

Boh-53 A. Bohr and B. R. Mottelson *Kgl. Danske Videnskab. Selskab, Mat. Fys. Medd.* **27,** No. 16 (1953), Chap. 3.

Bo-57a F. Boehm and A. H. Wapstra, *Phys. Rev.* **106,** 1364 (1957); **107,** 1202, 1462 (1957), Chap. 4.

Bo-57b Boehm, Novey, Barnes, and Stech, *Phys. Rev.* **108,** 1497 (1957), Chap. 4.

Bo-58 F. Boehm and A. H. Wapstra, *Phys. Rev.* **109,** 456 (1958), Chap. 4.

Boe-59 F. Boehm and U. Hauser, *Nucl. Phys.* **14,** 615 (1959), Chap. 7.

Bou-59 C. C. Bouchiat, *Phys. Rev. Letters* **3,** 516 (1959), Chap. 4.

Bo-60 C. C. Bouchiat, *Phys. Rev.* **118,** 540 (1960), Chap. 4.

Bo-62a F. Boehm, private communication, quoted in Blo-62, Chap. 4.

Bo-62b F. Boehm and J. Rogers, *Nucl. Phys.* **33,** 118 (1962), Chap. 4.

Bo-63 F. Boehm and J. Rogers, *Nucl. Phys.* **45,** 392 (1963), Chap. 3.

Bo-65 Bowen et al., Argonne Conference on Weak Interactions, October 1965.

Br-62 Brosi, Galonsky, Ketelle, and Willard, *Nucl. Phys.* **33,** 353 (1962), Chap. 4.

Bu-58 Burgy, Krohn, Novy, Ringo, and Telegdi, *Phys. Rev.* **110,** 1214 (1958); and *Phys. Rev.* **120,** 1829 (1960), Chaps. 1, 4.

Buhl-63 A. Buhler, N. Cabibbo, M. Fidecaro, T. Massam, Th. Muller, M. Schneegans, and A. Zichichi, *Phys. Letters* **7,** 368 (1963), Chap. 6.

Bühr-63 W. Bühring, *Nucl. Phys.* **40,** 473 (1963), Chaps. 2, 3.

Bü-65a W. Bühring, *Nucl. Phys.* **61,** 110 (1965), Chaps. 2, 3, 7.

Bü-65b W. Bühring and H. Schopper, preprint, Chap. 3,7.

Ca-53 E. Caianello, *Nuovo Cimento* **10,** 43 (1953), Chap. 7.

Ca-57 Cavanagh, Turner, Coleman, and Ridley, *Proc. Rehovoth Conf. on Nuclear Structure*, 1957, edited by H. J. Lipkin, North-Holland Publishing Co., Amsterdam, p. 394; and *Phil. Mag.* **21,** 1105 (1957), Chap. 4.

Ca-59 Carter, Reines, Wagner, and Wyman, *Phys. Rev.* **113,** 280 (1959), Chap. 5.

Ca-63 N. Cabibbo, *Phys. Rev. Letters* **10,** 531 (1963), Chap. 7.

Cab-64 N. Cabibbo, *Lecture Notes of Intern. School of Physics "Enrico Fermi,"* Varenna (Como), Italy, 1964 Academic Press, New York, Chap. 7.

Cam-64 Camerini, Cline, Fry, and Powell, *Phys. Rev. Letters* **13,** 318 (1964), Chap. 7.

Ce-62 *Proc. Intern. Conf. on High-Energy Physics* CERN, Geneva, 1962, Chap. 6.

Ce-63 CERN High-Energy Neutrino Experiments. *Proc. Intern Conf. on Fundamental Aspects of Weak Interactions*, Brookhaven Natl. Lab., Upton, N.Y., 1963; and *Proc. Intern. Conf. on Elementary Particles*, Sienna, Italy, 1963, Chaps. 1, 7.

Ch-14 V. Chadwick, *Phys. Gens.* **16,** 383 (1914), Chap. 1.

Ch-32 V. Chadwick, *Proc. Roy. Soc. (London)* **A136,** 692 (1932), Chap. 1.

Cham-62 M. Chambre and P. Depommier, *Compt. Rend.* **255,** 503 (1962), Chap. 4.

Ch-62 Charpak, Farley, Garwin, Muller, Sens, and Zichichi, *Phys. Letters* **1,** 16 (1962), Chap. 7.

Ch-64 J. H. Christensen, J. W. Cronin, V. L. Fitch, and R. Turlay, *Phys. Rev. Letters* **13,** 138 (1964), Chaps. 1, 4, 6.

Cl-58 M. A. Clark, J. M. Robson, and R. Nathans, *Intern. Conf. on Peaceful Uses of Atomic Energy*, Geneva, 1958, Vol. 30, p. 290, Chap. 4.

Cl-65 Cley, Keuffel, Wagner, and Edelstein, *Phys. Rev.* **140,** B586 (1965), Chap. 6.

Co-28 R. T. Cox, C. G. McIlwraith, and B. Kurrelmeyer, *Proc. Natl. Acad. Sci. U.S.* **14,** 544 (1928), Chap. 1.

Co-48 C. S. Cook, L. M. Langer, and H. C. Price, *Phys. Rev.* **73,** 1395 (1948), Chap. 2.

Cow-56 Cowan, Harrison, Langer, and Reines, *Nuovo Cimento* **3,** 649 (1956), Chap. 5.

Co-57 Coombes et al. *Phys. Rev.* **108,** 1348 (1957), Chap. 6.

Com-58 B. D. Commins and P. Kusch, *Phys. Rev. Letters* **1,** 208 (1958), Chap. 3.

Co-62 M. Conversi, L. di Lella, G. Penso, M. Toller, and C. Rubbia, *Phys. Rev. Letters* **8,** 125 (1962), Chap. 7.

Coh-64 R. Cohen, S. Devons, and A. Kanaris, *Nucl. Phys.* **57,** 255 (1964), Chap. 6.

Con-64 M. Conversi, R. Diebold, and L. di Lella, *Phys. Rev.* **136B,** 1077 (1964), Chap. 6.

Cr-38 H. R. Crane and J. Halpern, *Phys. Rev.* **53,** 789 (1938); **56,** 232 (1939); R. F. Christy, E. R. Cohen, W. A. Fowler, C. C. Lauritsen, and T. Lauritsen, *Phys. Rev.* **72,** 698 (1947), Chap. 1.

Cr-41 C. L. Critchfield and E. P. Wigner, *Phys. Rev.* **60,** 412 (1941), Chap. 7.

Cu-52 S. C. Curran, *Physica* **18,** 1161 (1952), Chap. 2.

Cul-57 Culligan, Frank, Holt, Kluyver, and Massam, *Nature (London)* **180,** 751 (1957), Chap. 6.

Cur-57 R. B. Curtis and R. R. Lewis, *Phys. Rev.* **107,** 1381 (1957), Chap. 7.

Cu-59 G. Culligan, S. G. F. Frank, and J. R. Holt, *Proc. Phys. Soc. (London)* **73,** 169 (1959), Chap. 6.

Da-51 J. P. Davidson, *Phys. Rev.* **82,** 48 (1951), Chap. 3.
Da-52 R. Davis, *Phys. Rev.* **86,** 976, (1952), Chap. 5.
Da-53 R. H. Dalitz, *Phil. Mag.* **44,** 1068 (1953), Chap. 1.
Dal-59 R. H. Dalitz, *Rev. Mod. Phys.* **31,** 823 (1959); and lecture notes from Varenna Summer School, 1959, Chap. 6.
Dav-55 R. Davis, *Phys. Rev.* **97,** 766 (1955); *Bull. Am. Phys. Soc., Ser. II,* **1,** 219 (1956), Chap. 5.
Da-61 H. Daniel and M. Kuntze, *Z. Physik* **162,** 229 (1961), Chap. 4.
Da-62 Danby, Gaillard, Goulianos, Lederman, Mistry, Schwartz, and Steinberger, *Phys. Rev. Letters* **9,** 36 (1962), Chaps. 1, 2, 4, 6, 7.
Da-63 Daniel, Mehling, Müller, Schmidlin, Schmitt, Subudhi, and Neuberger, *Nucl. Phys.* **45,** 529 (1963), Chap. 4.
Da-65 H. Daniel and H. Schmitt, *Nucl. Phys.* **65,** 481 (1965), Chap. 4.
De-55 J. F. Detoeuf and R. Moch, *J. Phys. Radium* **16** (12), 987 (1955), Chap. 5.
Deb-57 P. De Brunner and W. Kundig, *Helv. Phys. Acta* **30,** 261 (1957), Chap 4.
Des-57 A. De Shalit, S. Kuperman, H. J. Lipkin, and T. Rothein, *Phys. Rev.* **107,** 1459 (1957), Chap. 4.
Deu-57 Deutsch, Gittleman, Baver, Grodzins, and Sunyar, *Phys. Rev.* **107,** 1733 (1957), Chap. 4.
De-59 M. Deutsch and O. Kofoed-Hansen, *Experimental Nuclear Physics,* edited by E. Segri, Vol. 3, John Wiley and Son, New York (1953–1959), Chap. 7.
De-60 Devons, Gidal, Lederman, and Shapiro, *Phys. Rev. Letters,* **5,** 330 (1960), Chap. 7.
Dep-63 P. DePommier, J. Heintze, G. Rubbia, and V. Soergel, *Phys. Letters* **5,** 61 (1963), Chap. 7.
De-63 J. P. Deutsch and P. Lipnik, preprint, Chap. 3.
de-64 E. der Mateosian and M. Goldhaber, *Proc. Intern. Conf. on High-Energy Physics,* Dubna, 1964, $T_{\text{neutrinoless}} > 1.2 \times 10^{19}$ yr, Chap. 5.
De-65 Deutsch and Lipnik, *Nucl. Phys.* **61,** 97 (1965), Chap. 3.
Di-63 L. Dick, L. Feuvrais, and M. Spighel, *Phys. Letters* **7,** 150 (1963), Chaps. 4, 6.
Dica-64 Di Capua, Garland, Pondrom, and Strelzoff, *Phys. Rev.* **133,** B1333 (1964), Chap. 6.
Dick-64 L. Dick, L. Feuvrais, L. Di Lella, and M. Spighel, *Phys. Letters* **10,** 236 (1964), Chap. 6.
Dub-59 E. I. Dubrokhotov, V. R. Lazarenko, and S. Yu Lak'yanov, *J. Exptl. theoret. phys. (U.S.S.R.)* **36** (9), 54 (1959), Chap. 5.
Du-59 W. F. Dudziak, R. Sagane, and J. Vedder, *Phys. Rev.* **114,** 336 (1959), Chap. 6.
Dun-63 A. F. Dungitsev et al,. reported by I. V. Chuvilo, *Proc. Intern. Conf. on Fundamental Aspects of Weak Interactions,* Brookhaven Natl. Lab., Upton, N.Y., 1963, Chap. 7.
Du-63 L. Durand, L. F. Landovitz, and R. B. Marr, *Phys. Rev.* **130,** 1188 (1963), Chap 7.

Du-64 J. Duclos, J. Heintze, A. DeRujula, and V. Soergel, *Phys. Letters* **9,** 62 (1964), Chap. 6.

Dur-64 L. Durand, *Phys. Rev.* **135B,** 310 (1964), Chap. 7.

Dz-56 B. S. Dzhelepov and L. N. Zyrianova, "Influence of Atomic Electric Fields on Beta Decay" (in Russian), *Izd. Akad. Nauk. SSSR Moskva* (1956), Chaps. 2, 7.

Eb-57 M. E. Ebel and G. Feldman, *Nucl. Phys.* **4,** 213 (1957), Chap. 4.

Ed-63 R. Edelstein et al., *Proc. Intern. Conf. on Fundamental Aspects of Weak Interactions*, Brookhaven Natl. Lab., Upton, N.Y., 1963, Chap. 6.

Eh-31 P. Ehrenfest and J. R. Oppenheimer, *Phys. Rev.* **37,** 333 (1931), Chap. 1.

Ei-63 J. Eichler and S. Wahlborn, *Phys. Letters* **4,** 344 (1963); J. Eichler, *Z. Physik* **171,** 463 (1963); and S. Wahlborn, *Nucl. Phys.* **58,** 209 (1964), Chap. 3.

Ei-64 J. Eichler, T. A. Tombrello, and J. N. Bahcall, *Phys. Letters* **13,** 146 (1964), Chap. 7.

El-27 C. D. Ellis and W. A. Wooster, *Proc. Roy. Soc.* (*London*) **A117,** 109 (1927), Chap. 1.

El-57 J. P. Elliott and A. M. Lane, "The Nuclear Shell Model," *Handbuch der Physik*, Vol. 39, Springer, Berlin 1957, pp. 241-410, Chap. 3.

El-63 Ely, Gidal, Kalmus, Oswald, Powell, Singleton, Bullock, Henderson, Miller, and Stannard, *Phys. Rev.* **131,** 868 (1963), Chap. 6.

En-57 C. D. Enz, *Nuovo Cimento* **6,** 250 (1957), Chaps. 2, 4.

En-62 P. M. Endt and C. Van der Leun, *Nucl. Phys.* **34,** 1 (1962), Chap. 4

Fa-50 D. L. Falkoff and G. E. Uhlenbeck, *Phys. Rev.* **79,** 334 (1950), Chap. 3.

Fa-58 T. Fazzini, G. Fidecaro, A. W. Merrison, H. Paul, and A. V. Tollestrup, *Phys. Rev. Letters* **1,** 247 (1958), Chaps. 1, 6.

Fa-59 L. W. Fagg and S. S. Hanna, *Rev. Mod. Phys.* **31,** 711 (1959), Chap. 4.

Fa-62 Farley, Massam, Muller, and Zichichi, *Proc. Intern. Conf. on High-Energy Phys.* CERN, Geneva, 1962, p. 415, Chap. 7.

Fa-63 I. V. Falomkin, A. I. Filippov, M. M. Kulyukin, B. Pontecorvo, Yu. A. Scherbakov, R. M. Sulyaev, V. M. Tsupko-Sitnikov, and D. A. Zaimidoroga, *Phys. Letters* **3,** 229 (1963), Chap. 6.

Fe-34 E. Fermi, *Z. Physik* **88,** 161 (1934), Chap. 1.

Fe-49 L. Feldman and C. S. Wu, *Phys. Rev.* **76,** 698 (1949); **76,** 697 (1949), Chap. 1.

Fe-50 E. Feenberg and G. Trigg, *Rev. Mod. Phys.* **22,** 399 (1959), Chap. 3.

Fel-50 L. Feldman and C. S. Wu, *Phys. Rev.* **78,** 318 (1950), Chaps. 1, 3.

Fe-51 E. Fermi, *Elementary Particles*, Yale University Press, New Haven, Conn., 1951, Chap. 7.

Fe-52 L. Feldman and C. S. Wu, *Phys. Rev.* **87,** 1091 (1952), Chaps. 1, 3.

Fe-55 E. Feenberg, *Shell Theory of the Nucleus*, Princeton University Press, Princeton, N.J., 1955, Chap. 3.

Fe-57 B. T. Feld, *Phys. Rev.* **107,** 797 (1957), Chap. 4.

Fe-58 E. Feenberg and H. Primakoff, *Phil. Mag.* **3,** 328 (1958), Chap. 7.

Fei-58 G. Feinberg, *Phys. Rev.* **110,** 1482 (1958), Chap. 7.

Fey-58 R. P. Feynman and M. Gell-Mann, *Phys. Rev.* **109,** 193 (1958), Chaps. 1, 7.

Fe-63 G. Feinberg and L. M. Lederman, *Ann. Rev. Nucl. Sci.* **13,** 431 (1963), Chap. 7.

Fi-37 M. Fierz, *Z. Physik* **104,** 553 (1937), Chaps. 1, 3, 6.

Fi-52 E. L. Fireman and D. Schwarzer, *Phys. Rev.* **86,** 451 (1952), Chap. 5.

Fi-53 R. Finkelstein and P. Kaus, *Phys. Rev.* **92,** 1316 (1953), Chap. 7.

Fi-54 R. J. Finkelstein and S. A. Moszkowski, *Phys. Rev.* **95,** 1695 (1954), Chap. 7.

Fi-63 T. R. Fisher, *Phys. Rev.* **130,** 2388 (1963), Chap. 7.

Fl-55 M. Flugge and W. Jekle, *Z. Naturforsch.* **109,** 419 (1955), Chap. 2.

Fo-57 G. W. Ford and C. J. Mullin, *Phys. Rev.* **108,** 477 (1957), Chap. 4.

Fr-52 J. H. Fremlin and M. C. Walters, *Proc. Phys. Soc.* (*London*) **A65,** 911 (1952), Chap. 5.

Fra-57 S. Frankel, G. Hansen, O. Nathan, and G. Temmer, *Phys. Rev.* **108,** 1099 (1957), Chap. 4.

Frau-57a Frauenfelder, Bobone, Von Goeler, Levine, Lewis, Peacock, Rossi, and De Pasquali, *Phys. Rev.* **106,** 386 (1957), Chap. 4.

Frau-57b Frauenfelder, Hanson, Levine, Rossi, and De Pasquali, *Phys. Rev.* **107,** 643, 909, 910 (1957), Chap. 4.

Fri-57 J. I. Friedman and V. L. Telegdi, *Phys. Rev.*, **105,** 1681 (1957), Chaps. 1, 6.

Fri-58 L. Friedman and L. G. Smith, *Phys. Rev.* **109,** 2214 (1958), Chap. 3.

Fro-58 C. Fronsdal, and H. Uberall, *Phys. Rev.* **111,** 580 (1958), Chap. 4

Fra-62 Frankel, Halpern, Holloway, Wales, Yearian, Chamberlain, Lemonick, and Pipkin, *Phys. Rev. Letters* **8,** 123 (1962), Chap. 7.

Fre-62 Freeman, Montague, West, and White, *Phys. Letters* **3,** 136 (1962), Chap. 7.

Fra-64 H. Frauenfelder and R. Steffen, Chap. 19 of *Alpha, Beta and Gamma Spectroscopy*, North-Holland Publishing Co., Amsterdam, 1964, Chap. 3.

Fre-64 Freeman, White, Montague, Murray, and Burcham, *Phys. Letters* **8,** 115 (1964), Chap. 7.

Fr-65 J. M. Freeman, G. Murray, and W. E. Burcham, *Phys. Letters* **17,** 317 (1965), Chaps. 2, 7.

Fu-39 W. H. Furry, *Phys. Rev.* **56,** 1184 (1939), Chap. 5.

Fu-49 H. W. Fulbright and J. C. D. Milton, *Phys. Rev.* **76,** 1271 (1949), Chap. 1.

Fu-59 A. L. Fujii and H. Primakoff, *Nuovo Cimento* **12,** 327 (1959), Chap. 6

Fu-62 J. Fujita, *Phys. Rev.* **126,** 202 (1962), Chap. 3.

Fu-63 J. Fujita, *Phys. Rev.* **133,** B549 (1964), Chap. 3.

Ga-36 G. Gamow and E. Teller, *Phys. Rev.* **49,** 895 (1936), Chaps. 1, 3.

Ga-57 R. L. Garwin, L. M. Lederman, and M. Weinrich, *Phys. Rev.* **105,** 1415 (1957), Chaps. 1, 6.

Ga-62 C. J. Gallagher and V. G. Soloviev, *Kgl. Danske Videnskab. Selskab, Mat. Fys. Skrifter* **2,** No. 2 (1962), Chap. 3.

Ge-55 S. S. Gershtein and Ia. B. Zel'dovich, *JETP* (*USSR*) **29,** 698 (1955); translation in *Soviet Phys. JETP* **2,** 576 (1956), Chap. 7.

Gei-58 Geiger, Ewan, Graham, and MacKenzie, *Bull. Am. Phys. Soc.* **3,** 51 (1958), Chap. 4.

Ge-58 M. Gell-Mann, *Phys. Rev.* **111,** 362 (1958), Chaps. 3, 7.

Ge-59 M. Gell-Mann and S. M. Berman, *Phys. Rev. Letters* **3,** 99 (1959), Chap. 7.

Gl-63 N. W. Glass and R. W. Peterson, *Phys. Rev.* **130,** 299 (1963), Chap. 7.

Gle-63 Gleit, Tang, and Coryell, "Beta Decay Transition Probabilities," Supplement to Nuclear Data Tables, Nov. 1963, Chap. 3.

Go-35 M. Goeppert-Mayer, *Phys. Rev.* **48,** 512 (1935), Chap. 5.

Go-48 C. J. Gorter, *Physica* **14,** 504 (1948), Chap. 4.

Go-57 M. Goldhaber, L. Grodzins, and A. W. Sunyar, *Phys. Rev.* **106,** 826 (1957), Chap. 4.

Goldb-58 M. Goldberger and S. Treiman, *Phys. Rev.* **111,** 354 (1958), Chap. 6.

Goldh-58 M. Goldhaber, L. Grodzins, and A. W. Sunyar, *Phys. Rev.* **109,** 1015 (1958), Chaps. 1, 4.

Gro-59 L. Grodzins, *Prog. Nucl. Phys.* **7,** 243 (1959), Chap. 4.

Gre-60 J. S. Greenberg, D. P. Malone, R. L. Gluckstern, and V. W. Hughes, *Phys. Rev.* **120,** 1393 (1960), Chap. 4.

Gr-60 E. Greuling and R. C. Whitten, *Ann. Phys.* (*N.Y.*) **11,** 510 (1960), Chap. 5.

Gr-63 W. Gruhle, K. H. Lauterjung, and B. Schimmer *Nucl. Phys.* **42,** 321 (1963), Chap. 7.

Gu-53 S. B. Gunst, and L. A. Page, *Phys. Rev.* **92,** 970 (1953), Chap. 4.

Ha-53 D. R. Hamilton, W. P. Alford, and L. Gross, *Phys. Rev.* **92,** 1521 (1953), Chap. 2.

Hay-53 R. J. Hayden and M. G. Inghram, *Natl. Bur. Std.* (*U.S.*) *Circ.* **522,** 189 (1953), Chap. 5.

Ha-57 H. Hanna and R. S. Preston, *Phys. Rev.* **106,** 1363, 108, 160 (1957); **109,** 716 (1958), Chap. 4.

Hay-57 E. Hayward and E. G. Fuller, *Phys. Rev.* **106,** 991 (1957), Chap. 7.

Ha-62 E. L. Haase, H. A. Hill, and D. B. Knudsen, *Bull. Am. Phys. Soc., Ser. II,* **7,** 342 (1962), Chap. 4.

Ha-63 E. L. Haase, H. A. Hill, and D. B. Knudsen, *Phys. Letters* **4,** 338 (1963), Chap. 4.

Ha-64 A. Halpern, *Phys. Rev. Letters* **13,** 660 (1964), Chap. 6.

He-29 W. Heitler and G. Herzberg, *Naturwiss.* **17,** 673 (1929), Chap. 1.

He-32 W. Heisenberg, *Z. Physik* **77,** 1 (1932), Chap. 1.

He-57 Hermannsfelt, Maxson, Stähelin, and Allen, *Phys. Rev.* **107,** 641 (1957), Chaps. 1, 3.

He-58 Hermannsfelt, Burman, Stähelin, Allen, and Brand, *Phys. Rev. Letters* **1,** 61 (1958), Chaps. 1, 3.

Hi-62 R. H. Hildebrand, *Phys. Rev. Letters* **8,** 34 (1962), Chap. 6.

Hu-62 J. N. Huffaker and E. Grueling, *Trans. N.Y. Acad. Sci.* **24,** 591 (1962), Chap. 7.

Hu-63 J. N. Huffaker and E. Greuling, *Phys. Rev.* **132,** 738 (1963), Chap. 7.

Im-58 Impeduglia, Plano, Prodell, Samios, Schwartz, and Steinberger, *Phys. Rev. Letters* **1,** 249 (1958), Chap. 1.

In-49 M. G. Inghram and J. H. Reynolds, *Phys. Rev.* **76,** 1265 (1949); **78,** 822 (1950), Chap. 5.

Ja-57 J. D. Jackson, S. B. Treiman, and H. W. Wyld, *Phys. Rev.* **106,** 517 (1957), Chap. 4.

Ja-63 J. Janecke, *Phys. Letters* **6,** 69 (1963), Chaps. 2, 7.

Jo-63 Johnson, Pleasonton, and Carlson, *Phys. Rev.* **132,** 1149 (1963), Chap. 3.

Ju-58 W. Jungst and H. Schopper, *Z. Naturforsch.* **13a,** 505 (1958), Chap. 4.

Ka-57 S. Kahana and D. L. Pursey, *Nuovo Cimento* **6,** 1469 (1957), Chap. 4.

Ki-58 R. W. King and J. F. Perkins, *Phys. Rev.* **112,** 963 (1958), Chap. 5.

Ki-59 T. Kinoshita and A. Sirlin, *Phys. Rev.* **113,** 1652 (1959), Chaps. 6, 7.

Kis-59 O. C. Kistner and B. M. Rustad, *Phys. Rev.* **114,** 1329 (1959), Chap. 3.

Ki-60 L. S. Kisslinger and R. A. Sorenson, *Kgl. Danske Videnskab. Selskab, Mat. Fys. Medd.* **32,** No. 9 (1960), Chap. 3.

Kim-63 Y. E. Kim and J. O. Rasmussen, *Nucl. Phys.* **47,** 184 (1963), Chap. 3.

Kis-63 L. S. Kisslinger and R. A. Sorenson, *Rev. Mod. Phys.* **35,** 853 (1963), Chap. 3.

Ki-64 L. S. Kisslinger and C. S. Wu, preprint, Chap. 3.

Ki-65 C. W. Kim and H. Primakoff, *Phys. Rev.* **140,** B570 (1965), Chap. 6.

Kl-48 O. Klein, *Nature* **161,** 897 (1948), Chap. 7.

Ko-35 E. J. Konopinski and G. E. Uhlenbeck, *Phys. Rev.* **48,** 7 (1935), Chaps. 1, 3.

Ko-41 E. J. Konopinski and G. E. Uhlenbeck, *Phys. Rev.* **60,** 308 (1941), Chap. 3.

Ko-47 O. Kofoed-Hansen, *Phys. Rev.* **71,** 451 (1947), Chap. 2.

Ko-49 E. J. Konopinski, USAEC Report LAMS (1949), Chap. 5.

Ko-53 E. J. Konopinski, and H. M. Mahmoud, *Phys. Rev.* **92,** 1045 (1953), Chaps. 3, 4.

Ko-54a O. Kofoed-Hansen, *Kgl. Danske Videnskab. Selskab, Mat. Fys. Medd.* **28,** No. 9 (1954); *Phys. Rev.* **74,** 1785 (1948), Chap. 3.

Ko-54b O. Kofoed-Hansen, *Phys. Rev.* **96,** 1045 (1954), Chaps. 2, 5.

Koh-54 T. P. Kohman, USAEC Report NYO-3626 (1954), Chap. 5.

Ko-58 Koller, Schwarzchild, Vise, and Wu, *Phys. Rev.* **109,** 85 (1958), Chap. 4.

Kon-59 E. J. Konopinski, *Ann. Rev. Nucl. Sci.* **9,** (1959), Chap. 7.

Kot-59 T. Kotani and M. Ross, *Phys. Rev.* **113,** 622 (1959); T. Kotani, *Phys. Rev.* **114,** 795 (1959), Chap. 3.

Kr-59 H. Kruger and K. Crowe, *Phys. Rev.* **113,** 341 (1959), Chap. 6.

Ku-36 F. N. D. Kurie, J. R. Richardson, and H. C. Paxton, *Phys. Rev.* **49,** 368 (1936), Chap. 2.

Ku-60 D. Kurath, *Phys. Rev. Letters* **4,** 180 (1960), Chap. 7.

La-24 O. Laporte, *Z. Physik*, **23,** 135 (1924), Chap. 1.

La-40 J. L. Lawson and J. M. Cork, *Phys. Rev.* **57,** 982 (1940), Chap. 1.

La-49a L. M. Langer, R. D. Moffat, and H. C. Price, Jr., *Phys. Rev.* **76,** 1725 (1949), Chap. 1.

La-49b L. M. Langer and H. C. Price, Jr., *Phys. Rev.* **76,** 641 (1949), Chaps. 1, 3.

La-52 L. M. Langer and R. D. Moffat, *Phys. Rev.* **88,** 689 (1952), Chap. 2.

La-57 L. Landau, *Nucl. Phys.* **3,** 127 (1957), Chaps. 1, 4.

La-60a Lathrop, Lundy, Swanson, Telegdi, and Yovanovitch, *Proc. Intern. Conf. on High-Energy Physics*, Rochester, 1960, Chap. 7.

La-60b Lathrop, Lundy, Penman, Telegdi, Winston, Yovanovitch, and Bearden, *Nuovo Cimento* **17,** 114 (1960), Chap. 7.

Le-48 T. D. Lee, M. Rosenbluth, and C. N. Yang, *Phys. Rev.* **75,** 905 (1948), Chap. 7.

Le-50 C. A. Levine, A. Ghiorso, and G. T. Seaborg, *Phys. Rev.* **77,** 296 (1950), Chap. 5.

Le-56 T. D. Lee and C. N. Yang, *Phys. Rev.* **104,** 254 (1956), Chaps. 1, 4.

Le-57a T. D. Lee and C. N. Yang, *Phys. Rev.* **105,** 1671 (1957), Chaps. 1, 4, 7.

Le-57b T. D. Lee, *Proc. Rehovoth Conf. on Nuclear Structure*, 1957, edited by H. J. Lipkin, North-Holland Publishing Co., Amsterdam, pp. 336–345, Chap. 4.

Le-60a T. D. Lee and C. N. Yang, *Phys. Rev. Letters* **4,** 307 (1960), Chap. 7.

Le-60b T. D. Lee and C. N. Yang, *Phys. Rev.* **119,** 1410 (1960), Chap. 7.

Le-60 T. D. Lee and C. N. Yang, *Proc. Intern. Conf. on High-Energy Physics*, Rochester, 1960, Chap. 7.

Le-63 Y. K. Lee, Luke Mo, and C. S. Wu, *Phys. Rev. Letters* **10,** 253 (1963), Chap. 7.

Lee-63 Y. K. Lee and C. S. Wu, *Phys. Rev.* **132,** 1200 (1963), Chap. 4.

Le-64 T. D. Lee and A. Sirlin., *Rev. Mod. Phys.* **36,** 666 (1964), Chaps. 1, 7.

Le-65 T. D. Lee and L. Wolfenstein, *Phys. Rev.* **138,** B1490 (1965); and J. Bernstein, J. Feinberg, and T. D. Lee, *Phys. Rev.* **139,** B1650 (1965), Chap. 4.

Lee-65 T. D. Lee and C. S. Wu, *Ann. Rev. Nucl. Sci.*, **15,** 381 (1965). Chaps. 1, 4.

Li-62 H. Lipkin, *Beta Decay for Pedestrians*, North-Holland Publishing Co., Amsterdam, 1962, Chap. 3.

Li-64 P. Lipnik and J. W. Sunier, *Nucl. Phys.* **56,** 241 (1964), Chap. 3.

Lo-49 C. Longmire and H. Brown, *Phys. Rev.* **75,** 264 (1949), Chap. 2.

Lo-63 L. Lovitch, *Nucl. Phys.* **46,** 353 (1963), Chap. 7.

Lu-54 G. Luders, *Kgl. Danske Videnskab. Selskab, Mat. Fys. Medd.* **28,** No. 5 (1954), Chap. 4.

Lu-57 G. Luders, *Ann. Phys.* (*N.Y.*) **2,** 1 (1957), Chap. 4.

Lun-57 A. Lundby, A. P. Patro, and J. P. Stroot, *Nuovo Cimento* **6,** 745 (1957), Chap. 4.

Lu-62 R. A. Lundy, W. A. Carmer, G. Culligan, V. L. Telegdi, and R. Winston, *Nuovo Cimento* **24,** 549 (1962), Chap. 6.

Ma-37 E. Majorana, *Nuovo Cimento* **14,** 171 (1937), Chap. 5.

Ma-43 H. S. W. Massey, *Proc. Roy. Soc.* (*London*) **A181,** 14 (1943), Chap. 4.

Ma-52 H. M. Mahmoud and E. J. Konopinski, *Phys. Rev.* **88,** 1266 (1952), Chaps. 3, 7.

Ma-55 M. G. Mayer and J. H. D. Jensen, *Elementary Theory of Nuclear Shell Structure*, John Wiley, New York, 1955, Chap. 3.

Macd-58 W. M. MacDonald, *Phys. Rev.* 110, 1420 (1958); and in *Nuclear Spectroscopy*, Vol. 2, edited by F. Ajzenberg-Selove, Academic Press, New York, Chap. 7.

Macq-58 P. C. Macq, K. M. Crowe, and R. P. Haddock, *Phys. Rev.* **112,** 2061 (1958), Chap. 6.

Mar-58 R. Marshak and E. C. G. Sudarshan, *Proc. Intern. Conf. on Elementary Particles*, Padua-Venice, 1957; *Phys. Rev.* **109,** 1860 (1958), Chap. 7.

May-60 T. Mayer-Kuckuk et al., *Z. Physik* **157,** 586 (1960), Chap. 4.

Mar-61 R. Marshak and E. C. G. Sudarshan, *Introduction to Elementary Particle Physics*, Interscience, New York, 1961, Chap. 1.

Mai-62 E. J. Maier, Ph.D. Thesis, Carnegie Institute of Technology, 1962, Chap. 6.

Man-62 L. G. Mann, S. D. Bloom, and R. J. Nagle, *Nucl. Phys.* **30,** 636 (1962), Chap. 4.

May-62 T. Mayer-Kuckuk and F. C. Michel, *Phys. Rev.* **127,** 545 (1962), Chap. 7.

Ma-63 Mann, Bloom, Scott, Polichar, and Richardson, *Proc. Manchester Conf. on Low and Medium-Energy Physics*, Sept. 1963, Chap. 4.

Ma-64 E. J. Maier, R. M. Edelstein, and R. T. Siegel, *Phys. Rev.* **133,** B663 (1964).

Mc-53 J. A. McCarthy, *Phys. Rev.* **90,** 853 (1953), Chap. 5.

Mc-57 K. M. McVoy, *Phys. Rev.* **108,** 828 (1957); **110,** 1484 (1958), Chap. 4.

Mc-60 W. M. McMaster, *Nuovo Cimento* **17,** 395 (1960), Chap. 6.

Me-22 L. Meitner, *Z. Physik* **9,** 131, 145 (1922), Chap. 1.

Me-30 L. Meitner and W. Orthman, *Z. Physik* **60,** 143 (1930), Chap. 1.

Mi-50 L. Michel, *Proc. Phys. Soc.* (*London*) **A63,** 514, (1950); *Phys. Rev.* **86,** 814 (1952), Chap. 6.

Mi-54 L. Michel and A. Wightman, *Phys. Rev.* **93,** 354 (1954), Chap. 7.

Mi-58 J. H. Miller III and D. C. Sutton, *Bull. Am. Phys. Soc., Ser. II,* **3,** No. 3, 206 (1958), Chaps. 3, 7.

Mis-63 J. A. Miskel et al., preprint, February 1963. Chap. 4.

Mit-63 S. K. Mitra, *Bucl. Phys.* **47,** 293 (1963), Chap. 3.

Mi-64 F. C. Michel, *Phys. Rev.* **133,** B329 (1964), Chap. 7.

Mø-32 C. Møller, *Ann. Physik* **14,** 531 (1932), Chap. 4.

Mo-51 S. A. Moszkowski, *Phys. Rev.* **82,** 35 (1951), Chap. 3.

Mo-53 M. Morita and M. Yamada, *Progr. Theoret. Phys.* **10,** 111, 641 (1953); M. Morita, *Progr. Theoret. Phys.* **10,** 363 (1953), Chap. 3.

Mo-55 S. A. Moszkowski, and D. Jantzen, UCLA Technical Report 10, 26, 1955, Chap. 3.

Mo-56 M. Morita, *Progr. Theoret. Phys.* **15,** 445 (1956), Chap. 3.

Mor-57 M. Morita and R. S. Morita, *Phys. Rev.* **107,** 139, 1316, 1729; (1957), Chaps. 3, 4.

Mos-57 S. A. Moszkowski, *Handbuch der Physik* Vol. 39, 411, Springer, Berlin, 1957, Chap. 3.

Mo-58 M. Morita, R. S. Morita, and M. Yamada, *Phys. Rev.* **111,** 237 (1958), Chaps. 3, 4,

Mo-59 M. Morita, *Phys. Rev.* **113,** 1584 (1959), Chaps. 3, 7.

Mot-59 B. R. Mottelson and S. G. Nilsson, *Kgl. Danske Videnskab. Selskab, Mat. Fys. Medd.* **1,** No. 8 (1959), Chap. 3.

Mu-57 C. O. Muelhause and S. Oleksa, *Phys. Rev.* **105,** 1332 (1957), Chap. 5.

NBS-52 *Natl. Bur. Std.* (*U.S.*), *Appl. Math. Ser.* **13** "Tables for Analysis of Beta Spectra" (1952), Chap. 2.

Ne-59 N. Newby and E. J. Konopinski, *Phys. Rev.* **115,** 434 (1959), Chap. 3.

Ni-55 S. G. Nilsson, *Kgl. Danske Videnskab. Selskab, Mat. Fys. Medd.* **29,** No. 16 (1955), Chap. 3.

No-62 M. E. Nordburg Jr. F. B. Morinigo, and C. A. Barnes, *Phys. Rev.* **125,** 321 (1962), Chap. 7.

On-59 S. Oneda and J. C. Pati, *Phys. Rev. Letters* **2,** 125 (1959), Chap. 7.

Or-57 J. Orear, *Phys. Rev.* **107,** 322 (1957), Chap. 6.

Pa-30 W. Pauli. A letter written by Pauli; see Pa-30, page 385.

Pa-33a W. Pauli, *Handbuch der Physik*, Vol. 24, 226–227, Springer, Berlin, 1933, Chap. 4.

Pa-33b W. Pauli, *Proc. Solvay Congress*, Brussels, 1933, p. 324, Chap. 1.

Pa-55 W. Pauli, *Niels Bohr and the Development of Physics*, Pergamon, New York, 1955, Chap. 4.

Pag-57a L. A. Page, *Phys. Rev.* **106,** 394 (1957), Chap. 4.

Pag-57b L. A. Page and M. Heinberg *Phys. Rev.* **106,** 1220 (1957) Chap. 4.

Pau-57 W. Pauli, *Nuovo Cimento* **6,** 204 (1957), Chap. 4.

Pa-59 L. A. Page, *Rev. Med. Phys.* **31,** 759 (1959), Chap. 4.

Pa-62 L. A. Page, *Ann. Rev. Nucl. Sci.* **12,** 43, 290 (1962), Chap. 6.

Pe-52 A. G. Petschek and R. E. Marshak, *Phys. Rev.* **85,** 698 (1952), Chap. 3.

Pe-53 D. C. Peaslee, *Phys. Rev.* **91,** 1447 (1953), Chaps. 3, 7.

Pe-63 R. W. Peterson and N. W. Glass, *Phys. Rev.* **130,** 292 (1963), Chap. 7.

Pl-60 R. J. Plano, *Phys. Rev.* **119,** 1400 (1960), Chap. 6.

Po-58 Postma, Huiskamp, Miedema, Steenland, Tolhoek, and Gorter, *Physika* **24,** 157 (1958), Chap. 4.

Po-59 J. Pontecorvo, *Exptl. Theoret. Phys.* (*USSR*) **37,** 1751 (1959), Chap. 7.

Pr-59a H. Primakoff and S. P. Rosen, *Rept. Progv. Phys.* **22,** 121 (1959), Chap. 5.

Pr-59b H. Primakoff, *Rev. Mod. Phys.* **31,** 802 (1959), Chap. 6.

Pr-65 J. Prentki and M. Veltman, *Phys. Letters* **15,** 88 (1965), Chap. 4.

Pu-49 G. Puppi, *Nuovo Cimento* **6,** 194 (1949), Chap. 7.

Pu-51 D. L. Pursey, *Phil. Mag.* **42,** 1193 (1951), Chap. 3.

Pu-52 D. L. Pursey, *Physica* **18,** 1017 (1952), Chap. 7.

Ra-30 Z. Rasetti, *Z. Physik* **61,** 598 (1930), Chap. 1.

Re-50 J. R. Reitz, *Phys. Rev.* **77,** 10 (1950), Chaps. 2, 7.

Re-56 F. Reines and C. L. Cowan, Jr., *Science* **124,** 103 (1956); *Phys. Rev.* **113,** 273 (1959), Chaps. 1, 5.

Ri-56 B. W. Ridley, *Progr. Nucl. Phys.* **5,** 188 (1956), Chap. 1.

Ro-36 M. E. Rose, *Phys. Rev.* **49,** 727 (1936), Chaps. 2, 7.

Ro-37 M. E. Rose, *Phys. Rev.* **51,** 484 (1937), Chaps. 2, 7.
Ro-48 M. E. Rose, Report AECD, 2119 (1948); *Phys. Rev.* **75,** 213 (1949), Chap. 4.
Rob-51 J. H. Robson, *Phys. Rev.* **83,** 349 (1951), Chap. 2.
Ro-51a M. E. Rose and D. K. Holmes, *Phys. Rev.* **83,** 190 (1951), Chap. 2.
Ro-51b M. E. Rose and D. K. Holmes, ORNL 1022 (1951), unpublished, Chap. 2.
Rod-52 G. W. Rodebeck and J. S. Allen, *Phys. Rev.* **86,** 446 (1952), Chap. 5.
Ro-52 Rose, Dismuke, Perry, and Bell, ORNL 1222 (1952), Chap. 2.
Ro-53a M. E. Rose and C. L. Perry, *Phys. Rev.* **90,** 479 (1953), Chap. 2.
Ro-53b M. E. Rose, C. L. Perry, and N. M. Dismuke, ORNL 1459 (1953), Chap. 2.
Ro-54 M. E. Rose and R. K. Osborn, *Phys. Rev.* **93,** 1315, 1326 (1954), Chap. 3.
Ro-58 L. Rosensen, *Phys. Rev.* **109,** 958 (1958), Chaps. 6, 7.
Ro-63 J. Rothberg, *Phys. Rev.* **132,** 2664 (1963), Chap. 6.
Ru-49 M. Ruderman and R. Finkelstein, *Phys. Rev.* **76,** 1458 (1949), Chap. 6.
Rud-53 M. Ruderman, *Phys. Rev.* **89,** 1227 (1953), Chap. 3.
Rus-53 B. M. Rustad and S. L. Ruby, *Phys. Rev.* **89,** 880 (1953); **97,** 991 (1955), Chaps. 1, 3.
Ry-63 C. Ryan and S. Okubo, University of Rochester Report URPA-3 (1963), Chap. 5.
Sa-53 R. G. Sachs, *Nuclear Theory*, Addison-Wesley, Reading, Mass., 1953, Chap. 3.
Sa-57 A. Salam, *Nuovo Cimento* **5,** 299 (1957), Chaps. 1, 4.
Sa-58a J. J. Sakurai, *Nuovo Cimento* **7,** 649 (1958), Chaps. 1, 7.
Sa-58b J. J. Sakurai, *Phys. Rev. Letters* **1,** 40 (1958), Chap. 2.
Sa-63 M. Sakai and S. Yoshida, *I.N.S.* **49,** University of Tokyo (1963), Chap. 3.
Sa-64 J. J. Sakurai, *Phys. Rev. Letters* **12,** 79 (1964), Chap. 7.
Sa-65 A. Sachs, *Phys. Rev. Bull.* **10,** Sec. JB (1965), Chap. 6.
Sc-53 J. Schwinger, *Phys. Rev.* **91,** 713 (1953), Chap. 4.
Sc-56 Schwartzschild, Rustad, and Wu, *Bull. Am. Phys. Soc., Ser. II,* **1,** 366 (1956); Ph.D. thesis, Columbia University, 1957, CU-167, Chap. 2.
Scho-57 H. Schopper, *Phil. Mag.* **2,** 710 (1957), Chap. 4.
Sc-58 H. Schopper and S. Galster, *Nucl. Phys.* **6,** 125 (1958), Chap. 4.
Sc-60 H. Schopper, *Fortschr. Physik* **8,** 328 (1960), Chap. 7.
Schw-60 M. Schwartz, *Phys. Rev. Letters* **4,** 306 (1960), Chap. 7.
Se-54 H. Selig, Ph.D. thesis, Carnegie Institute of Technology, 1954, Chap. 5.
Sh-48 C. W. Sherwin, *Phys. Rev.* **73,** 1219, (1948); **75,** 1799 (1948), Chap. 2.
Sh-51 C. W. Sherwin, *Phys. Rev.* **82,** 52 (1951), Chap. 2.
Sh-53 R. Sherr and J. B. Gerhart, *Phys. Rev.* **91,** 909 (1953), Chap. 1.
Sh-54 R. Sherr and R. H. Miller, *Phys. Rev.* **93,** 1076 (1954), Chaps. 3, 5.
Sherm-56 N. Sherman, *Phys. Rev.* **103,** 1601 (1956), Chap. 4.
Sherr-56 R. Sherr and J. B. Gerhart, *Bull. Am. Phys. Soc.* **1,** 219 (1956), Chap. 3.

Sh-65 M. H. Shapiro, S. Frankel, S. Koicki, W. Wales, and G. T. Wood, *Bull. Am. Phys. Soc.* **10** (4), paper AB3; and M. Shapiro, Bull. *Am. Phys. Soc.* **10** (5), paper FA2, $T_{2\nu} > 4.3 \times 10^{18}$ yr, Chap. 5.

She-65 B. Sherwood, post deadline paper American Physics Society Meeting, New York, January 1965, $\rho = 0.746 \pm 0.011$ (systematic error is not included), Chap. 5.

Si-37 A. J. F. Siegert, *Phys. Rev.* **52,** 787 (1937), Chap. 3.

Si-65 P. C. Simms, *Phys. Rev.* **138,** B784 (1965); P. C. Simms, A. Nanienson, T. H. Wei, and C. S. Wu, *Phys. Rev.* **138,** B777 (1965), Chap. 3.

Sm-51 P. B. Smith and J. S. Allen, *Phys. Rev.* **81,** 381 (1951), Chap. 5.

Sm-51 A. M. Smith, *Phys. Rev.* **82,** 955(L) (1951), Chap. 3.

Sn-55 A. H. Snell and F. Pleasanton, *Phys. Rev.* **97,** 246 (1955); **100,** 1396 (1955), Chaps. 2, 5.

So-59 Sosnovskij, Spivak, Prokofiev, Kutikov, and Dobrinin, *Nucl. Phys.* **10,** 395 (1959), Chap. 2.

Sp-62a R. M. Spector and R. J. Blin-Stoyle, *Phys. Letters* **1,** 118 (1962), Chap. 3.

Sp-62b R. M. Spector, *Nucl. Phys.* **40,** 338 (1962), Chap. 3.

Sp-64 I. Spirn, W. Brandt, G. Present, and A. Schwartzchild, Bull. *Am. Phys. Soc.* **9,** 394 (Paper BC1) (1964), Chap. 4.

St-55 B. Stech and J. H. A. Jensen, *Z. Physik* **141,** 175 (1955), Chap. 7.

St-57 R. Steffen, *Proc. Rehovoth Conf. on Nuclear Structure*, 1957, edited by H. J. Lipkin, North-Holland Publishing Co., Amsterdam, Chap. 4.

St-59 R. H. Steffen, *Phys. Rev.* **115,** 980 (1959), Chap. 4.

St-63 R. Steffen, preprint (1963), Chap. 4.

St-64 J. Steinberger, "Experimental Survey of Strange Particle Decays," Varenna Summer School, 1964, Chap. 6.

Su-58 E. C. G. Sudershan and R. E. Marshak, *Proc. Intern. Conf. on Elementary Particles* Padua-Venice, 1957; *Phys. Rev.* **109,** 1860 (1958), Chaps. 1, 7.

Su-64 A. W. Sunyar, *Bull. Am. Phys. Soc.* **9,** BC5, 394 (1964), Chap. 4.

Ta-58 J. C. Taylor, *Phys. Rev.* **110,** 1216 (1958), Chap. 7.

Te-62 V. L. Telegdi, *Phys. Rev. Letters* **8,** 327 (1962), Chap. 6.

Ti-49 J. Tiomno and J. A. Wheeler, *Rev. Mod. Phys.* **21,** 153 (1949), Chap. 7.

To-56 H. A. Tolhoek, *Rev. Mod. Phys.* **28,** 177 (1956), Chap. 4.

Tr-56 S. Treiman and H. W. Wyld, *Phys. Rev.* **101,** 1552 (1956), Chap. 6.

Tr-58 S. B. Treiman, *Phys. Rev.* **110,** 448 (1958), Chap. 4.

Ul-61 J. D. Ullman, H. Frauenfelder, H. J. Lipkin, and A. Rossi, *Phys. Rev.* **122,** 536 (1961), Chap. 4.

Vi-57 V. M. Visscher and R. A. Ferrell, *Phys. Rev.* **107,** 781 (1957), Chap. 3.

We-29 H. Weyl, *Z. Physik* **56,** 330 (1929), Chap. 4. It was rejected on the grounds of parity violation.

We-52 H. Weyl, *Symmetry*, Princeton University Press, Princeton, N.J., 1952, Chap. 1.

Weg-58 H. Wegener, *Z. Physik* **151,** 252 (1958), Chap. 4.

Wei-58 S. Weinberg, *Phys. Rev.* **112,** 1375 (1958), Chap. 7.

We-60 H. Weidenmüller, *Phys. Rev. Letters* **4,** 299 (1960), Chap. 7.
We-61 H. Weidenmüller, *Rev. Mod. Phys.* **33,** 574 (1961), Chap. 3.
We-62 H. Weidenmüller, *Phys. Rev.* **127,** 537 (1962), Chap. 7.
We-64 W. R. Wessel and P. Phillipson, *Phys. Rev. Letters* **13,** 23 (1964), Chap. 6.
Wei-64 T. S. Wei, Ph.D. thesis, Columbia University (1964), Chap. 4.
We-65 W. I. Weisberger, *Phys. Rev. Letters* **14,** 1047 (1965), Chap. 7.
Wh-63 W. Whaling and T. R. Fisher, *Bull. Am. Phys. Soc.* **8,** No. 8 F7 (1963), Chap. 7.
Wi-27 E. P. Wigner, *Z. Physik*, **43,** 624 (1927), Chap. 1.
Wi-39 E. P. Wigner, *Phys. Rev.* **56,** 519 (1939), Chap. 3.
Wi-52 G. C. Wick, A. S. Wightman, and E. P. Wigner, *Phys. Rev.* **88,** 101 (1952), Chaps. 1, 4.
Wi-55 R. G. Winter, *Phys. Rev.* **99,** 88 (1955), Chap. 5.
Wi-57 E. P. Wigner, Proceedings of the R. Welsh Foundation Conference on Chemical Research, Nov. 1957 (unpublished), Chaps. 4, 7.
Wil-57 D. A. Wilkinson, *Phys. Rev.* **109,** 1603 (1957), Chap. 7.
Wi-64 Willis et al., *Phys. Rev. Letters* **13,** 291 (1964), Chap. 6.
Wo-59 L. Wolfenstein, *Nuovo Cimento* **13,** 319 (1959), Chap. 6.
Wo-63 *Proc. Intern. Conf. on Fundamental Aspects of Weak Interactions*, Brookhaven Natl. Lab., Upton, N.Y., 1963 (see summary talk by L. Wolfenstein), Chap. 7.
Wu-49 C. S. Wu and R. D. Albert, *Phys. Rev.* **75,** 315 (1949), Chap. 1.
Wu-50 C. S. Wu, *Rev. Mod. Phys.* **22,** 386 (1950), Chap. 1.
Wu-55 C. S. Wu, *Beta and Gamma Spectroscopy*, edited by Siegbahn, North-Holland Publishing Co., Amsterdam, 1955, Chap. 1 (see also the *Alpha, Beta and Gamma Spectroscopy*, revision of the above, 1964).
Wu-57 C. S. Wu, E. Ambler, R. W. Hayward, D. D. Hoppes, and R. F. Hudson, *Phys. Rev.* **105,** 1413 (1957), Chaps. 1, 4.
Wu-58a C. S. Wu, *Proc. Rehovoth Conf. on Nucl. Structure*, 1957, edited by H. J. Lipkin, North-Holland Publishing Co., Amsterdam; and Benczer-Koller, Schwartzschild, Vise, and Wu, *Phys. Rev.* **109,** 193 (1958), Chap. 4.
Wu-58b C. S. Wu and A. Schwartzschild, Columbia Univ. Report CU-173 (1958), Chap. 1.
Wu-59 C. S. Wu, *Rev. Mod. Phys.* **31,** 783 (1959); *Theoretical Physics in the Twentieth Century*, edited by M. Fierz and V. F. Weisskopf, Interscience Publishers, New York, 1960, pp. 249-303, Chap. 7.
Wu-64 C. S. Wu, *Rev. Mod. Phys.* **36,** 618 (1964), Chaps, 1, 7.
Ya-50 C. N. Yang and J. Tiomno, *Phys. Rev.* **79,** 495 (1950), Chap. 4.
Ya-52 M. Yamada and M. Morita, *Progr. Theoret. Phys.* **8,** 431 (1952), Chap. 3.
Ya-53a M. Yamada, *Prog. Theoret. Phys.* **10,** 241 (1953), Chap. 2.
Ya-53b M. Yamada, *Prog. Theoret. Phys.* **10,** 245 (1953), Chap. 2.
Ya-53c M. Yamada, *Prog. Theoret. Phys.* **10,** 252 (1953), Chaps. 2, 3.
Ya-56 C. N. Yang, *Proc. Seattle Congress*, Sept. 1956; *Rev. Mod. Phys.* **29,** 231 (1956), Chaps. 1, 4.

Ya-63 C. N. Yang, *Proc. Intern. Conf. on Fundamental Aspects of Weak Interactions*, Brookhaven Natl. Lab., Upton, N.Y., 1963, Chap. 7.

Ya-64 A. F. Yano, *Phys. Rev. Letters* **12,** 110 (1964), Chap. 6.

Yu-35 H. Yukawa, *Proc. Phys. Soc. Japan* **17,** 48 (1935), Chaps. 1, 4, 7.

Yu-35a H. Yukawa and S. Sakata, *Proc. Phys. Soc. Japan* **17,** 467 (1935) Chap. 5.

Za-63 Zaimidoroga, Kulyukin, Pontecorvo, Sulyaev, Falomkin, Fillippov, Tsupko-Sitnikov, and Scherbakov, *Phys. Letters* **6,** 100 (1963), Chap. 6.

Zw-57 Zweifel, *Proc. Rehovoth Conf. on Nuclear Structure*, 1957, edited by H. J. Lipkin, North-Holland Publishing Co., Amsterdam, p. 300, Chap. 5.

Pa-30 The following are parts of a letter which Pauli sent to friends participating in a congress:

Zürich, December 4, 1930

Dear radioactive ladies and gentlemen,

I beg you to most favorably listen to the carrier of this letter. He will tell you that, in view of the "wrong" statistics of the N and Li^6 nuclei and of the continuous beta spectrum, I have hit upon a desperate remedy to save the laws of conservation of energy and statistics. This is the possibility that electrically neutral particles exist which I will call neutrons,* which exist in nuclei, which have a spin $\frac{1}{2}$ and obey the exclusion principle, and which differ from the photons also in that they do not move with the velocity of light. The mass of the neutrons should be of the same order as those of the electrons and should in no case exceed 0.01 proton masses. The continuous beta spectrum would then be understandable if one assumes that during beta decay with each electron a neutron is emitted in such a way that the sum of the energies of neutron and electron is constant. . . .

I admit that my remedy may look very unlikely, because one would have seen these neutrons long ago if they really were to exist. But only he who dares wins and the seriousness of the situation caused by the continuous beta spectrum is illuminated by a remark of my honored predecessor, Mr. Debye, who recently said to me in Brussels: 'O, it is best not to think at all, just as with the new taxes.' Hence one should seriously discuss every possible path to rescue. So, dear radioactive people, examine and judge. Unfortunately I will not be able to appear in Tübingen personally, because I am indispensable here due to a ball which will take place in Zürich during the night from December 6 to 7.

Your most obedient servant,

W. Pauli

* The name neutrino was proposed by Fermi when a heavier "neutron" was discovered by Chadwick.

Books Mainly on Beta Decay and/or Weak Interactions

J. S. Allen, *The Neutrino*, Princton University Press, Princeton, N.J., 1958.

E. J. Konopinski, *The Theory of Beta Radioactivity*, Oxford University Press, New York, 1966.

H. J. Lipkin, *Beta Decay for Pedestrians*, North-Holland Publishing Co., Amsterdam, 1962.

R. Marshak and E. C. G. Sudershan, *Introduction to Elementary Particle Physics*, Interscience Publishers, New York, 1961.

A. Winther, *On the Theory of Nuclear Beta Decay*, Ejnar Munksgaard, Copenhagen, 1962.

Books Containing Chapter (or Chapters) on Beta Decay

F. Ajzenberg-Selove, editor, *Nuclear Spectroscopy*, Vols. 9A, 9B, Academic Press, New York, 1960.

J. M. Blatt and V. F. Weisskopf, "Beta Decay," *Theoretical Nuclear Physics*, John Wiley and Sons, New York, 1952.

S. DeBenedetti, *Nuclear Reactions*, John Wiley and Sons, New York, 1961.

M. Deutsch and O. Kofoed-Hansen, "Beta Decay," *Experimental Nuclear Physics*, Vol. 3, edited by E. Segre, John Wiley and Son, New York, 1959.

O. Kofoed-Hansen and C. J. Christensen, "Beta Decay," *Encyclopedia of Physics*, Vol. 40, edited by S. Flugge, Springer, Berlin, 1962.

M. A. Preston, *Physics of the Nucleus*, Addison-Wesley, Reading, Mass., 1962.

E. Segre, *Nuclei and Particles*, W. A. Benjamin, New York, 1964.

K. Siegbahn, editor, *Alpha, Beta and Gamma-Ray Spectroscopy*, North-Holland Publishing Co., Amsterdam, 1965.

C. S. Wu, "History of Beta Decay," *Beitrage Zur Physik and Chemie der* 20 *Jahrhunderts*, edited by O. R. Frisch et al., Friedr. Vieweg und Sohn, 1959.

C. S. Wu, "The Neutrino," *Memorial Volume for W. Pauli*, edited by V. P. Weisskopf, and M. Fierz, Pergamon Press, New York, 1960.

L. C. L. Yuan and C. S. Wu, editors, *Methods of Experimental Physics*, Vols. *V*A, *V*B, Academic Press, New York, 1962-1963.

Review Articles

R. J. Blin-Stoyle, "Present States of the Conserved Vector Current Theory," *Nuclear Physics*, **57**, 232 (1964).

R. H. Dalitz, "Strange Particle Decay," *Progress in Nuclear Physics*, **7**, 243-312 (1959).

R. H. Dalitz, "Strange Particle Decay Processes and the Fermi Interactions," *Reviews of Modern Physics*, **31**, 823 (1959).

L. W. Fagg and S. S. Hanna, "Polarization of Nuclear Gamma Rays," *Reviews of Modern Physics*, **31**, 711-758 (1959).

G. Feinberg and L. M. Lederman, "Physics of Muons and Muon Neutrinos," *Annual Reviews of Nuclear Science*, **13**, 431 (1963).

L. Grodzins, "Measurement of Helicity," *Progress in Nuclear Physics*, **7**, 163-242 (1959).

E. J. Konopinski, "The Experimental Clarification of the Laws of β-Radio-activity," *Annual Review of Nuclear Science*, **9**, 99-158 (1959).

T. D. Lee and C. S. Wu, "Weak Interactions," *Annual Review of Nuclear Science*, **15,** 381 (1965).

L. A. Page, "Electron and Positron Polarization," *Reviews of Modern Physics*, **31,** 759-781 (1959).

H. Primakoff, "Theory of Muon Capture," *Reviews of Modern Physics*, **31,** 802-822 (1959).

H. Primakoff and S. P. Rosen, "Double Beta Decay," *Reports of Progress in Physics*, **22,** 121-166 (1959).

J. J. Sakurai, "Weak Interactions," *Progress in Nuclear Physics*, **7,** 243-312 (1959).

H. A. Tolhoek, "Electron Polarization, Theory and Experiment," *Reviews of Modern Physics*, **33,** 277-298 (1956).

H. A. Weidemuller, "First Forbidden Beta Decay," *Reviews of Modern Physics*, **33,** 574-607 (1961).

C. S. Wu, "The Universal Fermi Interaction and the Conserved Vector Current in Beta Decay," *Reviews of Modern Physics*, **36,** 618 (1964).

General References on Invariance Principles and Conservation Laws

E. L. Hill, *Reviews of Modern Physics*, **23,** 253 (1951) (classical aspects).

J. J. Sakurai, "Symmetry Laws and Elementary Particle Interactions," from *Lectures in Theoretical Physics*, Vol. 2, edited by W. E. Britten and B. W. Downs, Interscience Publishers, New York, 1960.

G. C. Wick, *Annual Review of Nuclear Science*, **8,** 1 (1958).

E. P. Wigner, *Proceedings of the American Philosophical Society*, **93,** 521 (1949).

Conference and Lecture Notes

G. Alaga, "Beta Decay," *Nuclear Spectroscopy*, Lecture notes from Enrico Fermi School, Academic Press, New York, 1962.

J. S. Bell, "Very Elementary Theory of Weak Interactions," CERN, 62-17, May 1962.

N. Cabibbo and M. Veltman, "Weak Interactions," CERN 65-30, August 1965.

G. Charpak and M. Gourdin, "High Energy Neutrino Induced Reactions," *Proceedings of Cargese Summer School*, 1962, W. J. Benjamin, New York, 1963.

"Conference on Leptonic Interactions, February 1964," *Proceedings of the Royal Society* (*London*), **285** (1401), 175-262 (1965).

C. Fronsdal, editor, *Weak Interactions and Topics in Dispersion Physics*, Lectures given at Second Bergen International School of Physics, W. A. Benjamin, New York, 1963.

International Conference on Weak Interactions, Argonne National Laboratory, October 1965, ANL 7130.

Lecture Notes of the International School of Physics, "*Enrico Fermi*," Varenna (Como), Italy, Academic Press, New York, 1965, especially H. Primakoff, "Theoretical Survey of Muon Physics," J. Steinberger, "Experimental Survey on Strange Particle Decay," and C. S. Wu "Beta Decay."

Lectures from Weak Interaction Seminars, CERN, 1961.

T. D. Lee, "Space Inversion, Time Reversal and Particle-Antiparticle Conjugation," *Physics Today*, **19**(3), 23 (1966).

T. D. Lee and C. N. Yang, "Elementary Particles and Weak Interactions," *Lecture Notes*, Brookhaven National Laboratory, Upton, N.Y., 1957.

H. J. Lipkin, editor, *Proceedings of the Rehovoth Conference on Nuclear Structure*, North-Holland Publishing Co., Amsterdam, 1957.

L. B. Okum, "Theory of Weak Interactions," Atomic Energy Commission, Tr-5226, 1962, Davey and Co., New York, 1965.

Proceedings of the International Conference on Fundamental Aspects of Weak Interactions, Brookhaven National Laboratory, Upton, N.Y., September 1963.

A. Roberts and K. C. Wali, editors, *Proceedings of the International Conference on Weak Interactions*. Argonne National Laboratory, Chicago, September 1965.

H. A. Tolhoek, "Weak Interactions Amongst Nucleons and Leptons." *Selected Topics in Nuclear Theory*, 1962.

D. H. Wilkinson, "Interrelations of Nuclear Structure with Elementary Particle Physics," Rutherford Memorial Lecture, *Proceedings of the Physical Society (London)*, **80**, 997-1040 (1962).

Index